# Mathematical Methods 1

# Pearson

At Pearson, we have a simple mission: to help people make more of their lives through learning.

We combine innovative learning technology with trusted content and educational expertise to provide engaging and effective learning experience that serve people wherever and whenever they are learning.

We enable our customers to access a wide and expanding range of market-leading content from world-renowned authors and develop their own tailor-made book. From classroom to boardroom, our curriculum materials, digital learning tools and testing programmes help to educate millions of people worldwide — more than any other private enterprise.

Every day our work helps learning flourish, and wherever learning flourishes, so do people.

To learn more, please visit us at: www.pearson.com/uk

# Mathematical Methods 1

Selected chapters from:

*Linear Algebra and Its Applications*
Fifth Edition and Global Edition
David C. Lay, Steven R. Lay, and Judi J. McDonald

*Calculus 1*
Ninth Edition
Robert A. Adams and Christopher Essex

**Pearson**

Harlow, England • London • New York • Boston • San Francisco • Toronto • Sydney • Dubai • Singapore • Hong Kong
Tokyo • Seoul • Taipei • New Dehli • Cape Town • São Paulo • Mexico City • Madrid • Amsterdam • Munich • Paris • Milan

Pearson
KAO Two
KAO Park
Harlow
Essex CM17 9NA

And associated companies throughout the world

Visit us on the World Wide Web at:
www.pearson.com/uk

© Pearson Education Limited 2020

Compiled from:

*Linear Algebra and Its Applications*
Fifth edition and Global edition
David C. Lay, Steven R. Lay, and Judi J. McDonald
ISBN 978-1-292-09223-2
© Pearson Education Limited 2016

*Calculus 1*
Ninth Edition
Robert A. Adams and Christopher Essex
ISBN 978-1-78726-776-3
© Pearson Education Limited 2018

ISBN 978-1-83961-000-4

Printed and bound by Ovimex in The Netherlands.

# CONTENTS

# 1

# Linear Equations in Linear Algebra

## 1.1 SYSTEMS OF LINEAR EQUATIONS

A **linear equation** in the variables $x_1, \ldots, x_n$ is an equation that can be written in the form

$$a_1 x_1 + a_2 x_2 + \cdots + a_n x_n = b \tag{1}$$

where $b$ and the **coefficients** $a_1, \ldots, a_n$ are real or complex numbers, usually known in advance. The subscript $n$ may be any positive integer. In textbook examples and exercises, $n$ is normally between 2 and 5. In real-life problems, $n$ might be 50 or 5000, or even larger.

The equations

$$4x_1 - 5x_2 + 2 = x_1 \quad \text{and} \quad x_2 = 2\left(\sqrt{6} - x_1\right) + x_3$$

are both linear because they can be rearranged algebraically as in equation (1):

$$3x_1 - 5x_2 = -2 \quad \text{and} \quad 2x_1 + x_2 - x_3 = 2\sqrt{6}$$

The equations

$$4x_1 - 5x_2 = x_1 x_2 \quad \text{and} \quad x_2 = 2\sqrt{x_1} - 6$$

are not linear because of the presence of $x_1 x_2$ in the first equation and $\sqrt{x_1}$ in the second.

A **system of linear equations** (or a **linear system**) is a collection of one or more linear equations involving the same variables—say, $x_1, \ldots, x_n$. An example is

$$
\begin{aligned}
2x_1 - x_2 + 1.5x_3 &= 8 \\
x_1 \qquad\quad - 4x_3 &= -7
\end{aligned}
\tag{2}
$$

A **solution** of the system is a list $(s_1, s_2, \ldots, s_n)$ of numbers that makes each equation a true statement when the values $s_1, \ldots, s_n$ are substituted for $x_1, \ldots, x_n$, respectively. For instance, $(5, 6.5, 3)$ is a solution of system (2) because, when these values are substituted in (2) for $x_1, x_2, x_3$, respectively, the equations simplify to $8 = 8$ and $-7 = -7$.

The set of all possible solutions is called the **solution set** of the linear system. Two linear systems are called **equivalent** if they have the same solution set. That is, each solution of the first system is a solution of the second system, and each solution of the second system is a solution of the first.

Finding the solution set of a system of two linear equations in two variables is easy because it amounts to finding the intersection of two lines. A typical problem is

$$x_1 - 2x_2 = -1$$
$$-x_1 + 3x_2 = \ \ \ 3$$

The graphs of these equations are lines, which we denote by $\ell_1$ and $\ell_2$. A pair of numbers $(x_1, x_2)$ satisfies *both* equations in the system if and only if the point $(x_1, x_2)$ lies on both $\ell_1$ and $\ell_2$. In the system above, the solution is the single point $(3, 2)$, as you can easily verify. See Figure 1.

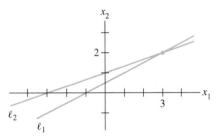

**FIGURE 1** Exactly one solution.

Of course, two lines need not intersect in a single point—they could be parallel, or they could coincide and hence "intersect" at every point on the line. Figure 2 shows the graphs that correspond to the following systems:

$$\text{(a)} \quad x_1 - 2x_2 = -1 \qquad \text{(b)} \quad x_1 - 2x_2 = -1$$
$$\qquad \qquad -x_1 + 2x_2 = \ \ \ 3 \qquad \qquad \qquad -x_1 + 2x_2 = \ \ \ 1$$

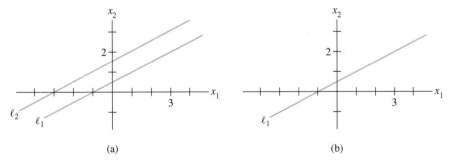

(a)                                           (b)

**FIGURE 2** (a) No solution. (b) Infinitely many solutions.

Figures 1 and 2 illustrate the following general fact about linear systems, to be verified in Section 1.2.

A system of linear equations has

**1.** no solution, or

**2.** exactly one solution, or

**3.** infinitely many solutions.

A system of linear equations is said to be **consistent** if it has either one solution or infinitely many solutions; a system is **inconsistent** if it has no solution.

## Matrix Notation

The essential information of a linear system can be recorded compactly in a rectangular array called a **matrix**. Given the system

$$
\begin{aligned}
x_1 - 2x_2 + x_3 &= 0 \\
2x_2 - 8x_3 &= 8 \\
5x_1 \quad\quad - 5x_3 &= 10
\end{aligned}
\tag{3}
$$

with the coefficients of each variable aligned in columns, the matrix

$$
\begin{bmatrix}
1 & -2 & 1 \\
0 & 2 & -8 \\
5 & 0 & -5
\end{bmatrix}
$$

is called the **coefficient matrix** (or **matrix of coefficients**) of the system (3), and

$$
\begin{bmatrix}
1 & -2 & 1 & 0 \\
0 & 2 & -8 & 8 \\
5 & 0 & -5 & 10
\end{bmatrix}
\tag{4}
$$

is called the **augmented matrix** of the system. (The second row here contains a zero because the second equation could be written as $0 \cdot x_1 + 2x_2 - 8x_3 = 8$.) An augmented matrix of a system consists of the coefficient matrix with an added column containing the constants from the right sides of the equations.

The **size** of a matrix tells how many rows and columns it has. The augmented matrix (4) above has 3 rows and 4 columns and is called a $3 \times 4$ (read "3 by 4") matrix. If $m$ and $n$ are positive integers, an $m \times n$ **matrix** is a rectangular array of numbers with $m$ rows and $n$ columns. (The number of rows always comes first.) Matrix notation will simplify the calculations in the examples that follow.

## Solving a Linear System

This section and the next describe an algorithm, or a systematic procedure, for solving linear systems. The basic strategy is *to replace one system with an equivalent system (i.e., one with the same solution set) that is easier to solve*.

Roughly speaking, use the $x_1$ term in the first equation of a system to eliminate the $x_1$ terms in the other equations. Then use the $x_2$ term in the second equation to eliminate the $x_2$ terms in the other equations, and so on, until you finally obtain a very simple equivalent system of equations.

Three basic operations are used to simplify a linear system: Replace one equation by the sum of itself and a multiple of another equation, interchange two equations, and multiply all the terms in an equation by a nonzero constant. After the first example, you will see why these three operations do not change the solution set of the system.

**EXAMPLE 1**   Solve system (3).

**SOLUTION**  The elimination procedure is shown here with and without matrix notation, and the results are placed side by side for comparison:

$$
\begin{aligned}
x_1 - 2x_2 + x_3 &= 0 \\
2x_2 - 8x_3 &= 8 \\
5x_1 \qquad\quad - 5x_3 &= 10
\end{aligned}
\qquad
\begin{bmatrix}
1 & -2 & 1 & 0 \\
0 & 2 & -8 & 8 \\
5 & 0 & -5 & 10
\end{bmatrix}
$$

*Keep $x_1$ in the first equation and eliminate it from the other equations.* To do so, add $-5$ times equation 1 to equation 3. After some practice, this type of calculation is usually performed mentally:

$$
\begin{array}{ll}
-5 \cdot \text{[equation 1]} & -5x_1 + 10x_2 - 5x_3 = 0 \\
+ \text{[equation 3]} & 5x_1 \qquad\quad - 5x_3 = 10 \\
\hline
\text{[new equation 3]} & \qquad\quad 10x_2 - 10x_3 = 10
\end{array}
$$

The result of this calculation is written in place of the original third equation:

$$
\begin{aligned}
x_1 - 2x_2 + x_3 &= 0 \\
2x_2 - 8x_3 &= 8 \\
10x_2 - 10x_3 &= 10
\end{aligned}
\qquad
\begin{bmatrix}
1 & -2 & 1 & 0 \\
0 & 2 & -8 & 8 \\
0 & 10 & -10 & 10
\end{bmatrix}
$$

Now, multiply equation 2 by $\frac{1}{2}$ in order to obtain 1 as the coefficient for $x_2$. (This calculation will simplify the arithmetic in the next step.)

$$
\begin{aligned}
x_1 - 2x_2 + x_3 &= 0 \\
x_2 - 4x_3 &= 4 \\
10x_2 - 10x_3 &= 10
\end{aligned}
\qquad
\begin{bmatrix}
1 & -2 & 1 & 0 \\
0 & 1 & -4 & 4 \\
0 & 10 & -10 & 10
\end{bmatrix}
$$

Use the $x_2$ in equation 2 to eliminate the $10x_2$ in equation 3. The "mental" computation is

$$
\begin{array}{ll}
-10 \cdot \text{[equation 2]} & -10x_2 + 40x_3 = -40 \\
+ \text{[equation 3]} & 10x_2 - 10x_3 = 10 \\
\hline
\text{[new equation 3]} & \qquad\quad 30x_3 = -30
\end{array}
$$

The result of this calculation is written in place of the previous third equation (row):

$$
\begin{aligned}
x_1 - 2x_2 + x_3 &= 0 \\
x_2 - 4x_3 &= 4 \\
30x_3 &= -30
\end{aligned}
\qquad
\begin{bmatrix}
1 & -2 & 1 & 0 \\
0 & 1 & -4 & 4 \\
0 & 0 & 30 & -30
\end{bmatrix}
$$

Now, multiply equation 3 by $\frac{1}{30}$ in order to obtain 1 as the coefficient for $x_3$. (This calculation will simplify the arithmetic in the next step.)

$$
\begin{aligned}
x_1 - 2x_2 + x_3 &= 0 \\
x_2 - 4x_3 &= 4 \\
x_3 &= -1
\end{aligned}
\qquad
\begin{bmatrix}
1 & -2 & 1 & 0 \\
0 & 1 & -4 & 4 \\
0 & 0 & 1 & -1
\end{bmatrix}
$$

The new system has a *triangular* form (the intuitive term *triangular* will be replaced by a precise term in the next section):

$$
\begin{aligned}
x_1 - 2x_2 + x_3 &= 0 \\
x_2 - 4x_3 &= 4 \\
x_3 &= -1
\end{aligned}
\qquad
\begin{bmatrix}
1 & -2 & 1 & 0 \\
0 & 1 & -4 & 4 \\
0 & 0 & 1 & -1
\end{bmatrix}
$$

Eventually, you want to eliminate the $-2x_2$ term from equation 1, but it is more efficient to use the $x_3$ in equation 3 first, to eliminate the $-4x_3$ and $+x_3$ terms in equations 2 and 1. The two "mental" calculations are

| $4 \cdot$ [equation 3] | $4x_3 = -4$ | $-1 \cdot$ [equation 3] | $-x_3 = 1$ |
|---|---|---|---|
| $+$ [equation 2] | $x_2 - 4x_3 = \phantom{-}4$ | $+$ [equation 1] | $x_1 - 2x_2 + x_3 = 0$ |
| [new equation 2] | $x_2 \phantom{- 4x_3} = 0$ | [new equation 1] | $x_1 - 2x_2 \phantom{+ x_3} = 1$ |

It is convenient to combine the results of these two operations:

$$\begin{array}{rcr} x_1 - 2x_2 & = & 1 \\ x_2 & = & 0 \\ x_3 & = & -1 \end{array} \qquad \begin{bmatrix} 1 & -2 & 0 & 1 \\ 0 & 1 & 0 & 0 \\ 0 & 0 & 1 & -1 \end{bmatrix}$$

Now, having cleaned out the column above the $x_3$ in equation 3, move back to the $x_2$ in equation 2 and use it to eliminate the $-2x_2$ above it. Because of the previous work with $x_3$, there is now no arithmetic involving $x_3$ terms. Add 2 times equation 2 to equation 1 and obtain the system:

$$\begin{array}{rcr} x_1 & = & 1 \\ x_2 & = & 0 \\ x_3 & = & -1 \end{array} \qquad \begin{bmatrix} 1 & 0 & 0 & 1 \\ 0 & 1 & 0 & 0 \\ 0 & 0 & 1 & -1 \end{bmatrix}$$

The work is essentially done. It shows that the only solution of the original system is $(1, 0, -1)$. However, since there are so many calculations involved, it is a good practice to check the work. To verify that $(1, 0, -1)$ *is* a solution, substitute these values into the left side of the original system, and compute:

$$\begin{array}{rcrcr} 1(1) - 2(0) + 1(-1) = 1 - 0 - 1 = & & 0 \\ 2(0) - 8(-1) = & 0 + 8 = & 8 \\ 5(1) \phantom{0} - 5(-1) = 5 & + 5 = & 10 \end{array}$$

The results agree with the right side of the original system, so $(1, 0, -1)$ is a solution of the system. ■

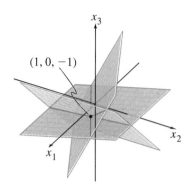

(1, 0, −1)

Each of the original equations determines a plane in three-dimensional space. The point $(1, 0, -1)$ lies in all three planes.

Example 1 illustrates how operations on equations in a linear system correspond to operations on the appropriate rows of the augmented matrix. The three basic operations listed earlier correspond to the following operations on the augmented matrix.

---
ELEMENTARY ROW OPERATIONS

**1.** (Replacement) Replace one row by the sum of itself and a multiple of another row.[1]

**2.** (Interchange) Interchange two rows.

**3.** (Scaling) Multiply all entries in a row by a nonzero constant.

---

Row operations can be applied to any matrix, not merely to one that arises as the augmented matrix of a linear system. Two matrices are called **row equivalent** if there is a sequence of elementary row operations that transforms one matrix into the other.

It is important to note that row operations are *reversible*. If two rows are interchanged, they can be returned to their original positions by another interchange. If a

---
[1] A common paraphrase of row replacement is "Add to one row a multiple of another row."

row is scaled by a nonzero constant $c$, then multiplying the new row by $1/c$ produces the original row. Finally, consider a replacement operation involving two rows—say, rows 1 and 2—and suppose that $c$ times row 1 is added to row 2 to produce a new row 2. To "reverse" this operation, add $-c$ times row 1 to (new) row 2 and obtain the original row 2. See Exercises 29–32 at the end of this section.

At the moment, we are interested in row operations on the augmented matrix of a system of linear equations. Suppose a system is changed to a new one via row operations. By considering each type of row operation, you can see that any solution of the original system remains a solution of the new system. Conversely, since the original system can be produced via row operations on the new system, each solution of the new system is also a solution of the original system. This discussion justifies the following statement.

> If the augmented matrices of two linear systems are row equivalent, then the two systems have the same solution set.

Though Example 1 is lengthy, you will find that after some practice, the calculations go quickly. Row operations in the text and exercises will usually be extremely easy to perform, allowing you to focus on the underlying concepts. Still, you must learn to perform row operations accurately because they will be used throughout the text.

The rest of this section shows how to use row operations to determine the size of a solution set, without completely solving the linear system.

## Existence and Uniqueness Questions

Section 1.2 will show why a solution set for a linear system contains either no solutions, one solution, or infinitely many solutions. Answers to the following two questions will determine the nature of the solution set for a linear system.

To determine which possibility is true for a particular system, we ask two questions.

> **TWO FUNDAMENTAL QUESTIONS ABOUT A LINEAR SYSTEM**
> **1.** Is the system consistent; that is, does at least one solution *exist*?
> **2.** If a solution exists, is it the *only* one; that is, is the solution *unique*?

These two questions will appear throughout the text, in many different guises. This section and the next will show how to answer these questions via row operations on the augmented matrix.

**EXAMPLE 2**   Determine if the following system is consistent:

$$\begin{aligned} x_1 - 2x_2 + x_3 &= 0 \\ 2x_2 - 8x_3 &= 8 \\ 5x_1 \qquad\quad - 5x_3 &= 10 \end{aligned}$$

**SOLUTION** This is the system from Example 1. Suppose that we have performed the row operations necessary to obtain the triangular form

$$\begin{aligned} x_1 - 2x_2 + x_3 &= 0 \\ x_2 - 4x_3 &= 4 \\ x_3 &= -1 \end{aligned} \qquad \begin{bmatrix} 1 & -2 & 1 & 0 \\ 0 & 1 & -4 & 4 \\ 0 & 0 & 1 & -1 \end{bmatrix}$$

At this point, we know $x_3$. Were we to substitute the value of $x_3$ into equation 2, we could compute $x_2$ and hence could determine $x_1$ from equation 1. So a solution exists; the system is consistent. (In fact, $x_2$ is uniquely determined by equation 2 since $x_3$ has only one possible value, and $x_1$ is therefore uniquely determined by equation 1. So the solution is unique.) ∎

**EXAMPLE 3**  Determine if the following system is consistent:

$$
\begin{aligned}
x_2 - \phantom{3}4x_3 &= 8 \\
2x_1 - 3x_2 + \phantom{1}2x_3 &= 1 \\
4x_1 - 8x_2 + 12x_3 &= 1
\end{aligned}
\tag{5}
$$

**SOLUTION**  The augmented matrix is

$$
\begin{bmatrix}
0 & 1 & -4 & 8 \\
2 & -3 & 2 & 1 \\
4 & -8 & 12 & 1
\end{bmatrix}
$$

To obtain an $x_1$ in the first equation, interchange rows 1 and 2:

$$
\begin{bmatrix}
2 & -3 & 2 & 1 \\
0 & 1 & -4 & 8 \\
4 & -8 & 12 & 1
\end{bmatrix}
$$

To eliminate the $4x_1$ term in the third equation, add $-2$ times row 1 to row 3:

$$
\begin{bmatrix}
2 & -3 & 2 & 1 \\
0 & 1 & -4 & 8 \\
0 & -2 & 8 & -1
\end{bmatrix}
\tag{6}
$$

Next, use the $x_2$ term in the second equation to eliminate the $-2x_2$ term from the third equation. Add 2 times row 2 to row 3:

$$
\begin{bmatrix}
2 & -3 & 2 & 1 \\
0 & 1 & -4 & 8 \\
0 & 0 & 0 & 15
\end{bmatrix}
\tag{7}
$$

The augmented matrix is now in triangular form. To interpret it correctly, go back to equation notation:

$$
\begin{aligned}
2x_1 - 3x_2 + 2x_3 &= 1 \\
x_2 - 4x_3 &= 8 \\
0 &= 15
\end{aligned}
\tag{8}
$$

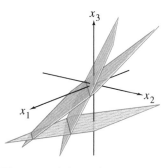

The system is inconsistent because there is no point that lies on all three planes.

The equation $0 = 15$ is a short form of $0x_1 + 0x_2 + 0x_3 = 15$. This system in triangular form obviously has a built-in contradiction. There are no values of $x_1, x_2, x_3$ that satisfy (8) because the equation $0 = 15$ is never true. Since (8) and (5) have the same solution set, the original system is inconsistent (i.e., has no solution). ∎

Pay close attention to the augmented matrix in (7). Its last row is typical of an inconsistent system in triangular form.

— NUMERICAL NOTE —

In real-world problems, systems of linear equations are solved by a computer. For a square coefficient matrix, computer programs nearly always use the elimination algorithm given here and in Section 1.2, modified slightly for improved accuracy.

The vast majority of linear algebra problems in business and industry are solved with programs that use *floating point arithmetic*. Numbers are represented as decimals $\pm .d_1 \cdots d_p \times 10^r$, where $r$ is an integer and the number $p$ of digits to the right of the decimal point is usually between 8 and 16. Arithmetic with such numbers typically is inexact, because the result must be rounded (or truncated) to the number of digits stored. "Roundoff error" is also introduced when a number such as $1/3$ is entered into the computer, since its decimal representation must be approximated by a finite number of digits. Fortunately, inaccuracies in floating point arithmetic seldom cause problems. The numerical notes in this book will occasionally warn of issues that you may need to consider later in your career.

## PRACTICE PROBLEMS

Throughout the text, practice problems should be attempted before working the exercises. Solutions appear after each exercise set.

**1.** State in words the next elementary row operation that should be performed on the system in order to solve it. [More than one answer is possible in (a).]

a.  $x_1 + 4x_2 - 2x_3 + 8x_4 = 12$  
  $x_2 - 7x_3 + 2x_4 = -4$  
  $5x_3 - x_4 = 7$  
  $x_3 + 3x_4 = -5$

b.  $x_1 - 3x_2 + 5x_3 - 2x_4 = 0$  
  $x_2 + 8x_3 = -4$  
  $2x_3 = 3$  
  $x_4 = 1$

**2.** The augmented matrix of a linear system has been transformed by row operations into the form below. Determine if the system is consistent.

$$\begin{bmatrix} 1 & 5 & 2 & -6 \\ 0 & 4 & -7 & 2 \\ 0 & 0 & 5 & 0 \end{bmatrix}$$

**3.** Is $(3, 4, -2)$ a solution of the following system?

$$\begin{aligned} 5x_1 - x_2 + 2x_3 &= 7 \\ -2x_1 + 6x_2 + 9x_3 &= 0 \\ -7x_1 + 5x_2 - 3x_3 &= -7 \end{aligned}$$

**4.** For what values of $h$ and $k$ is the following system consistent?

$$\begin{aligned} 2x_1 - x_2 &= h \\ -6x_1 + 3x_2 &= k \end{aligned}$$

## 1.1 EXERCISES

Solve each system in Exercises 1–4 by using elementary row operations on the equations or on the augmented matrix. Follow the systematic elimination procedure described in this section.

**1.**   $x_1 + 5x_2 = 7$
     $-2x_1 - 7x_2 = -5$

**2.** $2x_1 + 4x_2 = -4$
     $5x_1 + 7x_2 = 11$

**3.** Find the point $(x_1, x_2)$ that lies on the line $x_1 + 5x_2 = 7$ and on the line $x_1 - 2x_2 = -2$. See the figure.

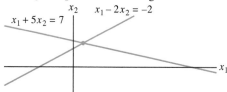

**4.** Find the point of intersection of the lines $x_1 - 5x_2 = 1$ and $3x_1 - 7x_2 = 5$.

Consider each matrix in Exercises 5 and 6 as the augmented matrix of a linear system. State in words the next two elementary row operations that should be performed in the process of solving the system.

**5.**
$$\begin{bmatrix} 1 & -4 & 5 & 0 & 7 \\ 0 & 1 & -3 & 0 & 6 \\ 0 & 0 & 1 & 0 & 2 \\ 0 & 0 & 0 & 1 & -5 \end{bmatrix}$$

**6.**
$$\begin{bmatrix} 1 & -6 & 4 & 0 & -1 \\ 0 & 2 & -7 & 0 & 4 \\ 0 & 0 & 1 & 2 & -3 \\ 0 & 0 & 3 & 1 & 6 \end{bmatrix}$$

In Exercises 7–10, the augmented matrix of a linear system has been reduced by row operations to the form shown. In each case, continue the appropriate row operations and describe the solution set of the original system.

**7.**
$$\begin{bmatrix} 1 & 7 & 3 & -4 \\ 0 & 1 & -1 & 3 \\ 0 & 0 & 0 & 1 \\ 0 & 0 & 1 & -2 \end{bmatrix}$$

**8.**
$$\begin{bmatrix} 1 & -4 & 9 & 0 \\ 0 & 1 & 7 & 0 \\ 0 & 0 & 2 & 0 \end{bmatrix}$$

**9.**
$$\begin{bmatrix} 1 & -1 & 0 & 0 & -4 \\ 0 & 1 & -3 & 0 & -7 \\ 0 & 0 & 1 & -3 & -1 \\ 0 & 0 & 0 & 2 & 4 \end{bmatrix}$$

**10.**
$$\begin{bmatrix} 1 & -2 & 0 & 3 & -2 \\ 0 & 1 & 0 & -4 & 7 \\ 0 & 0 & 1 & 0 & 6 \\ 0 & 0 & 0 & 1 & -3 \end{bmatrix}$$

Solve the systems in Exercises 11–14.

**11.**
$$x_2 + 4x_3 = -5$$
$$x_1 + 3x_2 + 5x_3 = -2$$
$$3x_1 + 7x_2 + 7x_3 = 6$$

**12.**
$$x_1 - 3x_2 + 4x_3 = -4$$
$$3x_1 - 7x_2 + 7x_3 = -8$$
$$-4x_1 + 6x_2 - x_3 = 7$$

**13.**
$$x_1 \qquad - 3x_3 = 8$$
$$2x_1 + 2x_2 + 9x_3 = 7$$
$$x_2 + 5x_3 = -2$$

**14.**
$$x_1 - 3x_2 \qquad = 5$$
$$-x_1 + x_2 + 5x_3 = 2$$
$$x_2 + x_3 = 0$$

Determine if the systems in Exercises 15 and 16 are consistent. Do not completely solve the systems.

**15.**
$$x_1 \qquad + 3x_3 \qquad = 2$$
$$x_2 \qquad - 3x_4 = 3$$
$$-2x_2 + 3x_3 + 2x_4 = 1$$
$$3x_1 \qquad + 7x_4 = -5$$

**16.**
$$x_1 \qquad - 2x_4 = -3$$
$$2x_2 + 2x_3 \qquad = 0$$
$$x_3 + 3x_4 = 1$$
$$-2x_1 + 3x_2 + 2x_3 + x_4 = 5$$

**17.** Do the three lines $x_1 - 4x_2 = 1$, $2x_1 - x_2 = -3$, and $-x_1 - 3x_2 = 4$ have a common point of intersection? Explain.

**18.** Do the three planes $x_1 + 2x_2 + x_3 = 4$, $x_2 - x_3 = 1$, and $x_1 + 3x_2 = 0$ have at least one common point of intersection? Explain.

In Exercises 19–22, determine the value(s) of $h$ such that the matrix is the augmented matrix of a consistent linear system.

**19.** $\begin{bmatrix} 1 & h & 4 \\ 3 & 6 & 8 \end{bmatrix}$

**20.** $\begin{bmatrix} 1 & h & -3 \\ -2 & 4 & 6 \end{bmatrix}$

**21.** $\begin{bmatrix} 1 & 3 & -2 \\ -4 & h & 8 \end{bmatrix}$

**22.** $\begin{bmatrix} 2 & -3 & h \\ -6 & 9 & 5 \end{bmatrix}$

In Exercises 23 and 24, key statements from this section are either quoted directly, restated slightly (but still true), or altered in some way that makes them false in some cases. Mark each statement True or False, and *justify* your answer. (If true, give the approximate location where a similar statement appears, or refer to a definition or theorem. If false, give the location of a statement that has been quoted or used incorrectly, or cite an example that shows the statement is not true in all cases.) Similar true/false questions will appear in many sections of the text.

**23.** a. Every elementary row operation is reversible.

b. A $5 \times 6$ matrix has six rows.

c. The solution set of a linear system involving variables $x_1, \ldots, x_n$ is a list of numbers $(s_1, \ldots, s_n)$ that makes each equation in the system a true statement when the values $s_1, \ldots, s_n$ are substituted for $x_1, \ldots, x_n$, respectively.

d. Two fundamental questions about a linear system involve existence and uniqueness.

**24.** a. Elementary row operations on an augmented matrix never change the solution set of the associated linear system.

b. Two matrices are row equivalent if they have the same number of rows.

c. An inconsistent system has more than one solution.

d. Two linear systems are equivalent if they have the same solution set.

**25.** Find an equation involving $g$, $h$, and $k$ that makes this augmented matrix correspond to a consistent system:

$$\begin{bmatrix} 1 & -4 & 7 & g \\ 0 & 3 & -5 & h \\ -2 & 5 & -9 & k \end{bmatrix}$$

**26.** Construct three different augmented matrices for linear systems whose solution set is $x_1 = -2, x_2 = 1, x_3 = 0$.

**27.** Suppose the system below is consistent for all possible values of $f$ and $g$. What can you say about the coefficients $c$ and $d$? Justify your answer.

$$x_1 + 3x_2 = f$$
$$cx_1 + dx_2 = g$$

**28.** Suppose $a, b, c$, and $d$ are constants such that $a$ is not zero and the system below is consistent for all possible values of $f$ and $g$. What can you say about the numbers $a, b, c$, and $d$? Justify your answer.

$$ax_1 + bx_2 = f$$
$$cx_1 + dx_2 = g$$

In Exercises 29–32, find the elementary row operation that transforms the first matrix into the second, and then find the reverse row operation that transforms the second matrix into the first.

**29.** $\begin{bmatrix} 0 & -2 & 5 \\ 1 & 4 & -7 \\ 3 & -1 & 6 \end{bmatrix}, \begin{bmatrix} 1 & 4 & -7 \\ 0 & -2 & 5 \\ 3 & -1 & 6 \end{bmatrix}$

**30.** $\begin{bmatrix} 1 & 3 & -4 \\ 0 & -2 & 6 \\ 0 & -5 & 9 \end{bmatrix}, \begin{bmatrix} 1 & 3 & -4 \\ 0 & 1 & -3 \\ 0 & -5 & 9 \end{bmatrix}$

**31.** $\begin{bmatrix} 1 & -2 & 1 & 0 \\ 0 & 5 & -2 & 8 \\ 4 & -1 & 3 & -6 \end{bmatrix}, \begin{bmatrix} 1 & -2 & 1 & 0 \\ 0 & 5 & -2 & 8 \\ 0 & 7 & -1 & -6 \end{bmatrix}$

**32.** $\begin{bmatrix} 1 & 2 & -5 & 0 \\ 0 & 1 & -3 & -2 \\ 0 & -3 & 9 & 5 \end{bmatrix}, \begin{bmatrix} 1 & 2 & -5 & 0 \\ 0 & 1 & -3 & -2 \\ 0 & 0 & 0 & -1 \end{bmatrix}$

An important concern in the study of heat transfer is to determine the steady-state temperature distribution of a thin plate when the temperature around the boundary is known. Assume the plate shown in the figure represents a cross section of a metal beam, with negligible heat flow in the direction perpendicular to the plate. Let $T_1, \ldots, T_4$ denote the temperatures at the four interior nodes of the mesh in the figure. The temperature at a node is approximately equal to the average of the four nearest nodes—to the left, above, to the right, and below.[2] For instance,

$$T_1 = (10 + 20 + T_2 + T_4)/4, \quad \text{or} \quad 4T_1 - T_2 - T_4 = 30$$

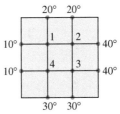

**33.** Write a system of four equations whose solution gives estimates for the temperatures $T_1, \ldots, T_4$.

**34.** Solve the system of equations from Exercise 33. [*Hint:* To speed up the calculations, interchange rows 1 and 4 before starting "replace" operations.]

_____

[2] See Frank M. White, *Heat and Mass Transfer* (Reading, MA: Addison-Wesley Publishing, 1991), pp. 145–149.

## SOLUTIONS TO PRACTICE PROBLEMS

**1.** a. For "hand computation," the best choice is to interchange equations 3 and 4. Another possibility is to multiply equation 3 by $1/5$. Or, replace equation 4 by its sum with $-1/5$ times row 3. (In any case, do not use the $x_2$ in equation 2 to eliminate the $4x_2$ in equation 1. Wait until a triangular form has been reached and the $x_3$ terms and $x_4$ terms have been eliminated from the first two equations.)

b. The system is in triangular form. Further simplification begins with the $x_4$ in the fourth equation. Use the $x_4$ to eliminate all $x_4$ terms above it. The appropriate step now is to add 2 times equation 4 to equation 1. (After that, move to equation 3, multiply it by $1/2$, and then use the equation to eliminate the $x_3$ terms above it.)

2. The system corresponding to the augmented matrix is

$$\begin{aligned}
x_1 + 5x_2 + 2x_3 &= -6 \\
4x_2 - 7x_3 &= 2 \\
5x_3 &= 0
\end{aligned}$$

The third equation makes $x_3 = 0$, which is certainly an allowable value for $x_3$. After eliminating the $x_3$ terms in equations 1 and 2, you could go on to solve for unique values for $x_2$ and $x_1$. Hence a solution exists, and it is unique. Contrast this situation with that in Example 3.

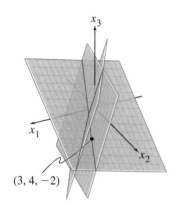

$(3, 4, -2)$

Since $(3, 4, -2)$ satisfies the first two equations, it is on the line of the intersection of the first two planes. Since $(3, 4, -2)$ does not satisfy all three equations, it does not lie on all three planes.

3. It is easy to check if a specific list of numbers is a solution. Set $x_1 = 3, x_2 = 4$, and $x_3 = -2$, and find that

$$\begin{aligned}
5(3) - (4) + 2(-2) &= 15 - 4 - 4 = 7 \\
-2(3) + 6(4) + 9(-2) &= -6 + 24 - 18 = 0 \\
-7(3) + 5(4) - 3(-2) &= -21 + 20 + 6 = 5
\end{aligned}$$

Although the first two equations are satisfied, the third is not, so $(3, 4, -2)$ is not a solution of the system. Notice the use of parentheses when making the substitutions. They are strongly recommended as a guard against arithmetic errors.

4. When the second equation is replaced by its sum with 3 times the first equation, the system becomes

$$\begin{aligned}
2x_1 - x_2 &= h \\
0 &= k + 3h
\end{aligned}$$

If $k + 3h$ is nonzero, the system has no solution. The system is consistent for any values of $h$ and $k$ that make $k + 3h = 0$.

## 1.2  ROW REDUCTION AND ECHELON FORMS

This section refines the method of Section 1.1 into a row reduction algorithm that will enable us to analyze any system of linear equations.[1] By using only the first part of the algorithm, we will be able to answer the fundamental existence and uniqueness questions posed in Section 1.1.

The algorithm applies to any matrix, whether or not the matrix is viewed as an augmented matrix for a linear system. So the first part of this section concerns an arbitrary rectangular matrix and begins by introducing two important classes of matrices that include the "triangular" matrices of Section 1.1. In the definitions that follow, a *nonzero* row or column in a matrix means a row or column that contains at least one nonzero entry; a **leading entry** of a row refers to the leftmost nonzero entry (in a nonzero row).

---

[1] The algorithm here is a variant of what is commonly called *Gaussian elimination*. A similar elimination method for linear systems was used by Chinese mathematicians in about 250 B.C. The process was unknown in Western culture until the nineteenth century, when a famous German mathematician, Carl Friedrich Gauss, discovered it. A German engineer, Wilhelm Jordan, popularized the algorithm in an 1888 text on geodesy.

**DEFINITION**

A rectangular matrix is in **echelon form** (or **row echelon form**) if it has the following three properties:

1. All nonzero rows are above any rows of all zeros.
2. Each leading entry of a row is in a column to the right of the leading entry of the row above it.
3. All entries in a column below a leading entry are zeros.

If a matrix in echelon form satisfies the following additional conditions, then it is in **reduced echelon form** (or **reduced row echelon form**):

4. The leading entry in each nonzero row is 1.
5. Each leading 1 is the only nonzero entry in its column.

An **echelon matrix** (respectively, **reduced echelon matrix**) is one that is in echelon form (respectively, reduced echelon form). Property 2 says that the leading entries form an *echelon* ("steplike") pattern that moves down and to the right through the matrix. Property 3 is a simple consequence of property 2, but we include it for emphasis.

The "triangular" matrices of Section 1.1, such as

$$\begin{bmatrix} 2 & -3 & 2 & 1 \\ 0 & 1 & -4 & 8 \\ 0 & 0 & 0 & 5/2 \end{bmatrix} \quad \text{and} \quad \begin{bmatrix} 1 & 0 & 0 & 29 \\ 0 & 1 & 0 & 16 \\ 0 & 0 & 1 & 3 \end{bmatrix}$$

are in echelon form. In fact, the second matrix is in reduced echelon form. Here are additional examples.

**EXAMPLE 1**    The following matrices are in echelon form. The leading entries (∎) may have any nonzero value; the starred entries (∗) may have any value (including zero).

$$\begin{bmatrix} ∎ & ∗ & ∗ & ∗ \\ 0 & ∎ & ∗ & ∗ \\ 0 & 0 & 0 & 0 \\ 0 & 0 & 0 & 0 \end{bmatrix}, \quad \begin{bmatrix} 0 & ∎ & ∗ & ∗ & ∗ & ∗ & ∗ & ∗ & ∗ & ∗ \\ 0 & 0 & 0 & ∎ & ∗ & ∗ & ∗ & ∗ & ∗ & ∗ \\ 0 & 0 & 0 & 0 & ∎ & ∗ & ∗ & ∗ & ∗ & ∗ \\ 0 & 0 & 0 & 0 & 0 & ∎ & ∗ & ∗ & ∗ & ∗ \\ 0 & 0 & 0 & 0 & 0 & 0 & 0 & 0 & ∎ & ∗ \end{bmatrix}$$

The following matrices are in reduced echelon form because the leading entries are 1's, and there are 0's below *and above* each leading 1.

$$\begin{bmatrix} 1 & 0 & ∗ & ∗ \\ 0 & 1 & ∗ & ∗ \\ 0 & 0 & 0 & 0 \\ 0 & 0 & 0 & 0 \end{bmatrix}, \quad \begin{bmatrix} 0 & 1 & ∗ & 0 & 0 & 0 & ∗ & ∗ & 0 & ∗ \\ 0 & 0 & 0 & 1 & 0 & 0 & ∗ & ∗ & 0 & ∗ \\ 0 & 0 & 0 & 0 & 1 & 0 & ∗ & ∗ & 0 & ∗ \\ 0 & 0 & 0 & 0 & 0 & 1 & ∗ & ∗ & 0 & ∗ \\ 0 & 0 & 0 & 0 & 0 & 0 & 0 & 0 & 1 & ∗ \end{bmatrix}$$

∎

Any nonzero matrix may be **row reduced** (that is, transformed by elementary row operations) into more than one matrix in echelon form, using different sequences of row operations. However, the reduced echelon form one obtains from a matrix is unique. The following theorem is proved in Appendix A at the end of the text.

**THEOREM 1**

Uniqueness of the Reduced Echelon Form

Each matrix is row equivalent to one and only one reduced echelon matrix.

If a matrix $A$ is row equivalent to an echelon matrix $U$, we call $U$ **an echelon form** (or row echelon form) **of** $A$; if $U$ is in reduced echelon form, we call $U$ **the reduced echelon form of** $A$. [Most matrix programs and calculators with matrix capabilities use the abbreviation RREF for reduced (row) echelon form. Some use REF for (row) echelon form.]

## Pivot Positions

When row operations on a matrix produce an echelon form, further row operations to obtain the reduced echelon form do not change the positions of the leading entries. Since the reduced echelon form is unique, *the leading entries are always in the same positions in any echelon form obtained from a given matrix.* These leading entries correspond to leading 1's in the reduced echelon form.

DEFINITION

> A **pivot position** in a matrix $A$ is a location in $A$ that corresponds to a leading 1 in the reduced echelon form of $A$. A **pivot column** is a column of $A$ that contains a pivot position.

In Example 1, the squares (■) identify the pivot positions. Many fundamental concepts in the first three chapters will be connected in one way or another with pivot positions in a matrix.

**EXAMPLE 2**    Row reduce the matrix $A$ below to echelon form, and locate the pivot columns of $A$.

$$A = \begin{bmatrix} 0 & -3 & -6 & 4 & 9 \\ -1 & -2 & -1 & 3 & 1 \\ -2 & -3 & 0 & 3 & -1 \\ 1 & 4 & 5 & -9 & -7 \end{bmatrix}$$

**SOLUTION**    Use the same basic strategy as in Section 1.1. The top of the leftmost nonzero column is the first pivot position. A nonzero entry, or *pivot*, must be placed in this position. A good choice is to interchange rows 1 and 4 (because the mental computations in the next step will not involve fractions).

Pivot
$$\begin{bmatrix} 1 & 4 & 5 & -9 & -7 \\ -1 & -2 & -1 & 3 & 1 \\ -2 & -3 & 0 & 3 & -1 \\ 0 & -3 & -6 & 4 & 9 \end{bmatrix}$$
Pivot column

Create zeros below the pivot, 1, by adding multiples of the first row to the rows below, and obtain matrix (1) below. The pivot position in the second row must be as far left as possible—namely, in the second column. Choose the 2 in this position as the next pivot.

Pivot
$$\begin{bmatrix} 1 & 4 & 5 & -9 & -7 \\ 0 & 2 & 4 & -6 & -6 \\ 0 & 5 & 10 & -15 & -15 \\ 0 & -3 & -6 & 4 & 9 \end{bmatrix} \qquad (1)$$
Next pivot column

Add $-5/2$ times row 2 to row 3, and add $3/2$ times row 2 to row 4.

$$\begin{bmatrix} 1 & 4 & 5 & -9 & -7 \\ 0 & 2 & 4 & -6 & -6 \\ 0 & 0 & 0 & 0 & 0 \\ 0 & 0 & 0 & -5 & 0 \end{bmatrix} \tag{2}$$

The matrix in (2) is different from any encountered in Section 1.1. There is no way to create a leading entry in column 3! (We can't use row 1 or 2 because doing so would destroy the echelon arrangement of the leading entries already produced.) However, if we interchange rows 3 and 4, we can produce a leading entry in column 4.

$$\begin{bmatrix} 1 & 4 & 5 & -9 & -7 \\ 0 & 2 & 4 & -6 & -6 \\ 0 & 0 & 0 & -5 & 0 \\ 0 & 0 & 0 & 0 & 0 \end{bmatrix} \quad \text{General form:} \quad \begin{bmatrix} \blacksquare & * & * & * & * \\ 0 & \blacksquare & * & * & * \\ 0 & 0 & 0 & \blacksquare & * \\ 0 & 0 & 0 & 0 & 0 \end{bmatrix}$$

The matrix is in echelon form and thus reveals that columns $1, 2$, and $4$ of $A$ are pivot columns.

$$A = \begin{bmatrix} 0 & -3 & -6 & 4 & 9 \\ -1 & -2 & -1 & 3 & 1 \\ -2 & -3 & 0 & 3 & -1 \\ 1 & 4 & 5 & -9 & -7 \end{bmatrix} \tag{3}$$

A **pivot**, as illustrated in Example 2, is a nonzero number in a pivot position that is used as needed to create zeros via row operations. The pivots in Example 2 were $1, 2$, and $-5$. Notice that these numbers are not the same as the actual elements of $A$ in the highlighted pivot positions shown in (3).

With Example 2 as a guide, we are ready to describe an efficient procedure for transforming a matrix into an echelon or reduced echelon matrix. Careful study and mastery of this procedure now will pay rich dividends later in the course.

## The Row Reduction Algorithm

The algorithm that follows consists of four steps, and it produces a matrix in echelon form. A fifth step produces a matrix in reduced echelon form. We illustrate the algorithm by an example.

**EXAMPLE 3**    Apply elementary row operations to transform the following matrix first into echelon form and then into reduced echelon form:

$$\begin{bmatrix} 0 & 3 & -6 & 6 & 4 & -5 \\ 3 & -7 & 8 & -5 & 8 & 9 \\ 3 & -9 & 12 & -9 & 6 & 15 \end{bmatrix}$$

SOLUTION

---

STEP 1

Begin with the leftmost nonzero column. This is a pivot column. The pivot position is at the top.

---

$$\begin{bmatrix} 0 & 3 & -6 & 6 & 4 & -5 \\ 3 & -7 & 8 & -5 & 8 & 9 \\ 3 & -9 & 12 & -9 & 6 & 15 \end{bmatrix}$$

↑
└── Pivot column

---

**STEP 2**

Select a nonzero entry in the pivot column as a pivot. If necessary, interchange rows to move this entry into the pivot position.

---

Interchange rows 1 and 3. (We could have interchanged rows 1 and 2 instead.)

┌── Pivot

$$\begin{bmatrix} 3 & -9 & 12 & -9 & 6 & 15 \\ 3 & -7 & 8 & -5 & 8 & 9 \\ 0 & 3 & -6 & 6 & 4 & -5 \end{bmatrix}$$

---

**STEP 3**

Use row replacement operations to create zeros in all positions below the pivot.

---

As a preliminary step, we could divide the top row by the pivot, 3. But with two 3's in column 1, it is just as easy to add $-1$ times row 1 to row 2.

┌── Pivot

$$\begin{bmatrix} 3 & -9 & 12 & -9 & 6 & 15 \\ 0 & 2 & -4 & 4 & 2 & -6 \\ 0 & 3 & -6 & 6 & 4 & -5 \end{bmatrix}$$

---

**STEP 4**

Cover (or ignore) the row containing the pivot position and cover all rows, if any, above it. Apply steps 1–3 to the submatrix that remains. Repeat the process until there are no more nonzero rows to modify.

---

With row 1 covered, step 1 shows that column 2 is the next pivot column; for step 2, select as a pivot the "top" entry in that column.

┌── Pivot

$$\begin{bmatrix} 3 & -9 & 12 & -9 & 6 & 15 \\ 0 & 2 & -4 & 4 & 2 & -6 \\ 0 & 3 & -6 & 6 & 4 & -5 \end{bmatrix}$$

↑
└── New pivot column

For step 3, we could insert an optional step of dividing the "top" row of the submatrix by the pivot, 2. Instead, we add $-3/2$ times the "top" row to the row below. This produces

$$\begin{bmatrix} 3 & -9 & 12 & -9 & 6 & 15 \\ 0 & 2 & -4 & 4 & 2 & -6 \\ 0 & 0 & 0 & 0 & 1 & 4 \end{bmatrix}$$

When we cover the row containing the second pivot position for step 4, we are left with a new submatrix having only one row:

$$\begin{bmatrix} 3 & -9 & 12 & -9 & 6 & 15 \\ 0 & 2 & -4 & 4 & 2 & -6 \\ 0 & 0 & 0 & 0 & 1 & 4 \end{bmatrix}$$

⎿— Pivot

Steps 1–3 require no work for this submatrix, and we have reached an echelon form of the full matrix. If we want the reduced echelon form, we perform one more step.

---

**STEP 5**

Beginning with the rightmost pivot and working upward and to the left, create zeros above each pivot. If a pivot is not 1, make it 1 by a scaling operation.

---

The rightmost pivot is in row 3. Create zeros above it, adding suitable multiples of row 3 to rows 2 and 1.

$$\begin{bmatrix} 3 & -9 & 12 & -9 & 0 & -9 \\ 0 & 2 & -4 & 4 & 0 & -14 \\ 0 & 0 & 0 & 0 & 1 & 4 \end{bmatrix}$$

←— Row 1 + (−6) · row 3
←— Row 2 + (−2) · row 3

The next pivot is in row 2. Scale this row, dividing by the pivot.

$$\begin{bmatrix} 3 & -9 & 12 & -9 & 0 & -9 \\ 0 & 1 & -2 & 2 & 0 & -7 \\ 0 & 0 & 0 & 0 & 1 & 4 \end{bmatrix}$$

←— Row scaled by $\frac{1}{2}$

Create a zero in column 2 by adding 9 times row 2 to row 1.

$$\begin{bmatrix} 3 & 0 & -6 & 9 & 0 & -72 \\ 0 & 1 & -2 & 2 & 0 & -7 \\ 0 & 0 & 0 & 0 & 1 & 4 \end{bmatrix}$$

←— Row 1 + (9) · row 2

Finally, scale row 1, dividing by the pivot, 3.

$$\begin{bmatrix} 1 & 0 & -2 & 3 & 0 & -24 \\ 0 & 1 & -2 & 2 & 0 & -7 \\ 0 & 0 & 0 & 0 & 1 & 4 \end{bmatrix}$$

←— Row scaled by $\frac{1}{3}$

This is the reduced echelon form of the original matrix.   ■

The combination of steps 1–4 is called the **forward phase** of the row reduction algorithm. Step 5, which produces the unique reduced echelon form, is called the **backward phase**.

---

**NUMERICAL NOTE**

In step 2 above, a computer program usually selects as a pivot the entry in a column having the largest absolute value. This strategy, called **partial pivoting**, is used because it reduces roundoff errors in the calculations.

## Solutions of Linear Systems

The row reduction algorithm leads directly to an explicit description of the solution set of a linear system when the algorithm is applied to the augmented matrix of the system.

Suppose, for example, that the augmented matrix of a linear system has been changed into the equivalent *reduced* echelon form

$$\begin{bmatrix} 1 & 0 & -5 & 1 \\ 0 & 1 & 1 & 4 \\ 0 & 0 & 0 & 0 \end{bmatrix}$$

There are three variables because the augmented matrix has four columns. The associated system of equations is

$$
\begin{aligned}
x_1 \quad - 5x_3 &= 1 \\
x_2 + x_3 &= 4 \\
0 &= 0
\end{aligned}
\tag{4}
$$

The variables $x_1$ and $x_2$ corresponding to pivot columns in the matrix are called **basic variables**.[2] The other variable, $x_3$, is called a **free variable**.

Whenever a system is consistent, as in (4), the solution set can be described explicitly by solving the *reduced* system of equations for the basic variables in terms of the free variables. This operation is possible because the reduced echelon form places each basic variable in one and only one equation. In (4), solve the first equation for $x_1$ and the second for $x_2$. (Ignore the third equation; it offers no restriction on the variables.)

$$
\begin{cases}
x_1 = 1 + 5x_3 \\
x_2 = 4 - x_3 \\
x_3 \text{ is free}
\end{cases}
\tag{5}
$$

The statement "$x_3$ is free" means that you are free to choose any value for $x_3$. Once that is done, the formulas in (5) determine the values for $x_1$ and $x_2$. For instance, when $x_3 = 0$, the solution is $(1, 4, 0)$; when $x_3 = 1$, the solution is $(6, 3, 1)$. *Each different choice of $x_3$ determines a (different) solution of the system, and every solution of the system is determined by a choice of $x_3$.*

**EXAMPLE 4**    Find the general solution of the linear system whose augmented matrix has been reduced to

$$\begin{bmatrix} 1 & 6 & 2 & -5 & -2 & -4 \\ 0 & 0 & 2 & -8 & -1 & 3 \\ 0 & 0 & 0 & 0 & 1 & 7 \end{bmatrix}$$

**SOLUTION** The matrix is in echelon form, but we want the reduced echelon form before solving for the basic variables. The row reduction is completed next. The symbol $\sim$ before a matrix indicates that the matrix is row equivalent to the preceding matrix.

$$
\begin{bmatrix} 1 & 6 & 2 & -5 & -2 & -4 \\ 0 & 0 & 2 & -8 & -1 & 3 \\ 0 & 0 & 0 & 0 & 1 & 7 \end{bmatrix}
\sim
\begin{bmatrix} 1 & 6 & 2 & -5 & 0 & 10 \\ 0 & 0 & 2 & -8 & 0 & 10 \\ 0 & 0 & 0 & 0 & 1 & 7 \end{bmatrix}
$$

$$
\sim
\begin{bmatrix} 1 & 6 & 2 & -5 & 0 & 10 \\ 0 & 0 & 1 & -4 & 0 & 5 \\ 0 & 0 & 0 & 0 & 1 & 7 \end{bmatrix}
\sim
\begin{bmatrix} 1 & 6 & 0 & 3 & 0 & 0 \\ 0 & 0 & 1 & -4 & 0 & 5 \\ 0 & 0 & 0 & 0 & 1 & 7 \end{bmatrix}
$$

---

[2] Some texts use the term *leading variables* because they correspond to the columns containing leading entries.

There are five variables because the augmented matrix has six columns. The associated system now is

$$\begin{aligned} x_1 + 6x_2 \quad + 3x_4 \quad &= 0 \\ x_3 - 4x_4 \quad &= 5 \\ x_5 &= 7 \end{aligned} \qquad (6)$$

The pivot columns of the matrix are $1, 3,$ and $5,$ so the basic variables are $x_1, x_3,$ and $x_5$. The remaining variables, $x_2$ and $x_4$, must be free. Solve for the basic variables to obtain the general solution:

$$\begin{cases} x_1 = -6x_2 - 3x_4 \\ x_2 \text{ is free} \\ x_3 = 5 + 4x_4 \\ x_4 \text{ is free} \\ x_5 = 7 \end{cases} \qquad (7)$$

Note that the value of $x_5$ is already fixed by the third equation in system (6).    ∎

## Parametric Descriptions of Solution Sets

The descriptions in (5) and (7) are *parametric descriptions* of solution sets in which the free variables act as parameters. *Solving a system* amounts to finding a parametric description of the solution set or determining that the solution set is empty.

Whenever a system is consistent and has free variables, the solution set has many parametric descriptions. For instance, in system (4), we may add 5 times equation 2 to equation 1 and obtain the equivalent system

$$\begin{aligned} x_1 + 5x_2 \quad &= 21 \\ x_2 + x_3 &= \phantom{0}4 \end{aligned}$$

We could treat $x_2$ as a parameter and solve for $x_1$ and $x_3$ in terms of $x_2$, and we would have an accurate description of the solution set. However, to be consistent, we make the (arbitrary) convention of always using the free variables as the parameters for describing a solution set. (The answer section at the end of the text also reflects this convention.)

Whenever a system is inconsistent, the solution set is empty, even when the system has free variables. In this case, the solution set has *no* parametric representation.

## Back-Substitution

Consider the following system, whose augmented matrix is in echelon form but is *not* in reduced echelon form:

$$\begin{aligned} x_1 - 7x_2 + 2x_3 - 5x_4 + 8x_5 &= \phantom{-}10 \\ x_2 - 3x_3 + 3x_4 + \phantom{0}x_5 &= -5 \\ x_4 - \phantom{0}x_5 &= \phantom{-0}4 \end{aligned}$$

A computer program would solve this system by back-substitution, rather than by computing the reduced echelon form. That is, the program would solve equation 3 for $x_4$ in terms of $x_5$ and substitute the expression for $x_4$ into equation 2, solve equation 2 for $x_2$, and then substitute the expressions for $x_2$ and $x_4$ into equation 1 and solve for $x_1$.

Our matrix format for the backward phase of row reduction, which produces the reduced echelon form, has the same number of arithmetic operations as back-substitution. But the discipline of the matrix format substantially reduces the likelihood of errors during hand computations. The best strategy is to use only the *reduced* echelon form to solve a system! The *Study Guide* that accompanies this text offers several helpful suggestions for performing row operations accurately and rapidly.

---

NUMERICAL NOTE

In general, the forward phase of row reduction takes much longer than the backward phase. An algorithm for solving a system is usually measured in flops (or floating point operations). A **flop** is one arithmetic operation $(+, -, *, /)$ on two real floating point numbers.[3] For an $n \times (n + 1)$ matrix, the reduction to echelon form can take $2n^3/3 + n^2/2 - 7n/6$ flops (which is approximately $2n^3/3$ flops when $n$ is moderately large—say, $n \geq 30$). In contrast, further reduction to reduced echelon form needs at most $n^2$ flops.

---

## Existence and Uniqueness Questions

Although a nonreduced echelon form is a poor tool for solving a system, this form is just the right device for answering two fundamental questions posed in Section 1.1.

**EXAMPLE 5** Determine the existence and uniqueness of the solutions to the system

$$3x_2 - 6x_3 + 6x_4 + 4x_5 = -5$$
$$3x_1 - 7x_2 + 8x_3 - 5x_4 + 8x_5 = 9$$
$$3x_1 - 9x_2 + 12x_3 - 9x_4 + 6x_5 = 15$$

**SOLUTION** The augmented matrix of this system was row reduced in Example 3 to

$$\begin{bmatrix} 3 & -9 & 12 & -9 & 6 & 15 \\ 0 & 2 & -4 & 4 & 2 & -6 \\ 0 & 0 & 0 & 0 & 1 & 4 \end{bmatrix} \tag{8}$$

The basic variables are $x_1$, $x_2$, and $x_5$; the free variables are $x_3$ and $x_4$. There is no equation such as $0 = 1$ that would indicate an inconsistent system, so we could use back-substitution to find a solution. But the *existence* of a solution is already clear in (8). Also, the solution is *not unique* because there are free variables. Each different choice of $x_3$ and $x_4$ determines a different solution. Thus the system has infinitely many solutions. ∎

When a system is in echelon form and contains no equation of the form $0 = b$, with $b$ nonzero, every nonzero equation contains a basic variable with a nonzero coefficient. Either the basic variables are completely determined (with no free variables) or at least one of the basic variables may be expressed in terms of one or more free variables. In the former case, there is a unique solution; in the latter case, there are infinitely many solutions (one for each choice of values for the free variables).

These remarks justify the following theorem.

---

[3] Traditionally, a *flop* was only a multiplication or division, because addition and subtraction took much less time and could be ignored. The definition of *flop* given here is preferred now, as a result of advances in computer architecture. See Golub and Van Loan, *Matrix Computations*, 2nd ed. (Baltimore: The Johns Hopkins Press, 1989), pp. 19–20.

THEOREM 2    **Existence and Uniqueness Theorem**

A linear system is consistent if and only if the rightmost column of the augmented matrix is *not* a pivot column—that is, if and only if an echelon form of the augmented matrix has *no* row of the form

$$[0 \ \cdots \ 0 \ b] \qquad \text{with } b \text{ nonzero}$$

If a linear system is consistent, then the solution set contains either (i) a unique solution, when there are no free variables, or (ii) infinitely many solutions, when there is at least one free variable.

The following procedure outlines how to find and describe all solutions of a linear system.

---

**USING ROW REDUCTION TO SOLVE A LINEAR SYSTEM**

1. Write the augmented matrix of the system.
2. Use the row reduction algorithm to obtain an equivalent augmented matrix in echelon form. Decide whether the system is consistent. If there is no solution, stop; otherwise, go to the next step.
3. Continue row reduction to obtain the reduced echelon form.
4. Write the system of equations corresponding to the matrix obtained in step 3.
5. Rewrite each nonzero equation from step 4 so that its one basic variable is expressed in terms of any free variables appearing in the equation.

---

**PRACTICE PROBLEMS**

1. Find the general solution of the linear system whose augmented matrix is

$$\begin{bmatrix} 1 & -3 & -5 & 0 \\ 0 & 1 & -1 & -1 \end{bmatrix}$$

2. Find the general solution of the system

$$\begin{aligned} x_1 - 2x_2 - \ \ x_3 + 3x_4 &= 0 \\ -2x_1 + 4x_2 + 5x_3 - 5x_4 &= 3 \\ 3x_1 - 6x_2 - 6x_3 + 8x_4 &= 2 \end{aligned}$$

3. Suppose a $4 \times 7$ coefficient matrix for a system of equations has 4 pivots. Is the system consistent? If the system is consistent, how many solutions are there?

## 1.2 EXERCISES

In Exercises 1 and 2, determine which matrices are in reduced echelon form and which others are only in echelon form.

**1. a.** $\begin{bmatrix} 1 & 0 & 0 & 0 \\ 0 & 1 & 0 & 0 \\ 0 & 0 & 1 & 1 \end{bmatrix}$ **b.** $\begin{bmatrix} 1 & 0 & 1 & 0 \\ 0 & 1 & 1 & 0 \\ 0 & 0 & 0 & 1 \end{bmatrix}$

**c.** $\begin{bmatrix} 1 & 0 & 0 & 0 \\ 0 & 1 & 1 & 0 \\ 0 & 0 & 0 & 0 \\ 0 & 0 & 0 & 1 \end{bmatrix}$ **d.** $\begin{bmatrix} 1 & 1 & 0 & 1 & 1 \\ 0 & 2 & 0 & 2 & 2 \\ 0 & 0 & 0 & 3 & 3 \\ 0 & 0 & 0 & 0 & 4 \end{bmatrix}$

**2. a.** $\begin{bmatrix} 1 & 1 & 0 & 1 \\ 0 & 0 & 1 & 1 \\ 0 & 0 & 0 & 0 \end{bmatrix}$  **b.** $\begin{bmatrix} 1 & 1 & 0 & 0 \\ 0 & 1 & 1 & 0 \\ 0 & 0 & 1 & 1 \end{bmatrix}$

**c.** $\begin{bmatrix} 1 & 0 & 0 & 0 \\ 1 & 1 & 0 & 0 \\ 0 & 1 & 1 & 0 \\ 0 & 0 & 1 & 1 \end{bmatrix}$

**d.** $\begin{bmatrix} 0 & 1 & 1 & 1 & 1 \\ 0 & 0 & 2 & 2 & 2 \\ 0 & 0 & 0 & 0 & 3 \\ 0 & 0 & 0 & 0 & 0 \end{bmatrix}$

Row reduce the matrices in Exercises 3 and 4 to reduced echelon form. Circle the pivot positions in the final matrix and in the original matrix, and list the pivot columns.

**3.** $\begin{bmatrix} 1 & 2 & 3 & 4 \\ 4 & 5 & 6 & 7 \\ 6 & 7 & 8 & 9 \end{bmatrix}$  **4.** $\begin{bmatrix} 1 & 3 & 5 & 7 \\ 3 & 5 & 7 & 9 \\ 5 & 7 & 9 & 1 \end{bmatrix}$

**5.** Describe the possible echelon forms of a nonzero $2 \times 2$ matrix. Use the symbols ■, ∗, and 0, as in the first part of Example 1.

**6.** Repeat Exercise 5 for a nonzero $3 \times 2$ matrix.

Find the general solutions of the systems whose augmented matrices are given in Exercises 7–14.

**7.** $\begin{bmatrix} 1 & 3 & 4 & 7 \\ 3 & 9 & 7 & 6 \end{bmatrix}$  **8.** $\begin{bmatrix} 1 & 4 & 0 & 7 \\ 2 & 7 & 0 & 10 \end{bmatrix}$

**9.** $\begin{bmatrix} 0 & 1 & -6 & 5 \\ 1 & -2 & 7 & -6 \end{bmatrix}$  **10.** $\begin{bmatrix} 1 & -2 & -1 & 3 \\ 3 & -6 & -2 & 2 \end{bmatrix}$

**11.** $\begin{bmatrix} 3 & -4 & 2 & 0 \\ -9 & 12 & -6 & 0 \\ -6 & 8 & -4 & 0 \end{bmatrix}$  **12.** $\begin{bmatrix} 1 & -7 & 0 & 6 & 5 \\ 0 & 0 & 1 & -2 & -3 \\ -1 & 7 & -4 & 2 & 7 \end{bmatrix}$

**13.** $\begin{bmatrix} 1 & -3 & 0 & -1 & 0 & -2 \\ 0 & 1 & 0 & 0 & -4 & 1 \\ 0 & 0 & 0 & 1 & 9 & 4 \\ 0 & 0 & 0 & 0 & 0 & 0 \end{bmatrix}$

**14.** $\begin{bmatrix} 1 & 2 & -5 & -6 & 0 & -5 \\ 0 & 1 & -6 & -3 & 0 & 2 \\ 0 & 0 & 0 & 0 & 1 & 0 \\ 0 & 0 & 0 & 0 & 0 & 0 \end{bmatrix}$

Exercises 15 and 16 use the notation of Example 1 for matrices in echelon form. Suppose each matrix represents the augmented matrix for a system of linear equations. In each case, determine if the system is consistent. If the system is consistent, determine if the solution is unique.

**15. a.** $\begin{bmatrix} ■ & ∗ & ∗ & ∗ \\ 0 & ■ & ∗ & ∗ \\ 0 & 0 & ■ & 0 \end{bmatrix}$

**b.** $\begin{bmatrix} 0 & ■ & ∗ & ∗ & ∗ \\ 0 & 0 & ■ & ∗ & ∗ \\ 0 & 0 & 0 & 0 & ■ \end{bmatrix}$

**16. a.** $\begin{bmatrix} ■ & ∗ & ∗ \\ 0 & ■ & ∗ \\ 0 & 0 & 0 \end{bmatrix}$

**b.** $\begin{bmatrix} ■ & ∗ & ∗ & ∗ & ∗ \\ 0 & 0 & ■ & ∗ & ∗ \\ 0 & 0 & 0 & ■ & ∗ \end{bmatrix}$

In Exercises 17 and 18, determine the value(s) of $h$ such that the matrix is the augmented matrix of a consistent linear system.

**17.** $\begin{bmatrix} 2 & 3 & h \\ 4 & 6 & 7 \end{bmatrix}$  **18.** $\begin{bmatrix} 1 & -3 & -2 \\ 5 & h & -7 \end{bmatrix}$

In Exercises 19 and 20, choose $h$ and $k$ such that the system has (a) no solution, (b) a unique solution, and (c) many solutions. Give separate answers for each part.

**19.** $x_1 + hx_2 = 2$
$4x_1 + 8x_2 = k$

**20.** $x_1 + 3x_2 = 2$
$3x_1 + hx_2 = k$

In Exercises 21 and 22, mark each statement True or False. Justify each answer.[4]

**21. a.** In some cases, a matrix may be row reduced to more than one matrix in reduced echelon form, using different sequences of row operations.

**b.** The row reduction algorithm applies only to augmented matrices for a linear system.

**c.** A basic variable in a linear system is a variable that corresponds to a pivot column in the coefficient matrix.

**d.** Finding a parametric description of the solution set of a linear system is the same as *solving* the system.

**e.** If one row in an echelon form of an augmented matrix is $[0 \ 0 \ 0 \ 5 \ 0]$, then the associated linear system is inconsistent.

**22. a.** The echelon form of a matrix is unique.

**b.** The pivot positions in a matrix depend on whether row interchanges are used in the row reduction process.

**c.** Reducing a matrix to echelon form is called the *forward phase* of the row reduction process.

**d.** Whenever a system has free variables, the solution set contains many solutions.

**e.** A general solution of a system is an explicit description of all solutions of the system.

**23.** Suppose a $3 \times 5$ *coefficient* matrix for a system has three pivot columns. Is the system consistent? Why or why not?

**24.** Suppose a system of linear equations has a $3 \times 5$ *augmented* matrix whose fifth column is a pivot column. Is the system consistent? Why (or why not)?

---

[4] True/false questions of this type will appear in many sections. Methods for justifying your answers were described before Exercises 23 and 24 in Section 1.1.

**25.** Suppose the coefficient matrix of a system of linear equations has a pivot position in every row. Explain why the system is consistent.

**26.** Suppose the coefficient matrix of a linear system of three equations in three variables has a pivot in each column. Explain why the system has a unique solution.

**27.** Restate the last sentence in Theorem 2 using the concept of pivot columns: "If a linear system is consistent, then the solution is unique if and only if _____."

**28.** What would you have to know about the pivot columns in an augmented matrix in order to know that the linear system is consistent and has a unique solution?

**29.** A system of linear equations with fewer equations than unknowns is sometimes called an *underdetermined system.* Suppose that such a system happens to be consistent. Explain why there must be an infinite number of solutions.

**30.** Give an example of an inconsistent underdetermined system of two equations in three unknowns.

**31.** A system of linear equations with more equations than unknowns is sometimes called an *overdetermined system.* Can such a system be consistent? Illustrate your answer with a specific system of three equations in two unknowns.

**32.** Suppose an $n \times (n + 1)$ matrix is row reduced to reduced echelon form. Approximately what fraction of the total number of operations (flops) is involved in the backward phase of the reduction when $n = 30$? when $n = 300$?

Suppose experimental data are represented by a set of points in the plane. An **interpolating polynomial** for the data is a polynomial whose graph passes through every point. In scientific work, such a polynomial can be used, for example, to estimate values between the known data points. Another use is to create curves for graphical images on a computer screen. One method for finding an interpolating polynomial is to solve a system of linear equations.

WEB

**33.** Find the interpolating polynomial $p(t) = a_0 + a_1 t + a_2 t^2$ for the data $(1, 12), (2, 15), (3, 16)$. That is, find $a_0, a_1,$ and $a_2$ such that

$$a_0 + a_1(1) + a_2(1)^2 = 12$$
$$a_0 + a_1(2) + a_2(2)^2 = 15$$
$$a_0 + a_1(3) + a_2(3)^2 = 16$$

**34.** [M] In a wind tunnel experiment, the force on a projectile due to air resistance was measured at different velocities:

| Velocity (100 ft/sec) | 0 | 2 | 4 | 6 | 8 | 10 |
|---|---|---|---|---|---|---|
| Force (100 lb) | 0 | 2.90 | 14.8 | 39.6 | 74.3 | 119 |

Find an interpolating polynomial for these data and estimate the force on the projectile when the projectile is traveling at 750 ft/sec. Use $p(t) = a_0 + a_1 t + a_2 t^2 + a_3 t^3 + a_4 t^4 + a_5 t^5$. What happens if you try to use a polynomial of degree less than 5? (Try a cubic polynomial, for instance.)[5]

———

[5] Exercises marked with the symbol [M] are designed to be worked with the aid of a "**M**atrix program" (a computer program, such as MATLAB, Maple, Mathematica, MathCad, or Derive, or a programmable calculator with matrix capabilities, such as those manufactured by Texas Instruments or Hewlett-Packard).

## SOLUTIONS TO PRACTICE PROBLEMS

**1.** The reduced echelon form of the augmented matrix and the corresponding system are

$$\begin{bmatrix} 1 & 0 & -8 & -3 \\ 0 & 1 & -1 & -1 \end{bmatrix} \quad \text{and} \quad \begin{array}{r} x_1 \quad - 8x_3 = -3 \\ x_2 - x_3 = -1 \end{array}$$

The basic variables are $x_1$ and $x_2$, and the general solution is

$$\begin{cases} x_1 = -3 + 8x_3 \\ x_2 = -1 + x_3 \\ x_3 \text{ is free} \end{cases}$$

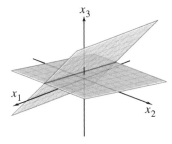

The general solution of the system of equations is the line of intersection of the two planes.

*Note:* It is essential that the general solution describe each variable, with any parameters clearly identified. The following statement does *not* describe the solution:

$$\begin{cases} x_1 = -3 + 8x_3 \\ x_2 = -1 + x_3 \\ x_3 = 1 + x_2 \quad \text{Incorrect solution} \end{cases}$$

This description implies that $x_2$ and $x_3$ are *both* free, which certainly is not the case.

**2.** Row reduce the system's augmented matrix:

$$\begin{bmatrix} 1 & -2 & -1 & 3 & 0 \\ -2 & 4 & 5 & -5 & 3 \\ 3 & -6 & -6 & 8 & 2 \end{bmatrix} \sim \begin{bmatrix} 1 & -2 & -1 & 3 & 0 \\ 0 & 0 & 3 & 1 & 3 \\ 0 & 0 & -3 & -1 & 2 \end{bmatrix}$$

$$\sim \begin{bmatrix} 1 & -2 & -1 & 3 & 0 \\ 0 & 0 & 3 & 1 & 3 \\ 0 & 0 & 0 & 0 & 5 \end{bmatrix}$$

This echelon matrix shows that the system is *inconsistent*, because its rightmost column is a pivot column; the third row corresponds to the equation $0 = 5$. There is no need to perform any more row operations. Note that the presence of the free variables in this problem is irrelevant because the system is inconsistent.

**3.** Since the coefficient matrix has four pivots, there is a pivot in every row of the coefficient matrix. This means that when the coefficient matrix is row reduced, it will *not* have a row of zeros, thus the corresponding row reduced augmented matrix can never have a row of the form $[0 \ 0 \ \cdots \ 0 \ b]$, where $b$ is a nonzero number. By Theorem 2, the system is consistent. Moreover, since there are seven columns in the coefficient matrix and only four pivot columns, there will be three free variables resulting in infinitely many solutions.

## 1.3 | VECTOR EQUATIONS

Important properties of linear systems can be described with the concept and notation of vectors. This section connects equations involving vectors to ordinary systems of equations. The term *vector* appears in a variety of mathematical and physical contexts. Until then, *vector* will mean an *ordered list of numbers*. This simple idea enables us to get to interesting and important applications as quickly as possible.

### Vectors in $\mathbb{R}^2$

A matrix with only one column is called a **column vector**, or simply a **vector**. Examples of vectors with two entries are

$$\mathbf{u} = \begin{bmatrix} 3 \\ -1 \end{bmatrix}, \qquad \mathbf{v} = \begin{bmatrix} .2 \\ .3 \end{bmatrix}, \qquad \mathbf{w} = \begin{bmatrix} w_1 \\ w_2 \end{bmatrix}$$

where $w_1$ and $w_2$ are any real numbers. The set of all vectors with two entries is denoted by $\mathbb{R}^2$ (read "r-two"). The $\mathbb{R}$ stands for the real numbers that appear as entries in the vectors, and the exponent 2 indicates that each vector contains two entries.[1]

Two vectors in $\mathbb{R}^2$ are **equal** if and only if their corresponding entries are equal. Thus $\begin{bmatrix} 4 \\ 7 \end{bmatrix}$ and $\begin{bmatrix} 7 \\ 4 \end{bmatrix}$ are *not* equal, because vectors in $\mathbb{R}^2$ are *ordered pairs* of real numbers.

---

[1] Most of the text concerns vectors and matrices that have only real entries. However, all definitions and theorems in Chapters 1–3, and in most of the rest of the text, remain valid if the entries are complex numbers. Complex vectors and matrices arise naturally, for example, in electrical engineering and physics.

Given two vectors $\mathbf{u}$ and $\mathbf{v}$ in $\mathbb{R}^2$, their **sum** is the vector $\mathbf{u} + \mathbf{v}$ obtained by adding corresponding entries of $\mathbf{u}$ and $\mathbf{v}$. For example,

$$\begin{bmatrix} 1 \\ -2 \end{bmatrix} + \begin{bmatrix} 2 \\ 5 \end{bmatrix} = \begin{bmatrix} 1+2 \\ -2+5 \end{bmatrix} = \begin{bmatrix} 3 \\ 3 \end{bmatrix}$$

Given a vector $\mathbf{u}$ and a real number $c$, the **scalar multiple** of $\mathbf{u}$ by $c$ is the vector $c\mathbf{u}$ obtained by multiplying each entry in $\mathbf{u}$ by $c$. For instance,

$$\text{if} \quad \mathbf{u} = \begin{bmatrix} 3 \\ -1 \end{bmatrix} \quad \text{and} \quad c = 5, \quad \text{then} \quad c\mathbf{u} = 5\begin{bmatrix} 3 \\ -1 \end{bmatrix} = \begin{bmatrix} 15 \\ -5 \end{bmatrix}$$

The number $c$ in $c\mathbf{u}$ is called a **scalar**; it is written in lightface type to distinguish it from the boldface vector $\mathbf{u}$.

The operations of scalar multiplication and vector addition can be combined, as in the following example.

**EXAMPLE 1** Given $\mathbf{u} = \begin{bmatrix} 1 \\ -2 \end{bmatrix}$ and $\mathbf{v} = \begin{bmatrix} 2 \\ -5 \end{bmatrix}$, find $4\mathbf{u}$, $(-3)\mathbf{v}$, and $4\mathbf{u} + (-3)\mathbf{v}$.

**SOLUTION**

$$4\mathbf{u} = \begin{bmatrix} 4 \\ -8 \end{bmatrix}, \qquad (-3)\mathbf{v} = \begin{bmatrix} -6 \\ 15 \end{bmatrix}$$

and

$$4\mathbf{u} + (-3)\mathbf{v} = \begin{bmatrix} 4 \\ -8 \end{bmatrix} + \begin{bmatrix} -6 \\ 15 \end{bmatrix} = \begin{bmatrix} -2 \\ 7 \end{bmatrix} \qquad \blacksquare$$

Sometimes, for convenience (and also to save space), this text may write a column vector such as $\begin{bmatrix} 3 \\ -1 \end{bmatrix}$ in the form $(3, -1)$. In this case, the parentheses and the comma distinguish the vector $(3, -1)$ from the $1 \times 2$ row matrix $\begin{bmatrix} 3 & -1 \end{bmatrix}$, written with brackets and no comma. Thus

$$\begin{bmatrix} 3 \\ -1 \end{bmatrix} \neq \begin{bmatrix} 3 & -1 \end{bmatrix}$$

because the matrices have different shapes, even though they have the same entries.

## Geometric Descriptions of $\mathbb{R}^2$

Consider a rectangular coordinate system in the plane. Because each point in the plane is determined by an ordered pair of numbers, *we can identify a geometric point $(a, b)$ with the column vector* $\begin{bmatrix} a \\ b \end{bmatrix}$. So we may regard $\mathbb{R}^2$ as the set of all points in the plane. See Figure 1.

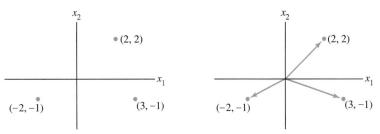

**FIGURE 1** Vectors as points.          **FIGURE 2** Vectors with arrows.

The geometric visualization of a vector such as $\begin{bmatrix} 3 \\ -1 \end{bmatrix}$ is often aided by including an arrow (directed line segment) from the origin $(0, 0)$ to the point $(3, -1)$, as in Figure 2. In this case, the individual points along the arrow itself have no special significance.[2]

The sum of two vectors has a useful geometric representation. The following rule can be verified by analytic geometry.

> ### Parallelogram Rule for Addition
>
> If $\mathbf{u}$ and $\mathbf{v}$ in $\mathbb{R}^2$ are represented as points in the plane, then $\mathbf{u} + \mathbf{v}$ corresponds to the fourth vertex of the parallelogram whose other vertices are $\mathbf{u}$, $\mathbf{0}$, and $\mathbf{v}$. See Figure 3.

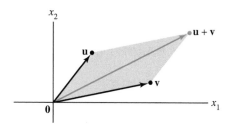

**FIGURE 3**  The parallelogram rule.

**EXAMPLE 2**  The vectors $\mathbf{u} = \begin{bmatrix} 2 \\ 2 \end{bmatrix}$, $\mathbf{v} = \begin{bmatrix} -6 \\ 1 \end{bmatrix}$, and $\mathbf{u} + \mathbf{v} = \begin{bmatrix} -4 \\ 3 \end{bmatrix}$ are displayed in Figure 4.  ∎

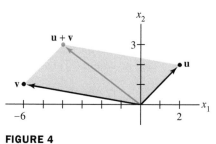

**FIGURE 4**

The next example illustrates the fact that the set of all scalar multiples of one fixed nonzero vector is a line through the origin, $(0, 0)$.

**EXAMPLE 3**  Let $\mathbf{u} = \begin{bmatrix} 3 \\ -1 \end{bmatrix}$. Display the vectors $\mathbf{u}$, $2\mathbf{u}$, and $-\frac{2}{3}\mathbf{u}$ on a graph.

**SOLUTION**  See Figure 5, where $\mathbf{u}$, $2\mathbf{u} = \begin{bmatrix} 6 \\ -2 \end{bmatrix}$, and $-\frac{2}{3}\mathbf{u} = \begin{bmatrix} -2 \\ 2/3 \end{bmatrix}$ are displayed. The arrow for $2\mathbf{u}$ is twice as long as the arrow for $\mathbf{u}$, and the arrows point in the same direction. The arrow for $-\frac{2}{3}\mathbf{u}$ is two-thirds the length of the arrow for $\mathbf{u}$, and the arrows point in opposite directions. In general, the length of the arrow for $c\mathbf{u}$ is $|c|$ times the length of the arrow for $\mathbf{u}$. [Recall that the length of the line segment from $(0, 0)$ to $(a, b)$ is $\sqrt{a^2 + b^2}$.]

---

[2] In physics, arrows can represent forces and usually are free to move about in space. This interpretation of vectors.

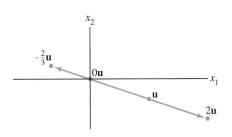

Typical multiples of **u**

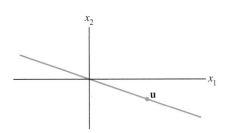

The set of all multiples of **u**

**FIGURE 5**

# Vectors in $\mathbb{R}^3$

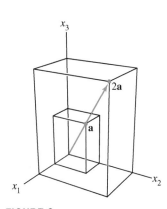

**FIGURE 6**

Scalar multiples.

Vectors in $\mathbb{R}^3$ are $3 \times 1$ column matrices with three entries. They are represented geometrically by points in a three-dimensional coordinate space, with arrows from the origin sometimes included for visual clarity. The vectors $\mathbf{a} = \begin{bmatrix} 2 \\ 3 \\ 4 \end{bmatrix}$ and $2\mathbf{a}$ are displayed in Figure 6.

# Vectors in $\mathbb{R}^n$

If $n$ is a positive integer, $\mathbb{R}^n$ (read "r-n") denotes the collection of all lists (or *ordered n-tuples*) of $n$ real numbers, usually written as $n \times 1$ column matrices, such as

$$\mathbf{u} = \begin{bmatrix} u_1 \\ u_2 \\ \vdots \\ u_n \end{bmatrix}$$

The vector whose entries are all zero is called the **zero vector** and is denoted by $\mathbf{0}$. (The number of entries in $\mathbf{0}$ will be clear from the context.)

Equality of vectors in $\mathbb{R}^n$ and the operations of scalar multiplication and vector addition in $\mathbb{R}^n$ are defined entry by entry just as in $\mathbb{R}^2$. These operations on vectors have the following properties, which can be verified directly from the corresponding properties for real numbers. See Practice Problem 1 and Exercises 33 and 34 at the end of this section.

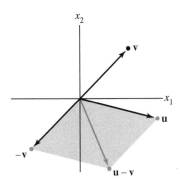

**FIGURE 7**

Vector subtraction.

> **Algebraic Properties of $\mathbb{R}^n$**
>
> For all $\mathbf{u}, \mathbf{v}, \mathbf{w}$ in $\mathbb{R}^n$ and all scalars $c$ and $d$:
>
> (i) $\mathbf{u} + \mathbf{v} = \mathbf{v} + \mathbf{u}$      (v) $c(\mathbf{u} + \mathbf{v}) = c\mathbf{u} + c\mathbf{v}$
>
> (ii) $(\mathbf{u} + \mathbf{v}) + \mathbf{w} = \mathbf{u} + (\mathbf{v} + \mathbf{w})$      (vi) $(c + d)\mathbf{u} = c\mathbf{u} + d\mathbf{u}$
>
> (iii) $\mathbf{u} + \mathbf{0} = \mathbf{0} + \mathbf{u} = \mathbf{u}$      (vii) $c(d\mathbf{u}) = (cd)\mathbf{u}$
>
> (iv) $\mathbf{u} + (-\mathbf{u}) = -\mathbf{u} + \mathbf{u} = \mathbf{0}$,      (viii) $1\mathbf{u} = \mathbf{u}$
>      where $-\mathbf{u}$ denotes $(-1)\mathbf{u}$

For simplicity of notation, a vector such as $\mathbf{u} + (-1)\mathbf{v}$ is often written as $\mathbf{u} - \mathbf{v}$. Figure 7 shows $\mathbf{u} - \mathbf{v}$ as the sum of $\mathbf{u}$ and $-\mathbf{v}$.

## Linear Combinations

Given vectors $\mathbf{v}_1, \mathbf{v}_2, \ldots, \mathbf{v}_p$ in $\mathbb{R}^n$ and given scalars $c_1, c_2, \ldots, c_p$, the vector $\mathbf{y}$ defined by

$$\mathbf{y} = c_1 \mathbf{v}_1 + \cdots + c_p \mathbf{v}_p$$

is called a **linear combination** of $\mathbf{v}_1, \ldots, \mathbf{v}_p$ with **weights** $c_1, \ldots, c_p$. Property (ii) above permits us to omit parentheses when forming such a linear combination. The weights in a linear combination can be any real numbers, including zero. For example, some linear combinations of vectors $\mathbf{v}_1$ and $\mathbf{v}_2$ are

$$\sqrt{3}\,\mathbf{v}_1 + \mathbf{v}_2, \quad \tfrac{1}{2}\mathbf{v}_1 \; (= \tfrac{1}{2}\mathbf{v}_1 + 0\mathbf{v}_2), \quad \text{and} \quad \mathbf{0} \; (= 0\mathbf{v}_1 + 0\mathbf{v}_2)$$

**EXAMPLE 4**   Figure 8 identifies selected linear combinations of $\mathbf{v}_1 = \begin{bmatrix} -1 \\ 1 \end{bmatrix}$ and $\mathbf{v}_2 = \begin{bmatrix} 2 \\ 1 \end{bmatrix}$. (Note that sets of parallel grid lines are drawn through integer multiples of $\mathbf{v}_1$ and $\mathbf{v}_2$.) Estimate the linear combinations of $\mathbf{v}_1$ and $\mathbf{v}_2$ that generate the vectors $\mathbf{u}$ and $\mathbf{w}$.

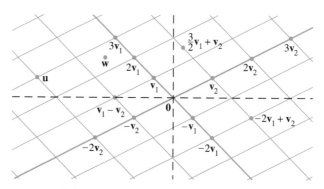

**FIGURE 8**   Linear combinations of $\mathbf{v}_1$ and $\mathbf{v}_2$.

**SOLUTION**   The parallelogram rule shows that $\mathbf{u}$ is the sum of $3\mathbf{v}_1$ and $-2\mathbf{v}_2$; that is,

$$\mathbf{u} = 3\mathbf{v}_1 - 2\mathbf{v}_2$$

This expression for $\mathbf{u}$ can be interpreted as instructions for traveling from the origin to $\mathbf{u}$ along two straight paths. First, travel 3 units in the $\mathbf{v}_1$ direction to $3\mathbf{v}_1$, and then travel $-2$ units in the $\mathbf{v}_2$ direction (parallel to the line through $\mathbf{v}_2$ and $\mathbf{0}$). Next, although the vector $\mathbf{w}$ is not on a grid line, $\mathbf{w}$ appears to be about halfway between two pairs of grid lines, at the vertex of a parallelogram determined by $(5/2)\mathbf{v}_1$ and $(-1/2)\mathbf{v}_2$. (See Figure 9.) Thus a reasonable estimate for $\mathbf{w}$ is

$$\mathbf{w} = \tfrac{5}{2}\mathbf{v}_1 - \tfrac{1}{2}\mathbf{v}_2 \qquad \blacksquare$$

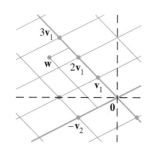

**FIGURE 9**

The next example connects a problem about linear combinations to the fundamental existence question studied in Sections 1.1 and 1.2.

**EXAMPLE 5**   Let $\mathbf{a}_1 = \begin{bmatrix} 1 \\ -2 \\ -5 \end{bmatrix}$, $\mathbf{a}_2 = \begin{bmatrix} 2 \\ 5 \\ 6 \end{bmatrix}$, and $\mathbf{b} = \begin{bmatrix} 7 \\ 4 \\ -3 \end{bmatrix}$. Determine whether $\mathbf{b}$ can be generated (or written) as a linear combination of $\mathbf{a}_1$ and $\mathbf{a}_2$. That is, determine whether weights $x_1$ and $x_2$ exist such that

$$x_1 \mathbf{a}_1 + x_2 \mathbf{a}_2 = \mathbf{b} \qquad (1)$$

If vector equation (1) has a solution, find it.

**SOLUTION**  Use the definitions of scalar multiplication and vector addition to rewrite the vector equation

$$x_1 \begin{bmatrix} 1 \\ -2 \\ -5 \end{bmatrix} + x_2 \begin{bmatrix} 2 \\ 5 \\ 6 \end{bmatrix} = \begin{bmatrix} 7 \\ 4 \\ -3 \end{bmatrix}$$

$$\uparrow \qquad\qquad \uparrow \qquad\quad \uparrow$$
$$\mathbf{a}_1 \qquad\qquad \mathbf{a}_2 \qquad\quad \mathbf{b}$$

which is the same as

$$\begin{bmatrix} x_1 \\ -2x_1 \\ -5x_1 \end{bmatrix} + \begin{bmatrix} 2x_2 \\ 5x_2 \\ 6x_2 \end{bmatrix} = \begin{bmatrix} 7 \\ 4 \\ -3 \end{bmatrix}$$

and

$$\begin{bmatrix} x_1 + 2x_2 \\ -2x_1 + 5x_2 \\ -5x_1 + 6x_2 \end{bmatrix} = \begin{bmatrix} 7 \\ 4 \\ -3 \end{bmatrix} \tag{2}$$

The vectors on the left and right sides of (2) are equal if and only if their corresponding entries are both equal. That is, $x_1$ and $x_2$ make the vector equation (1) true if and only if $x_1$ and $x_2$ satisfy the system

$$\begin{aligned} x_1 + 2x_2 &= 7 \\ -2x_1 + 5x_2 &= 4 \\ -5x_1 + 6x_2 &= -3 \end{aligned} \tag{3}$$

To solve this system, row reduce the augmented matrix of the system as follows:[3]

$$\begin{bmatrix} 1 & 2 & 7 \\ -2 & 5 & 4 \\ -5 & 6 & -3 \end{bmatrix} \sim \begin{bmatrix} 1 & 2 & 7 \\ 0 & 9 & 18 \\ 0 & 16 & 32 \end{bmatrix} \sim \begin{bmatrix} 1 & 2 & 7 \\ 0 & 1 & 2 \\ 0 & 16 & 32 \end{bmatrix} \sim \begin{bmatrix} 1 & 0 & 3 \\ 0 & 1 & 2 \\ 0 & 0 & 0 \end{bmatrix}$$

The solution of (3) is $x_1 = 3$ and $x_2 = 2$. Hence **b** is a linear combination of $\mathbf{a}_1$ and $\mathbf{a}_2$, with weights $x_1 = 3$ and $x_2 = 2$. That is,

$$3 \begin{bmatrix} 1 \\ -2 \\ -5 \end{bmatrix} + 2 \begin{bmatrix} 2 \\ 5 \\ 6 \end{bmatrix} = \begin{bmatrix} 7 \\ 4 \\ -3 \end{bmatrix} \qquad\blacksquare$$

Observe in Example 5 that the original vectors $\mathbf{a}_1$, $\mathbf{a}_2$, and **b** are the columns of the augmented matrix that we row reduced:

$$\begin{bmatrix} 1 & 2 & 7 \\ -2 & 5 & 4 \\ -5 & 6 & -3 \end{bmatrix}$$

$$\uparrow \quad \uparrow \quad \uparrow$$
$$\mathbf{a}_1 \quad \mathbf{a}_2 \quad \mathbf{b}$$

For brevity, write this matrix in a way that identifies its columns—namely,

$$[\,\mathbf{a}_1 \quad \mathbf{a}_2 \quad \mathbf{b}\,] \tag{4}$$

It is clear how to write this augmented matrix immediately from vector equation (1), without going through the intermediate steps of Example 5. Take the vectors in the order in which they appear in (1) and put them into the columns of a matrix as in (4).

The discussion above is easily modified to establish the following fundamental fact.

---

[3] The symbol $\sim$ between matrices denotes row equivalence (Section 1.2).

A vector equation

$$x_1\mathbf{a}_1 + x_2\mathbf{a}_2 + \cdots + x_n\mathbf{a}_n = \mathbf{b}$$

has the same solution set as the linear system whose augmented matrix is

$$\begin{bmatrix} \mathbf{a}_1 & \mathbf{a}_2 & \cdots & \mathbf{a}_n & \mathbf{b} \end{bmatrix} \tag{5}$$

In particular, $\mathbf{b}$ can be generated by a linear combination of $\mathbf{a}_1, \ldots, \mathbf{a}_n$ if and only if there exists a solution to the linear system corresponding to the matrix (5).

One of the key ideas in linear algebra is to study the set of all vectors that can be generated or written as a linear combination of a fixed set $\{\mathbf{v}_1, \ldots, \mathbf{v}_p\}$ of vectors.

DEFINITION

If $\mathbf{v}_1, \ldots, \mathbf{v}_p$ are in $\mathbb{R}^n$, then the set of all linear combinations of $\mathbf{v}_1, \ldots, \mathbf{v}_p$ is denoted by Span $\{\mathbf{v}_1, \ldots, \mathbf{v}_p\}$ and is called the **subset of $\mathbb{R}^n$ spanned** (or **generated**) **by** $\mathbf{v}_1, \ldots, \mathbf{v}_p$. That is, Span $\{\mathbf{v}_1, \ldots, \mathbf{v}_p\}$ is the collection of all vectors that can be written in the form

$$c_1\mathbf{v}_1 + c_2\mathbf{v}_2 + \cdots + c_p\mathbf{v}_p$$

with $c_1, \ldots, c_p$ scalars.

Asking whether a vector $\mathbf{b}$ is in Span $\{\mathbf{v}_1, \ldots, \mathbf{v}_p\}$ amounts to asking whether the vector equation

$$x_1\mathbf{v}_1 + x_2\mathbf{v}_2 + \cdots + x_p\mathbf{v}_p = \mathbf{b}$$

has a solution, or, equivalently, asking whether the linear system with augmented matrix $\begin{bmatrix} \mathbf{v}_1 & \cdots & \mathbf{v}_p & \mathbf{b} \end{bmatrix}$ has a solution.

Note that Span $\{\mathbf{v}_1, \ldots, \mathbf{v}_p\}$ contains every scalar multiple of $\mathbf{v}_1$ (for example), since $c\mathbf{v}_1 = c\mathbf{v}_1 + 0\mathbf{v}_2 + \cdots + 0\mathbf{v}_p$. In particular, the zero vector must be in Span $\{\mathbf{v}_1, \ldots, \mathbf{v}_p\}$.

## A Geometric Description of Span $\{\mathbf{v}\}$ and Span $\{\mathbf{u}, \mathbf{v}\}$

Let $\mathbf{v}$ be a nonzero vector in $\mathbb{R}^3$. Then Span $\{\mathbf{v}\}$ is the set of all scalar multiples of $\mathbf{v}$, which is the set of points on the line in $\mathbb{R}^3$ through $\mathbf{v}$ and $\mathbf{0}$. See Figure 10.

If $\mathbf{u}$ and $\mathbf{v}$ are nonzero vectors in $\mathbb{R}^3$, with $\mathbf{v}$ not a multiple of $\mathbf{u}$, then Span $\{\mathbf{u}, \mathbf{v}\}$ is the plane in $\mathbb{R}^3$ that contains $\mathbf{u}$, $\mathbf{v}$, and $\mathbf{0}$. In particular, Span $\{\mathbf{u}, \mathbf{v}\}$ contains the line in $\mathbb{R}^3$ through $\mathbf{u}$ and $\mathbf{0}$ and the line through $\mathbf{v}$ and $\mathbf{0}$. See Figure 11.

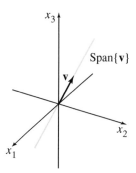

**FIGURE 10** Span $\{\mathbf{v}\}$ as a line through the origin.

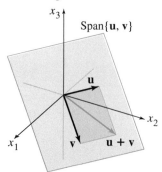

**FIGURE 11** Span $\{\mathbf{u}, \mathbf{v}\}$ as a plane through the origin.

**EXAMPLE 6**   Let   $\mathbf{a}_1 = \begin{bmatrix} 1 \\ -2 \\ 3 \end{bmatrix}$,   $\mathbf{a}_2 = \begin{bmatrix} 5 \\ -13 \\ -3 \end{bmatrix}$,   and   $\mathbf{b} = \begin{bmatrix} -3 \\ 8 \\ 1 \end{bmatrix}$.   Then

Span $\{\mathbf{a}_1, \mathbf{a}_2\}$ is a plane through the origin in $\mathbb{R}^3$. Is $\mathbf{b}$ in that plane?

**SOLUTION**   Does the equation $x_1\mathbf{a}_1 + x_2\mathbf{a}_2 = \mathbf{b}$ have a solution? To answer this, row reduce the augmented matrix $[\,\mathbf{a}_1 \quad \mathbf{a}_2 \quad \mathbf{b}\,]$:

$$\begin{bmatrix} 1 & 5 & -3 \\ -2 & -13 & 8 \\ 3 & -3 & 1 \end{bmatrix} \sim \begin{bmatrix} 1 & 5 & -3 \\ 0 & -3 & 2 \\ 0 & -18 & 10 \end{bmatrix} \sim \begin{bmatrix} 1 & 5 & -3 \\ 0 & -3 & 2 \\ 0 & 0 & -2 \end{bmatrix}$$

The third equation is $0 = -2$, which shows that the system has no solution. The vector equation $x_1\mathbf{a}_1 + x_2\mathbf{a}_2 = \mathbf{b}$ has no solution, and so $\mathbf{b}$ is *not* in Span $\{\mathbf{a}_1, \mathbf{a}_2\}$.   ■

## Linear Combinations in Applications

The final example shows how scalar multiples and linear combinations can arise when a quantity such as "cost" is broken down into several categories. The basic principle for the example concerns the cost of producing several units of an item when the cost per unit is known:

$$\left\{\begin{matrix} \text{number} \\ \text{of units} \end{matrix}\right\} \cdot \left\{\begin{matrix} \text{cost} \\ \text{per unit} \end{matrix}\right\} = \left\{\begin{matrix} \text{total} \\ \text{cost} \end{matrix}\right\}$$

**EXAMPLE 7**   A company manufactures two products. For \$1.00 worth of product B, the company spends \$.45 on materials, \$.25 on labor, and \$.15 on overhead. For \$1.00 worth of product C, the company spends \$.40 on materials, \$.30 on labor, and \$.15 on overhead. Let

$$\mathbf{b} = \begin{bmatrix} .45 \\ .25 \\ .15 \end{bmatrix} \quad \text{and} \quad \mathbf{c} = \begin{bmatrix} .40 \\ .30 \\ .15 \end{bmatrix}$$

Then $\mathbf{b}$ and $\mathbf{c}$ represent the "costs per dollar of income" for the two products.

a.  What economic interpretation can be given to the vector $100\mathbf{b}$?

b.  Suppose the company wishes to manufacture $x_1$ dollars worth of product B and $x_2$ dollars worth of product C. Give a vector that describes the various costs the company will have (for materials, labor, and overhead).

**SOLUTION**

a.  Compute

$$100\mathbf{b} = 100 \begin{bmatrix} .45 \\ .25 \\ .15 \end{bmatrix} = \begin{bmatrix} 45 \\ 25 \\ 15 \end{bmatrix}$$

The vector $100\mathbf{b}$ lists the various costs for producing \$100 worth of product B— namely, \$45 for materials, \$25 for labor, and \$15 for overhead.

b.  The costs of manufacturing $x_1$ dollars worth of B are given by the vector $x_1\mathbf{b}$, and the costs of manufacturing $x_2$ dollars worth of C are given by $x_2\mathbf{c}$. Hence the total costs for both products are given by the vector $x_1\mathbf{b} + x_2\mathbf{c}$.   ■

| PRACTICE PROBLEMS

**1.** Prove that $\mathbf{u} + \mathbf{v} = \mathbf{v} + \mathbf{u}$ for any $\mathbf{u}$ and $\mathbf{v}$ in $\mathbb{R}^n$.

**2.** For what value(s) of $h$ will $\mathbf{y}$ be in Span$\{\mathbf{v}_1, \mathbf{v}_2, \mathbf{v}_3\}$ if

$$\mathbf{v}_1 = \begin{bmatrix} 1 \\ -1 \\ -2 \end{bmatrix}, \qquad \mathbf{v}_2 = \begin{bmatrix} 5 \\ -4 \\ -7 \end{bmatrix}, \qquad \mathbf{v}_3 = \begin{bmatrix} -3 \\ 1 \\ 0 \end{bmatrix}, \quad \text{and} \quad \mathbf{y} = \begin{bmatrix} -4 \\ 3 \\ h \end{bmatrix}$$

**3.** Let $\mathbf{w}_1, \mathbf{w}_2, \mathbf{w}_3, \mathbf{u}$, and $\mathbf{v}$ be vectors in $\mathbb{R}^n$. Suppose the vectors $\mathbf{u}$ and $\mathbf{v}$ are in Span $\{\mathbf{w}_1, \mathbf{w}_2, \mathbf{w}_3\}$. Show that $\mathbf{u} + \mathbf{v}$ is also in Span $\{\mathbf{w}_1, \mathbf{w}_2, \mathbf{w}_3\}$. [*Hint:* The solution to Practice Problem 3 requires the use of the definition of the span of a set of vectors. It is useful to review this definition on Page 30 before starting this exercise.]

# 1.3 EXERCISES

In Exercises 1 and 2, compute $\mathbf{u} + \mathbf{v}$ and $\mathbf{u} - 2\mathbf{v}$.

**1.** $\mathbf{u} = \begin{bmatrix} -1 \\ 2 \end{bmatrix}, \mathbf{v} = \begin{bmatrix} -3 \\ -1 \end{bmatrix}$

**2.** $\mathbf{u} = \begin{bmatrix} 3 \\ 2 \end{bmatrix}, \mathbf{v} = \begin{bmatrix} 2 \\ -1 \end{bmatrix}$

In Exercises 3 and 4, display the following vectors using arrows on an $xy$-graph: $\mathbf{u}, \mathbf{v}, -\mathbf{v}, -2\mathbf{v}, \mathbf{u} + \mathbf{v}, \mathbf{u} - \mathbf{v}$, and $\mathbf{u} - 2\mathbf{v}$. Notice that $\mathbf{u} - \mathbf{v}$ is the vertex of a parallelogram whose other vertices are $\mathbf{u}, \mathbf{0}$, and $-\mathbf{v}$.

**3.** $\mathbf{u}$ and $\mathbf{v}$ as in Exercise 1      **4.** $\mathbf{u}$ and $\mathbf{v}$ as in Exercise 2

In Exercises 5 and 6, write a system of equations that is equivalent to the given vector equation.

**5.** $x_1 \begin{bmatrix} 6 \\ -1 \\ 5 \end{bmatrix} + x_2 \begin{bmatrix} -3 \\ 4 \\ 0 \end{bmatrix} = \begin{bmatrix} 1 \\ -7 \\ -5 \end{bmatrix}$

**6.** $x_1 \begin{bmatrix} -2 \\ 3 \end{bmatrix} + x_2 \begin{bmatrix} 8 \\ 5 \end{bmatrix} + x_3 \begin{bmatrix} 1 \\ -6 \end{bmatrix} = \begin{bmatrix} 0 \\ 0 \end{bmatrix}$

Use the accompanying figure to write each vector listed in Exercises 7 and 8 as a linear combination of $\mathbf{u}$ and $\mathbf{v}$. Is every vector in $\mathbb{R}^2$ a linear combination of $\mathbf{u}$ and $\mathbf{v}$?

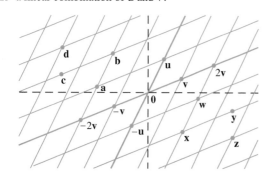

**7.** Vectors $\mathbf{a}, \mathbf{b}, \mathbf{c}$, and $\mathbf{d}$

**8.** Vectors $\mathbf{w}, \mathbf{x}, \mathbf{y}$, and $\mathbf{z}$

In Exercises 9 and 10, write a vector equation that is equivalent to the given system of equations.

**9.**
$$\begin{aligned} x_2 + 5x_3 &= 0 \\ 4x_1 + 6x_2 - x_3 &= 0 \\ -x_1 + 3x_2 - 8x_3 &= 0 \end{aligned}$$

**10.**
$$\begin{aligned} 4x_1 + x_2 + 3x_3 &= 9 \\ x_1 - 7x_2 - 2x_3 &= 2 \\ 8x_1 + 6x_2 - 5x_3 &= 15 \end{aligned}$$

In Exercises 11 and 12, determine if $\mathbf{b}$ is a linear combination of $\mathbf{a}_1, \mathbf{a}_2$, and $\mathbf{a}_3$.

**11.** $\mathbf{a}_1 = \begin{bmatrix} 1 \\ -2 \\ 0 \end{bmatrix}, \mathbf{a}_2 = \begin{bmatrix} 0 \\ 1 \\ 2 \end{bmatrix}, \mathbf{a}_3 = \begin{bmatrix} 5 \\ -6 \\ 8 \end{bmatrix}, \mathbf{b} = \begin{bmatrix} 2 \\ -1 \\ 6 \end{bmatrix}$

**12.** $\mathbf{a}_1 = \begin{bmatrix} 1 \\ -2 \\ 2 \end{bmatrix}, \mathbf{a}_2 = \begin{bmatrix} 0 \\ 5 \\ 5 \end{bmatrix}, \mathbf{a}_3 = \begin{bmatrix} 2 \\ 0 \\ 8 \end{bmatrix}, \mathbf{b} = \begin{bmatrix} -5 \\ 11 \\ -7 \end{bmatrix}$

In Exercises 13 and 14, determine if $\mathbf{b}$ is a linear combination of the vectors formed from the columns of the matrix $A$.

**13.** $A = \begin{bmatrix} 1 & -4 & 2 \\ 0 & 3 & 5 \\ -2 & 8 & -4 \end{bmatrix}, \mathbf{b} = \begin{bmatrix} 3 \\ -7 \\ -3 \end{bmatrix}$

**14.** $A = \begin{bmatrix} 1 & -2 & -6 \\ 0 & 3 & 7 \\ 1 & -2 & 5 \end{bmatrix}, \mathbf{b} = \begin{bmatrix} 11 \\ -5 \\ 9 \end{bmatrix}$

In Exercises 15 and 16, list five vectors in Span $\{\mathbf{v}_1, \mathbf{v}_2\}$. For each vector, show the weights on $\mathbf{v}_1$ and $\mathbf{v}_2$ used to generate the vector and list the three entries of the vector. Do not make a sketch.

**15.** $\mathbf{v}_1 = \begin{bmatrix} 7 \\ 1 \\ -6 \end{bmatrix}, \mathbf{v}_2 = \begin{bmatrix} -5 \\ 3 \\ 0 \end{bmatrix}$

**16.** $\mathbf{v}_1 = \begin{bmatrix} 3 \\ 0 \\ 2 \end{bmatrix}, \mathbf{v}_2 = \begin{bmatrix} -2 \\ 0 \\ 3 \end{bmatrix}$

**17.** Let $\mathbf{a}_1 = \begin{bmatrix} 1 \\ 4 \\ -2 \end{bmatrix}$, $\mathbf{a}_2 = \begin{bmatrix} -2 \\ -3 \\ 7 \end{bmatrix}$, and $\mathbf{b} = \begin{bmatrix} 4 \\ 1 \\ h \end{bmatrix}$. For what

value(s) of $h$ is $\mathbf{b}$ in the plane spanned by $\mathbf{a}_1$ and $\mathbf{a}_2$?

**18.** Let $\mathbf{v}_1 = \begin{bmatrix} 1 \\ 0 \\ -2 \end{bmatrix}$, $\mathbf{v}_2 = \begin{bmatrix} -3 \\ 1 \\ 8 \end{bmatrix}$, and $\mathbf{y} = \begin{bmatrix} h \\ -5 \\ -3 \end{bmatrix}$. For what

value(s) of $h$ is $\mathbf{y}$ in the plane generated by $\mathbf{v}_1$ and $\mathbf{v}_2$?

**19.** Give a geometric description of Span $\{\mathbf{v}_1, \mathbf{v}_2\}$ for the vectors

$$\mathbf{v}_1 = \begin{bmatrix} 8 \\ 2 \\ -6 \end{bmatrix} \text{ and } \mathbf{v}_2 = \begin{bmatrix} 12 \\ 3 \\ -9 \end{bmatrix}.$$

**20.** Give a geometric description of Span $\{\mathbf{v}_1, \mathbf{v}_2\}$ for the vectors in Exercise 16.

**21.** Let $\mathbf{u} = \begin{bmatrix} 2 \\ -1 \end{bmatrix}$ and $\mathbf{v} = \begin{bmatrix} 2 \\ 1 \end{bmatrix}$. Show that $\begin{bmatrix} h \\ k \end{bmatrix}$ is in

Span $\{\mathbf{u}, \mathbf{v}\}$ for all $h$ and $k$.

**22.** Construct a $3 \times 3$ matrix $A$, with nonzero entries, and a vector $\mathbf{b}$ in $\mathbb{R}^3$ such that $\mathbf{b}$ is *not* in the set spanned by the columns of $A$.

In Exercises 23 and 24, mark each statement True or False. Justify each answer.

**23. a.** Another notation for the vector $\begin{bmatrix} -4 \\ 3 \end{bmatrix}$ is $\begin{bmatrix} -4 & 3 \end{bmatrix}$.

   **b.** The points in the plane corresponding to $\begin{bmatrix} -2 \\ 5 \end{bmatrix}$ and

   $\begin{bmatrix} -5 \\ 2 \end{bmatrix}$ lie on a line through the origin.

   **c.** An example of a linear combination of vectors $\mathbf{v}_1$ and $\mathbf{v}_2$ is the vector $\frac{1}{2}\mathbf{v}_1$.

   **d.** The solution set of the linear system whose augmented matrix is $\begin{bmatrix} \mathbf{a}_1 & \mathbf{a}_2 & \mathbf{a}_3 & \mathbf{b} \end{bmatrix}$ is the same as the solution set of the equation $x_1\mathbf{a}_1 + x_2\mathbf{a}_2 + x_3\mathbf{a}_3 = \mathbf{b}$.

   **e.** The set Span $\{\mathbf{u}, \mathbf{v}\}$ is always visualized as a plane through the origin.

**24. a.** Any list of five real numbers is a vector in $\mathbb{R}^5$.

   **b.** The vector $\mathbf{u}$ results when a vector $\mathbf{u} - \mathbf{v}$ is added to the vector $\mathbf{v}$.

   **c.** The weights $c_1, \ldots, c_p$ in a linear combination $c_1\mathbf{v}_1 + \cdots + c_p\mathbf{v}_p$ cannot all be zero.

   **d.** When $\mathbf{u}$ and $\mathbf{v}$ are nonzero vectors, Span $\{\mathbf{u}, \mathbf{v}\}$ contains the line through $\mathbf{u}$ and the origin.

   **e.** Asking whether the linear system corresponding to an augmented matrix $\begin{bmatrix} \mathbf{a}_1 & \mathbf{a}_2 & \mathbf{a}_3 & \mathbf{b} \end{bmatrix}$ has a solution amounts to asking whether $\mathbf{b}$ is in Span $\{\mathbf{a}_1, \mathbf{a}_2, \mathbf{a}_3\}$.

**25.** Let $A = \begin{bmatrix} 1 & 0 & -4 \\ 0 & 3 & -2 \\ -2 & 6 & 3 \end{bmatrix}$ and $\mathbf{b} = \begin{bmatrix} 4 \\ 1 \\ -4 \end{bmatrix}$. Denote the

columns of $A$ by $\mathbf{a}_1, \mathbf{a}_2, \mathbf{a}_3$, and let $W = $ Span $\{\mathbf{a}_1, \mathbf{a}_2, \mathbf{a}_3\}$.

   **a.** Is $\mathbf{b}$ in $\{\mathbf{a}_1, \mathbf{a}_2, \mathbf{a}_3\}$? How many vectors are in $\{\mathbf{a}_1, \mathbf{a}_2, \mathbf{a}_3\}$?

   **b.** Is $\mathbf{b}$ in $W$? How many vectors are in $W$?

   **c.** Show that $\mathbf{a}_1$ is in $W$. [*Hint:* Row operations are unnecessary.]

**26.** Let $A = \begin{bmatrix} 2 & 0 & 6 \\ -1 & 8 & 5 \\ 1 & -2 & 1 \end{bmatrix}$, let $\mathbf{b} = \begin{bmatrix} 10 \\ 3 \\ 3 \end{bmatrix}$, and let $W$ be

the set of all linear combinations of the columns of $A$.

   **a.** Is $\mathbf{b}$ in $W$?

   **b.** Show that the third column of $A$ is in $W$.

**27.** A mining company has two mines. One day's operation at mine #1 produces ore that contains 20 metric tons of copper and 550 kilograms of silver, while one day's operation at mine #2 produces ore that contains 30 metric tons of copper and 500 kilograms of silver. Let $\mathbf{v}_1 = \begin{bmatrix} 20 \\ 550 \end{bmatrix}$ and

$\mathbf{v}_2 = \begin{bmatrix} 30 \\ 500 \end{bmatrix}$. Then $\mathbf{v}_1$ and $\mathbf{v}_2$ represent the "output per day"

of mine #1 and mine #2, respectively.

   **a.** What physical interpretation can be given to the vector $5\mathbf{v}_1$?

   **b.** Suppose the company operates mine #1 for $x_1$ days and mine #2 for $x_2$ days. Write a vector equation whose solution gives the number of days each mine should operate in order to produce 150 tons of copper and 2825 kilograms of silver. Do not solve the equation.

   **c.** [**M**] Solve the equation in (b).

**28.** A steam plant burns two types of coal: anthracite (A) and bituminous (B). For each ton of A burned, the plant produces 27.6 million Btu of heat, 3100 grams (g) of sulfur dioxide, and 250 g of particulate matter (solid-particle pollutants). For each ton of B burned, the plant produces 30.2 million Btu, 6400 g of sulfur dioxide, and 360 g of particulate matter.

   **a.** How much heat does the steam plant produce when it burns $x_1$ tons of A and $x_2$ tons of B?

   **b.** Suppose the output of the steam plant is described by a vector that lists the amounts of heat, sulfur dioxide, and particulate matter. Express this output as a linear combination of two vectors, assuming that the plant burns $x_1$ tons of A and $x_2$ tons of B.

   **c.** [**M**] Over a certain time period, the steam plant produced 162 million Btu of heat, 23,610 g of sulfur dioxide, and 1623 g of particulate matter. Determine how many tons of each type of coal the steam plant must have burned. Include a vector equation as part of your solution.

**29.** Let $\mathbf{v}_1, \ldots, \mathbf{v}_k$ be points in $\mathbb{R}^3$ and suppose that for $j = 1, \ldots, k$ an object with mass $m_j$ is located at point $\mathbf{v}_j$. Physicists call such objects *point masses*. The total mass of the system of point masses is

$$m = m_1 + \cdots + m_k$$

The *center of gravity* (or *center of mass*) of the system is

$$\bar{\mathbf{v}} = \frac{1}{m}[m_1\mathbf{v}_1 + \cdots + m_k\mathbf{v}_k]$$

Compute the center of gravity of the system consisting of the following point masses (see the figure):

| Point | Mass |
|---|---|
| $\mathbf{v}_1 = (5, -4, 3)$ | 2 g |
| $\mathbf{v}_2 = (4, 3, -2)$ | 5 g |
| $\mathbf{v}_3 = (-4, -3, -1)$ | 2 g |
| $\mathbf{v}_4 = (-9, 8, 6)$ | 1 g |

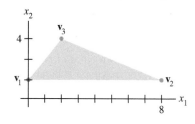

**30.** Let $\mathbf{v}$ be the center of mass of a system of point masses located at $\mathbf{v}_1, \ldots, \mathbf{v}_k$ as in Exercise 29. Is $\mathbf{v}$ in Span $\{\mathbf{v}_1, \ldots, \mathbf{v}_k\}$? Explain.

**31.** A thin triangular plate of uniform density and thickness has vertices at $\mathbf{v}_1 = (0, 1)$, $\mathbf{v}_2 = (8, 1)$, and $\mathbf{v}_3 = (2, 4)$, as in the figure below, and the mass of the plate is 3 g.

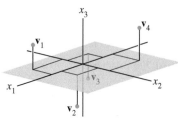

a. Find the $(x, y)$-coordinates of the center of mass of the plate. This "balance point" of the plate coincides with the center of mass of a system consisting of three 1-gram point masses located at the vertices of the plate.

b. Determine how to distribute an additional mass of 6 g at the three vertices of the plate to move the balance point of the plate to $(2, 2)$. [*Hint:* Let $w_1$, $w_2$, and $w_3$ denote the masses added at the three vertices, so that $w_1 + w_2 + w_3 = 6$.]

**32.** Consider the vectors $\mathbf{v}_1$, $\mathbf{v}_2$, $\mathbf{v}_3$, and $\mathbf{b}$ in $\mathbb{R}^2$, shown in the figure. Does the equation $x_1\mathbf{v}_1 + x_2\mathbf{v}_2 + x_3\mathbf{v}_3 = \mathbf{b}$ have a solution? Is the solution unique? Use the figure to explain your answers.

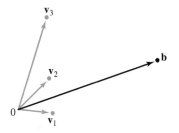

**33.** Use the vectors $\mathbf{u} = (u_1, \ldots, u_n)$, $\mathbf{v} = (v_1, \ldots, v_n)$, and $\mathbf{w} = (w_1, \ldots, w_n)$ to verify the following algebraic properties of $\mathbb{R}^n$.

a. $(\mathbf{u} + \mathbf{v}) + \mathbf{w} = \mathbf{u} + (\mathbf{v} + \mathbf{w})$

b. $c(\mathbf{u} + \mathbf{v}) = c\mathbf{u} + c\mathbf{v}$ for each scalar $c$

**34.** Use the vector $\mathbf{u} = (u_1, \ldots, u_n)$ to verify the following algebraic properties of $\mathbb{R}^n$.

a. $\mathbf{u} + (-\mathbf{u}) = (-\mathbf{u}) + \mathbf{u} = 0$

b. $c(d\mathbf{u}) = (cd)\mathbf{u}$ for all scalars $c$ and $d$

---

## SOLUTIONS TO PRACTICE PROBLEMS

**1.** Take arbitrary vectors $\mathbf{u} = (u_1, \ldots, u_n)$ and $\mathbf{v} = (v_1, \ldots, v_n)$ in $\mathbb{R}^n$, and compute

$$\mathbf{u} + \mathbf{v} = (u_1 + v_1, \ldots, u_n + v_n) \qquad \text{Definition of vector addition}$$
$$= (v_1 + u_1, \ldots, v_n + u_n) \qquad \text{Commutativity of addition in } \mathbb{R}$$
$$= \mathbf{v} + \mathbf{u} \qquad \text{Definition of vector addition}$$

The points $\begin{bmatrix} -4 \\ 3 \\ h \end{bmatrix}$ lie on a line that intersects the plane when $h = 5$.

**2.** The vector $\mathbf{y}$ belongs to Span $\{\mathbf{v}_1, \mathbf{v}_2, \mathbf{v}_3\}$ if and only if there exist scalars $x_1, x_2, x_3$ such that

$$x_1 \begin{bmatrix} 1 \\ -1 \\ -2 \end{bmatrix} + x_2 \begin{bmatrix} 5 \\ -4 \\ -7 \end{bmatrix} + x_3 \begin{bmatrix} -3 \\ 1 \\ 0 \end{bmatrix} = \begin{bmatrix} -4 \\ 3 \\ h \end{bmatrix}$$

This vector equation is equivalent to a system of three linear equations in three unknowns. If you row reduce the augmented matrix for this system, you find that

$$\begin{bmatrix} 1 & 5 & -3 & -4 \\ -1 & -4 & 1 & 3 \\ -2 & -7 & 0 & h \end{bmatrix} \sim \begin{bmatrix} 1 & 5 & -3 & -4 \\ 0 & 1 & -2 & -1 \\ 0 & 3 & -6 & h-8 \end{bmatrix} \sim \begin{bmatrix} 1 & 5 & -3 & -4 \\ 0 & 1 & -2 & -1 \\ 0 & 0 & 0 & h-5 \end{bmatrix}$$

The system is consistent if and only if there is no pivot in the fourth column. That is, $h - 5$ must be 0. So $\mathbf{y}$ is in Span $\{\mathbf{v}_1, \mathbf{v}_2, \mathbf{v}_3\}$ if and only if $h = 5$.

***Remember:***    The presence of a free variable in a system does not guarantee that the system is consistent.

3. Since the vectors $\mathbf{u}$ and $\mathbf{v}$ are in Span $\{\mathbf{w}_1, \mathbf{w}_2, \mathbf{w}_3\}$, there exist scalars $c_1, c_2, c_3$ and $d_1, d_2, d_3$ such that

$$\mathbf{u} = c_1\mathbf{w}_1 + c_2\mathbf{w}_2 + c_3\mathbf{w}_3 \quad \text{and} \quad \mathbf{v} = d_1\mathbf{w}_1 + d_2\mathbf{w}_2 + d_3\mathbf{w}_3.$$

Notice

$$\begin{aligned} \mathbf{u} + \mathbf{v} &= c_1\mathbf{w}_1 + c_2\mathbf{w}_2 + c_3\mathbf{w}_3 + d_1\mathbf{w}_1 + d_2\mathbf{w}_2 + d_3\mathbf{w}_3 \\ &= (c_1 + d_1)\mathbf{w}_1 + (c_2 + d_2)\mathbf{w}_2 + (c_3 + d_3)\mathbf{w}_3 \end{aligned}$$

Since $c_1 + d_1, c_2 + d_2$, and $c_3 + d_3$ are also scalars, the vector $\mathbf{u} + \mathbf{v}$ is in Span $\{\mathbf{w}_1, \mathbf{w}_2, \mathbf{w}_3\}$.

## 1.4 THE MATRIX EQUATION $A\mathbf{x} = \mathbf{b}$

A fundamental idea in linear algebra is to view a linear combination of vectors as the product of a matrix and a vector. The following definition permits us to rephrase some of the concepts of Section 1.3 in new ways.

DEFINITION

If $A$ is an $m \times n$ matrix, with columns $\mathbf{a}_1, \ldots, \mathbf{a}_n$, and if $\mathbf{x}$ is in $\mathbb{R}^n$, then the **product of $A$ and $\mathbf{x}$**, denoted by $A\mathbf{x}$, is **the linear combination of the columns of $A$ using the corresponding entries in x as weights**; that is,

$$A\mathbf{x} = \begin{bmatrix} \mathbf{a}_1 & \mathbf{a}_2 & \cdots & \mathbf{a}_n \end{bmatrix} \begin{bmatrix} x_1 \\ \vdots \\ x_n \end{bmatrix} = x_1\mathbf{a}_1 + x_2\mathbf{a}_2 + \cdots + x_n\mathbf{a}_n$$

Note that $A\mathbf{x}$ is defined only if the number of columns of $A$ equals the number of entries in $\mathbf{x}$.

**EXAMPLE 1**

a. $\begin{bmatrix} 1 & 2 & -1 \\ 0 & -5 & 3 \end{bmatrix} \begin{bmatrix} 4 \\ 3 \\ 7 \end{bmatrix} = 4\begin{bmatrix} 1 \\ 0 \end{bmatrix} + 3\begin{bmatrix} 2 \\ -5 \end{bmatrix} + 7\begin{bmatrix} -1 \\ 3 \end{bmatrix}$

$$= \begin{bmatrix} 4 \\ 0 \end{bmatrix} + \begin{bmatrix} 6 \\ -15 \end{bmatrix} + \begin{bmatrix} -7 \\ 21 \end{bmatrix} = \begin{bmatrix} 3 \\ 6 \end{bmatrix}$$

b. $\begin{bmatrix} 2 & -3 \\ 8 & 0 \\ -5 & 2 \end{bmatrix} \begin{bmatrix} 4 \\ 7 \end{bmatrix} = 4\begin{bmatrix} 2 \\ 8 \\ -5 \end{bmatrix} + 7\begin{bmatrix} -3 \\ 0 \\ 2 \end{bmatrix} = \begin{bmatrix} 8 \\ 32 \\ -20 \end{bmatrix} + \begin{bmatrix} -21 \\ 0 \\ 14 \end{bmatrix} = \begin{bmatrix} -13 \\ 32 \\ -6 \end{bmatrix}$    ∎

**EXAMPLE 2**    For $\mathbf{v}_1, \mathbf{v}_2, \mathbf{v}_3$ in $\mathbb{R}^m$, write the linear combination $3\mathbf{v}_1 - 5\mathbf{v}_2 + 7\mathbf{v}_3$ as a matrix times a vector.

**SOLUTION** Place $\mathbf{v}_1, \mathbf{v}_2, \mathbf{v}_3$ into the columns of a matrix $A$ and place the weights $3, -5$, and $7$ into a vector $\mathbf{x}$. That is,

$$3\mathbf{v}_1 - 5\mathbf{v}_2 + 7\mathbf{v}_3 = \begin{bmatrix} \mathbf{v}_1 & \mathbf{v}_2 & \mathbf{v}_3 \end{bmatrix} \begin{bmatrix} 3 \\ -5 \\ 7 \end{bmatrix} = A\mathbf{x} \qquad\blacksquare$$

Section 1.3 showed how to write a system of linear equations as a vector equation involving a linear combination of vectors. For example, the system

$$\begin{aligned} x_1 + 2x_2 - \phantom{3}x_3 &= 4 \\ -5x_2 + 3x_3 &= 1 \end{aligned} \tag{1}$$

is equivalent to

$$x_1 \begin{bmatrix} 1 \\ 0 \end{bmatrix} + x_2 \begin{bmatrix} 2 \\ -5 \end{bmatrix} + x_3 \begin{bmatrix} -1 \\ 3 \end{bmatrix} = \begin{bmatrix} 4 \\ 1 \end{bmatrix} \tag{2}$$

As in Example 2, the linear combination on the left side is a matrix times a vector, so that (2) becomes

$$\begin{bmatrix} 1 & 2 & -1 \\ 0 & -5 & 3 \end{bmatrix} \begin{bmatrix} x_1 \\ x_2 \\ x_3 \end{bmatrix} = \begin{bmatrix} 4 \\ 1 \end{bmatrix} \tag{3}$$

Equation (3) has the form $A\mathbf{x} = \mathbf{b}$. Such an equation is called a **matrix equation**, to distinguish it from a vector equation such as is shown in (2).

Notice how the matrix in (3) is just the matrix of coefficients of the system (1). Similar calculations show that any system of linear equations, or any vector equation such as (2), can be written as an equivalent matrix equation in the form $A\mathbf{x} = \mathbf{b}$. This simple observation will be used repeatedly throughout the text.

Here is the formal result.

**THEOREM 3**

If $A$ is an $m \times n$ matrix, with columns $\mathbf{a}_1, \ldots, \mathbf{a}_n$, and if $\mathbf{b}$ is in $\mathbb{R}^m$, the matrix equation

$$A\mathbf{x} = \mathbf{b} \tag{4}$$

has the same solution set as the vector equation

$$x_1\mathbf{a}_1 + x_2\mathbf{a}_2 + \cdots + x_n\mathbf{a}_n = \mathbf{b} \tag{5}$$

which, in turn, has the same solution set as the system of linear equations whose augmented matrix is

$$\begin{bmatrix} \mathbf{a}_1 & \mathbf{a}_2 & \cdots & \mathbf{a}_n & \mathbf{b} \end{bmatrix} \tag{6}$$

Theorem 3 provides a powerful tool for gaining insight into problems in linear algebra, because a system of linear equations may now be viewed in three different but equivalent ways: as a matrix equation, as a vector equation, or as a system of linear equations. Whenever you construct a mathematical model of a problem in real life, you are free to choose whichever viewpoint is most natural. Then you may switch from one formulation of a problem to another whenever it is convenient. In any case, the matrix equation (4), the vector equation (5), and the system of equations are all solved in the same way—by row reducing the augmented matrix (6). Other methods of solution will be discussed later.

## Existence of Solutions

The definition of $A\mathbf{x}$ leads directly to the following useful fact.

> The equation $A\mathbf{x} = \mathbf{b}$ has a solution if and only if $\mathbf{b}$ is a linear combination of the columns of $A$.

Section 1.3 considered the existence question, "Is $\mathbf{b}$ in Span $\{\mathbf{a}_1, \ldots, \mathbf{a}_n\}$?" Equivalently, "Is $A\mathbf{x} = \mathbf{b}$ consistent?" A harder existence problem is to determine whether the equation $A\mathbf{x} = \mathbf{b}$ is consistent *for all* possible $\mathbf{b}$.

**EXAMPLE 3**   Let $A = \begin{bmatrix} 1 & 3 & 4 \\ -4 & 2 & -6 \\ -3 & -2 & -7 \end{bmatrix}$ and $\mathbf{b} = \begin{bmatrix} b_1 \\ b_2 \\ b_3 \end{bmatrix}$. Is the equation $A\mathbf{x} = \mathbf{b}$ consistent for all possible $b_1, b_2, b_3$?

**SOLUTION**   Row reduce the augmented matrix for $A\mathbf{x} = \mathbf{b}$:

$$\begin{bmatrix} 1 & 3 & 4 & b_1 \\ -4 & 2 & -6 & b_2 \\ -3 & -2 & -7 & b_3 \end{bmatrix} \sim \begin{bmatrix} 1 & 3 & 4 & b_1 \\ 0 & 14 & 10 & b_2 + 4b_1 \\ 0 & 7 & 5 & b_3 + 3b_1 \end{bmatrix}$$

$$\sim \begin{bmatrix} 1 & 3 & 4 & b_1 \\ 0 & 14 & 10 & b_2 + 4b_1 \\ 0 & 0 & 0 & b_3 + 3b_1 - \frac{1}{2}(b_2 + 4b_1) \end{bmatrix}$$

The third entry in column 4 equals $b_1 - \frac{1}{2}b_2 + b_3$. The equation $A\mathbf{x} = \mathbf{b}$ is *not* consistent for every $\mathbf{b}$ because some choices of $\mathbf{b}$ can make $b_1 - \frac{1}{2}b_2 + b_3$ nonzero. ∎

The reduced matrix in Example 3 provides a description of all $\mathbf{b}$ for which the equation $A\mathbf{x} = \mathbf{b}$ *is* consistent: The entries in $\mathbf{b}$ must satisfy

$$b_1 - \tfrac{1}{2}b_2 + b_3 = 0$$

This is the equation of a plane through the origin in $\mathbb{R}^3$. The plane is the set of all linear combinations of the three columns of $A$. See Figure 1.

The equation $A\mathbf{x} = \mathbf{b}$ in Example 3 fails to be consistent for all $\mathbf{b}$ because the echelon form of $A$ has a row of zeros. If $A$ had a pivot in all three rows, we would not care about the calculations in the augmented column because in this case an echelon form of the augmented matrix could not have a row such as $\begin{bmatrix} 0 & 0 & 0 & 1 \end{bmatrix}$.

In the next theorem, the sentence "The columns of $A$ span $\mathbb{R}^m$" means that *every* $\mathbf{b}$ in $\mathbb{R}^m$ is a linear combination of the columns of $A$. In general, a set of vectors $\{\mathbf{v}_1, \ldots, \mathbf{v}_p\}$ in $\mathbb{R}^m$ **spans** (or **generates**) $\mathbb{R}^m$ if every vector in $\mathbb{R}^m$ is a linear combination of $\mathbf{v}_1, \ldots, \mathbf{v}_p$—that is, if Span $\{\mathbf{v}_1, \ldots, \mathbf{v}_p\} = \mathbb{R}^m$.

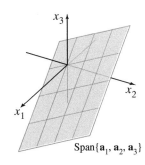

**FIGURE 1**

The columns of
$A = [\, \mathbf{a}_1 \ \ \mathbf{a}_2 \ \ \mathbf{a}_3 \,]$ span a plane
through $\mathbf{0}$.

Span$\{\mathbf{a}_1, \mathbf{a}_2, \mathbf{a}_3\}$

**THEOREM 4**

> Let $A$ be an $m \times n$ matrix. Then the following statements are logically equivalent. That is, for a particular $A$, either they are all true statements or they are all false.
>
> a.  For each $\mathbf{b}$ in $\mathbb{R}^m$, the equation $A\mathbf{x} = \mathbf{b}$ has a solution.
>
> b.  Each $\mathbf{b}$ in $\mathbb{R}^m$ is a linear combination of the columns of $A$.
>
> c.  The columns of $A$ span $\mathbb{R}^m$.
>
> d.  $A$ has a pivot position in every row.

Theorem 4 is one of the most useful theorems in this chapter. Statements (a), (b), and (c) are equivalent because of the definition of $A\mathbf{x}$ and what it means for a set of vectors to span $\mathbb{R}^m$. The discussion after Example 3 suggests why (a) and (d) are equivalent; a proof is given at the end of the section. The exercises will provide examples of how Theorem 4 is used.

***Warning:***   Theorem 4 is about a *coefficient matrix*, not an augmented matrix. If an augmented matrix $[\,A \quad \mathbf{b}\,]$ has a pivot position in every row, then the equation $A\mathbf{x} = \mathbf{b}$ may or may not be consistent.

## Computation of $A\mathbf{x}$

The calculations in Example 1 were based on the definition of the product of a matrix $A$ and a vector $\mathbf{x}$. The following simple example will lead to a more efficient method for calculating the entries in $A\mathbf{x}$ when working problems by hand.

**EXAMPLE 4**   Compute $A\mathbf{x}$, where $A = \begin{bmatrix} 2 & 3 & 4 \\ -1 & 5 & -3 \\ 6 & -2 & 8 \end{bmatrix}$ and $\mathbf{x} = \begin{bmatrix} x_1 \\ x_2 \\ x_3 \end{bmatrix}$.

**SOLUTION**   From the definition,

$$
\begin{bmatrix} 2 & 3 & 4 \\ -1 & 5 & -3 \\ 6 & -2 & 8 \end{bmatrix}\begin{bmatrix} x_1 \\ x_2 \\ x_3 \end{bmatrix} = x_1\begin{bmatrix} 2 \\ -1 \\ 6 \end{bmatrix} + x_2\begin{bmatrix} 3 \\ 5 \\ -2 \end{bmatrix} + x_3\begin{bmatrix} 4 \\ -3 \\ 8 \end{bmatrix}
$$

$$
= \begin{bmatrix} 2x_1 \\ -x_1 \\ 6x_1 \end{bmatrix} + \begin{bmatrix} 3x_2 \\ 5x_2 \\ -2x_2 \end{bmatrix} + \begin{bmatrix} 4x_3 \\ -3x_3 \\ 8x_3 \end{bmatrix} \qquad (7)
$$

$$
= \begin{bmatrix} 2x_1 + 3x_2 + 4x_3 \\ -x_1 + 5x_2 - 3x_3 \\ 6x_1 - 2x_2 + 8x_3 \end{bmatrix}
$$

The first entry in the product $A\mathbf{x}$ is a sum of products (sometimes called a *dot product*), using the first row of $A$ and the entries in $\mathbf{x}$. That is,

$$
\begin{bmatrix} 2 & 3 & 4 \end{bmatrix}\begin{bmatrix} x_1 \\ x_2 \\ x_3 \end{bmatrix} = \begin{bmatrix} 2x_1 + 3x_2 + 4x_3 \end{bmatrix}
$$

This matrix shows how to compute the first entry in $A\mathbf{x}$ directly, without writing down all the calculations shown in (7). Similarly, the second entry in $A\mathbf{x}$ can be calculated at once by multiplying the entries in the second row of $A$ by the corresponding entries in $\mathbf{x}$ and then summing the resulting products:

$$
\begin{bmatrix} -1 & 5 & -3 \end{bmatrix}\begin{bmatrix} x_1 \\ x_2 \\ x_3 \end{bmatrix} = \begin{bmatrix} -x_1 + 5x_2 - 3x_3 \end{bmatrix}
$$

Likewise, the third entry in $A\mathbf{x}$ can be calculated from the third row of $A$ and the entries in $\mathbf{x}$. ∎

Row–Vector Rule for Computing $A\mathbf{x}$

If the product $A\mathbf{x}$ is defined, then the $i$th entry in $A\mathbf{x}$ is the sum of the products of corresponding entries from row $i$ of $A$ and from the vector $\mathbf{x}$.

**EXAMPLE 5**

a. $\begin{bmatrix} 1 & 2 & -1 \\ 0 & -5 & 3 \end{bmatrix} \begin{bmatrix} 4 \\ 3 \\ 7 \end{bmatrix} = \begin{bmatrix} 1 \cdot 4 + 2 \cdot 3 + (-1) \cdot 7 \\ 0 \cdot 4 + (-5) \cdot 3 + 3 \cdot 7 \end{bmatrix} = \begin{bmatrix} 3 \\ 6 \end{bmatrix}$

b. $\begin{bmatrix} 2 & -3 \\ 8 & 0 \\ -5 & 2 \end{bmatrix} \begin{bmatrix} 4 \\ 7 \end{bmatrix} = \begin{bmatrix} 2 \cdot 4 + (-3) \cdot 7 \\ 8 \cdot 4 + 0 \cdot 7 \\ (-5) \cdot 4 + 2 \cdot 7 \end{bmatrix} = \begin{bmatrix} -13 \\ 32 \\ -6 \end{bmatrix}$

c. $\begin{bmatrix} 1 & 0 & 0 \\ 0 & 1 & 0 \\ 0 & 0 & 1 \end{bmatrix} \begin{bmatrix} r \\ s \\ t \end{bmatrix} = \begin{bmatrix} 1 \cdot r + 0 \cdot s + 0 \cdot t \\ 0 \cdot r + 1 \cdot s + 0 \cdot t \\ 0 \cdot r + 0 \cdot s + 1 \cdot t \end{bmatrix} = \begin{bmatrix} r \\ s \\ t \end{bmatrix}$ ∎

By definition, the matrix in Example 5(c) with 1's on the diagonal and 0's elsewhere is called an **identity matrix** and is denoted by $I$. The calculation in part (c) shows that $I\mathbf{x} = \mathbf{x}$ for every $\mathbf{x}$ in $\mathbb{R}^3$. There is an analogous $n \times n$ identity matrix, sometimes written as $I_n$. As in part (c), $I_n\mathbf{x} = \mathbf{x}$ for every $\mathbf{x}$ in $\mathbb{R}^n$.

## Properties of the Matrix–Vector Product $A\mathbf{x}$

The facts in the next theorem are important and will be used throughout the text. The proof relies on the definition of $A\mathbf{x}$ and the algebraic properties of $\mathbb{R}^n$.

**THEOREM 5**

If $A$ is an $m \times n$ matrix, $\mathbf{u}$ and $\mathbf{v}$ are vectors in $\mathbb{R}^n$, and $c$ is a scalar, then:

a. $A(\mathbf{u} + \mathbf{v}) = A\mathbf{u} + A\mathbf{v}$;

b. $A(c\mathbf{u}) = c(A\mathbf{u})$.

**PROOF** For simplicity, take $n = 3$, $A = [\, \mathbf{a}_1 \ \ \mathbf{a}_2 \ \ \mathbf{a}_3 \,]$, and $\mathbf{u}, \mathbf{v}$ in $\mathbb{R}^3$. (The proof of the general case is similar.) For $i = 1, 2, 3$, let $u_i$ and $v_i$ be the $i$th entries in $\mathbf{u}$ and $\mathbf{v}$, respectively. To prove statement (a), compute $A(\mathbf{u} + \mathbf{v})$ as a linear combination of the columns of $A$ using the entries in $\mathbf{u} + \mathbf{v}$ as weights.

$$A(\mathbf{u} + \mathbf{v}) = [\, \mathbf{a}_1 \ \ \mathbf{a}_2 \ \ \mathbf{a}_3 \,] \begin{bmatrix} u_1 + v_1 \\ u_2 + v_2 \\ u_3 + v_3 \end{bmatrix}$$

Entries in $\mathbf{u} + \mathbf{v}$

$$= (u_1 + v_1)\mathbf{a}_1 + (u_2 + v_2)\mathbf{a}_2 + (u_3 + v_3)\mathbf{a}_3$$

Columns of $A$

$$= (u_1\mathbf{a}_1 + u_2\mathbf{a}_2 + u_3\mathbf{a}_3) + (v_1\mathbf{a}_1 + v_2\mathbf{a}_2 + v_3\mathbf{a}_3)$$

$$= A\mathbf{u} + A\mathbf{v}$$

To prove statement (b), compute $A(c\mathbf{u})$ as a linear combination of the columns of $A$ using the entries in $c\mathbf{u}$ as weights.

$$A(c\mathbf{u}) = [\, \mathbf{a}_1 \ \ \mathbf{a}_2 \ \ \mathbf{a}_3 \,] \begin{bmatrix} cu_1 \\ cu_2 \\ cu_3 \end{bmatrix} = (cu_1)\mathbf{a}_1 + (cu_2)\mathbf{a}_2 + (cu_3)\mathbf{a}_3$$

$$= c(u_1\mathbf{a}_1) + c(u_2\mathbf{a}_2) + c(u_3\mathbf{a}_3)$$

$$= c(u_1\mathbf{a}_1 + u_2\mathbf{a}_2 + u_3\mathbf{a}_3)$$

$$= c(A\mathbf{u})$$ ∎

---

NUMERICAL NOTE

To optimize a computer algorithm to compute $A\mathbf{x}$, the sequence of calculations should involve data stored in contiguous memory locations. The most widely used professional algorithms for matrix computations are written in Fortran, a language that stores a matrix as a set of columns. Such algorithms compute $A\mathbf{x}$ as a linear combination of the columns of $A$. In contrast, if a program is written in the popular language C, which stores matrices by rows, $A\mathbf{x}$ should be computed via the alternative rule that uses the rows of $A$.

---

**PROOF OF THEOREM 4** As was pointed out after Theorem 4, statements (a), (b), and (c) are logically equivalent. So, it suffices to show (for an arbitrary matrix $A$) that (a) and (d) are either both true or both false. This will tie all four statements together.

Let $U$ be an echelon form of $A$. Given $\mathbf{b}$ in $\mathbb{R}^m$, we can row reduce the augmented matrix $[\,A \quad \mathbf{b}\,]$ to an augmented matrix $[\,U \quad \mathbf{d}\,]$ for some $\mathbf{d}$ in $\mathbb{R}^m$:

$$[\,A \quad \mathbf{b}\,] \sim \cdots \sim [\,U \quad \mathbf{d}\,]$$

If statement (d) is true, then each row of $U$ contains a pivot position and there can be no pivot in the augmented column. So $A\mathbf{x} = \mathbf{b}$ has a solution for any $\mathbf{b}$, and (a) is true. If (d) is false, the last row of $U$ is all zeros. Let $\mathbf{d}$ be any vector with a 1 in its last entry. Then $[\,U \quad \mathbf{d}\,]$ represents an *inconsistent* system. Since row operations are reversible, $[\,U \quad \mathbf{d}\,]$ can be transformed into the form $[\,A \quad \mathbf{b}\,]$. The new system $A\mathbf{x} = \mathbf{b}$ is also inconsistent, and (a) is false. ∎

---

PRACTICE PROBLEMS

**1.** Let $A = \begin{bmatrix} 1 & 5 & -2 & 0 \\ -3 & 1 & 9 & -5 \\ 4 & -8 & -1 & 7 \end{bmatrix}$, $\mathbf{p} = \begin{bmatrix} 3 \\ -2 \\ 0 \\ -4 \end{bmatrix}$, and $\mathbf{b} = \begin{bmatrix} -7 \\ 9 \\ 0 \end{bmatrix}$. It can be shown that

$\mathbf{p}$ is a solution of $A\mathbf{x} = \mathbf{b}$. Use this fact to exhibit $\mathbf{b}$ as a specific linear combination of the columns of $A$.

**2.** Let $A = \begin{bmatrix} 2 & 5 \\ 3 & 1 \end{bmatrix}$, $\mathbf{u} = \begin{bmatrix} 4 \\ -1 \end{bmatrix}$, and $\mathbf{v} = \begin{bmatrix} -3 \\ 5 \end{bmatrix}$. Verify Theorem 5(a) in this case by computing $A(\mathbf{u} + \mathbf{v})$ and $A\mathbf{u} + A\mathbf{v}$.

**3.** Construct a $3 \times 3$ matrix $A$ and vectors $\mathbf{b}$ and $\mathbf{c}$ in $\mathbb{R}^3$ so that $A\mathbf{x} = \mathbf{b}$ has a solution, but $A\mathbf{x} = \mathbf{c}$ does not.

## 1.4 EXERCISES

Compute the products in Exercises 1–4 using (a) the definition, as in Example 1, and (b) the row–vector rule for computing $A\mathbf{x}$. If a product is undefined, explain why.

**1.** $\begin{bmatrix} -4 & 2 \\ 1 & 6 \\ 0 & 1 \end{bmatrix} \begin{bmatrix} 3 \\ -2 \\ 7 \end{bmatrix}$ 
**2.** $\begin{bmatrix} 2 \\ 6 \\ -1 \end{bmatrix} \begin{bmatrix} 5 \\ -1 \end{bmatrix}$

**3.** $\begin{bmatrix} 6 & 5 \\ -4 & -3 \\ 7 & 6 \end{bmatrix} \begin{bmatrix} 2 \\ -3 \end{bmatrix}$ 
**4.** $\begin{bmatrix} 8 & 3 & -4 \\ 5 & 1 & 2 \end{bmatrix} \begin{bmatrix} 1 \\ 1 \\ 1 \end{bmatrix}$

In Exercises 5–8, use the definition of $A\mathbf{x}$ to write the matrix equation as a vector equation, or vice versa.

**5.** $\begin{bmatrix} 5 & 1 & -8 & 4 \\ -2 & -7 & 3 & -5 \end{bmatrix} \begin{bmatrix} 5 \\ -1 \\ 3 \\ -2 \end{bmatrix} = \begin{bmatrix} -8 \\ 16 \end{bmatrix}$

**6.** $\begin{bmatrix} 7 & -3 \\ 2 & 1 \\ 9 & -6 \\ -3 & 2 \end{bmatrix} \begin{bmatrix} -2 \\ -5 \end{bmatrix} = \begin{bmatrix} 1 \\ -9 \\ 12 \\ -4 \end{bmatrix}$

**7.** $x_1 \begin{bmatrix} 4 \\ -1 \\ 7 \\ -4 \end{bmatrix} + x_2 \begin{bmatrix} -5 \\ 3 \\ -5 \\ 1 \end{bmatrix} + x_3 \begin{bmatrix} 7 \\ -8 \\ 0 \\ 2 \end{bmatrix} = \begin{bmatrix} 6 \\ -8 \\ 0 \\ -7 \end{bmatrix}$

**8.** $z_1 \begin{bmatrix} 4 \\ -2 \end{bmatrix} + z_2 \begin{bmatrix} -4 \\ 5 \end{bmatrix} + z_3 \begin{bmatrix} -5 \\ 4 \end{bmatrix} + z_4 \begin{bmatrix} 3 \\ 0 \end{bmatrix} = \begin{bmatrix} 4 \\ 13 \end{bmatrix}$

In Exercises 9 and 10, write the system first as a vector equation and then as a matrix equation.

**9.** $3x_1 + x_2 - 5x_3 = 9$
$\phantom{3x_1 + {}} x_2 + 4x_3 = 0$

**10.** $8x_1 - \phantom{4}x_2 = 4$
$\phantom{8}5x_1 + 4x_2 = 1$
$\phantom{8}x_1 - 3x_2 = 2$

Given $A$ and **b** in Exercises 11 and 12, write the augmented matrix for the linear system that corresponds to the matrix equation $A\mathbf{x} = \mathbf{b}$. Then solve the system and write the solution as a vector.

**11.** $A = \begin{bmatrix} 1 & 2 & 4 \\ 0 & 1 & 5 \\ -2 & -4 & -3 \end{bmatrix}, \mathbf{b} = \begin{bmatrix} -2 \\ 2 \\ 9 \end{bmatrix}$

**12.** $A = \begin{bmatrix} 1 & 2 & 1 \\ -3 & -1 & 2 \\ 0 & 5 & 3 \end{bmatrix}, \mathbf{b} = \begin{bmatrix} 0 \\ 1 \\ -1 \end{bmatrix}$

**13.** Let $\mathbf{u} = \begin{bmatrix} 0 \\ 4 \\ 4 \end{bmatrix}$ and $A = \begin{bmatrix} 3 & -5 \\ -2 & 6 \\ 1 & 1 \end{bmatrix}$. Is **u** in the plane $\mathbb{R}^3$

spanned by the columns of $A$? (See the figure.) Why or why not?

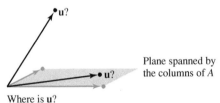

Plane spanned by the columns of $A$

Where is **u**?

**14.** Let $\mathbf{u} = \begin{bmatrix} 2 \\ -3 \\ 2 \end{bmatrix}$ and $A = \begin{bmatrix} 5 & 8 & 7 \\ 0 & 1 & -1 \\ 1 & 3 & 0 \end{bmatrix}$. Is **u** in the subset

of $\mathbb{R}^3$ spanned by the columns of $A$? Why or why not?

**15.** Let $A = \begin{bmatrix} 2 & -1 \\ -6 & 3 \end{bmatrix}$ and $\mathbf{b} = \begin{bmatrix} b_1 \\ b_2 \end{bmatrix}$. Show that the equation

$A\mathbf{x} = \mathbf{b}$ does not have a solution for all possible **b**, and describe the set of all **b** for which $A\mathbf{x} = \mathbf{b}$ *does* have a solution.

**16.** Repeat Exercise 15: $A = \begin{bmatrix} 1 & -3 & -4 \\ -3 & 2 & 6 \\ 5 & -1 & -8 \end{bmatrix}, \mathbf{b} = \begin{bmatrix} b_1 \\ b_2 \\ b_3 \end{bmatrix}$.

Exercises 17–20 refer to the matrices $A$ and $B$ below. Make appropriate calculations that justify your answers and mention an appropriate theorem.

$A = \begin{bmatrix} 1 & 3 & 0 & 3 \\ -1 & -1 & -1 & 1 \\ 0 & -4 & 2 & -8 \\ 2 & 0 & 3 & -1 \end{bmatrix}$ $B = \begin{bmatrix} 1 & 3 & -2 & 2 \\ 0 & 1 & 1 & -5 \\ 1 & 2 & -3 & 7 \\ -2 & -8 & 2 & -1 \end{bmatrix}$

**17.** How many rows of $A$ contain a pivot position? Does the equation $A\mathbf{x} = \mathbf{b}$ have a solution for each **b** in $\mathbb{R}^4$?

**18.** Do the columns of $B$ span $\mathbb{R}^4$? Does the equation $B\mathbf{x} = \mathbf{y}$ have a solution for each **y** in $\mathbb{R}^4$?

**19.** Can each vector in $\mathbb{R}^4$ be written as a linear combination of the columns of the matrix $A$ above? Do the columns of $A$ span $\mathbb{R}^4$?

**20.** Can every vector in $\mathbb{R}^4$ be written as a linear combination of the columns of the matrix $B$ above? Do the columns of $B$ span $\mathbb{R}^3$?

**21.** Let $\mathbf{v}_1 = \begin{bmatrix} 1 \\ 0 \\ -1 \\ 0 \end{bmatrix}, \mathbf{v}_2 = \begin{bmatrix} 0 \\ -1 \\ 0 \\ 1 \end{bmatrix}, \mathbf{v}_3 = \begin{bmatrix} 1 \\ 0 \\ 0 \\ -1 \end{bmatrix}$.

Does $\{\mathbf{v}_1, \mathbf{v}_2, \mathbf{v}_3\}$ span $\mathbb{R}^4$? Why or why not?

**22.** Let $\mathbf{v}_1 = \begin{bmatrix} 0 \\ 0 \\ -2 \end{bmatrix}, \mathbf{v}_2 = \begin{bmatrix} 0 \\ -3 \\ 8 \end{bmatrix}, \mathbf{v}_3 = \begin{bmatrix} 4 \\ -1 \\ -5 \end{bmatrix}$.

Does $\{\mathbf{v}_1, \mathbf{v}_2, \mathbf{v}_3\}$ span $\mathbb{R}^3$? Why or why not?

In Exercises 23 and 24, mark each statement True or False. Justify each answer.

**23.** a. The equation $A\mathbf{x} = \mathbf{b}$ is referred to as a *vector equation*.

b. A vector **b** is a linear combination of the columns of a matrix $A$ if and only if the equation $A\mathbf{x} = \mathbf{b}$ has at least one solution.

c. The equation $A\mathbf{x} = \mathbf{b}$ is consistent if the augmented matrix $[\,A \quad \mathbf{b}\,]$ has a pivot position in every row.

d. The first entry in the product $A\mathbf{x}$ is a sum of products.

e. If the columns of an $m \times n$ matrix $A$ span $\mathbb{R}^m$, then the equation $A\mathbf{x} = \mathbf{b}$ is consistent for each **b** in $\mathbb{R}^m$.

f. If $A$ is an $m \times n$ matrix and if the equation $A\mathbf{x} = \mathbf{b}$ is inconsistent for some **b** in $\mathbb{R}^m$, then $A$ cannot have a pivot position in every row.

**24.** a. Every matrix equation $A\mathbf{x} = \mathbf{b}$ corresponds to a vector equation with the same solution set.

b. Any linear combination of vectors can always be written in the form $A\mathbf{x}$ for a suitable matrix $A$ and vector **x**.

c. The solution set of a linear system whose augmented matrix is $[\, \mathbf{a}_1 \quad \mathbf{a}_2 \quad \mathbf{a}_3 \quad \mathbf{b} \,]$ is the same as the solution set of $A\mathbf{x} = \mathbf{b}$, if $A = [\, \mathbf{a}_1 \quad \mathbf{a}_2 \quad \mathbf{a}_3 \,]$.

d. If the equation $A\mathbf{x} = \mathbf{b}$ is inconsistent, then **b** is not in the set spanned by the columns of $A$.

e. If the augmented matrix $[\, A \quad \mathbf{b} \,]$ has a pivot position in every row, then the equation $A\mathbf{x} = \mathbf{b}$ is inconsistent.

f.  If $A$ is an $m \times n$ matrix whose columns do not span $\mathbb{R}^m$, then the equation $A\mathbf{x} = \mathbf{b}$ is inconsistent for some $\mathbf{b}$ in $\mathbb{R}^m$.

25. Note that $\begin{bmatrix} 4 & -3 & 1 \\ 5 & -2 & 5 \\ -6 & 2 & -3 \end{bmatrix} \begin{bmatrix} -3 \\ -1 \\ 2 \end{bmatrix} = \begin{bmatrix} -7 \\ -3 \\ 10 \end{bmatrix}$. Use this fact (and no row operations) to find scalars $c_1$, $c_2$, $c_3$ such that

$$\begin{bmatrix} -7 \\ -3 \\ 10 \end{bmatrix} = c_1 \begin{bmatrix} 4 \\ 5 \\ -6 \end{bmatrix} + c_2 \begin{bmatrix} -3 \\ -2 \\ 2 \end{bmatrix} + c_3 \begin{bmatrix} 1 \\ 5 \\ -3 \end{bmatrix}.$$

26. Let $\mathbf{u} = \begin{bmatrix} 7 \\ 2 \\ 5 \end{bmatrix}$, $\mathbf{v} = \begin{bmatrix} 3 \\ 1 \\ 3 \end{bmatrix}$, and $\mathbf{w} = \begin{bmatrix} 6 \\ 1 \\ 0 \end{bmatrix}$.

It can be shown that $3\mathbf{u} - 5\mathbf{v} - \mathbf{w} = \mathbf{0}$. Use this fact (and no row operations) to find $x_1$ and $x_2$ that satisfy the equation

$$\begin{bmatrix} 7 & 3 \\ 2 & 1 \\ 5 & 3 \end{bmatrix} \begin{bmatrix} x_1 \\ x_2 \end{bmatrix} = \begin{bmatrix} 6 \\ 1 \\ 0 \end{bmatrix}.$$

27. Let $\mathbf{q}_1$, $\mathbf{q}_2$, $\mathbf{q}_3$, and $\mathbf{v}$ represent vectors in $\mathbb{R}^5$, and let $x_1$, $x_2$, and $x_3$ denote scalars. Write the following vector equation as a matrix equation. Identify any symbols you choose to use.

$$x_1\mathbf{q}_1 + x_2\mathbf{q}_2 + x_3\mathbf{q}_3 = \mathbf{v}$$

28. Rewrite the (numerical) matrix equation below in symbolic form as a vector equation, using symbols $\mathbf{v}_1, \mathbf{v}_2, \ldots$ for the vectors and $c_1, c_2, \ldots$ for scalars. Define what each symbol represents, using the data given in the matrix equation.

$$\begin{bmatrix} -3 & 5 & -4 & 9 & 7 \\ 5 & 8 & 1 & -2 & -4 \end{bmatrix} \begin{bmatrix} -3 \\ 2 \\ 4 \\ -1 \\ 2 \end{bmatrix} = \begin{bmatrix} 8 \\ -1 \end{bmatrix}$$

29. Construct a $3 \times 3$ matrix, not in echelon form, whose columns span $\mathbb{R}^3$. Show that the matrix you construct has the desired property.

30. Construct a $3 \times 3$ matrix, not in echelon form, whose columns do *not* span $\mathbb{R}^3$. Show that the matrix you construct has the desired property.

31. Let $A$ be a $3 \times 2$ matrix. Explain why the equation $A\mathbf{x} = \mathbf{b}$ cannot be consistent for all $\mathbf{b}$ in $\mathbb{R}^3$. Generalize your argument to the case of an arbitrary $A$ with more rows than columns.

32. Could a set of three vectors in $\mathbb{R}^4$ span all of $\mathbb{R}^4$? Explain. What about $n$ vectors in $\mathbb{R}^m$ when $n$ is less than $m$?

33. Suppose $A$ is a $4 \times 3$ matrix and $\mathbf{b}$ is a vector in $\mathbb{R}^4$ with the property that $A\mathbf{x} = \mathbf{b}$ has a unique solution. What can you say about the reduced echelon form of $A$? Justify your answer.

34. Suppose $A$ is a $3 \times 3$ matrix and $\mathbf{b}$ is a vector in $\mathbb{R}^3$ with the property that $A\mathbf{x} = \mathbf{b}$ has a unique solution. Explain why the columns of $A$ must span $\mathbb{R}^3$.

35. Let $A$ be a $3 \times 4$ matrix, let $\mathbf{y}_1$ and $\mathbf{y}_2$ be vectors in $\mathbb{R}^3$, and let $\mathbf{w} = \mathbf{y}_1 + \mathbf{y}_2$. Suppose $\mathbf{y}_1 = A\mathbf{x}_1$ and $\mathbf{y}_2 = A\mathbf{x}_2$ for some vectors $\mathbf{x}_1$ and $\mathbf{x}_2$ in $\mathbb{R}^4$. What fact allows you to conclude that the system $A\mathbf{x} = \mathbf{w}$ is consistent? (*Note:* $\mathbf{x}_1$ and $\mathbf{x}_2$ denote vectors, not scalar entries in vectors.)

36. Let $A$ be a $5 \times 3$ matrix, let $\mathbf{y}$ be a vector in $\mathbb{R}^3$, and let $\mathbf{z}$ be a vector in $\mathbb{R}^5$. Suppose $A\mathbf{y} = \mathbf{z}$. What fact allows you to conclude that the system $A\mathbf{x} = 4\mathbf{z}$ is consistent?

**[M]** In Exercises 37–40, determine if the columns of the matrix span $\mathbb{R}^4$.

37. $\begin{bmatrix} 7 & 2 & -5 & 8 \\ -5 & -3 & 4 & -9 \\ 6 & 10 & -2 & 7 \\ -7 & 9 & 2 & 15 \end{bmatrix}$   38. $\begin{bmatrix} 5 & -7 & -4 & 9 \\ 6 & -8 & -7 & 5 \\ 4 & -4 & -9 & -9 \\ -9 & 11 & 16 & 7 \end{bmatrix}$

39. $\begin{bmatrix} 12 & -7 & 11 & -9 & 5 \\ -9 & 4 & -8 & 7 & -3 \\ -6 & 11 & -7 & 3 & -9 \\ 4 & -6 & 10 & -5 & 12 \end{bmatrix}$

40. $\begin{bmatrix} 8 & 11 & -6 & -7 & 13 \\ -7 & -8 & 5 & 6 & -9 \\ 11 & 7 & -7 & -9 & -6 \\ -3 & 4 & 1 & 8 & 7 \end{bmatrix}$

41. **[M]** Find a column of the matrix in Exercise 39 that can be deleted and yet have the remaining matrix columns still span $\mathbb{R}^4$.

42. **[M]** Find a column of the matrix in Exercise 40 that can be deleted and yet have the remaining matrix columns still span $\mathbb{R}^4$. Can you delete more than one column?

**SG**   Mastering Linear Algebra Concepts: Span 1–18

**WEB**

---

### SOLUTIONS TO PRACTICE PROBLEMS

**1.** The matrix equation

$$\begin{bmatrix} 1 & 5 & -2 & 0 \\ -3 & 1 & 9 & -5 \\ 4 & -8 & -1 & 7 \end{bmatrix} \begin{bmatrix} 3 \\ -2 \\ 0 \\ -4 \end{bmatrix} = \begin{bmatrix} -7 \\ 9 \\ 0 \end{bmatrix}$$

is equivalent to the vector equation

$$3\begin{bmatrix} 1 \\ -3 \\ 4 \end{bmatrix} - 2\begin{bmatrix} 5 \\ 1 \\ -8 \end{bmatrix} + 0\begin{bmatrix} -2 \\ 9 \\ -1 \end{bmatrix} - 4\begin{bmatrix} 0 \\ -5 \\ 7 \end{bmatrix} = \begin{bmatrix} -7 \\ 9 \\ 0 \end{bmatrix}$$

which expresses **b** as a linear combination of the columns of $A$.

**2.**  
$$\mathbf{u} + \mathbf{v} = \begin{bmatrix} 4 \\ -1 \end{bmatrix} + \begin{bmatrix} -3 \\ 5 \end{bmatrix} = \begin{bmatrix} 1 \\ 4 \end{bmatrix}$$

$$A(\mathbf{u} + \mathbf{v}) = \begin{bmatrix} 2 & 5 \\ 3 & 1 \end{bmatrix}\begin{bmatrix} 1 \\ 4 \end{bmatrix} = \begin{bmatrix} 2 + 20 \\ 3 + 4 \end{bmatrix} = \begin{bmatrix} 22 \\ 7 \end{bmatrix}$$

$$A\mathbf{u} + A\mathbf{v} = \begin{bmatrix} 2 & 5 \\ 3 & 1 \end{bmatrix}\begin{bmatrix} 4 \\ -1 \end{bmatrix} + \begin{bmatrix} 2 & 5 \\ 3 & 1 \end{bmatrix}\begin{bmatrix} -3 \\ 5 \end{bmatrix}$$

$$= \begin{bmatrix} 3 \\ 11 \end{bmatrix} + \begin{bmatrix} 19 \\ -4 \end{bmatrix} = \begin{bmatrix} 22 \\ 7 \end{bmatrix}$$

*Remark:* There are, in fact, infinitely many correct solutions to Practice Problem 3. When creating matrices to satisfy specified criteria, it is often useful to create matrices that are straightforward, such as those already in reduced echelon form. Here is one possible solution:

**3.** Let

$$A = \begin{bmatrix} 1 & 0 & 1 \\ 0 & 1 & 1 \\ 0 & 0 & 0 \end{bmatrix}, \mathbf{b} = \begin{bmatrix} 3 \\ 2 \\ 0 \end{bmatrix}, \text{ and } \mathbf{c} = \begin{bmatrix} 3 \\ 2 \\ 1 \end{bmatrix}.$$

Notice the reduced echelon form of the augmented matrix corresponding to $A\mathbf{x} = \mathbf{b}$ is

$$\begin{bmatrix} 1 & 0 & 1 & 3 \\ 0 & 1 & 1 & 2 \\ 0 & 0 & 0 & 0 \end{bmatrix},$$

which corresponds to a consistent system, and hence $A\mathbf{x} = \mathbf{b}$ has solutions. The reduced echelon form of the augmented matrix corresponding to $A\mathbf{x} = \mathbf{c}$ is

$$\begin{bmatrix} 1 & 0 & 1 & 3 \\ 0 & 1 & 1 & 2 \\ 0 & 0 & 0 & 1 \end{bmatrix},$$

which corresponds to an inconsistent system, and hence $A\mathbf{x} = \mathbf{c}$ does not have any solutions.

## 1.5  SOLUTION SETS OF LINEAR SYSTEMS

Solution sets of linear systems are important objects of study in linear algebra. They will appear later in several different contexts. This section uses vector notation to give explicit and geometric descriptions of such solution sets.

### Homogeneous Linear Systems

A system of linear equations is said to be **homogeneous** if it can be written in the form $A\mathbf{x} = \mathbf{0}$, where $A$ is an $m \times n$ matrix and $\mathbf{0}$ is the zero vector in $\mathbb{R}^m$. Such a system $A\mathbf{x} = \mathbf{0}$ *always* has at least one solution, namely, $\mathbf{x} = \mathbf{0}$ (the zero vector in $\mathbb{R}^n$). This zero solution is usually called the **trivial solution**. For a given equation $A\mathbf{x} = \mathbf{0}$, the important question is whether there exists a **nontrivial solution**, that is, a nonzero vector $\mathbf{x}$ that satisfies $A\mathbf{x} = \mathbf{0}$. The Existence and Uniqueness Theorem in Section 1.2 (Theorem 2) leads immediately to the following fact.

> The homogeneous equation $A\mathbf{x} = \mathbf{0}$ has a nontrivial solution if and only if the equation has at least one free variable.

**EXAMPLE 1**   Determine if the following homogeneous system has a nontrivial solution. Then describe the solution set.

$$3x_1 + 5x_2 - 4x_3 = 0$$
$$-3x_1 - 2x_2 + 4x_3 = 0$$
$$6x_1 + \phantom{2}x_2 - 8x_3 = 0$$

**SOLUTION** Let $A$ be the matrix of coefficients of the system and row reduce the augmented matrix $[\,A \quad \mathbf{0}\,]$ to echelon form:

$$\begin{bmatrix} 3 & 5 & -4 & 0 \\ -3 & -2 & 4 & 0 \\ 6 & 1 & -8 & 0 \end{bmatrix} \sim \begin{bmatrix} 3 & 5 & -4 & 0 \\ 0 & 3 & 0 & 0 \\ 0 & -9 & 0 & 0 \end{bmatrix} \sim \begin{bmatrix} 3 & 5 & -4 & 0 \\ 0 & 3 & 0 & 0 \\ 0 & 0 & 0 & 0 \end{bmatrix}$$

Since $x_3$ is a free variable, $A\mathbf{x} = \mathbf{0}$ has nontrivial solutions (one for each choice of $x_3$). To describe the solution set, continue the row reduction of $[\,A \quad \mathbf{0}\,]$ to *reduced* echelon form:

$$\begin{bmatrix} 1 & 0 & -\frac{4}{3} & 0 \\ 0 & 1 & 0 & 0 \\ 0 & 0 & 0 & 0 \end{bmatrix} \qquad \begin{aligned} x_1 \phantom{xx} - \tfrac{4}{3}x_3 &= 0 \\ x_2 \phantom{xxxx} &= 0 \\ 0 &= 0 \end{aligned}$$

Solve for the basic variables $x_1$ and $x_2$ and obtain $x_1 = \frac{4}{3}x_3$, $x_2 = 0$, with $x_3$ free. As a vector, the general solution of $A\mathbf{x} = \mathbf{0}$ has the form

$$\mathbf{x} = \begin{bmatrix} x_1 \\ x_2 \\ x_3 \end{bmatrix} = \begin{bmatrix} \frac{4}{3}x_3 \\ 0 \\ x_3 \end{bmatrix} = x_3 \begin{bmatrix} \frac{4}{3} \\ 0 \\ 1 \end{bmatrix} = x_3\mathbf{v}, \quad \text{where } \mathbf{v} = \begin{bmatrix} \frac{4}{3} \\ 0 \\ 1 \end{bmatrix}$$

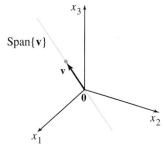

Span{**v**}

**FIGURE 1**

Here $x_3$ is factored out of the expression for the general solution vector. This shows that every solution of $A\mathbf{x} = \mathbf{0}$ in this case is a scalar multiple of $\mathbf{v}$. The trivial solution is obtained by choosing $x_3 = 0$. Geometrically, the solution set is a line through $\mathbf{0}$ in $\mathbb{R}^3$. See Figure 1.   ∎

Notice that a nontrivial solution $\mathbf{x}$ can have some zero entries so long as not all of its entries are zero.

**EXAMPLE 2**   A single linear equation can be treated as a very simple system of equations. Describe all solutions of the homogeneous "system"

$$10x_1 - 3x_2 - 2x_3 = 0 \tag{1}$$

**SOLUTION** There is no need for matrix notation. Solve for the basic variable $x_1$ in terms of the free variables. The general solution is $x_1 = .3x_2 + .2x_3$, with $x_2$ and $x_3$

free. As a vector, the general solution is

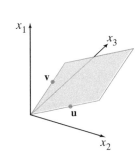

**FIGURE 2**

$$\mathbf{x} = \begin{bmatrix} x_1 \\ x_2 \\ x_3 \end{bmatrix} = \begin{bmatrix} .3x_2 + .2x_3 \\ x_2 \\ x_3 \end{bmatrix} = \begin{bmatrix} .3x_2 \\ x_2 \\ 0 \end{bmatrix} + \begin{bmatrix} .2x_3 \\ 0 \\ x_3 \end{bmatrix}$$

$$= x_2 \underbrace{\begin{bmatrix} .3 \\ 1 \\ 0 \end{bmatrix}}_{\mathbf{u}} + x_3 \underbrace{\begin{bmatrix} .2 \\ 0 \\ 1 \end{bmatrix}}_{\mathbf{v}} \quad \text{(with } x_2, x_3 \text{ free)} \tag{2}$$

This calculation shows that every solution of (1) is a linear combination of the vectors $\mathbf{u}$ and $\mathbf{v}$, shown in (2). That is, the solution set is Span $\{\mathbf{u}, \mathbf{v}\}$. Since neither $\mathbf{u}$ nor $\mathbf{v}$ is a scalar multiple of the other, the solution set is a plane through the origin. See Figure 2. ∎

Examples 1 and 2, along with the exercises, illustrate the fact that the solution set of a homogeneous equation $A\mathbf{x} = \mathbf{0}$ can always be expressed explicitly as Span $\{\mathbf{v}_1, \dots, \mathbf{v}_p\}$ for suitable vectors $\mathbf{v}_1, \dots, \mathbf{v}_p$. If the only solution is the zero vector, then the solution set is Span $\{\mathbf{0}\}$. If the equation $A\mathbf{x} = \mathbf{0}$ has only one free variable, the solution set is a line through the origin, as in Figure 1. A plane through the origin, as in Figure 2, provides a good mental image for the solution set of $A\mathbf{x} = \mathbf{0}$ when there are two or more free variables. Note, however, that a similar figure can be used to visualize Span $\{\mathbf{u}, \mathbf{v}\}$ even when $\mathbf{u}$ and $\mathbf{v}$ do not arise as solutions of $A\mathbf{x} = \mathbf{0}$. See Figure 11 in Section 1.3.

## Parametric Vector Form

The original equation (1) for the plane in Example 2 is an *implicit* description of the plane. Solving this equation amounts to finding an *explicit* description of the plane as the set spanned by $\mathbf{u}$ and $\mathbf{v}$. Equation (2) is called a **parametric vector equation** of the plane. Sometimes such an equation is written as

$$\mathbf{x} = s\mathbf{u} + t\mathbf{v} \quad (s, t \text{ in } \mathbb{R})$$

to emphasize that the parameters vary over all real numbers. In Example 1, the equation $\mathbf{x} = x_3\mathbf{v}$ (with $x_3$ free), or $\mathbf{x} = t\mathbf{v}$ (with $t$ in $\mathbb{R}$), is a parametric vector equation of a line. Whenever a solution set is described explicitly with vectors as in Examples 1 and 2, we say that the solution is in **parametric vector form**.

## Solutions of Nonhomogeneous Systems

When a nonhomogeneous linear system has many solutions, the general solution can be written in parametric vector form as one vector plus an arbitrary linear combination of vectors that satisfy the corresponding homogeneous system.

**EXAMPLE 3**   Describe all solutions of $A\mathbf{x} = \mathbf{b}$, where

$$A = \begin{bmatrix} 3 & 5 & -4 \\ -3 & -2 & 4 \\ 6 & 1 & -8 \end{bmatrix} \quad \text{and} \quad \mathbf{b} = \begin{bmatrix} 7 \\ -1 \\ -4 \end{bmatrix}$$

**SOLUTION** Here $A$ is the matrix of coefficients from Example 1. Row operations on $[\,A \quad \mathbf{b}\,]$ produce

$$\begin{bmatrix} 3 & 5 & -4 & 7 \\ -3 & -2 & 4 & -1 \\ 6 & 1 & -8 & -4 \end{bmatrix} \sim \begin{bmatrix} 1 & 0 & -\frac{4}{3} & -1 \\ 0 & 1 & 0 & 2 \\ 0 & 0 & 0 & 0 \end{bmatrix}, \qquad \begin{aligned} x_1 \quad -\tfrac{4}{3}x_3 &= -1 \\ x_2 \qquad\quad &= 2 \\ 0 &= 0 \end{aligned}$$

Thus $x_1 = -1 + \frac{4}{3}x_3$, $x_2 = 2$, and $x_3$ is free. As a vector, the general solution of $A\mathbf{x} = \mathbf{b}$ has the form

$$\mathbf{x} = \begin{bmatrix} x_1 \\ x_2 \\ x_3 \end{bmatrix} = \begin{bmatrix} -1 + \frac{4}{3}x_3 \\ 2 \\ x_3 \end{bmatrix} = \begin{bmatrix} -1 \\ 2 \\ 0 \end{bmatrix} + \begin{bmatrix} \frac{4}{3}x_3 \\ 0 \\ x_3 \end{bmatrix} = \underset{\underset{\mathbf{p}}{\uparrow}}{\begin{bmatrix} -1 \\ 2 \\ 0 \end{bmatrix}} + x_3 \underset{\underset{\mathbf{v}}{\uparrow}}{\begin{bmatrix} \frac{4}{3} \\ 0 \\ 1 \end{bmatrix}}$$

The equation $\mathbf{x} = \mathbf{p} + x_3\mathbf{v}$, or, writing $t$ as a general parameter,

$$\mathbf{x} = \mathbf{p} + t\mathbf{v} \quad (t \text{ in } \mathbb{R}) \tag{3}$$

describes the solution set of $A\mathbf{x} = \mathbf{b}$ in parametric vector form. Recall from Example 1 that the solution set of $A\mathbf{x} = \mathbf{0}$ has the parametric vector equation

$$\mathbf{x} = t\mathbf{v} \quad (t \text{ in } \mathbb{R}) \tag{4}$$

[with the same $\mathbf{v}$ that appears in (3)]. Thus the solutions of $A\mathbf{x} = \mathbf{b}$ are obtained by adding the vector $\mathbf{p}$ to the solutions of $A\mathbf{x} = \mathbf{0}$. The vector $\mathbf{p}$ itself is just one particular solution of $A\mathbf{x} = \mathbf{b}$ [corresponding to $t = 0$ in (3)]. ∎

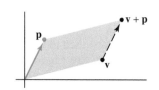

**FIGURE 3**

Adding $\mathbf{p}$ to $\mathbf{v}$ translates $\mathbf{v}$ to $\mathbf{v} + \mathbf{p}$.

To describe the solution set of $A\mathbf{x} = \mathbf{b}$ geometrically, we can think of vector addition as a *translation*. Given $\mathbf{v}$ and $\mathbf{p}$ in $\mathbb{R}^2$ or $\mathbb{R}^3$, the effect of adding $\mathbf{p}$ to $\mathbf{v}$ is to *move* $\mathbf{v}$ in a direction parallel to the line through $\mathbf{p}$ and $\mathbf{0}$. We say that $\mathbf{v}$ is **translated by $\mathbf{p}$** to $\mathbf{v} + \mathbf{p}$. See Figure 3. If each point on a line $L$ in $\mathbb{R}^2$ or $\mathbb{R}^3$ is translated by a vector $\mathbf{p}$, the result is a line parallel to $L$. See Figure 4.

Suppose $L$ is the line through $\mathbf{0}$ and $\mathbf{v}$, described by equation (4). Adding $\mathbf{p}$ to each point on $L$ produces the translated line described by equation (3). Note that $\mathbf{p}$ is on the line in equation (3). We call (3) **the equation of the line through $\mathbf{p}$ parallel to $\mathbf{v}$**. Thus *the solution set of $A\mathbf{x} = \mathbf{b}$ is a line through $\mathbf{p}$ parallel to the solution set of $A\mathbf{x} = \mathbf{0}$.* Figure 5 illustrates this case.

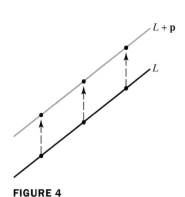

**FIGURE 4**

Translated line.

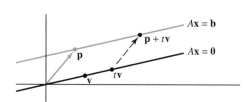

**FIGURE 5** Parallel solution sets of $A\mathbf{x} = \mathbf{b}$ and $A\mathbf{x} = \mathbf{0}$.

The relation between the solution sets of $A\mathbf{x} = \mathbf{b}$ and $A\mathbf{x} = \mathbf{0}$ shown in Figure 5 generalizes to any *consistent* equation $A\mathbf{x} = \mathbf{b}$, although the solution set will be larger than a line when there are several free variables. The following theorem gives the precise statement. See Exercise 25 for a proof.

**THEOREM 6**

Suppose the equation $A\mathbf{x} = \mathbf{b}$ is consistent for some given $\mathbf{b}$, and let $\mathbf{p}$ be a solution. Then the solution set of $A\mathbf{x} = \mathbf{b}$ is the set of all vectors of the form $\mathbf{w} = \mathbf{p} + \mathbf{v}_h$, where $\mathbf{v}_h$ is any solution of the homogeneous equation $A\mathbf{x} = \mathbf{0}$.

Theorem 6 says that if $A\mathbf{x} = \mathbf{b}$ has a solution, then the solution set is obtained by translating the solution set of $A\mathbf{x} = \mathbf{0}$, using any particular solution $\mathbf{p}$ of $A\mathbf{x} = \mathbf{b}$ for the translation. Figure 6 illustrates the case in which there are two free variables. Even when $n > 3$, our mental image of the solution set of a consistent system $A\mathbf{x} = \mathbf{b}$ (with $\mathbf{b} \neq \mathbf{0}$) is either a single nonzero point or a line or plane not passing through the origin.

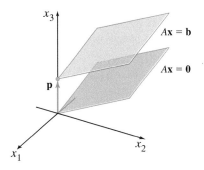

**FIGURE 6** Parallel solution sets of $A\mathbf{x} = \mathbf{b}$ and $A\mathbf{x} = \mathbf{0}$.

***Warning:*** Theorem 6 and Figure 6 apply only to an equation $A\mathbf{x} = \mathbf{b}$ that has at least one nonzero solution $\mathbf{p}$. When $A\mathbf{x} = \mathbf{b}$ has no solution, the solution set is empty.

The following algorithm outlines the calculations shown in Examples 1, 2, and 3.

---

**WRITING A SOLUTION SET (OF A CONSISTENT SYSTEM) IN PARAMETRIC VECTOR FORM**

1. Row reduce the augmented matrix to reduced echelon form.
2. Express each basic variable in terms of any free variables appearing in an equation.
3. Write a typical solution $\mathbf{x}$ as a vector whose entries depend on the free variables, if any.
4. Decompose $\mathbf{x}$ into a linear combination of vectors (with numeric entries) using the free variables as parameters.

---

**PRACTICE PROBLEMS**

1. Each of the following equations determines a plane in $\mathbb{R}^3$. Do the two planes intersect? If so, describe their intersection.

$$x_1 + 4x_2 - 5x_3 = 0$$
$$2x_1 - x_2 + 8x_3 = 9$$

2. Write the general solution of $10x_1 - 3x_2 - 2x_3 = 7$ in parametric vector form, and relate the solution set to the one found in Example 2.

3. Prove the first part of Theorem 6: Suppose that $\mathbf{p}$ is a solution of $A\mathbf{x} = \mathbf{b}$, so that $A\mathbf{p} = \mathbf{b}$. Let $\mathbf{v}_h$ be any solution to the homogeneous equation $A\mathbf{x} = \mathbf{0}$, and let $\mathbf{w} = \mathbf{p} + \mathbf{v}_h$. Show that $\mathbf{w}$ is a solution to $A\mathbf{x} = \mathbf{b}$.

## 1.5 EXERCISES

In Exercises 1–4, determine if the system has a nontrivial solution. Try to use as few row operations as possible.

**1.**
$$2x_1 - 5x_2 + 8x_3 = 0$$
$$-2x_1 - 7x_2 + x_3 = 0$$
$$4x_1 + 2x_2 + 7x_3 = 0$$

**2.**
$$x_1 - 3x_2 + 7x_3 = 0$$
$$-2x_1 + x_2 - 4x_3 = 0$$
$$x_1 + 2x_2 + 9x_3 = 0$$

**3.**
$$-3x_1 + 5x_2 - 7x_3 = 0$$
$$-6x_1 + 7x_2 + x_3 = 0$$

**4.**
$$-5x_1 + 7x_2 + 9x_3 = 0$$
$$x_1 - 2x_2 + 6x_3 = 0$$

In Exercises 5 and 6, follow the method of Examples 1 and 2 to write the solution set of the given homogeneous system in parametric vector form.

**5.**
$$x_1 + 3x_2 + x_3 = 0$$
$$-4x_1 - 9x_2 + 2x_3 = 0$$
$$- 3x_2 - 6x_3 = 0$$

**6.**
$$x_1 + 3x_2 - 5x_3 = 0$$
$$x_1 + 4x_2 - 8x_3 = 0$$
$$-3x_1 - 7x_2 + 9x_3 = 0$$

In Exercises 7–12, describe all solutions of $A\mathbf{x} = \mathbf{0}$ in parametric vector form, where $A$ is row equivalent to the given matrix.

**7.** $\begin{bmatrix} 1 & 3 & -3 & 7 \\ 0 & 1 & -4 & 5 \end{bmatrix}$

**8.** $\begin{bmatrix} 1 & -2 & -9 & 5 \\ 0 & 1 & 2 & -6 \end{bmatrix}$

**9.** $\begin{bmatrix} 3 & -9 & 6 \\ -1 & 3 & -2 \end{bmatrix}$

**10.** $\begin{bmatrix} 1 & 3 & 0 & -4 \\ 2 & 6 & 0 & -8 \end{bmatrix}$

**11.** $\begin{bmatrix} 1 & -4 & -2 & 0 & 3 & -5 \\ 0 & 0 & 1 & 0 & 0 & -1 \\ 0 & 0 & 0 & 0 & 1 & -4 \\ 0 & 0 & 0 & 0 & 0 & 0 \end{bmatrix}$

**12.** $\begin{bmatrix} 1 & 5 & 2 & -6 & 9 & 0 \\ 0 & 0 & 1 & -7 & 4 & -8 \\ 0 & 0 & 0 & 0 & 0 & 1 \\ 0 & 0 & 0 & 0 & 0 & 0 \end{bmatrix}$

**13.** Suppose the solution set of a certain system of linear equations can be described as $x_1 = 5 + 4x_3, x_2 = -2 - 7x_3$, with $x_3$ free. Use vectors to describe this set as a line in $\mathbb{R}^3$.

**14.** Suppose the solution set of a certain system of linear equations can be described as $x_1 = 3x_4$, $x_2 = 8 + x_4$, $x_3 = 2 - 5x_4$, with $x_4$ free. Use vectors to describe this set as a "line" in $\mathbb{R}^4$.

**15.** Follow the method of Example 3 to describe the solutions of the following system in parametric vector form. Also, give a geometric description of the solution set and compare it to that in Exercise 5.
$$x_1 + 3x_2 + x_3 = 1$$
$$-4x_1 - 9x_2 + 2x_3 = -1$$
$$- 3x_2 - 6x_3 = -3$$

**16.** As in Exercise 15, describe the solutions of the following system in parametric vector form, and provide a geometric comparison with the solution set in Exercise 6.

$$x_1 + 3x_2 - 5x_3 = 4$$
$$x_1 + 4x_2 - 8x_3 = 7$$
$$-3x_1 - 7x_2 + 9x_3 = -6$$

**17.** Describe and compare the solution sets of $x_1 + 9x_2 - 4x_3 = 0$ and $x_1 + 9x_2 - 4x_3 = -2$.

**18.** Describe and compare the solution sets of $x_1 - 3x_2 + 5x_3 = 0$ and $x_1 - 3x_2 + 5x_3 = 4$.

In Exercises 19 and 20, find the parametric equation of the line through **a** parallel to **b**.

**19.** $\mathbf{a} = \begin{bmatrix} -2 \\ 0 \end{bmatrix}, \mathbf{b} = \begin{bmatrix} -5 \\ 3 \end{bmatrix}$

**20.** $\mathbf{a} = \begin{bmatrix} 3 \\ -4 \end{bmatrix}, \mathbf{b} = \begin{bmatrix} -7 \\ 8 \end{bmatrix}$

In Exercises 21 and 22, find a parametric equation of the line $M$ through **p** and **q**. [*Hint:* $M$ is parallel to the vector $\mathbf{q} - \mathbf{p}$. See the figure below.]

**21.** $\mathbf{p} = \begin{bmatrix} 2 \\ -5 \end{bmatrix}, \mathbf{q} = \begin{bmatrix} -3 \\ 1 \end{bmatrix}$

**22.** $\mathbf{p} = \begin{bmatrix} -6 \\ 3 \end{bmatrix}, \mathbf{q} = \begin{bmatrix} 0 \\ -4 \end{bmatrix}$

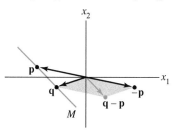

The line through **p** and **q**.

In Exercises 23 and 24, mark each statement True or False. Justify each answer.

**23.** a. A homogeneous equation is always consistent.

  b. The equation $A\mathbf{x} = \mathbf{0}$ gives an explicit description of its solution set.

  c. The homogeneous equation $A\mathbf{x} = \mathbf{0}$ has the trivial solution if and only if the equation has at least one free variable.

  d. The equation $\mathbf{x} = \mathbf{p} + t\mathbf{v}$ describes a line through **v** parallel to **p**.

  e. The solution set of $A\mathbf{x} = \mathbf{b}$ is the set of all vectors of the form $\mathbf{w} = \mathbf{p} + \mathbf{v}_h$, where $\mathbf{v}_h$ is any solution of the equation $A\mathbf{x} = \mathbf{0}$.

**24.** a. If **x** is a nontrivial solution of $A\mathbf{x} = \mathbf{0}$, then every entry in **x** is nonzero.

  b. The equation $\mathbf{x} = x_2\mathbf{u} + x_3\mathbf{v}$, with $x_2$ and $x_3$ free (and neither **u** nor **v** a multiple of the other), describes a plane through the origin.

  c. The equation $A\mathbf{x} = \mathbf{b}$ is homogeneous if the zero vector is a solution.

  d. The effect of adding **p** to a vector is to move the vector in a direction parallel to **p**.

e. The solution set of $A\mathbf{x} = \mathbf{b}$ is obtained by translating the solution set of $A\mathbf{x} = \mathbf{0}$.

**25.** Prove the second part of Theorem 6: Let $\mathbf{w}$ be any solution of $A\mathbf{x} = \mathbf{b}$, and define $\mathbf{v}_h = \mathbf{w} - \mathbf{p}$. Show that $\mathbf{v}_h$ is a solution of $A\mathbf{x} = \mathbf{0}$. This shows that every solution of $A\mathbf{x} = \mathbf{b}$ has the form $\mathbf{w} = \mathbf{p} + \mathbf{v}_h$, with $\mathbf{p}$ a particular solution of $A\mathbf{x} = \mathbf{b}$ and $\mathbf{v}_h$ a solution of $A\mathbf{x} = \mathbf{0}$.

**26.** Suppose $A\mathbf{x} = \mathbf{b}$ has a solution. Explain why the solution is unique precisely when $A\mathbf{x} = \mathbf{0}$ has only the trivial solution.

**27.** Suppose $A$ is the $3 \times 3$ *zero* matrix (with all zero entries). Describe the solution set of the equation $A\mathbf{x} = \mathbf{0}$.

**28.** If $\mathbf{b} \neq \mathbf{0}$, can the solution set of $A\mathbf{x} = \mathbf{b}$ be a plane through the origin? Explain.

In Exercises 29–32, (a) does the equation $A\mathbf{x} = \mathbf{0}$ have a nontrivial solution and (b) does the equation $A\mathbf{x} = \mathbf{b}$ have at least one solution for every possible $\mathbf{b}$?

**29.** $A$ is a $3 \times 3$ matrix with three pivot positions.

**30.** $A$ is a $3 \times 3$ matrix with two pivot positions.

**31.** $A$ is a $3 \times 2$ matrix with two pivot positions.

**32.** $A$ is a $2 \times 4$ matrix with two pivot positions.

**33.** Given $A = \begin{bmatrix} -2 & -6 \\ 7 & 21 \\ -3 & -9 \end{bmatrix}$, find one nontrivial solution of $A\mathbf{x} = \mathbf{0}$ by inspection. [*Hint:* Think of the equation $A\mathbf{x} = \mathbf{0}$ written as a vector equation.]

**34.** Given $A = \begin{bmatrix} 4 & -6 \\ -8 & 12 \\ 6 & -9 \end{bmatrix}$, find one nontrivial solution of $A\mathbf{x} = \mathbf{0}$ by inspection.

**35.** Construct a $3 \times 3$ nonzero matrix $A$ such that the vector $\begin{bmatrix} 1 \\ 1 \\ 1 \end{bmatrix}$ is a solution of $A\mathbf{x} = \mathbf{0}$.

**36.** Construct a $3 \times 3$ nonzero matrix $A$ such that the vector $\begin{bmatrix} 1 \\ -2 \\ 1 \end{bmatrix}$ is a solution of $A\mathbf{x} = \mathbf{0}$.

**37.** Construct a $2 \times 2$ matrix $A$ such that the solution set of the equation $A\mathbf{x} = \mathbf{0}$ is the line in $\mathbb{R}^2$ through $(4, 1)$ and the origin. Then, find a vector $\mathbf{b}$ in $\mathbb{R}^2$ such that the solution set of $A\mathbf{x} = \mathbf{b}$ is *not* a line in $\mathbb{R}^2$ parallel to the solution set of $A\mathbf{x} = \mathbf{0}$. Why does this *not* contradict Theorem 6?

**38.** Suppose $A$ is a $3 \times 3$ matrix and $\mathbf{y}$ is a vector in $\mathbb{R}^3$ such that the equation $A\mathbf{x} = \mathbf{y}$ does *not* have a solution. Does there exist a vector $\mathbf{z}$ in $\mathbb{R}^3$ such that the equation $A\mathbf{x} = \mathbf{z}$ has a unique solution? Discuss.

**39.** Let $A$ be an $m \times n$ matrix and let $\mathbf{u}$ be a vector in $\mathbb{R}^n$ that satisfies the equation $A\mathbf{x} = \mathbf{0}$. Show that for any scalar $c$, the vector $c\mathbf{u}$ also satisfies $A\mathbf{x} = \mathbf{0}$. [That is, show that $A(c\mathbf{u}) = \mathbf{0}$.]

**40.** Let $A$ be an $m \times n$ matrix, and let $\mathbf{u}$ and $\mathbf{v}$ be vectors in $\mathbb{R}^n$ with the property that $A\mathbf{u} = \mathbf{0}$ and $A\mathbf{v} = \mathbf{0}$. Explain why $A(\mathbf{u} + \mathbf{v})$ must be the zero vector. Then explain why $A(c\mathbf{u} + d\mathbf{v}) = \mathbf{0}$ for each pair of scalars $c$ and $d$.

---

**SOLUTIONS TO PRACTICE PROBLEMS**

**1.** Row reduce the augmented matrix:

$$\begin{bmatrix} 1 & 4 & -5 & 0 \\ 2 & -1 & 8 & 9 \end{bmatrix} \sim \begin{bmatrix} 1 & 4 & -5 & 0 \\ 0 & -9 & 18 & 9 \end{bmatrix} \sim \begin{bmatrix} 1 & 0 & 3 & 4 \\ 0 & 1 & -2 & -1 \end{bmatrix}$$

$$\begin{aligned} x_1 \quad + 3x_3 &= 4 \\ x_2 - 2x_3 &= -1 \end{aligned}$$

Thus $x_1 = 4 - 3x_3$, $x_2 = -1 + 2x_3$, with $x_3$ free. The general solution in parametric vector form is

$$\begin{bmatrix} x_1 \\ x_2 \\ x_3 \end{bmatrix} = \begin{bmatrix} 4 - 3x_3 \\ -1 + 2x_3 \\ x_3 \end{bmatrix} = \underset{\mathbf{p}}{\begin{bmatrix} 4 \\ -1 \\ 0 \end{bmatrix}} + x_3 \underset{\mathbf{v}}{\begin{bmatrix} -3 \\ 2 \\ 1 \end{bmatrix}}$$

The intersection of the two planes is the line through $\mathbf{p}$ in the direction of $\mathbf{v}$.

2.  The augmented matrix $\begin{bmatrix} 10 & -3 & -2 & 7 \end{bmatrix}$ is row equivalent to $\begin{bmatrix} 1 & -.3 & -.2 & .7 \end{bmatrix}$, and the general solution is $x_1 = .7 + .3x_2 + .2x_3$, with $x_2$ and $x_3$ free. That is,

$$
\mathbf{x} = \begin{bmatrix} x_1 \\ x_2 \\ x_3 \end{bmatrix} = \begin{bmatrix} .7 + .3x_2 + .2x_3 \\ x_2 \\ x_3 \end{bmatrix} = \begin{bmatrix} .7 \\ 0 \\ 0 \end{bmatrix} + x_2 \begin{bmatrix} .3 \\ 1 \\ 0 \end{bmatrix} + x_3 \begin{bmatrix} .2 \\ 0 \\ 1 \end{bmatrix}
$$

$$
= \quad \mathbf{p} \quad + \quad x_2\mathbf{u} \quad + \quad x_3\mathbf{v}
$$

The solution set of the nonhomogeneous equation $A\mathbf{x} = \mathbf{b}$ is the translated plane $\mathbf{p} + \text{Span}\{\mathbf{u}, \mathbf{v}\}$, which passes through $\mathbf{p}$ and is parallel to the solution set of the homogeneous equation in Example 2.

3.  Using Theorem 5 from Section 1.4, notice

$$
A(\mathbf{p} + \mathbf{v}_h) = A\mathbf{p} + A\mathbf{v}_h = \mathbf{b} + \mathbf{0} = \mathbf{b},
$$

hence $\mathbf{p} + \mathbf{v}_h$ is a solution to $A\mathbf{x} = \mathbf{b}$.

# 1.6 APPLICATIONS OF LINEAR SYSTEMS

You might expect that a real-life problem involving linear algebra would have only one solution, or perhaps no solution. The purpose of this section is to show how linear systems with many solutions can arise naturally. The applications here come from economics, chemistry, and network flow.

## A Homogeneous System in Economics

WEB

The system of 500 equations in 500 variables, mentioned in this chapter's introduction, is now known as a Leontief "input–output" (or "production") model.[1] For now, we look at a simpler "exchange model," also due to Leontief.

Suppose a nation's economy is divided into many sectors, such as various manufacturing, communication, entertainment, and service industries. Suppose that for each sector we know its total output for one year and we know exactly how this output is divided or "exchanged" among the other sectors of the economy. Let the total dollar value of a sector's output be called the **price** of that output. Leontief proved the following result.

> There exist *equilibrium prices* that can be assigned to the total outputs of the various sectors in such a way that the income of each sector exactly balances its expenses.

The following example shows how to find the equilibrium prices.

**EXAMPLE 1**   Suppose an economy consists of the Coal, Electric (power), and Steel sectors, and the output of each sector is distributed among the various sectors as shown in Table 1, where the entries in a column represent the fractional parts of a sector's total output.

The second column of Table 1, for instance, says that the total output of the Electric sector is divided as follows: 40% to Coal, 50% to Steel, and the remaining 10% to Electric. (Electric treats this 10% as an expense it incurs in order to operate its

---

[1] See Wassily W. Leontief, "Input–Output Economics," *Scientific American*, October 1951, pp. 15–21.

business.) Since all output must be taken into account, the decimal fractions in each column must sum to 1.

Denote the prices (i.e., dollar values) of the total annual outputs of the Coal, Electric, and Steel sectors by $p_C$, $p_E$, and $p_S$, respectively. If possible, find equilibrium prices that make each sector's income match its expenditures.

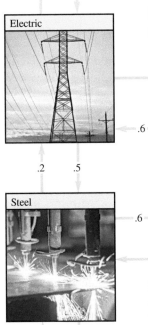

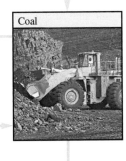

| TABLE 1 | A Simple Economy | | |
|---------|------------------|---|---|
| **Distribution of Output from:** | | | |
| **Coal** | **Electric** | **Steel** | **Purchased by:** |
| .0 | .4 | .6 | Coal |
| .6 | .1 | .2 | Electric |
| .4 | .5 | .2 | Steel |

**SOLUTION** A sector looks down a column to see where its output goes, and it looks across a row to see what it needs as inputs. For instance, the first row of Table 1 says that Coal receives (and pays for) 40% of the Electric output and 60% of the Steel output. Since the respective values of the total outputs are $p_E$ and $p_S$, Coal must spend $.4p_E$ dollars for its share of Electric's output and $.6p_S$ for its share of Steel's output. Thus Coal's total expenses are $.4p_E + .6p_S$. To make Coal's income, $p_C$, equal to its expenses, we want

$$p_C = .4p_E + .6p_S \tag{1}$$

The second row of the exchange table shows that the Electric sector spends $.6p_C$ for coal, $.1p_E$ for electricity, and $.2p_S$ for steel. Hence the income/expense requirement for Electric is

$$p_E = .6p_C + .1p_E + .2p_S \tag{2}$$

Finally, the third row of the exchange table leads to the final requirement:

$$p_S = .4p_C + .5p_E + .2p_S \tag{3}$$

To solve the system of equations (1), (2), and (3), move all the unknowns to the left sides of the equations and combine like terms. [For instance, on the left side of (2), write $p_E - .1p_E$ as $.9p_E$.]

$$p_C - .4p_E - .6p_S = 0$$
$$-.6p_C + .9p_E - .2p_S = 0$$
$$-.4p_C - .5p_E + .8p_S = 0$$

Row reduction is next. For simplicity here, decimals are rounded to two places.

$$\begin{bmatrix} 1 & -.4 & -.6 & 0 \\ -.6 & .9 & -.2 & 0 \\ -.4 & -.5 & .8 & 0 \end{bmatrix} \sim \begin{bmatrix} 1 & -.4 & -.6 & 0 \\ 0 & .66 & -.56 & 0 \\ 0 & -.66 & .56 & 0 \end{bmatrix} \sim \begin{bmatrix} 1 & -.4 & -.6 & 0 \\ 0 & .66 & -.56 & 0 \\ 0 & 0 & 0 & 0 \end{bmatrix}$$

$$\sim \begin{bmatrix} 1 & -.4 & -.6 & 0 \\ 0 & 1 & -.85 & 0 \\ 0 & 0 & 0 & 0 \end{bmatrix} \sim \begin{bmatrix} 1 & 0 & -.94 & 0 \\ 0 & 1 & -.85 & 0 \\ 0 & 0 & 0 & 0 \end{bmatrix}$$

The general solution is $p_C = .94 p_S$, $p_E = .85 p_S$, and $p_S$ is free. The equilibrium price vector for the economy has the form

$$\mathbf{p} = \begin{bmatrix} p_C \\ p_E \\ p_S \end{bmatrix} = \begin{bmatrix} .94 p_S \\ .85 p_S \\ p_S \end{bmatrix} = p_S \begin{bmatrix} .94 \\ .85 \\ 1 \end{bmatrix}$$

Any (nonnegative) choice for $p_S$ results in a choice of equilibrium prices. For instance, if we take $p_S$ to be 100 (or \$100 million), then $p_C = 94$ and $p_E = 85$. The incomes and expenditures of each sector will be equal if the output of Coal is priced at \$94 million, that of Electric at \$85 million, and that of Steel at \$100 million. ∎

## Balancing Chemical Equations

Chemical equations describe the quantities of substances consumed and produced by chemical reactions. For instance, when propane gas burns, the propane ($C_3H_8$) combines with oxygen ($O_2$) to form carbon dioxide ($CO_2$) and water ($H_2O$), according to an equation of the form

$$(x_1)C_3H_8 + (x_2)O_2 \rightarrow (x_3)CO_2 + (x_4)H_2O \tag{4}$$

To "balance" this equation, a chemist must find whole numbers $x_1, \ldots, x_4$ such that the total numbers of carbon (C), hydrogen (H), and oxygen (O) atoms on the left match the corresponding numbers of atoms on the right (because atoms are neither destroyed nor created in the reaction).

A systematic method for balancing chemical equations is to set up a vector equation that describes the numbers of atoms of each type present in a reaction. Since equation (4) involves three types of atoms (carbon, hydrogen, and oxygen), construct a vector in $\mathbb{R}^3$ for each reactant and product in (4) that lists the numbers of "atoms per molecule," as follows:

$$C_3H_8: \begin{bmatrix} 3 \\ 8 \\ 0 \end{bmatrix}, \ O_2: \begin{bmatrix} 0 \\ 0 \\ 2 \end{bmatrix}, \ CO_2: \begin{bmatrix} 1 \\ 0 \\ 2 \end{bmatrix}, \ H_2O: \begin{bmatrix} 0 \\ 2 \\ 1 \end{bmatrix} \begin{matrix} \leftarrow \text{Carbon} \\ \leftarrow \text{Hydrogen} \\ \leftarrow \text{Oxygen} \end{matrix}$$

To balance equation (4), the coefficients $x_1, \ldots, x_4$ must satisfy

$$x_1 \begin{bmatrix} 3 \\ 8 \\ 0 \end{bmatrix} + x_2 \begin{bmatrix} 0 \\ 0 \\ 2 \end{bmatrix} = x_3 \begin{bmatrix} 1 \\ 0 \\ 2 \end{bmatrix} + x_4 \begin{bmatrix} 0 \\ 2 \\ 1 \end{bmatrix}$$

To solve, move all the terms to the left (changing the signs in the third and fourth vectors):

$$x_1 \begin{bmatrix} 3 \\ 8 \\ 0 \end{bmatrix} + x_2 \begin{bmatrix} 0 \\ 0 \\ 2 \end{bmatrix} + x_3 \begin{bmatrix} -1 \\ 0 \\ -2 \end{bmatrix} + x_4 \begin{bmatrix} 0 \\ -2 \\ -1 \end{bmatrix} = \begin{bmatrix} 0 \\ 0 \\ 0 \end{bmatrix}$$

Row reduction of the augmented matrix for this equation leads to the general solution

$$x_1 = \tfrac{1}{4} x_4, \ x_2 = \tfrac{5}{4} x_4, \ x_3 = \tfrac{3}{4} x_4, \ \text{with } x_4 \text{ free}$$

Since the coefficients in a chemical equation must be integers, take $x_4 = 4$, in which case $x_1 = 1$, $x_2 = 5$, and $x_3 = 3$. The balanced equation is

$$C_3H_8 + 5O_2 \rightarrow 3CO_2 + 4H_2O$$

The equation would also be balanced if, for example, each coefficient were doubled. For most purposes, however, chemists prefer to use a balanced equation whose coefficients are the smallest possible whole numbers.

## Network Flow

Systems of linear equations arise naturally when scientists, engineers, or economists study the flow of some quantity through a network. For instance, urban planners and traffic engineers monitor the pattern of traffic flow in a grid of city streets. Electrical engineers calculate current flow through electrical circuits. And economists analyze the distribution of products from manufacturers to consumers through a network of wholesalers and retailers. For many networks, the systems of equations involve hundreds or even thousands of variables and equations.

A *network* consists of a set of points called *junctions*, or *nodes*, with lines or arcs called *branches* connecting some or all of the junctions. The direction of flow in each branch is indicated, and the flow amount (or rate) is either shown or is denoted by a variable.

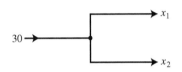

The basic assumption of network flow is that the total flow into the network equals the total flow out of the network and that the total flow into a junction equals the total flow out of the junction. For example, Figure 1 shows 30 units flowing into a junction through one branch, with $x_1$ and $x_2$ denoting the flows out of the junction through other branches. Since the flow is "conserved" at each junction, we must have $x_1 + x_2 = 30$. In a similar fashion, the flow at each junction is described by a linear equation. The problem of network analysis is to determine the flow in each branch when partial information (such as the flow into and out of the network) is known.

**FIGURE 1**

A junction, or node.

**EXAMPLE 2**   The network in Figure 2 shows the traffic flow (in vehicles per hour) over several one-way streets in downtown Baltimore during a typical early afternoon. Determine the general flow pattern for the network.

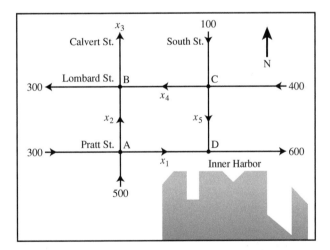

**FIGURE 2**  Baltimore streets.

**SOLUTION** Write equations that describe the flow, and then find the general solution of the system. Label the street intersections (junctions) and the unknown flows in the branches, as shown in Figure 2. At each intersection, set the flow in equal to the flow out.

| Intersection | Flow in | | Flow out |
|:---:|:---:|:---:|:---:|
| A | $300 + 500$ | $=$ | $x_1 + x_2$ |
| B | $x_2 + x_4$ | $=$ | $300 + x_3$ |
| C | $100 + 400$ | $=$ | $x_4 + x_5$ |
| D | $x_1 + x_5$ | $=$ | $600$ |

Also, the total flow into the network $(500 + 300 + 100 + 400)$ equals the total flow out of the network $(300 + x_3 + 600)$, which simplifies to $x_3 = 400$. Combine this equation with a rearrangement of the first four equations to obtain the following system of equations:

$$
\begin{aligned}
x_1 + x_2 \quad\quad\quad\quad\quad\quad &= 800 \\
x_2 - x_3 + x_4 \quad\quad &= 300 \\
x_4 + x_5 &= 500 \\
x_1 \quad\quad\quad\quad\quad\quad + x_5 &= 600 \\
x_3 \quad\quad\quad\quad\quad &= 400
\end{aligned}
$$

Row reduction of the associated augmented matrix leads to

$$
\begin{aligned}
x_1 \quad\quad\quad\quad + x_5 &= 600 \\
x_2 \quad\quad\quad - x_5 &= 200 \\
x_3 \quad\quad\quad &= 400 \\
x_4 + x_5 &= 500
\end{aligned}
$$

The general flow pattern for the network is described by

$$
\begin{cases}
x_1 = 600 - x_5 \\
x_2 = 200 + x_5 \\
x_3 = 400 \\
x_4 = 500 - x_5 \\
x_5 \text{ is free}
\end{cases}
$$

A negative flow in a network branch corresponds to flow in the direction opposite to that shown on the model. Since the streets in this problem are one-way, none of the variables here can be negative. This fact leads to certain limitations on the possible values of the variables. For instance, $x_5 \le 500$ because $x_4$ cannot be negative. Other constraints on the variables are considered in Practice Problem 2. ■

## PRACTICE PROBLEMS

1. Suppose an economy has three sectors: Agriculture, Mining, and Manufacturing. Agriculture sells 5% of its output to Mining and 30% to Manufacturing, and retains the rest. Mining sells 20% of its output to Agriculture and 70% to Manufacturing, and retains the rest. Manufacturing sells 20% of its output to Agriculture and 30% to Mining, and retains the rest. Determine the exchange table for this economy, where the columns describe how the output of each sector is exchanged among the three sectors.

2. Consider the network flow studied in Example 2. Determine the possible range of values of $x_1$ and $x_2$. [*Hint:* The example showed that $x_5 \le 500$. What does this imply about $x_1$ and $x_2$? Also, use the fact that $x_5 \ge 0$.]

# 1.6 EXERCISES

1. Suppose an economy has only two sectors, Goods and Services. Each year, Goods sells 80% of its output to Services and keeps the rest, while Services sells 70% of its output to Goods and retains the rest. Find equilibrium prices for the annual outputs of the Goods and Services sectors that make each sector's income match its expenditures.

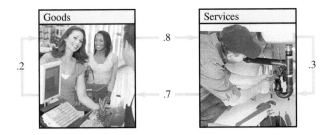

2. Find another set of equilibrium prices for the economy in Example 1. Suppose the same economy used Japanese yen instead of dollars to measure the value of the various sectors' outputs. Would this change the problem in any way? Discuss.

3. Consider an economy with three sectors, Chemicals & Metals, Fuels & Power, and Machinery. Chemicals sells 30% of its output to Fuels and 50% to Machinery and retains the rest. Fuels sells 80% of its output to Chemicals and 10% to Machinery and retains the rest. Machinery sells 40% to Chemicals and 40% to Fuels and retains the rest.

   a. Construct the exchange table for this economy.

   b. Develop a system of equations that leads to prices at which each sector's income matches its expenses. Then write the augmented matrix that can be row reduced to find these prices.

   c. [M] Find a set of equilibrium prices when the price for the Machinery output is 100 units.

4. Suppose an economy has four sectors, Agriculture (A), Energy (E), Manufacturing (M), and Transportation (T). Sector A sells 10% of its output to E and 25% to M and retains the rest. Sector E sells 30% of its output to A, 35% to M, and 25% to T and retains the rest. Sector M sells 30% of its output to A, 15% to E, and 40% to T and retains the rest. Sector T sells 20% of its output to A, 10% to E, and 30% to M and retains the rest.

   a. Construct the exchange table for this economy.

   b. [M] Find a set of equilibrium prices for the economy.

Balance the chemical equations in Exercises 5–10 using the vector equation approach discussed in this section.

5. Boron sulfide reacts violently with water to form boric acid and hydrogen sulfide gas (the smell of rotten eggs). The unbalanced equation is

$$B_2S_3 + H_2O \rightarrow H_3BO_3 + H_2S$$

[For each compound, construct a vector that lists the numbers of atoms of boron, sulfur, hydrogen, and oxygen.]

6. When solutions of sodium phosphate and barium nitrate are mixed, the result is barium phosphate (as a precipitate) and sodium nitrate. The unbalanced equation is

$$Na_3PO_4 + Ba(NO_3)_2 \rightarrow Ba_3(PO_4)_2 + NaNO_3$$

[For each compound, construct a vector that lists the numbers of atoms of sodium (Na), phosphorus, oxygen, barium, and nitrogen. For instance, barium nitrate corresponds to $(0, 0, 6, 1, 2)$.]

7. Alka-Seltzer contains sodium bicarbonate ($NaHCO_3$) and citric acid ($H_3C_6H_5O_7$). When a tablet is dissolved in water, the following reaction produces sodium citrate, water, and carbon dioxide (gas):

$$NaHCO_3 + H_3C_6H_5O_7 \rightarrow Na_3C_6H_5O_7 + H_2O + CO_2$$

8. The following reaction between potassium permanganate ($KMnO_4$) and manganese sulfate in water produces manganese dioxide, potassium sulfate, and sulfuric acid:

$$KMnO_4 + MnSO_4 + H_2O \rightarrow MnO_2 + K_2SO_4 + H_2SO_4$$

[For each compound, construct a vector that lists the numbers of atoms of potassium (K), manganese, oxygen, sulfur, and hydrogen.]

9. [M] If possible, use exact arithmetic or rational format for calculations in balancing the following chemical reaction:

$$PbN_6 + CrMn_2O_8 \rightarrow Pb_3O_4 + Cr_2O_3 + MnO_2 + NO$$

10. [M] The chemical reaction below can be used in some industrial processes, such as the production of arsene ($AsH_3$). Use exact arithmetic or rational format for calculations to balance this equation.

$$MnS + As_2Cr_{10}O_{35} + H_2SO_4$$
$$\rightarrow HMnO_4 + AsH_3 + CrS_3O_{12} + H_2O$$

11. Find the general flow pattern of the network shown in the figure. Assuming that the flows are all nonnegative, what is the largest possible value for $x_3$?

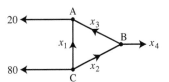

12. a. Find the general traffic pattern in the freeway network shown in the figure. (Flow rates are in cars/minute.)

    b. Describe the general traffic pattern when the road whose flow is $x_4$ is closed.

c. When $x_4 = 0$, what is the minimum value of $x_1$?

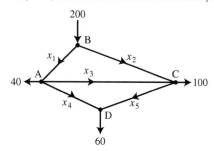

**13. a.** Find the general flow pattern in the network shown in the figure.

b. Assuming that the flow must be in the directions indicated, find the minimum flows in the branches denoted by $x_2, x_3, x_4$, and $x_5$.

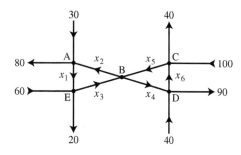

**14.** Intersections in England are often constructed as one-way "roundabouts," such as the one shown in the figure. Assume that traffic must travel in the directions shown. Find the general solution of the network flow. Find the smallest possible value for $x_6$.

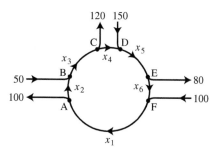

---

SOLUTIONS TO PRACTICE PROBLEMS

**1.** Write the percentages as decimals. Since all output must be taken into account, each column must sum to 1. This fact helps to fill in any missing entries.

**Distribution of Output from:**

| Agriculture | Mining | Manufacturing | Purchased by: |
|---|---|---|---|
| .65 | .20 | .20 | Agriculture |
| .05 | .10 | .30 | Mining |
| .30 | .70 | .50 | Manufacturing |

**2.** Since $x_5 \leq 500$, the equations D and A for $x_1$ and $x_2$ imply that $x_1 \geq 100$ and $x_2 \leq 700$. The fact that $x_5 \geq 0$ implies that $x_1 \leq 600$ and $x_2 \geq 200$. So, $100 \leq x_1 \leq 600$, and $200 \leq x_2 \leq 700$.

# 2 Matrix Algebra

## 2.1 | MATRIX OPERATIONS

If $A$ is an $m \times n$ matrix—that is, a matrix with $m$ rows and $n$ columns—then the scalar entry in the $i$th row and $j$th column of $A$ is denoted by $a_{ij}$ and is called the $(i, j)$-entry of $A$. See Figure 1. For instance, the $(3, 2)$-entry is the number $a_{32}$ in the third row, second column. Each column of $A$ is a list of $m$ real numbers, which identifies a vector in $\mathbb{R}^m$. Often, these columns are denoted by $\mathbf{a}_1, \ldots, \mathbf{a}_n$, and the matrix $A$ is written as

$$A = \begin{bmatrix} \mathbf{a}_1 & \mathbf{a}_2 & \cdots & \mathbf{a}_n \end{bmatrix}$$

Observe that the number $a_{ij}$ is the $i$th entry (from the top) of the $j$th column vector $\mathbf{a}_j$.

The **diagonal entries** in an $m \times n$ matrix $A = [a_{ij}]$ are $a_{11}, a_{22}, a_{33}, \ldots$, and they form the **main diagonal** of $A$. A **diagonal matrix** is a square $n \times n$ matrix whose nondiagonal entries are zero. An example is the $n \times n$ identity matrix, $I_n$. An $m \times n$ matrix whose entries are all zero is a **zero matrix** and is written as $0$. The size of a zero matrix is usually clear from the context.

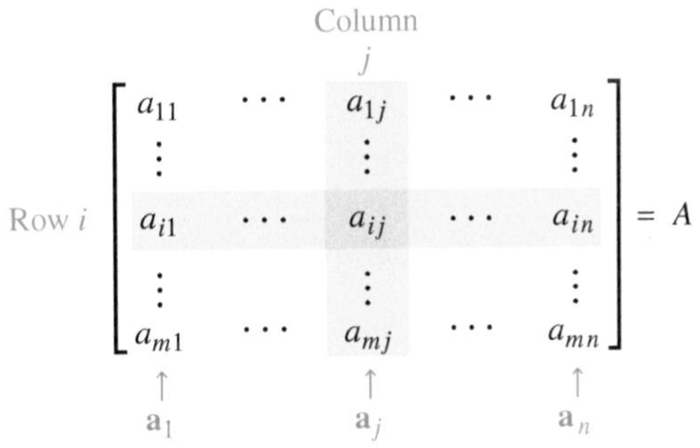

**FIGURE 1** Matrix notation.

## Sums and Scalar Multiples

The arithmetic for vectors described earlier has a natural extension to matrices. We say that two matrices are **equal** if they have the same size (i.e., the same number of rows and the same number of columns) and if their corresponding columns are equal, which amounts to saying that their corresponding entries are equal. If $A$ and $B$ are $m \times n$ matrices, then the **sum** $A + B$ is the $m \times n$ matrix whose columns are the sums of the corresponding columns in $A$ and $B$. Since vector addition of the columns is done entrywise, each entry in $A + B$ is the sum of the corresponding entries in $A$ and $B$. The sum $A + B$ is defined only when $A$ and $B$ are the same size.

**EXAMPLE 1**  Let

$$A = \begin{bmatrix} 4 & 0 & 5 \\ -1 & 3 & 2 \end{bmatrix}, \qquad B = \begin{bmatrix} 1 & 1 & 1 \\ 3 & 5 & 7 \end{bmatrix}, \qquad C = \begin{bmatrix} 2 & -3 \\ 0 & 1 \end{bmatrix}$$

Then

$$A + B = \begin{bmatrix} 5 & 1 & 6 \\ 2 & 8 & 9 \end{bmatrix}$$

but $A + C$ is not defined because $A$ and $C$ have different sizes.  ■

If $r$ is a scalar and $A$ is a matrix, then the **scalar multiple** $rA$ is the matrix whose columns are $r$ times the corresponding columns in $A$. As with vectors, $-A$ stands for $(-1)A$, and $A - B$ is the same as $A + (-1)B$.

**EXAMPLE 2**  If $A$ and $B$ are the matrices in Example 1, then

$$2B = 2 \begin{bmatrix} 1 & 1 & 1 \\ 3 & 5 & 7 \end{bmatrix} = \begin{bmatrix} 2 & 2 & 2 \\ 6 & 10 & 14 \end{bmatrix}$$

$$A - 2B = \begin{bmatrix} 4 & 0 & 5 \\ -1 & 3 & 2 \end{bmatrix} - \begin{bmatrix} 2 & 2 & 2 \\ 6 & 10 & 14 \end{bmatrix} = \begin{bmatrix} 2 & -2 & 3 \\ -7 & -7 & -12 \end{bmatrix} \qquad ■$$

It was unnecessary in Example 2 to compute $A - 2B$ as $A + (-1)2B$ because the usual rules of algebra apply to sums and scalar multiples of matrices, as the following theorem shows.

**THEOREM 1**  Let $A$, $B$, and $C$ be matrices of the same size, and let $r$ and $s$ be scalars.

a. $A + B = B + A$

b. $(A + B) + C = A + (B + C)$

c. $A + 0 = A$

d. $r(A + B) = rA + rB$

e. $(r + s)A = rA + sA$

f. $r(sA) = (rs)A$

Each equality in Theorem 1 is verified by showing that the matrix on the left side has the same size as the matrix on the right and that corresponding columns are equal. Size is no problem because $A$, $B$, and $C$ are equal in size. The equality of columns follows immediately from analogous properties of vectors. For instance, if the $j$th columns of $A$, $B$, and $C$ are $\mathbf{a}_j$, $\mathbf{b}_j$, and $\mathbf{c}_j$, respectively, then the $j$th columns of $(A + B) + C$ and $A + (B + C)$ are

$$(\mathbf{a}_j + \mathbf{b}_j) + \mathbf{c}_j \quad \text{and} \quad \mathbf{a}_j + (\mathbf{b}_j + \mathbf{c}_j)$$

respectively. Since these two vector sums are equal for each $j$, property (b) is verified.

Because of the associative property of addition, we can simply write $A + B + C$ for the sum, which can be computed either as $(A + B) + C$ or as $A + (B + C)$. The same applies to sums of four or more matrices.

## Matrix Multiplication

When a matrix $B$ multiplies a vector $\mathbf{x}$, it transforms $\mathbf{x}$ into the vector $B\mathbf{x}$. If this vector is then multiplied in turn by a matrix $A$, the resulting vector is $A(B\mathbf{x})$. See Figure 2.

**FIGURE 2** Multiplication by $B$ and then $A$.

Thus $A(B\mathbf{x})$ is produced from $\mathbf{x}$ by a *composition* of mappings—the linear transformations studied. Our goal is to represent this composite mapping as multiplication by a single matrix, denoted by $AB$, so that

$$A(B\mathbf{x}) = (AB)\mathbf{x} \tag{1}$$

See Figure 3.

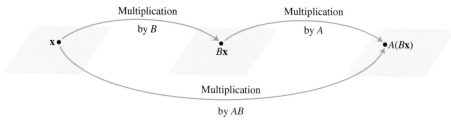

**FIGURE 3** Multiplication by $AB$.

If $A$ is $m \times n$, $B$ is $n \times p$, and $\mathbf{x}$ is in $\mathbb{R}^p$, denote the columns of $B$ by $\mathbf{b}_1, \ldots, \mathbf{b}_p$ and the entries in $\mathbf{x}$ by $x_1, \ldots, x_p$. Then

$$B\mathbf{x} = x_1\mathbf{b}_1 + \cdots + x_p\mathbf{b}_p$$

By the linearity of multiplication by $A$,

$$A(B\mathbf{x}) = A(x_1\mathbf{b}_1) + \cdots + A(x_p\mathbf{b}_p)$$
$$= x_1 A\mathbf{b}_1 + \cdots + x_p A\mathbf{b}_p$$

The vector $A(B\mathbf{x})$ is a linear combination of the vectors $A\mathbf{b}_1, \ldots, A\mathbf{b}_p$, using the entries in $\mathbf{x}$ as weights. In matrix notation, this linear combination is written as

$$A(B\mathbf{x}) = [\, A\mathbf{b}_1 \quad A\mathbf{b}_2 \quad \cdots \quad A\mathbf{b}_p \,]\mathbf{x}$$

Thus multiplication by $[\, A\mathbf{b}_1 \quad A\mathbf{b}_2 \quad \cdots \quad A\mathbf{b}_p \,]$ transforms $\mathbf{x}$ into $A(B\mathbf{x})$. We have found the matrix we sought!

DEFINITION

If $A$ is an $m \times n$ matrix, and if $B$ is an $n \times p$ matrix with columns $\mathbf{b}_1, \ldots, \mathbf{b}_p$, then the product $AB$ is the $m \times p$ matrix whose columns are $A\mathbf{b}_1, \ldots, A\mathbf{b}_p$. That is,

$$AB = A[\, \mathbf{b}_1 \quad \mathbf{b}_2 \quad \cdots \quad \mathbf{b}_p \,] = [\, A\mathbf{b}_1 \quad A\mathbf{b}_2 \quad \cdots \quad A\mathbf{b}_p \,]$$

This definition makes equation (1) true for all $\mathbf{x}$ in $\mathbb{R}^p$. Equation (1) proves that the composite mapping in Figure 3 is a linear transformation and that its standard matrix is $AB$. *Multiplication of matrices corresponds to composition of linear transformations.*

**EXAMPLE 3**   Compute $AB$, where $A = \begin{bmatrix} 2 & 3 \\ 1 & -5 \end{bmatrix}$ and $B = \begin{bmatrix} 4 & 3 & 6 \\ 1 & -2 & 3 \end{bmatrix}$.

**SOLUTION**   Write $B = [\, \mathbf{b}_1 \quad \mathbf{b}_2 \quad \mathbf{b}_3 \,]$, and compute:

$$A\mathbf{b}_1 = \begin{bmatrix} 2 & 3 \\ 1 & -5 \end{bmatrix}\begin{bmatrix} 4 \\ 1 \end{bmatrix}, \quad A\mathbf{b}_2 = \begin{bmatrix} 2 & 3 \\ 1 & -5 \end{bmatrix}\begin{bmatrix} 3 \\ -2 \end{bmatrix}, \quad A\mathbf{b}_3 = \begin{bmatrix} 2 & 3 \\ 1 & -5 \end{bmatrix}\begin{bmatrix} 6 \\ 3 \end{bmatrix}$$

$$= \begin{bmatrix} 11 \\ -1 \end{bmatrix} \qquad\qquad = \begin{bmatrix} 0 \\ 13 \end{bmatrix} \qquad\qquad = \begin{bmatrix} 21 \\ -9 \end{bmatrix}$$

Then

$$AB = A[\, \mathbf{b}_1 \quad \mathbf{b}_2 \quad \mathbf{b}_3 \,] = \begin{bmatrix} 11 & 0 & 21 \\ -1 & 13 & -9 \end{bmatrix}$$

$$\uparrow \qquad \uparrow \qquad \uparrow$$
$$A\mathbf{b}_1 \quad A\mathbf{b}_2 \quad A\mathbf{b}_3$$

Notice that since the first column of $AB$ is $A\mathbf{b}_1$, this column is a linear combination of the columns of $A$ using the entries in $\mathbf{b}_1$ as weights. A similar statement is true for each column of $AB$.

Each column of $AB$ is a linear combination of the columns of $A$ using weights from the corresponding column of $B$.

Obviously, the number of columns of $A$ must match the number of rows in $B$ in order for a linear combination such as $A\mathbf{b}_1$ to be defined. Also, the definition of $AB$ shows that $AB$ has the same number of rows as $A$ and the same number of columns as $B$.

**EXAMPLE 4**   If $A$ is a $3 \times 5$ matrix and $B$ is a $5 \times 2$ matrix, what are the sizes of $AB$ and $BA$, if they are defined?

**SOLUTION** Since $A$ has 5 columns and $B$ has 5 rows, the product $AB$ is defined and is a $3 \times 2$ matrix:

$$
\underset{3\times 5}{\begin{bmatrix} * & * & * & * & * \\ * & * & * & * & * \\ * & * & * & * & * \end{bmatrix}}^{A}
\underset{5\times 2}{\begin{bmatrix} * & * \\ * & * \\ * & * \\ * & * \\ * & * \end{bmatrix}}^{B}
=
\underset{3\times 2}{\begin{bmatrix} * & * \\ * & * \\ * & * \end{bmatrix}}^{AB}
$$

Match — Size of $AB$

The product $BA$ is *not* defined because the 2 columns of $B$ do not match the 3 rows of $A$. ∎

The definition of $AB$ is important for theoretical work and applications, but the following rule provides a more efficient method for calculating the individual entries in $AB$ when working small problems by hand.

---

**ROW–COLUMN RULE FOR COMPUTING *AB***

If the product $AB$ is defined, then the entry in row $i$ and column $j$ of $AB$ is the sum of the products of corresponding entries from row $i$ of $A$ and column $j$ of $B$. If $(AB)_{ij}$ denotes the $(i, j)$-entry in $AB$, and if $A$ is an $m \times n$ matrix, then

$$(AB)_{ij} = a_{i1}b_{1j} + a_{i2}b_{2j} + \cdots + a_{in}b_{nj}$$

---

To verify this rule, let $B = [\,\mathbf{b}_1 \;\cdots\; \mathbf{b}_p\,]$. Column $j$ of $AB$ is $A\mathbf{b}_j$, and we can compute $A\mathbf{b}_j$ by the row–vector rule for computing $A\mathbf{x}$ from Section 1.4. The $i$th entry in $A\mathbf{b}_j$ is the sum of the products of corresponding entries from row $i$ of $A$ and the vector $\mathbf{b}_j$, which is precisely the computation described in the rule for computing the $(i, j)$-entry of $AB$.

**EXAMPLE 5** Use the row–column rule to compute two of the entries in $AB$ for the matrices in Example 3. An inspection of the numbers involved will make it clear how the two methods for calculating $AB$ produce the same matrix.

**SOLUTION** To find the entry in row 1 and column 3 of $AB$, consider row 1 of $A$ and column 3 of $B$. Multiply corresponding entries and add the results, as shown below:

$$
AB = \begin{bmatrix} 2 & 3 \\ 1 & -5 \end{bmatrix}\begin{bmatrix} 4 & 3 & 6 \\ 1 & -2 & 3 \end{bmatrix} = \begin{bmatrix} \square & \square & 2(6)+3(3) \\ \square & \square & \square \end{bmatrix} = \begin{bmatrix} \square & \square & 21 \\ \square & \square & \square \end{bmatrix}
$$

For the entry in row 2 and column 2 of $AB$, use row 2 of $A$ and column 2 of $B$:

$$
\begin{bmatrix} 2 & 3 \\ 1 & -5 \end{bmatrix}\begin{bmatrix} 4 & 3 & 6 \\ 1 & -2 & 3 \end{bmatrix} = \begin{bmatrix} \square & \square & 21 \\ \square & 1(3)+-5(-2) & \square \end{bmatrix} = \begin{bmatrix} \square & \square & 21 \\ \square & 13 & \square \end{bmatrix}
$$
∎

**EXAMPLE 6**  Find the entries in the second row of $AB$, where

$$A = \begin{bmatrix} 2 & -5 & 0 \\ -1 & 3 & -4 \\ 6 & -8 & -7 \\ -3 & 0 & 9 \end{bmatrix}, \qquad B = \begin{bmatrix} 4 & -6 \\ 7 & 1 \\ 3 & 2 \end{bmatrix}$$

**SOLUTION**  By the row–column rule, the entries of the second row of $AB$ come from row 2 of $A$ (and the columns of $B$):

$$\rightarrow \begin{bmatrix} 2 & -5 & 0 \\ -1 & 3 & -4 \\ 6 & -8 & -7 \\ -3 & 0 & 9 \end{bmatrix} \begin{bmatrix} 4 & -6 \\ 7 & 1 \\ 3 & 2 \end{bmatrix}$$

$$= \begin{bmatrix} \square & \square \\ -4+21-12 & 6+3-8 \\ \square & \square \\ \square & \square \end{bmatrix} = \begin{bmatrix} \square & \square \\ 5 & 1 \\ \square & \square \\ \square & \square \end{bmatrix} \qquad \blacksquare$$

Notice that since Example 6 requested only the second row of $AB$, we could have written just the second row of $A$ to the left of $B$ and computed

$$\begin{bmatrix} -1 & 3 & -4 \end{bmatrix} \begin{bmatrix} 4 & -6 \\ 7 & 1 \\ 3 & 2 \end{bmatrix} = \begin{bmatrix} 5 & 1 \end{bmatrix}$$

This observation about rows of $AB$ is true in general and follows from the row–column rule. Let $\text{row}_i(A)$ denote the $i$th row of a matrix $A$. Then

$$\text{row}_i(AB) = \text{row}_i(A) \cdot B \tag{2}$$

## Properties of Matrix Multiplication

The following theorem lists the standard properties of matrix multiplication. Recall that $I_m$ represents the $m \times m$ identity matrix and $I_m\mathbf{x} = \mathbf{x}$ for all $\mathbf{x}$ in $\mathbb{R}^m$.

**THEOREM 2**

Let $A$ be an $m \times n$ matrix, and let $B$ and $C$ have sizes for which the indicated sums and products are defined.

a. $A(BC) = (AB)C$ (associative law of multiplication)
b. $A(B + C) = AB + AC$ (left distributive law)
c. $(B + C)A = BA + CA$ (right distributive law)
d. $r(AB) = (rA)B = A(rB)$
   for any scalar $r$
e. $I_mA = A = AI_n$ (identity for matrix multiplication)

**PROOF**  Properties (b)–(e) are considered in the exercises. Property (a) follows from the fact that matrix multiplication corresponds to composition of linear transformations (which are functions), and it is known (or easy to check) that the composition of functions is associative. Here is another proof of (a) that rests on the "column definition" of the product of two matrices. Let

$$C = [\, \mathbf{c}_1 \quad \cdots \quad \mathbf{c}_p \,]$$

By the definition of matrix multiplication,

$$BC = [\, B\mathbf{c}_1 \quad \cdots \quad B\mathbf{c}_p \,]$$
$$A(BC) = [\, A(B\mathbf{c}_1) \quad \cdots \quad A(B\mathbf{c}_p) \,]$$

Recall from equation (1) that the definition of $AB$ makes $A(B\mathbf{x}) = (AB)\mathbf{x}$ for all $\mathbf{x}$, so

$$A(BC) = [\, (AB)\mathbf{c}_1 \quad \cdots \quad (AB)\mathbf{c}_p \,] = (AB)C \qquad \blacksquare$$

The associative and distributive laws in Theorems 1 and 2 say essentially that pairs of parentheses in matrix expressions can be inserted and deleted in the same way as in the algebra of real numbers. In particular, we can write $ABC$ for the product, which can be computed either as $A(BC)$ or as $(AB)C$.[1] Similarly, a product $ABCD$ of four matrices can be computed as $A(BCD)$ or $(ABC)D$ or $A(BC)D$, and so on. It does not matter how we group the matrices when computing the product, so long as the left-to-right order of the matrices is preserved.

The left-to-right order in products is critical because $AB$ and $BA$ are usually not the same. This is not surprising, because the columns of $AB$ are linear combinations of the columns of $A$, whereas the columns of $BA$ are constructed from the columns of $B$. The position of the factors in the product $AB$ is emphasized by saying that $A$ is *right-multiplied* by $B$ or that $B$ is *left-multiplied* by $A$. If $AB = BA$, we say that $A$ and $B$ **commute** with one another.

**EXAMPLE 7**   Let $A = \begin{bmatrix} 5 & 1 \\ 3 & -2 \end{bmatrix}$ and $B = \begin{bmatrix} 2 & 0 \\ 4 & 3 \end{bmatrix}$. Show that these matrices do not commute. That is, verify that $AB \neq BA$.

**SOLUTION**

$$AB = \begin{bmatrix} 5 & 1 \\ 3 & -2 \end{bmatrix}\begin{bmatrix} 2 & 0 \\ 4 & 3 \end{bmatrix} = \begin{bmatrix} 14 & 3 \\ -2 & -6 \end{bmatrix}$$
$$BA = \begin{bmatrix} 2 & 0 \\ 4 & 3 \end{bmatrix}\begin{bmatrix} 5 & 1 \\ 3 & -2 \end{bmatrix} = \begin{bmatrix} 10 & 2 \\ 29 & -2 \end{bmatrix} \qquad \blacksquare$$

Example 7 illustrates the first of the following list of important differences between matrix algebra and the ordinary algebra of real numbers. See Exercises 9–12 for examples of these situations.

**WARNINGS:**

1. In general, $AB \neq BA$.

2. The cancellation laws do *not* hold for matrix multiplication. That is, if $AB = AC$, then it is *not* true in general that $B = C$. (See Exercise 10.)

3. If a product $AB$ is the zero matrix, you *cannot* conclude in general that either $A = 0$ or $B = 0$. (See Exercise 12.)

---

[1] When $B$ is square and $C$ has fewer columns than $A$ has rows, it is more efficient to compute $A(BC)$ than $(AB)C$.

## Powers of a Matrix

If $A$ is an $n \times n$ matrix and if $k$ is a positive integer, then $A^k$ denotes the product of $k$ copies of $A$:

$$A^k = \underbrace{A \cdots A}_{k}$$

If $A$ is nonzero and if $\mathbf{x}$ is in $\mathbb{R}^n$, then $A^k\mathbf{x}$ is the result of left-multiplying $\mathbf{x}$ by $A$ repeatedly $k$ times. If $k = 0$, then $A^0\mathbf{x}$ should be $\mathbf{x}$ itself. Thus $A^0$ is interpreted as the identity matrix. Matrix powers are useful in both theory and applications.

## The Transpose of a Matrix

Given an $m \times n$ matrix $A$, the **transpose** of $A$ is the $n \times m$ matrix, denoted by $A^T$, whose columns are formed from the corresponding rows of $A$.

**EXAMPLE 8**   Let

$$A = \begin{bmatrix} a & b \\ c & d \end{bmatrix}, \quad B = \begin{bmatrix} -5 & 2 \\ 1 & -3 \\ 0 & 4 \end{bmatrix}, \quad C = \begin{bmatrix} 1 & 1 & 1 & 1 \\ -3 & 5 & -2 & 7 \end{bmatrix}$$

Then

$$A^T = \begin{bmatrix} a & c \\ b & d \end{bmatrix}, \quad B^T = \begin{bmatrix} -5 & 1 & 0 \\ 2 & -3 & 4 \end{bmatrix}, \quad C^T = \begin{bmatrix} 1 & -3 \\ 1 & 5 \\ 1 & -2 \\ 1 & 7 \end{bmatrix} \qquad ■$$

**THEOREM 3**

Let $A$ and $B$ denote matrices whose sizes are appropriate for the following sums and products.

a. $(A^T)^T = A$

b. $(A + B)^T = A^T + B^T$

c. For any scalar $r$, $(rA)^T = rA^T$

d. $(AB)^T = B^T A^T$

Proofs of (a)–(c) are straightforward and are omitted. For (d), see Exercise 33. Usually, $(AB)^T$ is not equal to $A^T B^T$, even when $A$ and $B$ have sizes such that the product $A^T B^T$ is defined.

The generalization of Theorem 3(d) to products of more than two factors can be stated in words as follows:

The transpose of a product of matrices equals the product of their transposes in the *reverse* order.

The exercises contain numerical examples that illustrate properties of transposes.

┌─ NUMERICAL NOTES ─────────────────────────────────────

1. The fastest way to obtain $AB$ on a computer depends on the way in which the computer stores matrices in its memory. The standard high-performance algorithms, such as in LAPACK, calculate $AB$ by columns, as in our definition of the product. (A version of LAPACK written in C++ calculates $AB$ by rows.)

2. The definition of $AB$ lends itself well to parallel processing on a computer. The columns of $B$ are assigned individually or in groups to different processors, which independently and hence simultaneously compute the corresponding columns of $AB$.

└───────────────────────────────────────────────────────

**PRACTICE PROBLEMS**

1. Since vectors in $\mathbb{R}^n$ may be regarded as $n \times 1$ matrices, the properties of transposes in Theorem 3 apply to vectors, too. Let

$$A = \begin{bmatrix} 1 & -3 \\ -2 & 4 \end{bmatrix} \quad \text{and} \quad \mathbf{x} = \begin{bmatrix} 5 \\ 3 \end{bmatrix}$$

Compute $(A\mathbf{x})^T$, $\mathbf{x}^T A^T$, $\mathbf{x}\mathbf{x}^T$, and $\mathbf{x}^T\mathbf{x}$. Is $A^T\mathbf{x}^T$ defined?

2. Let $A$ be a $4 \times 4$ matrix and let $\mathbf{x}$ be a vector in $\mathbb{R}^4$. What is the fastest way to compute $A^2\mathbf{x}$? Count the multiplications.

3. Suppose $A$ is an $m \times n$ matrix, all of whose rows are identical. Suppose $B$ is an $n \times p$ matrix, all of whose columns are identical. What can be said about the entries in $AB$?

# 2.1 EXERCISES

In Exercises 1 and 2, compute each matrix sum or product if it is defined. If an expression is undefined, explain why. Let

$$A = \begin{bmatrix} 2 & 0 & -1 \\ 4 & -5 & 2 \end{bmatrix}, \quad B = \begin{bmatrix} 7 & -5 & 1 \\ 1 & -4 & -3 \end{bmatrix},$$

$$C = \begin{bmatrix} 1 & 2 \\ -2 & 1 \end{bmatrix}, \quad D = \begin{bmatrix} 3 & 5 \\ -1 & 4 \end{bmatrix}, \quad E = \begin{bmatrix} -5 \\ 3 \end{bmatrix}$$

1. $-2A, \quad B - 2A, \quad AC, \quad CD$

2. $A + 2B, \quad 3C - E, \quad CB, \quad EB$

In the rest of this exercise set and in those to follow, you should assume that each matrix expression is defined. That is, the sizes of the matrices (and vectors) involved "match" appropriately.

3. Let $A = \begin{bmatrix} 4 & -1 \\ 5 & -2 \end{bmatrix}$. Compute $3I_2 - A$ and $(3I_2)A$.

4. Compute $A - 5I_3$ and $(5I_3)A$, when

$$A = \begin{bmatrix} 9 & -1 & 3 \\ -8 & 7 & -6 \\ -4 & 1 & 8 \end{bmatrix}.$$

In Exercises 5 and 6, compute the product $AB$ in two ways: (a) by the definition, where $A\mathbf{b}_1$ and $A\mathbf{b}_2$ are computed separately, and (b) by the row–column rule for computing $AB$.

5. $A = \begin{bmatrix} -1 & 2 \\ 5 & 4 \\ 2 & -3 \end{bmatrix}, B = \begin{bmatrix} 3 & -2 \\ -2 & 1 \end{bmatrix}$

6. $A = \begin{bmatrix} 4 & -2 \\ -3 & 0 \\ 3 & 5 \end{bmatrix}, B = \begin{bmatrix} 1 & 3 \\ 2 & -1 \end{bmatrix}$

7. If a matrix $A$ is $5 \times 3$ and the product $AB$ is $5 \times 7$, what is the size of $B$?

8. How many rows does $B$ have if $BC$ is a $3 \times 4$ matrix?

9. Let $A = \begin{bmatrix} 2 & 5 \\ -3 & 1 \end{bmatrix}$ and $B = \begin{bmatrix} 4 & -5 \\ 3 & k \end{bmatrix}$. What value(s) of $k$, if any, will make $AB = BA$?

10. Let $A = \begin{bmatrix} 2 & -3 \\ -4 & 6 \end{bmatrix}$, $B = \begin{bmatrix} 8 & 4 \\ 5 & 5 \end{bmatrix}$, and $C = \begin{bmatrix} 5 & -2 \\ 3 & 1 \end{bmatrix}$. Verify that $AB = AC$ and yet $B \neq C$.

11. Let $A = \begin{bmatrix} 1 & 1 & 1 \\ 1 & 2 & 3 \\ 1 & 4 & 5 \end{bmatrix}$ and $D = \begin{bmatrix} 2 & 0 & 0 \\ 0 & 3 & 0 \\ 0 & 0 & 5 \end{bmatrix}$. Compute $AD$ and $DA$. Explain how the columns or rows of $A$ change when $A$ is multiplied by $D$ on the right or on the left. Find a $3 \times 3$ matrix $B$, not the identity matrix or the zero matrix, such that $AB = BA$.

12. Let $A = \begin{bmatrix} 3 & -6 \\ -1 & 2 \end{bmatrix}$. Construct a $2 \times 2$ matrix $B$ such that $AB$ is the zero matrix. Use two different nonzero columns for $B$.

13. Let $\mathbf{r}_1, \ldots, \mathbf{r}_p$ be vectors in $\mathbb{R}^n$, and let $Q$ be an $m \times n$ matrix. Write the matrix $[\, Q\mathbf{r}_1 \cdots Q\mathbf{r}_p \,]$ as a *product* of two matrices (neither of which is an identity matrix).

14. Let $U$ be the $3 \times 2$ cost matrix. The first column of $U$ lists the costs per dollar of output for manufacturing product $B$, and the second column lists the costs per dollar of output for product $C$. (The costs are categorized as materials, labor, and overhead.) Let $\mathbf{q}_1$ be a vector in $\mathbb{R}^2$ that lists the output (measured in dollars) of products B and C manufactured during the first quarter of the year, and let $\mathbf{q}_2, \mathbf{q}_3,$ and $\mathbf{q}_4$ be the analogous vectors that list the amounts of products B and C manufactured in the second, third, and fourth quarters, respectively. Give an economic description of the data in the matrix $UQ$, where $Q = [\mathbf{q}_1 \quad \mathbf{q}_2 \quad \mathbf{q}_3 \quad \mathbf{q}_4]$.

Exercises 15 and 16 concern arbitrary matrices $A$, $B$, and $C$ for which the indicated sums and products are defined. Mark each statement True or False. Justify each answer.

15. a. If $A$ and $B$ are $2 \times 2$ with columns $\mathbf{a}_1, \mathbf{a}_2,$ and $\mathbf{b}_1, \mathbf{b}_2,$ respectively, then $AB = [\mathbf{a}_1\mathbf{b}_1 \quad \mathbf{a}_2\mathbf{b}_2]$.

  b. Each column of $AB$ is a linear combination of the columns of $B$ using weights from the corresponding column of $A$.

  c. $AB + AC = A(B + C)$

  d. $A^T + B^T = (A + B)^T$

  e. The transpose of a product of matrices equals the product of their transposes in the same order.

16. a. If $A$ and $B$ are $3 \times 3$ and $B = [\mathbf{b}_1 \ \mathbf{b}_2 \ \mathbf{b}_3],$ then $AB = [A\mathbf{b}_1 + A\mathbf{b}_2 + A\mathbf{b}_3]$.

  b. The second row of $AB$ is the second row of $A$ multiplied on the right by $B$.

  c. $(AB)C = (AC)B$

  d. $(AB)^T = A^T B^T$

  e. The transpose of a sum of matrices equals the sum of their transposes.

17. If $A = \begin{bmatrix} 1 & -2 \\ -2 & 5 \end{bmatrix}$ and $AB = \begin{bmatrix} -1 & 2 & -1 \\ 6 & -9 & 3 \end{bmatrix}$, determine the first and second columns of $B$.

18. Suppose the first two columns, $\mathbf{b}_1$ and $\mathbf{b}_2$, of $B$ are equal. What can you say about the columns of $AB$ (if $AB$ is defined)? Why?

19. Suppose the third column of $B$ is the sum of the first two columns. What can you say about the third column of $AB$? Why?

20. Suppose the second column of $B$ is all zeros. What can you say about the second column of $AB$?

21. Suppose the last column of $AB$ is entirely zero but $B$ itself has no column of zeros. What can you say about the columns of $A$?

22. Show that if the columns of $B$ are linearly dependent, then so are the columns of $AB$.

23. Suppose $CA = I_n$ (the $n \times n$ identity matrix). Show that the equation $A\mathbf{x} = \mathbf{0}$ has only the trivial solution. Explain why $A$ cannot have more columns than rows.

24. Suppose $AD = I_m$ (the $m \times m$ identity matrix). Show that for any $\mathbf{b}$ in $\mathbb{R}^m$, the equation $A\mathbf{x} = \mathbf{b}$ has a solution. [*Hint:* Think about the equation $AD\mathbf{b} = \mathbf{b}$.] Explain why $A$ cannot have more rows than columns.

25. Suppose $A$ is an $m \times n$ matrix and there exist $n \times m$ matrices $C$ and $D$ such that $CA = I_n$ and $AD = I_m$. Prove that $m = n$ and $C = D$. [*Hint:* Think about the product $CAD$.]

26. Suppose $A$ is a $3 \times n$ matrix whose columns span $\mathbb{R}^3$. Explain how to construct an $n \times 3$ matrix $D$ such that $AD = I_3$.

In Exercises 27 and 28, view vectors in $\mathbb{R}^n$ as $n \times 1$ matrices. For $\mathbf{u}$ and $\mathbf{v}$ in $\mathbb{R}^n$, the matrix product $\mathbf{u}^T\mathbf{v}$ is a $1 \times 1$ matrix, called the **scalar product**, or **inner product**, of $\mathbf{u}$ and $\mathbf{v}$. It is usually written as a single real number without brackets. The matrix product $\mathbf{u}\mathbf{v}^T$ is an $n \times n$ matrix, called the **outer product** of $\mathbf{u}$ and $\mathbf{v}$. The products $\mathbf{u}^T\mathbf{v}$ and $\mathbf{u}\mathbf{v}^T$ will appear later in the text.

27. Let $\mathbf{u} = \begin{bmatrix} -2 \\ 3 \\ -4 \end{bmatrix}$ and $\mathbf{v} = \begin{bmatrix} a \\ b \\ c \end{bmatrix}$. Compute $\mathbf{u}^T\mathbf{v}, \mathbf{v}^T\mathbf{u}, \mathbf{u}\mathbf{v}^T,$ and $\mathbf{v}\mathbf{u}^T$.

28. If $\mathbf{u}$ and $\mathbf{v}$ are in $\mathbb{R}^n$, how are $\mathbf{u}^T\mathbf{v}$ and $\mathbf{v}^T\mathbf{u}$ related? How are $\mathbf{u}\mathbf{v}^T$ and $\mathbf{v}\mathbf{u}^T$ related?

29. Prove Theorem 2(b) and 2(c). Use the row–column rule. The $(i,j)$-entry in $A(B + C)$ can be written as

$$a_{i1}(b_{1j} + c_{1j}) + \cdots + a_{in}(b_{nj} + c_{nj}) \text{ or } \sum_{k=1}^{n} a_{ik}(b_{kj} + c_{kj})$$

30. Prove Theorem 2(d). [*Hint:* The $(i, j)$-entry in $(rA)B$ is $(ra_{i1})b_{1j} + \cdots + (ra_{in})b_{nj}$.]

31. Show that $I_m A = A$ when $A$ is an $m \times n$ matrix. You can assume $I_m\mathbf{x} = \mathbf{x}$ for all $\mathbf{x}$ in $\mathbb{R}^m$.

32. Show that $AI_n = A$ when $A$ is an $m \times n$ matrix. [*Hint:* Use the (column) definition of $AI_n$.]

33. Prove Theorem 3(d). [*Hint:* Consider the $j$th row of $(AB)^T$.]

34. Give a formula for $(AB\mathbf{x})^T$, where $\mathbf{x}$ is a vector and $A$ and $B$ are matrices of appropriate sizes.

35. [M] Read the documentation for your matrix program, and write the commands that will produce the following matrices (without keying in each entry of the matrix).

  a. A $5 \times 6$ matrix of zeros

  b. A $3 \times 5$ matrix of ones

c. The $6 \times 6$ identity matrix

d. A $5 \times 5$ diagonal matrix, with diagonal entries $3, 5, 7, 2, 4$

A useful way to test new ideas in matrix algebra, or to make conjectures, is to make calculations with matrices selected at random. Checking a property for a few matrices does not prove that the property holds in general, but it makes the property more believable. Also, if the property is actually false, you may discover this when you make a few calculations.

36. **[M]** Write the command(s) that will create a $6 \times 4$ matrix with random entries. In what range of numbers do the entries lie? Tell how to create a $3 \times 3$ matrix with random integer entries between $-9$ and $9$. [*Hint:* If $x$ is a random number such that $0 < x < 1$, then $-9.5 < 19(x - .5) < 9.5$.]

37. **[M]** Construct a random $4 \times 4$ matrix $A$ and test whether $(A + I)(A - I) = A^2 - I$. The best way to do this is to compute $(A + I)(A - I) - (A^2 - I)$ and verify that this difference is the zero matrix. Do this for three random matrices. Then test $(A + B)(A - B) = A^2 - B^2$ the same way for

three pairs of random $4 \times 4$ matrices. Report your conclusions.

38. **[M]** Use at least three pairs of random $4 \times 4$ matrices $A$ and $B$ to test the equalities $(A + B)^T = A^T + B^T$ and $(AB)^T = A^T B^T$. (See Exercise 37.) Report your conclusions. [*Note:* Most matrix programs use $A'$ for $A^T$.]

39. **[M]** Let
$$S = \begin{bmatrix} 0 & 1 & 0 & 0 & 0 \\ 0 & 0 & 1 & 0 & 0 \\ 0 & 0 & 0 & 1 & 0 \\ 0 & 0 & 0 & 0 & 1 \\ 0 & 0 & 0 & 0 & 0 \end{bmatrix}$$
Compute $S^k$ for $k = 2, \ldots, 6$.

40. **[M]** Describe in words what happens when you compute $A^5$, $A^{10}$, $A^{20}$, and $A^{30}$ for
$$A = \begin{bmatrix} 1/6 & 1/2 & 1/3 \\ 1/2 & 1/4 & 1/4 \\ 1/3 & 1/4 & 5/12 \end{bmatrix}$$

---

**SOLUTIONS TO PRACTICE PROBLEMS**

1. $Ax = \begin{bmatrix} 1 & -3 \\ -2 & 4 \end{bmatrix} \begin{bmatrix} 5 \\ 3 \end{bmatrix} = \begin{bmatrix} -4 \\ 2 \end{bmatrix}$. So $(Ax)^T = \begin{bmatrix} -4 & 2 \end{bmatrix}$. Also,

$$\mathbf{x}^T A^T = \begin{bmatrix} 5 & 3 \end{bmatrix} \begin{bmatrix} 1 & -2 \\ -3 & 4 \end{bmatrix} = \begin{bmatrix} -4 & 2 \end{bmatrix}.$$

The quantities $(Ax)^T$ and $\mathbf{x}^T A^T$ are equal, by Theorem 3(d). Next,

$$\mathbf{xx}^T = \begin{bmatrix} 5 \\ 3 \end{bmatrix} \begin{bmatrix} 5 & 3 \end{bmatrix} = \begin{bmatrix} 25 & 15 \\ 15 & 9 \end{bmatrix}$$

$$\mathbf{x}^T \mathbf{x} = \begin{bmatrix} 5 & 3 \end{bmatrix} \begin{bmatrix} 5 \\ 3 \end{bmatrix} = [25 + 9] = 34$$

A $1 \times 1$ matrix such as $\mathbf{x}^T \mathbf{x}$ is usually written without the brackets. Finally, $A^T \mathbf{x}^T$ is not defined, because $\mathbf{x}^T$ does not have two rows to match the two columns of $A^T$.

2. The fastest way to compute $A^2 \mathbf{x}$ is to compute $A(A\mathbf{x})$. The product $A\mathbf{x}$ requires 16 multiplications, 4 for each entry, and $A(A\mathbf{x})$ requires 16 more. In contrast, the product $A^2$ requires 64 multiplications, 4 for each of the 16 entries in $A^2$. After that, $A^2 \mathbf{x}$ takes 16 more multiplications, for a total of 80.

3. First observe that by the definition of matrix multiplication,
$$AB = [A\mathbf{b}_1 \quad A\mathbf{b}_2 \quad \cdots \quad A\mathbf{b}_n] = [A\mathbf{b}_1 \quad A\mathbf{b}_1 \quad \cdots \quad A\mathbf{b}_1],$$

so the columns of $AB$ are identical. Next, recall that $\text{row}_i(AB) = \text{row}_i(A) \cdot B$. Since all the rows of $A$ are identical, all the rows of $AB$ are identical. Putting this information about the rows and columns together, it follows that all the entries in $AB$ are the same.

# 2.2 THE INVERSE OF A MATRIX

Matrix algebra provides tools for manipulating matrix equations and creating various useful formulas in ways similar to doing ordinary algebra with real numbers. This section investigates the matrix analogue of the reciprocal, or multiplicative inverse, of a nonzero number.

Recall that the multiplicative inverse of a number such as 5 is $1/5$ or $5^{-1}$. This inverse satisfies the equations

$$5^{-1} \cdot 5 = 1 \quad \text{and} \quad 5 \cdot 5^{-1} = 1$$

The matrix generalization requires *both* equations and avoids the slanted-line notation (for division) because matrix multiplication is not commutative. Furthermore, a full generalization is possible only if the matrices involved are square.[1]

An $n \times n$ matrix $A$ is said to be **invertible** if there is an $n \times n$ matrix $C$ such that

$$CA = I \quad \text{and} \quad AC = I$$

where $I = I_n$, the $n \times n$ identity matrix. In this case, $C$ is an **inverse** of $A$. In fact, $C$ is uniquely determined by $A$, because if $B$ were another inverse of $A$, then $B = BI = B(AC) = (BA)C = IC = C$. This unique inverse is denoted by $A^{-1}$, so that

$$A^{-1}A = I \quad \text{and} \quad AA^{-1} = I$$

A matrix that is *not* invertible is sometimes called a **singular matrix**, and an invertible matrix is called a **nonsingular matrix**.

**EXAMPLE 1**   If $A = \begin{bmatrix} 2 & 5 \\ -3 & -7 \end{bmatrix}$ and $C = \begin{bmatrix} -7 & -5 \\ 3 & 2 \end{bmatrix}$, then

$$AC = \begin{bmatrix} 2 & 5 \\ -3 & -7 \end{bmatrix}\begin{bmatrix} -7 & -5 \\ 3 & 2 \end{bmatrix} = \begin{bmatrix} 1 & 0 \\ 0 & 1 \end{bmatrix} \quad \text{and}$$

$$CA = \begin{bmatrix} -7 & -5 \\ 3 & 2 \end{bmatrix}\begin{bmatrix} 2 & 5 \\ -3 & -7 \end{bmatrix} = \begin{bmatrix} 1 & 0 \\ 0 & 1 \end{bmatrix}$$

Thus $C = A^{-1}$.                                                                   ∎

Here is a simple formula for the inverse of a $2 \times 2$ matrix, along with a test to tell if the inverse exists.

**THEOREM 4**

Let $A = \begin{bmatrix} a & b \\ c & d \end{bmatrix}$. If $ad - bc \neq 0$, then $A$ is invertible and

$$A^{-1} = \frac{1}{ad - bc}\begin{bmatrix} d & -b \\ -c & a \end{bmatrix}$$

If $ad - bc = 0$, then $A$ is not invertible.

The simple proof of Theorem 4 is outlined in Exercises 25 and 26. The quantity $ad - bc$ is called the **determinant** of $A$, and we write

$$\det A = ad - bc$$

Theorem 4 says that a $2 \times 2$ matrix $A$ is invertible if and only if $\det A \neq 0$.

---

[1] One could say that an $m \times n$ matrix $A$ is invertible if there exist $n \times m$ matrices $C$ and $D$ such that $CA = I_n$ and $AD = I_m$. However, these equations imply that $A$ is square and $C = D$. Thus $A$ is invertible as defined above. See Exercises 23–25 in Section 2.1.

**EXAMPLE 2** Find the inverse of $A = \begin{bmatrix} 3 & 4 \\ 5 & 6 \end{bmatrix}$.

**SOLUTION** Since $\det A = 3(6) - 4(5) = -2 \neq 0$, $A$ is invertible, and

$$A^{-1} = \frac{1}{-2}\begin{bmatrix} 6 & -4 \\ -5 & 3 \end{bmatrix} = \begin{bmatrix} 6/(-2) & -4/(-2) \\ -5/(-2) & 3/(-2) \end{bmatrix} = \begin{bmatrix} -3 & 2 \\ 5/2 & -3/2 \end{bmatrix} \qquad ■$$

Invertible matrices are indispensable in linear algebra—mainly for algebraic calculations and formula derivations, as in the next theorem. There are also occasions when an inverse matrix provides insight into a mathematical model of a real-life situation, as in Example 3, below.

**THEOREM 5**

If $A$ is an invertible $n \times n$ matrix, then for each $\mathbf{b}$ in $\mathbb{R}^n$, the equation $A\mathbf{x} = \mathbf{b}$ has the unique solution $\mathbf{x} = A^{-1}\mathbf{b}$.

**PROOF** Take any $\mathbf{b}$ in $\mathbb{R}^n$. A solution exists because if $A^{-1}\mathbf{b}$ is substituted for $\mathbf{x}$, then $A\mathbf{x} = A(A^{-1}\mathbf{b}) = (AA^{-1})\mathbf{b} = I\mathbf{b} = \mathbf{b}$. So $A^{-1}\mathbf{b}$ is a solution. To prove that the solution is unique, show that if $\mathbf{u}$ is any solution, then $\mathbf{u}$, in fact, must be $A^{-1}\mathbf{b}$. Indeed, if $A\mathbf{u} = \mathbf{b}$, we can multiply both sides by $A^{-1}$ and obtain

$$A^{-1}A\mathbf{u} = A^{-1}\mathbf{b}, \quad I\mathbf{u} = A^{-1}\mathbf{b}, \quad \text{and} \quad \mathbf{u} = A^{-1}\mathbf{b} \qquad ■$$

**EXAMPLE 3** A horizontal elastic beam is supported at each end and is subjected to forces at points 1, 2, and 3, as shown in Figure 1. Let $\mathbf{f}$ in $\mathbb{R}^3$ list the forces at these points, and let $\mathbf{y}$ in $\mathbb{R}^3$ list the amounts of deflection (that is, movement) of the beam at the three points. Using Hooke's law from physics, it can be shown that

$$\mathbf{y} = D\mathbf{f}$$

where $D$ is a *flexibility matrix*. Its inverse is called the *stiffness matrix*. Describe the physical significance of the columns of $D$ and $D^{-1}$.

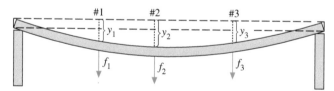

**FIGURE 1** Deflection of an elastic beam.

**SOLUTION** Write $I_3 = [\,\mathbf{e}_1 \quad \mathbf{e}_2 \quad \mathbf{e}_3\,]$ and observe that

$$D = DI_3 = [\,D\mathbf{e}_1 \quad D\mathbf{e}_2 \quad D\mathbf{e}_3\,]$$

Interpret the vector $\mathbf{e}_1 = (1, 0, 0)$ as a unit force applied downward at point 1 on the beam (with zero force at the other two points). Then $D\mathbf{e}_1$, the first column of $D$, lists the beam deflections due to a unit force at point 1. Similar descriptions apply to the second and third columns of $D$.

To study the stiffness matrix $D^{-1}$, observe that the equation $\mathbf{f} = D^{-1}\mathbf{y}$ computes a force vector $\mathbf{f}$ when a deflection vector $\mathbf{y}$ is given. Write

$$D^{-1} = D^{-1}I_3 = [\,D^{-1}\mathbf{e}_1 \quad D^{-1}\mathbf{e}_2 \quad D^{-1}\mathbf{e}_3\,]$$

Now interpret $\mathbf{e}_1$ as a deflection vector. Then $D^{-1}\mathbf{e}_1$ lists the forces that create the deflection. That is, the first column of $D^{-1}$ lists the forces that must be applied at the three points to produce a unit deflection at point 1 and zero deflections at the other points. Similarly, columns 2 and 3 of $D^{-1}$ list the forces required to produce unit deflections at points 2 and 3, respectively. In each column, one or two of the forces must be negative (point upward) to produce a unit deflection at the desired point and zero deflections at the other two points. If the flexibility is measured, for example, in inches of deflection per pound of load, then the stiffness matrix entries are given in pounds of load per inch of deflection. ■

The formula in Theorem 5 is seldom used to solve an equation $A\mathbf{x} = \mathbf{b}$ numerically because row reduction of $[\,A \quad \mathbf{b}\,]$ is nearly always faster. (Row reduction is usually more accurate, too, when computations involve rounding off numbers.) One possible exception is the $2 \times 2$ case. In this case, mental computations to solve $A\mathbf{x} = \mathbf{b}$ are sometimes easier using the formula for $A^{-1}$, as in the next example.

**EXAMPLE 4**   Use the inverse of the matrix $A$ in Example 2 to solve the system

$$3x_1 + 4x_2 = 3$$
$$5x_1 + 6x_2 = 7$$

**SOLUTION** This system is equivalent to $A\mathbf{x} = \mathbf{b}$, so

$$\mathbf{x} = A^{-1}\mathbf{b} = \begin{bmatrix} -3 & 2 \\ 5/2 & -3/2 \end{bmatrix} \begin{bmatrix} 3 \\ 7 \end{bmatrix} = \begin{bmatrix} 5 \\ -3 \end{bmatrix}$$   ■

The next theorem provides three useful facts about invertible matrices.

**THEOREM 6**

a. If $A$ is an invertible matrix, then $A^{-1}$ is invertible and

$$(A^{-1})^{-1} = A$$

b. If $A$ and $B$ are $n \times n$ invertible matrices, then so is $AB$, and the inverse of $AB$ is the product of the inverses of $A$ and $B$ in the reverse order. That is,

$$(AB)^{-1} = B^{-1}A^{-1}$$

c. If $A$ is an invertible matrix, then so is $A^T$, and the inverse of $A^T$ is the transpose of $A^{-1}$. That is,

$$(A^T)^{-1} = (A^{-1})^T$$

**PROOF** To verify statement (a), find a matrix $C$ such that

$$A^{-1}C = I \quad \text{and} \quad CA^{-1} = I$$

In fact, these equations are satisfied with $A$ in place of $C$. Hence $A^{-1}$ is invertible, and $A$ is its inverse. Next, to prove statement (b), compute:

$$(AB)(B^{-1}A^{-1}) = A(BB^{-1})A^{-1} = AIA^{-1} = AA^{-1} = I$$

A similar calculation shows that $(B^{-1}A^{-1})(AB) = I$. For statement (c), use Theorem 3(d), read from right to left, $(A^{-1})^T A^T = (AA^{-1})^T = I^T = I$. Similarly, $A^T(A^{-1})^T = I^T = I$. Hence $A^T$ is invertible, and its inverse is $(A^{-1})^T$. ■

*Remark:* Part (b) illustrates the important role that definitions play in proofs. The theorem claims that $B^{-1}A^{-1}$ is the inverse of $AB$. The proof establishes this by showing that $B^{-1}A^{-1}$ satisfies the definition of what it means to be the inverse of $AB$. Now, the inverse of $AB$ is a matrix that when multiplied on the left (or right) by $AB$, the product is the identity matrix $I$. So the proof consists of showing that $B^{-1}A^{-1}$ has this property.

The following generalization of Theorem 6(b) is needed later.

The product of $n \times n$ invertible matrices is invertible, and the inverse is the product of their inverses in the reverse order.

There is an important connection between invertible matrices and row operations that leads to a method for computing inverses. As we shall see, an invertible matrix $A$ is row equivalent to an identity matrix, and we can find $A^{-1}$ by *watching the row reduction of $A$ to $I$.*

## Elementary Matrices

An **elementary matrix** is one that is obtained by performing a single elementary row operation on an identity matrix. The next example illustrates the three kinds of elementary matrices.

**EXAMPLE 5**  Let

$$E_1 = \begin{bmatrix} 1 & 0 & 0 \\ 0 & 1 & 0 \\ -4 & 0 & 1 \end{bmatrix}, \quad E_2 = \begin{bmatrix} 0 & 1 & 0 \\ 1 & 0 & 0 \\ 0 & 0 & 1 \end{bmatrix}, \quad E_3 = \begin{bmatrix} 1 & 0 & 0 \\ 0 & 1 & 0 \\ 0 & 0 & 5 \end{bmatrix},$$

$$A = \begin{bmatrix} a & b & c \\ d & e & f \\ g & h & i \end{bmatrix}$$

Compute $E_1 A$, $E_2 A$, and $E_3 A$, and describe how these products can be obtained by elementary row operations on $A$.

**SOLUTION**  Verify that

$$E_1 A = \begin{bmatrix} a & b & c \\ d & e & f \\ g-4a & h-4b & i-4c \end{bmatrix}, \quad E_2 A = \begin{bmatrix} d & e & f \\ a & b & c \\ g & h & i \end{bmatrix},$$

$$E_3 A = \begin{bmatrix} a & b & c \\ d & e & f \\ 5g & 5h & 5i \end{bmatrix}.$$

Addition of $-4$ times row 1 of $A$ to row 3 produces $E_1 A$. (This is a row replacement operation.) An interchange of rows 1 and 2 of $A$ produces $E_2 A$, and multiplication of row 3 of $A$ by 5 produces $E_3 A$.  ∎

Left-multiplication (that is, multiplication on the left) by $E_1$ in Example 5 has the same effect on any $3 \times n$ matrix. It adds $-4$ times row 1 to row 3. In particular, since $E_1 \cdot I = E_1$, we see that $E_1$ *itself* is produced by this same row operation on the identity. Thus Example 5 illustrates the following general fact about elementary matrices. See Exercises 27 and 28.

If an elementary row operation is performed on an $m \times n$ matrix $A$, the resulting matrix can be written as $EA$, where the $m \times m$ matrix $E$ is created by performing the same row operation on $I_m$.

Since row operations are reversible, as shown in Section 1.1, elementary matrices are invertible, for if $E$ is produced by a row operation on $I$, then there is another row operation of the same type that changes $E$ back into $I$. Hence there is an elementary matrix $F$ such that $FE = I$. Since $E$ and $F$ correspond to reverse operations, $EF = I$, too.

Each elementary matrix $E$ is invertible. The inverse of $E$ is the elementary matrix of the same type that transforms $E$ back into $I$.

**EXAMPLE 6**　Find the inverse of $E_1 = \begin{bmatrix} 1 & 0 & 0 \\ 0 & 1 & 0 \\ -4 & 0 & 1 \end{bmatrix}$.

**SOLUTION**　To transform $E_1$ into $I$, add $+4$ times row 1 to row 3. The elementary matrix that does this is

$$E_1^{-1} = \begin{bmatrix} 1 & 0 & 0 \\ 0 & 1 & 0 \\ +4 & 0 & 1 \end{bmatrix}$$
∎

The following theorem provides the best way to "visualize" an invertible matrix, and the theorem leads immediately to a method for finding the inverse of a matrix.

**THEOREM 7**

An $n \times n$ matrix $A$ is invertible if and only if $A$ is row equivalent to $I_n$, and in this case, any sequence of elementary row operations that reduces $A$ to $I_n$ also transforms $I_n$ into $A^{-1}$.

**PROOF**　Suppose that $A$ is invertible. Then, since the equation $A\mathbf{x} = \mathbf{b}$ has a solution for each $\mathbf{b}$ (Theorem 5), $A$ has a pivot position in every row (Theorem 4 in Section 1.4). Because $A$ is square, the $n$ pivot positions must be on the diagonal, which implies that the reduced echelon form of $A$ is $I_n$. That is, $A \sim I_n$.

Now suppose, conversely, that $A \sim I_n$. Then, since each step of the row reduction of $A$ corresponds to left-multiplication by an elementary matrix, there exist elementary matrices $E_1, \ldots, E_p$ such that

$$A \sim E_1 A \sim E_2(E_1 A) \sim \cdots \sim E_p(E_{p-1} \cdots E_1 A) = I_n$$

That is,

$$E_p \cdots E_1 A = I_n \tag{1}$$

Since the product $E_p \cdots E_1$ of invertible matrices is invertible, (1) leads to

$$(E_p \cdots E_1)^{-1}(E_p \cdots E_1)A = (E_p \cdots E_1)^{-1} I_n$$
$$A = (E_p \cdots E_1)^{-1}$$

Thus $A$ is invertible, as it is the inverse of an invertible matrix (Theorem 6). Also,

$$A^{-1} = \left[ (E_p \cdots E_1)^{-1} \right]^{-1} = E_p \cdots E_1$$

Then $A^{-1} = E_p \cdots E_1 \cdot I_n$, which says that $A^{-1}$ results from applying $E_1, \ldots, E_p$ successively to $I_n$. This is the same sequence in (1) that reduced $A$ to $I_n$.
∎

# An Algorithm for Finding $A^{-1}$

If we place $A$ and $I$ side by side to form an augmented matrix $[\,A\quad I\,]$, then row operations on this matrix produce identical operations on $A$ and on $I$. By Theorem 7, either there are row operations that transform $A$ to $I_n$ and $I_n$ to $A^{-1}$ or else $A$ is not invertible.

---

**ALGORITHM FOR FINDING $A^{-1}$**

Row reduce the augmented matrix $[\,A\quad I\,]$. If $A$ is row equivalent to $I$, then $[\,A\quad I\,]$ is row equivalent to $[\,I\quad A^{-1}\,]$. Otherwise, $A$ does not have an inverse.

---

**EXAMPLE 7**   Find the inverse of the matrix $A = \begin{bmatrix} 0 & 1 & 2 \\ 1 & 0 & 3 \\ 4 & -3 & 8 \end{bmatrix}$, if it exists.

**SOLUTION**

$$[\,A\quad I\,] = \begin{bmatrix} 0 & 1 & 2 & 1 & 0 & 0 \\ 1 & 0 & 3 & 0 & 1 & 0 \\ 4 & -3 & 8 & 0 & 0 & 1 \end{bmatrix} \sim \begin{bmatrix} 1 & 0 & 3 & 0 & 1 & 0 \\ 0 & 1 & 2 & 1 & 0 & 0 \\ 4 & -3 & 8 & 0 & 0 & 1 \end{bmatrix}$$

$$\sim \begin{bmatrix} 1 & 0 & 3 & 0 & 1 & 0 \\ 0 & 1 & 2 & 1 & 0 & 0 \\ 0 & -3 & -4 & 0 & -4 & 1 \end{bmatrix} \sim \begin{bmatrix} 1 & 0 & 3 & 0 & 1 & 0 \\ 0 & 1 & 2 & 1 & 0 & 0 \\ 0 & 0 & 2 & 3 & -4 & 1 \end{bmatrix}$$

$$\sim \begin{bmatrix} 1 & 0 & 3 & 0 & 1 & 0 \\ 0 & 1 & 2 & 1 & 0 & 0 \\ 0 & 0 & 1 & 3/2 & -2 & 1/2 \end{bmatrix}$$

$$\sim \begin{bmatrix} 1 & 0 & 0 & -9/2 & 7 & -3/2 \\ 0 & 1 & 0 & -2 & 4 & -1 \\ 0 & 0 & 1 & 3/2 & -2 & 1/2 \end{bmatrix}$$

Theorem 7 shows, since $A \sim I$, that $A$ is invertible, and

$$A^{-1} = \begin{bmatrix} -9/2 & 7 & -3/2 \\ -2 & 4 & -1 \\ 3/2 & -2 & 1/2 \end{bmatrix}$$

It is a good idea to check the final answer:

$$AA^{-1} = \begin{bmatrix} 0 & 1 & 2 \\ 1 & 0 & 3 \\ 4 & -3 & 8 \end{bmatrix} \begin{bmatrix} -9/2 & 7 & -3/2 \\ -2 & 4 & -1 \\ 3/2 & -2 & 1/2 \end{bmatrix} = \begin{bmatrix} 1 & 0 & 0 \\ 0 & 1 & 0 \\ 0 & 0 & 1 \end{bmatrix}$$

It is not necessary to check that $A^{-1}A = I$ since $A$ is invertible. ∎

# Another View of Matrix Inversion

Denote the columns of $I_n$ by $\mathbf{e}_1, \ldots, \mathbf{e}_n$. Then row reduction of $[\,A\quad I\,]$ to $[\,I\quad A^{-1}\,]$ can be viewed as the simultaneous solution of the $n$ systems

$$A\mathbf{x} = \mathbf{e}_1, \quad A\mathbf{x} = \mathbf{e}_2, \quad \ldots, \quad A\mathbf{x} = \mathbf{e}_n \tag{2}$$

where the "augmented columns" of these systems have all been placed next to $A$ to form $[\,A\quad \mathbf{e}_1\quad \mathbf{e}_2\quad \cdots\quad \mathbf{e}_n\,] = [\,A\quad I\,]$. The equation $AA^{-1} = I$ and the definition of matrix multiplication show that the columns of $A^{-1}$ are precisely the solutions of the systems in (2). This observation is useful because some applied problems may require finding only one or two columns of $A^{-1}$. In this case, only the corresponding systems in (2) need be solved.

> ── NUMERICAL NOTE ──────────────────────
>
> **WEB**
>
> In practical work, $A^{-1}$ is seldom computed, unless the entries of $A^{-1}$ are needed. Computing both $A^{-1}$ and $A^{-1}\mathbf{b}$ takes about three times as many arithmetic operations as solving $A\mathbf{x} = \mathbf{b}$ by row reduction, and row reduction may be more accurate.

### PRACTICE PROBLEMS

1. Use determinants to determine which of the following matrices are invertible.

   a. $\begin{bmatrix} 3 & -9 \\ 2 & 6 \end{bmatrix}$    b. $\begin{bmatrix} 4 & -9 \\ 0 & 5 \end{bmatrix}$    c. $\begin{bmatrix} 6 & -9 \\ -4 & 6 \end{bmatrix}$

2. Find the inverse of the matrix $A = \begin{bmatrix} 1 & -2 & -1 \\ -1 & 5 & 6 \\ 5 & -4 & 5 \end{bmatrix}$, if it exists.

3. If $A$ is an invertible matrix, prove that $5A$ is an invertible matrix.

## 2.2 EXERCISES

Find the inverses of the matrices in Exercises 1–4.

1. $\begin{bmatrix} 8 & 6 \\ 5 & 4 \end{bmatrix}$    2. $\begin{bmatrix} 3 & 2 \\ 7 & 4 \end{bmatrix}$

3. $\begin{bmatrix} 8 & 5 \\ -7 & -5 \end{bmatrix}$    4. $\begin{bmatrix} 3 & -4 \\ 7 & -8 \end{bmatrix}$

5. Use the inverse found in Exercise 1 to solve the system

   $8x_1 + 6x_2 = 2$
   $5x_1 + 4x_2 = -1$

6. Use the inverse found in Exercise 3 to solve the system

   $8x_1 + 5x_2 = -9$
   $-7x_1 - 5x_2 = 11$

7. Let $A = \begin{bmatrix} 1 & 2 \\ 5 & 12 \end{bmatrix}$, $\mathbf{b}_1 = \begin{bmatrix} -1 \\ 3 \end{bmatrix}$, $\mathbf{b}_2 = \begin{bmatrix} 1 \\ -5 \end{bmatrix}$, $\mathbf{b}_3 = \begin{bmatrix} 2 \\ 6 \end{bmatrix}$, and $\mathbf{b}_4 = \begin{bmatrix} 3 \\ 5 \end{bmatrix}$.

   a. Find $A^{-1}$, and use it to solve the four equations $A\mathbf{x} = \mathbf{b}_1$, $A\mathbf{x} = \mathbf{b}_2$, $A\mathbf{x} = \mathbf{b}_3$, $A\mathbf{x} = \mathbf{b}_4$.

   b. The four equations in part (a) can be solved by the *same* set of row operations, since the coefficient matrix is the same in each case. Solve the four equations in part (a) by row reducing the augmented matrix $[A \ \mathbf{b}_1 \ \mathbf{b}_2 \ \mathbf{b}_3 \ \mathbf{b}_4]$.

8. Use matrix algebra to show that if $A$ is invertible and $D$ satisfies $AD = I$, then $D = A^{-1}$.

In Exercises 9 and 10, mark each statement True or False. Justify each answer.

9. a. In order for a matrix $B$ to be the inverse of $A$, both equations $AB = I$ and $BA = I$ must be true.

   b. If $A$ and $B$ are $n \times n$ and invertible, then $A^{-1}B^{-1}$ is the inverse of $AB$.

   c. If $A = \begin{bmatrix} a & b \\ c & d \end{bmatrix}$ and $ab - cd \neq 0$, then $A$ is invertible.

   d. If $A$ is an invertible $n \times n$ matrix, then the equation $A\mathbf{x} = \mathbf{b}$ is consistent for *each* $\mathbf{b}$ in $\mathbb{R}^n$.

   e. Each elementary matrix is invertible.

10. a. A product of invertible $n \times n$ matrices is invertible, and the inverse of the product is the product of their inverses in the same order.

    b. If $A$ is invertible, then the inverse of $A^{-1}$ is $A$ itself.

    c. If $A = \begin{bmatrix} a & b \\ c & d \end{bmatrix}$ and $ad = bc$, then $A$ is not invertible.

    d. If $A$ can be row reduced to the identity matrix, then $A$ must be invertible.

    e. If $A$ is invertible, then elementary row operations that reduce $A$ to the identity $I_n$ also reduce $A^{-1}$ to $I_n$.

11. Let $A$ be an invertible $n \times n$ matrix, and let $B$ be an $n \times p$ matrix. Show that the equation $AX = B$ has a unique solution $A^{-1}B$.

12. Let $A$ be an invertible $n \times n$ matrix, and let $B$ be an $n \times p$ matrix. Explain why $A^{-1}B$ can be computed by row reduction:

If $[A \ B] \sim \cdots \sim [I \ X]$, then $X = A^{-1}B$.

If $A$ is larger than $2 \times 2$, then row reduction of $[A \ B]$ is much faster than computing both $A^{-1}$ and $A^{-1}B$.

**13.** Suppose $AB = AC$, where $B$ and $C$ are $n \times p$ matrices and $A$ is invertible. Show that $B = C$. Is this true, in general, when $A$ is not invertible?

**14.** Suppose $(B - C)D = 0$, where $B$ and $C$ are $m \times n$ matrices and $D$ is invertible. Show that $B = C$.

**15.** Suppose $A$, $B$, and $C$ are invertible $n \times n$ matrices. Show that $ABC$ is also invertible by producing a matrix $D$ such that $(ABC)D = I$ and $D(ABC) = I$.

**16.** Suppose $A$ and $B$ are $n \times n$, $B$ is invertible, and $AB$ is invertible. Show that $A$ is invertible. [*Hint:* Let $C = AB$, and solve this equation for $A$.]

**17.** Solve the equation $AB = BC$ for $A$, assuming that $A$, $B$, and $C$ are square and $B$ is invertible.

**18.** Suppose $P$ is invertible and $A = PBP^{-1}$. Solve for $B$ in terms of $A$.

**19.** If $A$, $B$, and $C$ are $n \times n$ invertible matrices, does the equation $C^{-1}(A + X)B^{-1} = I_n$ have a solution, $X$? If so, find it.

**20.** Suppose $A$, $B$, and $X$ are $n \times n$ matrices with $A$, $X$, and $A - AX$ invertible, and suppose

$$(A - AX)^{-1} = X^{-1}B \tag{3}$$

a. Explain why $B$ is invertible.

b. Solve (3) for $X$. If you need to invert a matrix, explain why that matrix is invertible.

**21.** Explain why the columns of an $n \times n$ matrix $A$ are linearly independent when $A$ is invertible.

**22.** Explain why the columns of an $n \times n$ matrix $A$ span $\mathbb{R}^n$ when $A$ is invertible. [*Hint:* Review Theorem 4 in Section 1.4.]

**23.** Suppose $A$ is $n \times n$ and the equation $A\mathbf{x} = \mathbf{0}$ has only the trivial solution. Explain why $A$ has $n$ pivot columns and $A$ is row equivalent to $I_n$. By Theorem 7, this shows that $A$ must be invertible.

**24.** Suppose $A$ is $n \times n$ and the equation $A\mathbf{x} = \mathbf{b}$ has a solution for each $\mathbf{b}$ in $\mathbb{R}^n$. Explain why $A$ must be invertible. [*Hint:* Is $A$ row equivalent to $I_n$?]

Exercises 25 and 26 prove Theorem 4 for $A = \begin{bmatrix} a & b \\ c & d \end{bmatrix}$.

**25.** Show that if $ad - bc = 0$, then the equation $A\mathbf{x} = \mathbf{0}$ has more than one solution. Why does this imply that $A$ is not invertible? [*Hint:* First, consider $a = b = 0$. Then, if $a$ and $b$ are not both zero, consider the vector $\mathbf{x} = \begin{bmatrix} -b \\ a \end{bmatrix}$.]

**26.** Show that if $ad - bc \neq 0$, the formula for $A^{-1}$ works.

Exercises 27 and 28 prove special cases of the facts about elementary matrices stated in the box following Example 5. Here $A$ is a

$3 \times 3$ matrix and $I = I_3$. (A general proof would require slightly more notation.)

**27.** a. Use equation (1) from Section 2.1 to show that $\text{row}_i(A) = \text{row}_i(I) \cdot A$, for $i = 1, 2, 3$.

b. Show that if rows 1 and 2 of $A$ are interchanged, then the result may be written as $EA$, where $E$ is an elementary matrix formed by interchanging rows 1 and 2 of $I$.

c. Show that if row 3 of $A$ is multiplied by 5, then the result may be written as $EA$, where $E$ is formed by multiplying row 3 of $I$ by 5.

**28.** Show that if row 3 of $A$ is replaced by $\text{row}_3(A) - 4 \cdot \text{row}_1(A)$, the result is $EA$, where $E$ is formed from $I$ by replacing $\text{row}_3(I)$ by $\text{row}_3(I) - 4 \cdot \text{row}_1(I)$.

Find the inverses of the matrices in Exercises 29–32, if they exist. Use the algorithm introduced in this section.

**29.** $\begin{bmatrix} 1 & 2 \\ 4 & 7 \end{bmatrix}$ **30.** $\begin{bmatrix} 5 & 10 \\ 4 & 7 \end{bmatrix}$

**31.** $\begin{bmatrix} 1 & 0 & -2 \\ -3 & 1 & 4 \\ 2 & -3 & 4 \end{bmatrix}$ **32.** $\begin{bmatrix} 1 & -2 & 1 \\ 4 & -7 & 3 \\ -2 & 6 & -4 \end{bmatrix}$

**33.** Use the algorithm from this section to find the inverses of

$$\begin{bmatrix} 1 & 0 & 0 \\ 1 & 1 & 0 \\ 1 & 1 & 1 \end{bmatrix} \quad \text{and} \quad \begin{bmatrix} 1 & 0 & 0 & 0 \\ 1 & 1 & 0 & 0 \\ 1 & 1 & 1 & 0 \\ 1 & 1 & 1 & 1 \end{bmatrix}.$$

Let $A$ be the corresponding $n \times n$ matrix, and let $B$ be its inverse. Guess the form of $B$, and then prove that $AB = I$ and $BA = I$.

**34.** Repeat the strategy of Exercise 33 to guess the inverse of

$$A = \begin{bmatrix} 1 & 0 & 0 & \cdots & 0 \\ 1 & 2 & 0 & & 0 \\ 1 & 2 & 3 & & 0 \\ \vdots & & & \ddots & \vdots \\ 1 & 2 & 3 & \cdots & n \end{bmatrix}. \text{ Prove that your guess is}$$

correct.

**35.** Let $A = \begin{bmatrix} -2 & -7 & -9 \\ 2 & 5 & 6 \\ 1 & 3 & 4 \end{bmatrix}$. Find the third column of $A^{-1}$ without computing the other columns.

**36.** **[M]** Let $A = \begin{bmatrix} -25 & -9 & -27 \\ 546 & 180 & 537 \\ 154 & 50 & 149 \end{bmatrix}$. Find the second and third columns of $A^{-1}$ without computing the first column.

**37.** Let $A = \begin{bmatrix} 1 & 2 \\ 1 & 3 \\ 1 & 5 \end{bmatrix}$. Construct a $2 \times 3$ matrix $C$ (by trial and error) using only 1, −1, and 0 as entries, such that $CA = I_2$. Compute $AC$ and note that $AC \neq I_3$.

**38.** Let $A = \begin{bmatrix} 1 & 1 & 1 & 0 \\ 0 & 1 & 1 & 1 \end{bmatrix}$. Construct a $4 \times 2$ matrix $D$

using only 1 and 0 as entries, such that $AD = I_2$. Is it possible that $CA = I_4$ for some $4 \times 2$ matrix $C$? Why or why not?

**39.** Let $D = \begin{bmatrix} .005 & .002 & .001 \\ .002 & .004 & .002 \\ .001 & .002 & .005 \end{bmatrix}$ be a flexibility matrix,

with flexibility measured in inches per pound. Suppose that forces of 30, 50, and 20 lb are applied at points 1, 2, and 3, respectively, in Figure 1 of Example 3. Find the corresponding deflections.

**40.** **[M]** Compute the stiffness matrix $D^{-1}$ for $D$ in Exercise 39. List the forces needed to produce a deflection of .04 in. at point 3, with zero deflections at the other points.

**41.** **[M]** Let $D = \begin{bmatrix} .0040 & .0030 & .0010 & .0005 \\ .0030 & .0050 & .0030 & .0010 \\ .0010 & .0030 & .0050 & .0030 \\ .0005 & .0010 & .0030 & .0040 \end{bmatrix}$ be a

flexibility matrix for an elastic beam with four points at which force is applied. Units are centimeters per newton of force. Measurements at the four points show deflections of .08, .12, .16, and .12 cm. Determine the forces at the four points.

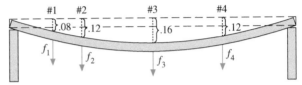

Deflection of elastic beam in Exercises 41 and 42.

**42.** **[M]** With $D$ as in Exercise 41, determine the forces that produce a deflection of .24 cm at the second point on the beam, with zero deflections at the other three points. How is the answer related to the entries in $D^{-1}$? [*Hint:* First answer the question when the deflection is 1 cm at the second point.]

---

**SOLUTIONS TO PRACTICE PROBLEMS**

**1.** a. $\det \begin{bmatrix} 3 & -9 \\ 2 & 6 \end{bmatrix} = 3 \cdot 6 - (-9) \cdot 2 = 18 + 18 = 36$. The determinant is nonzero, so the matrix is invertible.

b. $\det \begin{bmatrix} 4 & -9 \\ 0 & 5 \end{bmatrix} = 4 \cdot 5 - (-9) \cdot 0 = 20 \neq 0$. The matrix is invertible.

c. $\det \begin{bmatrix} 6 & -9 \\ -4 & 6 \end{bmatrix} = 6 \cdot 6 - (-9)(-4) = 36 - 36 = 0$. The matrix is not invertible.

**2.** $[\, A \quad I \,] \sim \begin{bmatrix} 1 & -2 & -1 & 1 & 0 & 0 \\ -1 & 5 & 6 & 0 & 1 & 0 \\ 5 & -4 & 5 & 0 & 0 & 1 \end{bmatrix}$

$\sim \begin{bmatrix} 1 & -2 & -1 & 1 & 0 & 0 \\ 0 & 3 & 5 & 1 & 1 & 0 \\ 0 & 6 & 10 & -5 & 0 & 1 \end{bmatrix}$

$\sim \begin{bmatrix} 1 & -2 & -1 & 1 & 0 & 0 \\ 0 & 3 & 5 & 1 & 1 & 0 \\ 0 & 0 & 0 & -7 & -2 & 1 \end{bmatrix}$

So $[\, A \quad I \,]$ is row equivalent to a matrix of the form $[\, B \quad D \,]$, where $B$ is square and has a row of zeros. Further row operations will not transform $B$ into $I$, so we stop. $A$ does not have an inverse.

**3.** Since $A$ is an invertible matrix, there exists a matrix $C$ such that $AC = I = CA$. The goal is to find a matrix $D$ so that $(5A)D = I = D(5A)$. Set $D = 1/5\, C$. Applying Theorem 2 from Section 2.1 establishes that $(5A)(1/5\, C) = (5)(1/5)(AC) = 1\, I = I$, and $(1/5\, C)(5A) = (1/5)(5)(CA) = 1\, I = I$. Thus $1/5\, C$ is indeed the inverse of $A$, proving that $A$ is invertible.

# 3 Determinants

## 3.1 INTRODUCTION TO DETERMINANTS

Recall from Section 2.2 that a $2 \times 2$ matrix is invertible if and only if its determinant is nonzero. To extend this useful fact to larger matrices, we need a definition for the determinant of an $n \times n$ matrix. We can discover the definition for the $3 \times 3$ case by watching what happens when an invertible $3 \times 3$ matrix $A$ is row reduced.

Consider $A = [a_{ij}]$ with $a_{11} \neq 0$. If we multiply the second and third rows of $A$ by $a_{11}$ and then subtract appropriate multiples of the first row from the other two rows, we find that $A$ is row equivalent to the following two matrices:

$$\begin{bmatrix} a_{11} & a_{12} & a_{13} \\ a_{11}a_{21} & a_{11}a_{22} & a_{11}a_{23} \\ a_{11}a_{31} & a_{11}a_{32} & a_{11}a_{33} \end{bmatrix} \sim \begin{bmatrix} a_{11} & a_{12} & a_{13} \\ 0 & a_{11}a_{22} - a_{12}a_{21} & a_{11}a_{23} - a_{13}a_{21} \\ 0 & a_{11}a_{32} - a_{12}a_{31} & a_{11}a_{33} - a_{13}a_{31} \end{bmatrix} \quad (1)$$

Since $A$ is invertible, either the $(2, 2)$-entry or the $(3, 2)$-entry on the right in (1) is nonzero. Let us suppose that the $(2, 2)$-entry is nonzero. (Otherwise, we can make a row interchange before proceeding.) Multiply row 3 by $a_{11}a_{22} - a_{12}a_{21}$, and then to the new row 3 add $-(a_{11}a_{32} - a_{12}a_{31})$ times row 2. This will show that

$$A \sim \begin{bmatrix} a_{11} & a_{12} & a_{13} \\ 0 & a_{11}a_{22} - a_{12}a_{21} & a_{11}a_{23} - a_{13}a_{21} \\ 0 & 0 & a_{11}\Delta \end{bmatrix}$$

where

$$\Delta = a_{11}a_{22}a_{33} + a_{12}a_{23}a_{31} + a_{13}a_{21}a_{32} - a_{11}a_{23}a_{32} - a_{12}a_{21}a_{33} - a_{13}a_{22}a_{31} \quad (2)$$

Since $A$ is invertible, $\Delta$ must be nonzero. The converse is true, too, as we will see in Section 3.2. We call $\Delta$ in (2) the **determinant** of the $3 \times 3$ matrix $A$.

Recall that the determinant of a $2 \times 2$ matrix, $A = [a_{ij}]$, is the number

$$\det A = a_{11}a_{22} - a_{12}a_{21}$$

For a $1 \times 1$ matrix—say, $A = [a_{11}]$—we define $\det A = a_{11}$. To generalize the definition of the determinant to larger matrices, we'll use $2 \times 2$ determinants to rewrite the $3 \times 3$ determinant $\Delta$ described above. Since the terms in $\Delta$ can be grouped as $(a_{11}a_{22}a_{33} - a_{11}a_{23}a_{32}) - (a_{12}a_{21}a_{33} - a_{12}a_{23}a_{31}) + (a_{13}a_{21}a_{32} - a_{13}a_{22}a_{31})$,

$$\Delta = a_{11} \cdot \det \begin{bmatrix} a_{22} & a_{23} \\ a_{32} & a_{33} \end{bmatrix} - a_{12} \cdot \det \begin{bmatrix} a_{21} & a_{23} \\ a_{31} & a_{33} \end{bmatrix} + a_{13} \cdot \det \begin{bmatrix} a_{21} & a_{22} \\ a_{31} & a_{32} \end{bmatrix}$$

For brevity, write

$$\Delta = a_{11} \cdot \det A_{11} - a_{12} \cdot \det A_{12} + a_{13} \cdot \det A_{13} \quad (3)$$

where $A_{11}$, $A_{12}$, and $A_{13}$ are obtained from $A$ by deleting the first row and one of the three columns. For any square matrix $A$, let $A_{ij}$ denote the submatrix formed by deleting the $i$th row and $j$th column of $A$. For instance, if

$$A = \begin{bmatrix} 1 & -2 & 5 & 0 \\ 2 & 0 & 4 & -1 \\ 3 & 1 & 0 & 7 \\ 0 & 4 & -2 & 0 \end{bmatrix}$$

then $A_{32}$ is obtained by crossing out row 3 and column 2,

$$\begin{bmatrix} 1 & -2 & 5 & 0 \\ 2 & 0 & 4 & -1 \\ 3 & 1 & 0 & 7 \\ 0 & 4 & -2 & 0 \end{bmatrix}$$

so that

$$A_{32} = \begin{bmatrix} 1 & 5 & 0 \\ 2 & 4 & -1 \\ 0 & -2 & 0 \end{bmatrix}$$

We can now give a *recursive* definition of a determinant. When $n = 3$, det $A$ is defined using determinants of the $2 \times 2$ submatrices $A_{1j}$, as in (3) above. When $n = 4$, det $A$ uses determinants of the $3 \times 3$ submatrices $A_{1j}$. In general, an $n \times n$ determinant is defined by determinants of $(n - 1) \times (n - 1)$ submatrices.

**DEFINITION**

For $n \geq 2$, the **determinant** of an $n \times n$ matrix $A = [a_{ij}]$ is the sum of $n$ terms of the form $\pm a_{1j}$ det $A_{1j}$, with plus and minus signs alternating, where the entries $a_{11}, a_{12}, \dots, a_{1n}$ are from the first row of $A$. In symbols,

$$\det A = a_{11} \det A_{11} - a_{12} \det A_{12} + \cdots + (-1)^{1+n} a_{1n} \det A_{1n}$$

$$= \sum_{j=1}^{n} (-1)^{1+j} a_{1j} \det A_{1j}$$

**EXAMPLE 1**   Compute the determinant of

$$A = \begin{bmatrix} 1 & 5 & 0 \\ 2 & 4 & -1 \\ 0 & -2 & 0 \end{bmatrix}$$

**SOLUTION** Compute $\det A = a_{11} \det A_{11} - a_{12} \det A_{12} + a_{13} \det A_{13}$:

$$\det A = 1 \cdot \det \begin{bmatrix} 4 & -1 \\ -2 & 0 \end{bmatrix} - 5 \cdot \det \begin{bmatrix} 2 & -1 \\ 0 & 0 \end{bmatrix} + 0 \cdot \det \begin{bmatrix} 2 & 4 \\ 0 & -2 \end{bmatrix}$$

$$= 1(0 - 2) - 5(0 - 0) + 0(-4 - 0) = -2 \qquad \blacksquare$$

Another common notation for the determinant of a matrix uses a pair of vertical lines in place of brackets. Thus the calculation in Example 1 can be written as

$$\det A = 1 \begin{vmatrix} 4 & -1 \\ -2 & 0 \end{vmatrix} - 5 \begin{vmatrix} 2 & -1 \\ 0 & 0 \end{vmatrix} + 0 \begin{vmatrix} 2 & 4 \\ 0 & -2 \end{vmatrix} = \cdots = -2$$

To state the next theorem, it is convenient to write the definition of det $A$ in a slightly different form. Given $A = [a_{ij}]$, the $(i, j)$-**cofactor** of $A$ is the number $C_{ij}$ given by

$$C_{ij} = (-1)^{i+j} \det A_{ij} \qquad (4)$$

Then

$$\det A = a_{11}C_{11} + a_{12}C_{12} + \cdots + a_{1n}C_{1n}$$

This formula is called a **cofactor expansion across the first row** of $A$. We omit the proof of the following fundamental theorem to avoid a lengthy digression.

The determinant of an $n \times n$ matrix $A$ can be computed by a cofactor expansion across any row or down any column. The expansion across the $i$th row using the cofactors in (4) is

$$\det A = a_{i1}C_{i1} + a_{i2}C_{i2} + \cdots + a_{in}C_{in}$$

The cofactor expansion down the $j$th column is

$$\det A = a_{1j}C_{1j} + a_{2j}C_{2j} + \cdots + a_{nj}C_{nj}$$

The plus or minus sign in the $(i, j)$-cofactor depends on the position of $a_{ij}$ in the matrix, regardless of the sign of $a_{ij}$ itself. The factor $(-1)^{i+j}$ determines the following checkerboard pattern of signs:

$$\begin{bmatrix} + & - & + & \cdots \\ - & + & - & \\ + & - & + & \\ \vdots & & & \ddots \end{bmatrix}$$

**EXAMPLE 2**  Use a cofactor expansion across the third row to compute $\det A$, where

$$A = \begin{bmatrix} 1 & 5 & 0 \\ 2 & 4 & -1 \\ 0 & -2 & 0 \end{bmatrix}$$

**SOLUTION**  Compute

$$\det A = a_{31}C_{31} + a_{32}C_{32} + a_{33}C_{33}$$

$$= (-1)^{3+1}a_{31} \det A_{31} + (-1)^{3+2}a_{32} \det A_{32} + (-1)^{3+3}a_{33} \det A_{33}$$

$$= 0 \begin{vmatrix} 5 & 0 \\ 4 & -1 \end{vmatrix} - (-2) \begin{vmatrix} 1 & 0 \\ 2 & -1 \end{vmatrix} + 0 \begin{vmatrix} 1 & 5 \\ 2 & 4 \end{vmatrix}$$

$$= 0 + 2(-1) + 0 = -2 \qquad \blacksquare$$

Theorem 1 is helpful for computing the determinant of a matrix that contains many zeros. For example, if a row is mostly zeros, then the cofactor expansion across that row has many terms that are zero, and the cofactors in those terms need not be calculated. The same approach works with a column that contains many zeros.

**EXAMPLE 3**  Compute $\det A$, where

$$A = \begin{bmatrix} 3 & -7 & 8 & 9 & -6 \\ 0 & 2 & -5 & 7 & 3 \\ 0 & 0 & 1 & 5 & 0 \\ 0 & 0 & 2 & 4 & -1 \\ 0 & 0 & 0 & -2 & 0 \end{bmatrix}$$

**SOLUTION**  The cofactor expansion down the first column of $A$ has all terms equal to zero except the first. Thus

$$\det A = 3 \cdot \begin{vmatrix} 2 & -5 & 7 & 3 \\ 0 & 1 & 5 & 0 \\ 0 & 2 & 4 & -1 \\ 0 & 0 & -2 & 0 \end{vmatrix} + 0 \cdot C_{21} + 0 \cdot C_{31} + 0 \cdot C_{41} + 0 \cdot C_{51}$$

Henceforth we will omit the zero terms in the cofactor expansion. Next, expand this $4 \times 4$ determinant down the first column, in order to take advantage of the zeros there. We have

$$\det A = 3 \cdot 2 \cdot \begin{vmatrix} 1 & 5 & 0 \\ 2 & 4 & -1 \\ 0 & -2 & 0 \end{vmatrix}$$

This $3 \times 3$ determinant was computed in Example 1 and found to equal $-2$. Hence $\det A = 3 \cdot 2 \cdot (-2) = -12$. ∎

The matrix in Example 3 was nearly triangular. The method in that example is easily adapted to prove the following theorem.

**THEOREM 2**    If $A$ is a triangular matrix, then $\det A$ is the product of the entries on the main diagonal of $A$.

The strategy in Example 3 of looking for zeros works extremely well when an entire row or column consists of zeros. In such a case, the cofactor expansion along such a row or column is a sum of zeros! So the determinant is zero. Unfortunately, most cofactor expansions are not so quickly evaluated.

---

**NUMERICAL NOTE**

By today's standards, a $25 \times 25$ matrix is small. Yet it would be impossible to calculate a $25 \times 25$ determinant by cofactor expansion. In general, a cofactor expansion requires more than $n!$ multiplications, and $25!$ is approximately $1.5 \times 10^{25}$.

If a computer performs one trillion multiplications per second, it would have to run for more than 500,000 years to compute a $25 \times 25$ determinant by this method. Fortunately, there are faster methods, as we'll soon discover.

---

Exercises 19–38 explore important properties of determinants, mostly for the $2 \times 2$ case. The results from Exercises 33–36 will be used in the next section to derive the analogous properties for $n \times n$ matrices.

**PRACTICE PROBLEM**

Compute $\begin{vmatrix} 5 & -7 & 2 & 2 \\ 0 & 3 & 0 & -4 \\ -5 & -8 & 0 & 3 \\ 0 & 5 & 0 & -6 \end{vmatrix}$.

# 3.1 EXERCISES

Compute the determinants in Exercises 1–8 using a cofactor expansion across the first row. In Exercises 1–4, also compute the determinant by a cofactor expansion down the second column.

**1.** $\begin{vmatrix} 3 & 0 & 4 \\ 2 & 3 & 2 \\ 0 & 5 & -1 \end{vmatrix}$

**2.** $\begin{vmatrix} 0 & 4 & 1 \\ 5 & -3 & 0 \\ 2 & 3 & 1 \end{vmatrix}$

**3.** $\begin{vmatrix} 2 & -2 & 3 \\ 3 & 1 & 2 \\ 1 & 3 & -1 \end{vmatrix}$

**4.** $\begin{vmatrix} 1 & 2 & 4 \\ 3 & 1 & 1 \\ 2 & 4 & 2 \end{vmatrix}$

**5.** $\begin{vmatrix} 2 & 3 & -3 \\ 4 & 0 & 3 \\ 6 & 1 & 5 \end{vmatrix}$

**6.** $\begin{vmatrix} 5 & -2 & 2 \\ 0 & 3 & -3 \\ 2 & -4 & 7 \end{vmatrix}$

**7.** $\begin{vmatrix} 4 & 3 & 0 \\ 6 & 5 & 2 \\ 9 & 7 & 3 \end{vmatrix}$  **8.** $\begin{vmatrix} 4 & 1 & 2 \\ 4 & 0 & 3 \\ 3 & -2 & 5 \end{vmatrix}$

Compute the determinants in Exercises 9–14 by cofactor expansions. At each step, choose a row or column that involves the least amount of computation.

**9.** $\begin{vmatrix} 4 & 0 & 0 & 5 \\ 1 & 7 & 2 & -5 \\ 3 & 0 & 0 & 0 \\ 8 & 3 & 1 & 7 \end{vmatrix}$  **10.** $\begin{vmatrix} 1 & -2 & 5 & 2 \\ 0 & 0 & 3 & 0 \\ 2 & -4 & -3 & 5 \\ 2 & 0 & 3 & 5 \end{vmatrix}$

**11.** $\begin{vmatrix} 3 & 5 & -6 & 4 \\ 0 & -2 & 3 & -3 \\ 0 & 0 & 1 & 5 \\ 0 & 0 & 0 & 3 \end{vmatrix}$  **12.** $\begin{vmatrix} 3 & 0 & 0 & 0 \\ 7 & -2 & 0 & 0 \\ 2 & 6 & 3 & 0 \\ 3 & -8 & 4 & -3 \end{vmatrix}$

**13.** $\begin{vmatrix} 4 & 0 & -7 & 3 & -5 \\ 0 & 0 & 2 & 0 & 0 \\ 7 & 3 & -6 & 4 & -8 \\ 5 & 0 & 5 & 2 & -3 \\ 0 & 0 & 9 & -1 & 2 \end{vmatrix}$

**14.** $\begin{vmatrix} 6 & 3 & 2 & 4 & 0 \\ 9 & 0 & -4 & 1 & 0 \\ 8 & -5 & 6 & 7 & 1 \\ 2 & 0 & 0 & 0 & 0 \\ 4 & 2 & 3 & 2 & 0 \end{vmatrix}$

The expansion of a $3 \times 3$ determinant can be remembered by the following device. Write a second copy of the first two columns to the right of the matrix, and compute the determinant by multiplying entries on six diagonals:

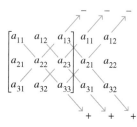

Add the downward diagonal products and subtract the upward products. Use this method to compute the determinants in Exercises 15–18. *Warning: This trick does not generalize in any reasonable way to $4 \times 4$ or larger matrices.*

**15.** $\begin{vmatrix} 1 & 0 & 4 \\ 2 & 3 & 2 \\ 0 & 5 & -2 \end{vmatrix}$  **16.** $\begin{vmatrix} 0 & 3 & 1 \\ 4 & -5 & 0 \\ 3 & 4 & 1 \end{vmatrix}$

**17.** $\begin{vmatrix} 2 & -3 & 3 \\ 3 & 2 & 2 \\ 1 & 3 & -1 \end{vmatrix}$  **18.** $\begin{vmatrix} 1 & 3 & 4 \\ 2 & 3 & 1 \\ 3 & 3 & 2 \end{vmatrix}$

In Exercises 19–24, explore the effect of an elementary row operation on the determinant of a matrix. In each case, state the row operation and describe how it affects the determinant.

**19.** $\begin{bmatrix} a & b \\ c & d \end{bmatrix}, \begin{bmatrix} c & d \\ a & b \end{bmatrix}$

**20.** $\begin{bmatrix} a & b \\ c & d \end{bmatrix}, \begin{bmatrix} a + kc & b + kd \\ c & d \end{bmatrix}$

**21.** $\begin{bmatrix} a & b \\ c & d \end{bmatrix}, \begin{bmatrix} a & b \\ kc & kd \end{bmatrix}$

**22.** $\begin{bmatrix} 3 & 2 \\ 5 & 4 \end{bmatrix}, \begin{bmatrix} 3 & 2 \\ 5 + 3k & 4 + 2k \end{bmatrix}$

**23.** $\begin{bmatrix} a & b & c \\ 3 & 2 & 1 \\ 4 & 5 & 6 \end{bmatrix}, \begin{bmatrix} 3 & 2 & 1 \\ a & b & c \\ 4 & 5 & 6 \end{bmatrix}$

**24.** $\begin{bmatrix} 1 & 0 & 1 \\ -3 & 4 & -4 \\ 2 & -3 & 1 \end{bmatrix}, \begin{bmatrix} k & 0 & k \\ -3 & 4 & -4 \\ 2 & -3 & 1 \end{bmatrix}$

Compute the determinants of the elementary matrices given in Exercises 25–30. (See Section 2.2.)

**25.** $\begin{bmatrix} 1 & 0 & 0 \\ 0 & 1 & 0 \\ 0 & k & 1 \end{bmatrix}$  **26.** $\begin{bmatrix} 0 & 0 & 1 \\ 0 & 1 & 0 \\ 1 & 0 & 0 \end{bmatrix}$

**27.** $\begin{bmatrix} 1 & 0 & 0 \\ 0 & 1 & 0 \\ k & 0 & 1 \end{bmatrix}$  **28.** $\begin{bmatrix} k & 0 & 0 \\ 0 & 1 & 0 \\ 0 & 0 & 1 \end{bmatrix}$

**29.** $\begin{bmatrix} 1 & 0 & 0 \\ 0 & k & 0 \\ 0 & 0 & 1 \end{bmatrix}$  **30.** $\begin{bmatrix} 0 & 1 & 0 \\ 1 & 0 & 0 \\ 0 & 0 & 1 \end{bmatrix}$

Use Exercises 25–28 to answer the questions in Exercises 31 and 32. Give reasons for your answers.

**31.** What is the determinant of an elementary row replacement matrix?

**32.** What is the determinant of an elementary scaling matrix with $k$ on the diagonal?

In Exercises 33–36, verify that $\det EA = (\det E)(\det A)$, where $E$ is the elementary matrix shown and $A = \begin{bmatrix} a & b \\ c & d \end{bmatrix}$.

**33.** $\begin{bmatrix} 1 & k \\ 0 & 1 \end{bmatrix}$  **34.** $\begin{bmatrix} 1 & 0 \\ k & 1 \end{bmatrix}$

**35.** $\begin{bmatrix} 0 & 1 \\ 1 & 0 \end{bmatrix}$  **36.** $\begin{bmatrix} 1 & 0 \\ 0 & k \end{bmatrix}$

**37.** Let $A = \begin{bmatrix} 3 & 1 \\ 4 & 2 \end{bmatrix}$. Write $5A$. Is $\det 5A = 5 \det A$?

**38.** Let $A = \begin{bmatrix} a & b \\ c & d \end{bmatrix}$ and let $k$ be a scalar. Find a formula that relates $\det kA$ to $k$ and $\det A$.

In Exercises 39 and 40, $A$ is an $n \times n$ matrix. Mark each statement True or False. Justify each answer.

**39.** a. An $n \times n$ determinant is defined by determinants of $(n-1) \times (n-1)$ submatrices.

b. The $(i, j)$-cofactor of a matrix $A$ is the matrix $A_{ij}$ obtained by deleting from $A$ its $i$th row and $j$th column.

**40.** a. The cofactor expansion of det $A$ down a column is equal to the cofactor expansion along a row.

   b. The determinant of a triangular matrix is the sum of the entries on the main diagonal.

**41.** Let $\mathbf{u} = \begin{bmatrix} 3 \\ 0 \end{bmatrix}$ and $\mathbf{v} = \begin{bmatrix} 1 \\ 2 \end{bmatrix}$. Compute the area of the parallelogram determined by $\mathbf{u}, \mathbf{v}, \mathbf{u} + \mathbf{v}$, and $\mathbf{0}$, and compute the determinant of $[\,\mathbf{u} \quad \mathbf{v}\,]$. How do they compare? Replace the first entry of $\mathbf{v}$ by an arbitrary number $x$, and repeat the problem. Draw a picture and explain what you find.

**42.** Let $\mathbf{u} = \begin{bmatrix} a \\ b \end{bmatrix}$ and $\mathbf{v} = \begin{bmatrix} c \\ 0 \end{bmatrix}$, where $a, b$, and $c$ are positive (for simplicity). Compute the area of the parallelogram determined by $\mathbf{u}, \mathbf{v}, \mathbf{u} + \mathbf{v}$, and $\mathbf{0}$, and compute the determinants of the matrices $[\,\mathbf{u} \quad \mathbf{v}\,]$ and $[\,\mathbf{v} \quad \mathbf{u}\,]$. Draw a picture and explain what you find.

**43.** **[M]** Construct a random $4 \times 4$ matrix $A$ with integer entries between $-9$ and $9$. How is det $A^{-1}$ related to det $A$? Experiment with random $n \times n$ integer matrices for $n = 4$,

5, and 6, and make a conjecture. *Note:* In the unlikely event that you encounter a matrix with a zero determinant, reduce it to echelon form and discuss what you find.

**44.** **[M]** Is it true that $\det AB = (\det A)(\det B)$? To find out, generate random $5 \times 5$ matrices $A$ and $B$, and compute $\det AB - (\det A \det B)$. Repeat the calculations for three other pairs of $n \times n$ matrices, for various values of $n$. Report your results.

**45.** **[M]** Is it true that $\det(A + B) = \det A + \det B$? Experiment with four pairs of random matrices as in Exercise 44, and make a conjecture.

**46.** **[M]** Construct a random $4 \times 4$ matrix $A$ with integer entries between $-9$ and $9$, and compare det $A$ with det $A^T$, $\det(-A)$, $\det(2A)$, and $\det(10A)$. Repeat with two other random $4 \times 4$ integer matrices, and make conjectures about how these determinants are related. (Refer to Exercise 36 in Section 2.1.) Then check your conjectures with several random $5 \times 5$ and $6 \times 6$ integer matrices. Modify your conjectures, if necessary, and report your results.

---

**SOLUTION TO PRACTICE PROBLEM**

Take advantage of the zeros. Begin with a cofactor expansion down the third column to obtain a $3 \times 3$ matrix, which may be evaluated by an expansion down its first column.

$$\begin{vmatrix} 5 & -7 & 2 & 2 \\ 0 & 3 & 0 & -4 \\ -5 & -8 & 0 & 3 \\ 0 & 5 & 0 & -6 \end{vmatrix} = (-1)^{1+3} 2 \begin{vmatrix} 0 & 3 & -4 \\ -5 & -8 & 3 \\ 0 & 5 & -6 \end{vmatrix}$$

$$= 2 \cdot (-1)^{2+1} (-5) \begin{vmatrix} 3 & -4 \\ 5 & -6 \end{vmatrix} = 20$$

The $(-1)^{2+1}$ in the next-to-last calculation came from the $(2, 1)$-position of the $-5$ in the $3 \times 3$ determinant.

---

# 3.2  PROPERTIES OF DETERMINANTS

The secret of determinants lies in how they change when row operations are performed. The following theorem generalizes the results of Exercises 19–24 in Section 3.1. The proof is at the end of this section.

**THEOREM 3**     **Row Operations**

Let $A$ be a square matrix.

   a. If a multiple of one row of $A$ is added to another row to produce a matrix $B$, then det $B = $ det $A$.

   b. If two rows of $A$ are interchanged to produce $B$, then det $B = -$ det $A$.

   c. If one row of $A$ is multiplied by $k$ to produce $B$, then det $B = k \cdot $ det $A$.

The following examples show how to use Theorem 3 to find determinants efficiently.

**EXAMPLE 1** Compute det $A$, where $A = \begin{bmatrix} 1 & -4 & 2 \\ -2 & 8 & -9 \\ -1 & 7 & 0 \end{bmatrix}$.

**SOLUTION** The strategy is to reduce $A$ to echelon form and then to use the fact that the determinant of a triangular matrix is the product of the diagonal entries. The first two row replacements in column 1 do not change the determinant:

$$\det A = \begin{vmatrix} 1 & -4 & 2 \\ -2 & 8 & -9 \\ -1 & 7 & 0 \end{vmatrix} = \begin{vmatrix} 1 & -4 & 2 \\ 0 & 0 & -5 \\ -1 & 7 & 0 \end{vmatrix} = \begin{vmatrix} 1 & -4 & 2 \\ 0 & 0 & -5 \\ 0 & 3 & 2 \end{vmatrix}$$

An interchange of rows 2 and 3 reverses the sign of the determinant, so

$$\det A = - \begin{vmatrix} 1 & -4 & 2 \\ 0 & 3 & 2 \\ 0 & 0 & -5 \end{vmatrix} = -(1)(3)(-5) = 15 \qquad \blacksquare$$

A common use of Theorem 3(c) in hand calculations is to *factor out a common multiple of one row* of a matrix. For instance,

$$\begin{vmatrix} * & * & * \\ 5k & -2k & 3k \\ * & * & * \end{vmatrix} = k \begin{vmatrix} * & * & * \\ 5 & -2 & 3 \\ * & * & * \end{vmatrix}$$

where the starred entries are unchanged. We use this step in the next example.

**EXAMPLE 2** Compute det $A$, where $A = \begin{bmatrix} 2 & -8 & 6 & 8 \\ 3 & -9 & 5 & 10 \\ -3 & 0 & 1 & -2 \\ 1 & -4 & 0 & 6 \end{bmatrix}$.

**SOLUTION** To simplify the arithmetic, we want a 1 in the upper-left corner. We could interchange rows 1 and 4. Instead, we factor out 2 from the top row, and then proceed with row replacements in the first column:

$$\det A = 2 \begin{vmatrix} 1 & -4 & 3 & 4 \\ 3 & -9 & 5 & 10 \\ -3 & 0 & 1 & -2 \\ 1 & -4 & 0 & 6 \end{vmatrix} = 2 \begin{vmatrix} 1 & -4 & 3 & 4 \\ 0 & 3 & -4 & -2 \\ 0 & -12 & 10 & 10 \\ 0 & 0 & -3 & 2 \end{vmatrix}$$

Next, we could factor out another 2 from row 3 or use the 3 in the second column as a pivot. We choose the latter operation, adding 4 times row 2 to row 3:

$$\det A = 2 \begin{vmatrix} 1 & -4 & 3 & 4 \\ 0 & 3 & -4 & -2 \\ 0 & 0 & -6 & 2 \\ 0 & 0 & -3 & 2 \end{vmatrix}$$

Finally, adding $-1/2$ times row 3 to row 4, and computing the "triangular" determinant, we find that

$$\det A = 2 \begin{vmatrix} 1 & -4 & 3 & 4 \\ 0 & 3 & -4 & -2 \\ 0 & 0 & -6 & 2 \\ 0 & 0 & 0 & 1 \end{vmatrix} = 2 \cdot (1)(3)(-6)(1) = -36 \qquad \blacksquare$$

$$U = \begin{bmatrix} \blacksquare & * & * & * \\ 0 & \blacksquare & * & * \\ 0 & 0 & \blacksquare & * \\ 0 & 0 & 0 & \blacksquare \end{bmatrix}$$
$$\det U \neq 0$$

$$U = \begin{bmatrix} \blacksquare & * & * & * \\ 0 & \blacksquare & * & * \\ 0 & 0 & 0 & \blacksquare \\ 0 & 0 & 0 & 0 \end{bmatrix}$$
$$\det U = 0$$

**FIGURE 1**

Typical echelon forms of square matrices.

Suppose a square matrix $A$ has been reduced to an echelon form $U$ by row replacements and row interchanges. (This is always possible. See the row reduction algorithm in Section 1.2.) If there are $r$ interchanges, then Theorem 3 shows that

$$\det A = (-1)^r \det U$$

Since $U$ is in echelon form, it is triangular, and so $\det U$ is the product of the diagonal entries $u_{11}, \ldots, u_{nn}$. If $A$ is invertible, the entries $u_{ii}$ are all pivots (because $A \sim I_n$ and the $u_{ii}$ have not been scaled to 1's). Otherwise, at least $u_{nn}$ is zero, and the product $u_{11} \cdots u_{nn}$ is zero. See Figure 1. Thus

$$\det A = \begin{cases} (-1)^r \cdot \begin{pmatrix} \text{product of} \\ \text{pivots in } U \end{pmatrix} & \text{when } A \text{ is invertible} \\ 0 & \text{when } A \text{ is not invertible} \end{cases} \tag{1}$$

It is interesting to note that although the echelon form $U$ described above is not unique (because it is not completely row reduced), and the pivots are not unique, the *product* of the pivots *is* unique, except for a possible minus sign.

Formula (1) not only gives a concrete interpretation of det $A$ but also proves the main theorem of this section:

**THEOREM 4**

A square matrix $A$ is invertible if and only if $\det A \neq 0$.

Theorem 4 adds the statement "$\det A \neq 0$" to the Invertible Matrix Theorem. A useful corollary is that $\det A = 0$ when the columns of $A$ are linearly dependent. Also, $\det A = 0$ when the *rows* of $A$ are linearly dependent. (Rows of $A$ are columns of $A^T$, and linearly dependent columns of $A^T$ make $A^T$ singular. When $A^T$ is singular, so is $A$, by the Invertible Matrix Theorem.) In practice, linear dependence is obvious when two columns or two rows are the same or a column or a row is zero.

**EXAMPLE 3** Compute det $A$, where $A = \begin{bmatrix} 3 & -1 & 2 & -5 \\ 0 & 5 & -3 & -6 \\ -6 & 7 & -7 & 4 \\ -5 & -8 & 0 & 9 \end{bmatrix}$.

**SOLUTION** Add 2 times row 1 to row 3 to obtain

$$\det A = \det \begin{bmatrix} 3 & -1 & 2 & -5 \\ 0 & 5 & -3 & -6 \\ 0 & 5 & -3 & -6 \\ -5 & -8 & 0 & 9 \end{bmatrix} = 0$$

because the second and third rows of the second matrix are equal. ∎

— NUMERICAL NOTES —

1. Most computer programs that compute det $A$ for a general matrix $A$ use the method of formula (1) above.

2. It can be shown that evaluation of an $n \times n$ determinant using row operations requires about $2n^3/3$ arithmetic operations. Any modern microcomputer can calculate a $25 \times 25$ determinant in a fraction of a second, since only about 10,000 operations are required.

WEB

Computers can also handle large "sparse" matrices, with special routines that take advantage of the presence of many zeros. Of course, zero entries can speed hand computations, too. The calculations in the next example combine the power of row operations with the strategy from Section 3.1 of using zero entries in cofactor expansions.

**EXAMPLE 4**   Compute det $A$, where $A = \begin{bmatrix} 0 & 1 & 2 & -1 \\ 2 & 5 & -7 & 3 \\ 0 & 3 & 6 & 2 \\ -2 & -5 & 4 & -2 \end{bmatrix}$.

**SOLUTION** A good way to begin is to use the 2 in column 1 as a pivot, eliminating the $-2$ below it. Then use a cofactor expansion to reduce the size of the determinant, followed by another row replacement operation. Thus

$$\det A = \begin{vmatrix} 0 & 1 & 2 & -1 \\ 2 & 5 & -7 & 3 \\ 0 & 3 & 6 & 2 \\ 0 & 0 & -3 & 1 \end{vmatrix} = -2\begin{vmatrix} 1 & 2 & -1 \\ 3 & 6 & 2 \\ 0 & -3 & 1 \end{vmatrix} = -2\begin{vmatrix} 1 & 2 & -1 \\ 0 & 0 & 5 \\ 0 & -3 & 1 \end{vmatrix}$$

An interchange of rows 2 and 3 would produce a "triangular determinant." Another approach is to make a cofactor expansion down the first column:

$$\det A = (-2)(1)\begin{vmatrix} 0 & 5 \\ -3 & 1 \end{vmatrix} = -2 \cdot (15) = -30 \qquad \blacksquare$$

## Column Operations

We can perform operations on the columns of a matrix in a way that is analogous to the row operations we have considered. The next theorem shows that column operations have the same effects on determinants as row operations.

*Remark:* The Principle of Mathematical Induction says the following: Let $P(n)$ be a statement that is either true or false for each natural number $n$. Then $P(n)$ is true for all $n \geq 1$ provided that $P(1)$ is true, and for each natural number $k$, if $P(k)$ is true, then $P(k+1)$ is true. The Principle of Mathematical Induction is used to prove the next theorem.

**THEOREM 5**      If $A$ is an $n \times n$ matrix, then $\det A^T = \det A$.

**PROOF** The theorem is obvious for $n = 1$. Suppose the theorem is true for $k \times k$ determinants and let $n = k + 1$. Then the cofactor of $a_{1j}$ in $A$ equals the cofactor of $a_{j1}$ in $A^T$, because the cofactors involve $k \times k$ determinants. Hence the cofactor expansion of $\det A$ along the first *row* equals the cofactor expansion of $\det A^T$ down the first *column*. That is, $A$ and $A^T$ have equal determinants. The theorem is true for $n = 1$, and the truth of the theorem for one value of $n$ implies its truth for the next value of $n$. By the Principle of Mathematical Induction, the theorem is true for all $n \geq 1$.    ■

Because of Theorem 5, each statement in Theorem 3 is true when the word *row* is replaced everywhere by *column*. To verify this property, one merely applies the original Theorem 3 to $A^T$. A row operation on $A^T$ amounts to a column operation on $A$.

Column operations are useful for both theoretical purposes and hand computations. However, for simplicity we'll perform only row operations in numerical calculations.

## Determinants and Matrix Products

The proof of the following useful theorem is at the end of the section. Applications are in the exercises.

**THEOREM 6**

**Multiplicative Property**

If $A$ and $B$ are $n \times n$ matrices, then $\det AB = (\det A)(\det B)$.

**EXAMPLE 5**  Verify Theorem 6 for $A = \begin{bmatrix} 6 & 1 \\ 3 & 2 \end{bmatrix}$ and $B = \begin{bmatrix} 4 & 3 \\ 1 & 2 \end{bmatrix}$.

**SOLUTION**

$$AB = \begin{bmatrix} 6 & 1 \\ 3 & 2 \end{bmatrix} \begin{bmatrix} 4 & 3 \\ 1 & 2 \end{bmatrix} = \begin{bmatrix} 25 & 20 \\ 14 & 13 \end{bmatrix}$$

and

$$\det AB = 25 \cdot 13 - 20 \cdot 14 = 325 - 280 = 45$$

Since $\det A = 9$ and $\det B = 5$,

$$(\det A)(\det B) = 9 \cdot 5 = 45 = \det AB \qquad \blacksquare$$

*Warning:* A common misconception is that Theorem 6 has an analogue for *sums* of matrices. However, $\det(A + B)$ is *not* equal to $\det A + \det B$, in general.

## A Linearity Property of the Determinant Function

For an $n \times n$ matrix $A$, we can consider $\det A$ as a function of the $n$ column vectors in $A$. We will show that if all columns except one are held fixed, then $\det A$ is a *linear function* of that one (vector) variable.

Suppose that the $j$th column of $A$ is allowed to vary, and write

$$A = \begin{bmatrix} \mathbf{a}_1 & \cdots & \mathbf{a}_{j-1} & \mathbf{x} & \mathbf{a}_{j+1} & \cdots & \mathbf{a}_n \end{bmatrix}$$

Define a transformation $T$ from $\mathbb{R}^n$ to $\mathbb{R}$ by

$$T(\mathbf{x}) = \det \begin{bmatrix} \mathbf{a}_1 & \cdots & \mathbf{a}_{j-1} & \mathbf{x} & \mathbf{a}_{j+1} & \cdots & \mathbf{a}_n \end{bmatrix}$$

Then,

$$T(c\mathbf{x}) = cT(\mathbf{x}) \quad \text{for all scalars } c \text{ and all } \mathbf{x} \text{ in } \mathbb{R}^n \qquad (2)$$

$$T(\mathbf{u} + \mathbf{v}) = T(\mathbf{u}) + T(\mathbf{v}) \quad \text{for all } \mathbf{u}, \mathbf{v} \text{ in } \mathbb{R}^n \qquad (3)$$

Property (2) is Theorem 3(c) applied to the columns of $A$. A proof of property (3) follows from a cofactor expansion of $\det A$ down the $j$th column. (See Exercise 43.) This (multi-) linearity property of the determinant turns out to have many useful consequences that are studied in more advanced courses.

## Proofs of Theorems 3 and 6

It is convenient to prove Theorem 3 when it is stated in terms of the elementary matrices discussed in Section 2.2. We call an elementary matrix $E$ a *row replacement (matrix)* if $E$ is obtained from the identity $I$ by adding a multiple of one row to another row; $E$ is an *interchange* if $E$ is obtained by interchanging two rows of $I$; and $E$ is *a scale by r* if $E$ is obtained by multiplying a row of $I$ by a nonzero scalar $r$. With this terminology, Theorem 3 can be reformulated as follows:

*If A is an n × n matrix and E is an n × n elementary matrix, then*

$$\det EA = (\det E)(\det A)$$

*where*

$$\det E = \begin{cases} 1 & \text{if } E \text{ is a row replacement} \\ -1 & \text{if } E \text{ is an interchange} \\ r & \text{if } E \text{ is a scale by } r \end{cases}$$

PROOF OF THEOREM 3   The proof is by induction on the size of $A$. The case of a $2 \times 2$ matrix was verified in Exercises 33–36 of Section 3.1. Suppose the theorem has been verified for determinants of $k \times k$ matrices with $k \geq 2$, let $n = k + 1$, and let $A$ be $n \times n$. The action of $E$ on $A$ involves either two rows or only one row. So we can expand $\det EA$ across a row that is unchanged by the action of $E$, say, row $i$. Let $A_{ij}$ (respectively, $B_{ij}$) be the matrix obtained by deleting row $i$ and column $j$ from $A$ (respectively, $EA$). Then the rows of $B_{ij}$ are obtained from the rows of $A_{ij}$ by the same type of elementary row operation that $E$ performs on $A$. Since these submatrices are only $k \times k$, the induction assumption implies that

$$\det B_{ij} = \alpha \cdot \det A_{ij}$$

where $\alpha = 1, -1$, or $r$, depending on the nature of $E$. The cofactor expansion across row $i$ is

$$\det EA = a_{i1}(-1)^{i+1} \det B_{i1} + \cdots + a_{in}(-1)^{i+n} \det B_{in}$$
$$= \alpha a_{i1}(-1)^{i+1} \det A_{i1} + \cdots + \alpha a_{in}(-1)^{i+n} \det A_{in}$$
$$= \alpha \cdot \det A$$

In particular, taking $A = I_n$, we see that $\det E = 1, -1$, or $r$, depending on the nature of $E$. Thus the theorem is true for $n = 2$, and the truth of the theorem for one value of $n$ implies its truth for the next value of $n$. By the principle of induction, the theorem must be true for $n \geq 2$. The theorem is trivially true for $n = 1$.  ■

PROOF OF THEOREM 6   In this case, $\det AB = (\det A)(\det B)$, because both sides are zero, by Theorem 4. If $A$ is invertible, then $A$ and the identity matrix $I_n$ are row equivalent by the Invertible Matrix Theorem. So there exist elementary matrices $E_1, \ldots, E_p$ such that

$$A = E_p E_{p-1} \cdots E_1 \cdot I_n = E_p E_{p-1} \cdots E_1$$

For brevity, write $|A|$ for $\det A$. Then repeated application of Theorem 3, as rephrased above, shows that

$$|AB| = |E_p \cdots E_1 B| = |E_p||E_{p-1} \cdots E_1 B| = \cdots$$
$$= |E_p| \cdots |E_1||B| = \cdots = |E_p \cdots E_1||B|$$
$$= |A||B|$$  ■

## PRACTICE PROBLEMS

**1.** Compute $\begin{vmatrix} 1 & -3 & 1 & -2 \\ 2 & -5 & -1 & -2 \\ 0 & -4 & 5 & 1 \\ -3 & 10 & -6 & 8 \end{vmatrix}$ in as few steps as possible.

**2.** Use a determinant to decide if $\mathbf{v}_1$, $\mathbf{v}_2$, and $\mathbf{v}_3$ are linearly independent, when

$$\mathbf{v}_1 = \begin{bmatrix} 5 \\ -7 \\ 9 \end{bmatrix}, \qquad \mathbf{v}_2 = \begin{bmatrix} -3 \\ 3 \\ -5 \end{bmatrix}, \qquad \mathbf{v}_3 = \begin{bmatrix} 2 \\ -7 \\ 5 \end{bmatrix}$$

**3.** Let $A$ be an $n \times n$ matrix such that $A^2 = I$. Show that det $A = \pm 1$.

## 3.2 EXERCISES

Each equation in Exercises 1–4 illustrates a property of determinants. State the property.

**1.** $\begin{vmatrix} 0 & 5 & -2 \\ 1 & -3 & 6 \\ 4 & -1 & 8 \end{vmatrix} = - \begin{vmatrix} 1 & -3 & 6 \\ 0 & 5 & -2 \\ 4 & -1 & 8 \end{vmatrix}$

**2.** $\begin{vmatrix} 1 & 2 & 2 \\ 0 & 3 & -4 \\ 3 & 7 & 4 \end{vmatrix} = \begin{vmatrix} 1 & 2 & 2 \\ 0 & 3 & -4 \\ 0 & 1 & -2 \end{vmatrix}$

**3.** $\begin{vmatrix} 3 & -6 & 9 \\ 3 & 5 & -5 \\ 1 & 3 & 3 \end{vmatrix} = 3 \begin{vmatrix} 1 & -2 & 3 \\ 3 & 5 & -5 \\ 1 & 3 & 3 \end{vmatrix}$

**4.** $\begin{vmatrix} 1 & 3 & -4 \\ 2 & 0 & -3 \\ 3 & -5 & 2 \end{vmatrix} = \begin{vmatrix} 1 & 3 & -4 \\ 0 & -6 & 5 \\ 3 & -5 & 2 \end{vmatrix}$

Find the determinants in Exercises 5–10 by row reduction to echelon form.

**5.** $\begin{vmatrix} 1 & 5 & -4 \\ -1 & -4 & 5 \\ -2 & -8 & 7 \end{vmatrix}$

**6.** $\begin{vmatrix} 3 & 3 & -3 \\ 3 & 4 & -4 \\ 2 & -3 & -5 \end{vmatrix}$

**7.** $\begin{vmatrix} 1 & 3 & 0 & 2 \\ -2 & -5 & 7 & 4 \\ 3 & 5 & 2 & 1 \\ 1 & -1 & 2 & -3 \end{vmatrix}$

**8.** $\begin{vmatrix} 1 & 3 & 2 & -4 \\ 0 & 1 & 2 & -5 \\ 2 & 7 & 6 & -3 \\ -3 & -10 & -7 & 2 \end{vmatrix}$

**9.** $\begin{vmatrix} 1 & -1 & -3 & 0 \\ 0 & 1 & 5 & 4 \\ -1 & 0 & 5 & 3 \\ 3 & -3 & -2 & 3 \end{vmatrix}$

**10.** $\begin{vmatrix} 1 & 3 & -1 & 0 & -2 \\ 0 & 2 & -4 & -2 & -6 \\ -2 & -6 & 2 & 3 & 10 \\ 1 & 5 & -6 & 2 & -3 \\ 0 & 2 & -4 & 5 & 9 \end{vmatrix}$

Combine the methods of row reduction and cofactor expansion to compute the determinants in Exercises 11–14.

**11.** $\begin{vmatrix} 3 & 4 & -3 & -1 \\ 3 & 0 & 1 & -3 \\ -6 & 0 & -4 & 3 \\ 6 & 8 & -4 & -1 \end{vmatrix}$

**12.** $\begin{vmatrix} -1 & 2 & 3 & 0 \\ 3 & 4 & 3 & 0 \\ 11 & 4 & 6 & 6 \\ 4 & 2 & 4 & 3 \end{vmatrix}$

**13.** $\begin{vmatrix} 2 & 5 & 4 & 1 \\ 4 & 7 & 6 & 2 \\ 6 & -2 & -4 & 0 \\ -6 & 7 & 7 & 0 \end{vmatrix}$

**14.** $\begin{vmatrix} 1 & 5 & 4 & 1 \\ 0 & -2 & -4 & 0 \\ 3 & 5 & 4 & 1 \\ -6 & 5 & 5 & 0 \end{vmatrix}$

Find the determinants in Exercises 15–20, where

$$\begin{vmatrix} a & b & c \\ d & e & f \\ g & h & i \end{vmatrix} = 7.$$

**15.** $\begin{vmatrix} a & b & c \\ d & e & f \\ 3g & 3h & 3i \end{vmatrix}$

**16.** $\begin{vmatrix} a & b & c \\ 5d & 5e & 5f \\ g & h & i \end{vmatrix}$

**17.** $\begin{bmatrix} a+d & b+e & c+f \\ d & e & f \\ g & h & i \end{bmatrix}$

**18.** $\begin{vmatrix} d & e & f \\ a & b & c \\ g & h & i \end{vmatrix}$

**19.** $\begin{vmatrix} a & b & c \\ 2d+a & 2e+b & 2f+c \\ g & h & i \end{vmatrix}$

**20.** $\begin{vmatrix} a & b & c \\ d+3g & e+3h & f+3i \\ g & h & i \end{vmatrix}$

In Exercises 21–23, use determinants to find out if the matrix is invertible.

**21.** $\begin{bmatrix} 2 & 6 & 0 \\ 1 & 3 & 2 \\ 3 & 9 & 2 \end{bmatrix}$

**22.** $\begin{bmatrix} 5 & 1 & -1 \\ 1 & -3 & -2 \\ 0 & 5 & 3 \end{bmatrix}$

**23.** $\begin{bmatrix} 2 & 0 & 0 & 6 \\ 1 & -7 & -5 & 0 \\ 3 & 8 & 6 & 0 \\ 0 & 7 & 5 & 4 \end{bmatrix}$

In Exercises 24–26, use determinants to decide if the set of vectors is linearly independent.

**24.** $\begin{bmatrix} 4 \\ 6 \\ 2 \end{bmatrix}, \begin{bmatrix} -7 \\ 0 \\ 7 \end{bmatrix}, \begin{bmatrix} -3 \\ -5 \\ -2 \end{bmatrix}$

**25.** $\begin{bmatrix} 7 \\ -4 \\ -6 \end{bmatrix}, \begin{bmatrix} -8 \\ 5 \\ 7 \end{bmatrix}, \begin{bmatrix} 7 \\ 0 \\ -5 \end{bmatrix}$

**26.** $\begin{bmatrix} 3 \\ 5 \\ -6 \\ 4 \end{bmatrix}, \begin{bmatrix} 2 \\ -6 \\ 0 \\ 7 \end{bmatrix}, \begin{bmatrix} -2 \\ -1 \\ 3 \\ 0 \end{bmatrix}, \begin{bmatrix} 0 \\ 0 \\ 0 \\ -2 \end{bmatrix}$

In Exercises 27 and 28, $A$ and $B$ are $n \times n$ matrices. Mark each statement True or False. Justify each answer.

**27. a.** A row replacement operation does not affect the determinant of a matrix.

   **b.** The determinant of $A$ is the product of the pivots in any echelon form $U$ of $A$, multiplied by $(-1)^r$, where $r$ is the number of row interchanges made during row reduction from $A$ to $U$.

   **c.** If the columns of $A$ are linearly dependent, then $\det A = 0$.

   **d.** $\det(A + B) = \det A + \det B$.

**28. a.** If three row interchanges are made in succession, then the new determinant equals the old determinant.

   **b.** The determinant of $A$ is the product of the diagonal entries in $A$.

   **c.** If $\det A$ is zero, then two rows or two columns are the same, or a row or a column is zero.

   **d.** $\det A^{-1} = (-1) \det A$.

**29.** Compute $\det B^4$, where $B = \begin{bmatrix} 1 & 0 & 1 \\ 1 & 1 & 2 \\ 1 & 2 & 1 \end{bmatrix}$.

**30.** Use Theorem 3 (but not Theorem 4) to show that if two rows of a square matrix $A$ are equal, then $\det A = 0$. The same is true for two columns. Why?

In Exercises 31–36, mention an appropriate theorem in your explanation.

**31.** Show that if $A$ is invertible, then $\det A^{-1} = \dfrac{1}{\det A}$.

**32.** Suppose that $A$ is a square matrix such that $\det A^3 = 0$. Explain why $A$ cannot be invertible.

**33.** Let $A$ and $B$ be square matrices. Show that even though $AB$ and $BA$ may not be equal, it is always true that $\det AB = \det BA$.

**34.** Let $A$ and $P$ be square matrices, with $P$ invertible. Show that $\det(PAP^{-1}) = \det A$.

**35.** Let $U$ be a square matrix such that $U^T U = I$. Show that $\det U = \pm 1$.

**36.** Find a formula for $\det(rA)$ when $A$ is an $n \times n$ matrix.

Verify that $\det AB = (\det A)(\det B)$ for the matrices in Exercises 37 and 38. (Do not use Theorem 6.)

**37.** $A = \begin{bmatrix} 3 & 0 \\ 6 & 1 \end{bmatrix}, B = \begin{bmatrix} 2 & 0 \\ 5 & 4 \end{bmatrix}$

**38.** $A = \begin{bmatrix} 3 & 6 \\ -1 & -2 \end{bmatrix}, B = \begin{bmatrix} 4 & 3 \\ -1 & -3 \end{bmatrix}$

**39.** Let $A$ and $B$ be $3 \times 3$ matrices, with $\det A = -3$ and $\det B = 4$. Use properties of determinants (in the text and in the exercises above) to compute:
   a. $\det AB$   b. $\det 5A$   c. $\det B^T$
   d. $\det A^{-1}$   e. $\det A^3$

**40.** Let $A$ and $B$ be $4 \times 4$ matrices, with $\det A = -3$ and $\det B = -1$. Compute:
   a. $\det AB$   b. $\det B^5$   c. $\det 2A$
   d. $\det A^T BA$   e. $\det B^{-1}AB$

**41.** Verify that $\det A = \det B + \det C$, where
$$A = \begin{bmatrix} a+e & b+f \\ c & d \end{bmatrix}, \ B = \begin{bmatrix} a & b \\ c & d \end{bmatrix}, \ C = \begin{bmatrix} e & f \\ c & d \end{bmatrix}$$

**42.** Let $A = \begin{bmatrix} 1 & 0 \\ 0 & 1 \end{bmatrix}$ and $B = \begin{bmatrix} a & b \\ c & d \end{bmatrix}$. Show that $\det(A + B) = \det A + \det B$ if and only if $a + d = 0$.

**43.** Verify that $\det A = \det B + \det C$, where
$$A = \begin{bmatrix} a_{11} & a_{12} & u_1 + v_1 \\ a_{21} & a_{22} & u_2 + v_2 \\ a_{31} & a_{32} & u_3 + v_3 \end{bmatrix},$$
$$B = \begin{bmatrix} a_{11} & a_{12} & u_1 \\ a_{21} & a_{22} & u_2 \\ a_{31} & a_{32} & u_3 \end{bmatrix}, \ C = \begin{bmatrix} a_{11} & a_{12} & v_1 \\ a_{21} & a_{22} & v_2 \\ a_{31} & a_{32} & v_3 \end{bmatrix}$$

Note, however, that $A$ is *not* the same as $B + C$.

**44.** Right-multiplication by an elementary matrix $E$ affects the *columns* of $A$ in the same way that left-multiplication affects the *rows*. Use Theorems 5 and 3 and the obvious fact that $E^T$ is another elementary matrix to show that
$$\det AE = (\det E)(\det A)$$
Do not use Theorem 6.

**45.** [M] Compute $\det A^T A$ and $\det AA^T$ for several random $4 \times 5$ matrices and several random $5 \times 6$ matrices. What can you say about $A^T A$ and $AA^T$ when $A$ has more columns than rows?

**46.** [M] If $\det A$ is close to zero, is the matrix $A$ nearly singular? Experiment with the nearly singular $4 \times 4$ matrix
$$A = \begin{bmatrix} 4 & 0 & -7 & -7 \\ -6 & 1 & 11 & 9 \\ 7 & -5 & 10 & 19 \\ -1 & 2 & 3 & -1 \end{bmatrix}$$

Compute the determinants of $A$, $10A$, and $0.1A$. In contrast, compute the condition numbers of these matrices. Repeat these calculations when $A$ is the $4 \times 4$ identity matrix. Discuss your results.

## SOLUTIONS TO PRACTICE PROBLEMS

1. Perform row replacements to create zeros in the first column, and then create a row of zeros.

$$\begin{vmatrix} 1 & -3 & 1 & -2 \\ 2 & -5 & -1 & -2 \\ 0 & -4 & 5 & 1 \\ -3 & 10 & -6 & 8 \end{vmatrix} = \begin{vmatrix} 1 & -3 & 1 & -2 \\ 0 & 1 & -3 & 2 \\ 0 & -4 & 5 & 1 \\ 0 & 1 & -3 & 2 \end{vmatrix} = \begin{vmatrix} 1 & -3 & 1 & -2 \\ 0 & 1 & -3 & 2 \\ 0 & -4 & 5 & 1 \\ 0 & 0 & 0 & 0 \end{vmatrix} = 0$$

2. $\det \begin{bmatrix} \mathbf{v}_1 & \mathbf{v}_2 & \mathbf{v}_3 \end{bmatrix} = \begin{vmatrix} 5 & -3 & 2 \\ -7 & 3 & -7 \\ 9 & -5 & 5 \end{vmatrix} = \begin{vmatrix} 5 & -3 & 2 \\ -2 & 0 & -5 \\ 9 & -5 & 5 \end{vmatrix}$   Row 1 added to row 2

$$= -(-3)\begin{vmatrix} -2 & -5 \\ 9 & 5 \end{vmatrix} - (-5)\begin{vmatrix} 5 & 2 \\ -2 & -5 \end{vmatrix} \quad \text{Cofactors of column 2}$$

$$= 3 \cdot (35) + 5 \cdot (-21) = 0$$

By Theorem 4, the matrix $\begin{bmatrix} \mathbf{v}_1 & \mathbf{v}_2 & \mathbf{v}_3 \end{bmatrix}$ is not invertible. The columns are linearly dependent, by the Invertible Matrix Theorem.

3. Recall that $\det I = 1$. By Theorem 6, $\det (AA) = (\det A)(\det A)$. Putting these two observations together results in

$$1 = \det I = \det A^2 = \det (AA) = (\det A)(\det A) = (\det A)^2$$

Taking the square root of both sides establishes that $\det A = \pm 1$.

## 3.3 | CRAMER'S RULE, VOLUME, AND LINEAR TRANSFORMATIONS

This section applies the theory of the preceding sections to obtain important theoretical formulas and a geometric interpretation of the determinant.

### Cramer's Rule

Cramer's rule is needed in a variety of theoretical calculations. For instance, it can be used to study how the solution of $A\mathbf{x} = \mathbf{b}$ is affected by changes in the entries of $\mathbf{b}$. However, the formula is inefficient for hand calculations, except for $2 \times 2$ or perhaps $3 \times 3$ matrices.

For any $n \times n$ matrix $A$ and any $\mathbf{b}$ in $\mathbb{R}^n$, let $A_i(\mathbf{b})$ be the matrix obtained from $A$ by replacing column $i$ by the vector $\mathbf{b}$.

$$A_i(\mathbf{b}) = [\mathbf{a}_1 \quad \cdots \quad \mathbf{b} \quad \cdots \quad \mathbf{a}_n]$$
$$\underset{\text{col } i}{\uparrow}$$

**THEOREM 7**    **Cramer's Rule**

Let $A$ be an invertible $n \times n$ matrix. For any $\mathbf{b}$ in $\mathbb{R}^n$, the unique solution $\mathbf{x}$ of $A\mathbf{x} = \mathbf{b}$ has entries given by

$$x_i = \frac{\det A_i(\mathbf{b})}{\det A}, \qquad i = 1, 2, \dots, n \tag{1}$$

PROOF Denote the columns of $A$ by $\mathbf{a}_1, \ldots, \mathbf{a}_n$ and the columns of the $n \times n$ identity matrix $I$ by $\mathbf{e}_1, \ldots, \mathbf{e}_n$. If $A\mathbf{x} = \mathbf{b}$, the definition of matrix multiplication shows that

$$A \cdot I_i(\mathbf{x}) = A \begin{bmatrix} \mathbf{e}_1 & \cdots & \mathbf{x} & \cdots & \mathbf{e}_n \end{bmatrix} = \begin{bmatrix} A\mathbf{e}_1 & \cdots & A\mathbf{x} & \cdots & A\mathbf{e}_n \end{bmatrix}$$

$$= \begin{bmatrix} \mathbf{a}_1 & \cdots & \mathbf{b} & \cdots & \mathbf{a}_n \end{bmatrix} = A_i(\mathbf{b})$$

By the multiplicative property of determinants,

$$(\det A)(\det I_i(\mathbf{x})) = \det A_i(\mathbf{b})$$

The second determinant on the left is simply $x_i$. (Make a cofactor expansion along the $i$th row.) Hence $(\det A) \cdot x_i = \det A_i(\mathbf{b})$. This proves (1) because $A$ is invertible and $\det A \neq 0$. ∎

**EXAMPLE 1** Use Cramer's rule to solve the system

$$3x_1 - 2x_2 = 6$$
$$-5x_1 + 4x_2 = 8$$

SOLUTION View the system as $A\mathbf{x} = \mathbf{b}$. Using the notation introduced above,

$$A = \begin{bmatrix} 3 & -2 \\ -5 & 4 \end{bmatrix}, \qquad A_1(\mathbf{b}) = \begin{bmatrix} 6 & -2 \\ 8 & 4 \end{bmatrix}, \qquad A_2(\mathbf{b}) = \begin{bmatrix} 3 & 6 \\ -5 & 8 \end{bmatrix}$$

Since $\det A = 2$, the system has a unique solution. By Cramer's rule,

$$x_1 = \frac{\det A_1(\mathbf{b})}{\det A} = \frac{24 + 16}{2} = 20$$

$$x_2 = \frac{\det A_2(\mathbf{b})}{\det A} = \frac{24 + 30}{2} = 27$$

∎

# Application to Engineering

A number of important engineering problems, particularly in electrical engineering and control theory, can be analyzed by *Laplace transforms*. This approach converts an appropriate system of linear differential equations into a system of linear algebraic equations whose coefficients involve a parameter. The next example illustrates the type of algebraic system that may arise.

**EXAMPLE 2** Consider the following system in which $s$ is an unspecified parameter. Determine the values of $s$ for which the system has a unique solution, and use Cramer's rule to describe the solution.

$$3sx_1 - 2x_2 = 4$$
$$-6x_1 + sx_2 = 1$$

SOLUTION View the system as $A\mathbf{x} = \mathbf{b}$. Then

$$A = \begin{bmatrix} 3s & -2 \\ -6 & s \end{bmatrix}, \qquad A_1(\mathbf{b}) = \begin{bmatrix} 4 & -2 \\ 1 & s \end{bmatrix}, \qquad A_2(\mathbf{b}) = \begin{bmatrix} 3s & 4 \\ -6 & 1 \end{bmatrix}$$

Since

$$\det A = 3s^2 - 12 = 3(s + 2)(s - 2)$$

the system has a unique solution precisely when $s \neq \pm 2$. For such an $s$, the solution is $(x_1, x_2)$, where

$$x_1 = \frac{\det A_1(\mathbf{b})}{\det A} = \frac{4s + 2}{3(s + 2)(s - 2)}$$

$$x_2 = \frac{\det A_2(\mathbf{b})}{\det A} = \frac{3s + 24}{3(s + 2)(s - 2)} = \frac{s + 8}{(s + 2)(s - 2)}$$

∎

# A Formula for $A^{-1}$

Cramer's rule leads easily to a general formula for the inverse of an $n \times n$ matrix $A$. The $j$th column of $A^{-1}$ is a vector $\mathbf{x}$ that satisfies

$$A\mathbf{x} = \mathbf{e}_j$$

where $\mathbf{e}_j$ is the $j$th column of the identity matrix, and the $i$th entry of $\mathbf{x}$ is the $(i, j)$-entry of $A^{-1}$. By Cramer's rule,

$$\{(i, j)\text{-entry of } A^{-1}\} = x_i = \frac{\det A_i(\mathbf{e}_j)}{\det A} \tag{2}$$

Recall that $A_{ji}$ denotes the submatrix of $A$ formed by deleting row $j$ and column $i$. A cofactor expansion down column $i$ of $A_i(\mathbf{e}_j)$ shows that

$$\det A_i(\mathbf{e}_j) = (-1)^{i+j} \det A_{ji} = C_{ji} \tag{3}$$

where $C_{ji}$ is a cofactor of $A$. By (2), the $(i, j)$-entry of $A^{-1}$ is the cofactor $C_{ji}$ divided by $\det A$. [Note that the subscripts on $C_{ji}$ are the reverse of $(i, j)$.] Thus

$$A^{-1} = \frac{1}{\det A} \begin{bmatrix} C_{11} & C_{21} & \cdots & C_{n1} \\ C_{12} & C_{22} & \cdots & C_{n2} \\ \vdots & \vdots & & \vdots \\ C_{1n} & C_{2n} & \cdots & C_{nn} \end{bmatrix} \tag{4}$$

The matrix of cofactors on the right side of (4) is called the **adjugate** (or **classical adjoint**) of $A$, denoted by adj $A$. (The term *adjoint* also has another meaning in advanced texts on linear transformations.) The next theorem simply restates (4).

**THEOREM 8**  **An Inverse Formula**

Let $A$ be an invertible $n \times n$ matrix. Then

$$A^{-1} = \frac{1}{\det A} \text{ adj } A$$

**EXAMPLE 3**  Find the inverse of the matrix $A = \begin{bmatrix} 2 & 1 & 3 \\ 1 & -1 & 1 \\ 1 & 4 & -2 \end{bmatrix}$.

**SOLUTION**  The nine cofactors are

$$C_{11} = +\begin{vmatrix} -1 & 1 \\ 4 & -2 \end{vmatrix} = -2, \quad C_{12} = -\begin{vmatrix} 1 & 1 \\ 1 & -2 \end{vmatrix} = 3, \quad C_{13} = +\begin{vmatrix} 1 & -1 \\ 1 & 4 \end{vmatrix} = 5$$

$$C_{21} = -\begin{vmatrix} 1 & 3 \\ 4 & -2 \end{vmatrix} = 14, \quad C_{22} = +\begin{vmatrix} 2 & 3 \\ 1 & -2 \end{vmatrix} = -7, \quad C_{23} = -\begin{vmatrix} 2 & 1 \\ 1 & 4 \end{vmatrix} = -7$$

$$C_{31} = +\begin{vmatrix} 1 & 3 \\ -1 & 1 \end{vmatrix} = 4, \quad C_{32} = -\begin{vmatrix} 2 & 3 \\ 1 & 1 \end{vmatrix} = 1, \quad C_{33} = +\begin{vmatrix} 2 & 1 \\ 1 & -1 \end{vmatrix} = -3$$

The adjugate matrix is the *transpose* of the matrix of cofactors. [For instance, $C_{12}$ goes in the $(2, 1)$ position.] Thus

$$\text{adj } A = \begin{bmatrix} -2 & 14 & 4 \\ 3 & -7 & 1 \\ 5 & -7 & -3 \end{bmatrix}$$

We could compute det $A$ directly, but the following computation provides a check on the calculations on page 93 *and* produces det $A$:

$$(\text{adj } A) \cdot A = \begin{bmatrix} -2 & 14 & 4 \\ 3 & -7 & 1 \\ 5 & -7 & -3 \end{bmatrix} \begin{bmatrix} 2 & 1 & 3 \\ 1 & -1 & 1 \\ 1 & 4 & -2 \end{bmatrix} = \begin{bmatrix} 14 & 0 & 0 \\ 0 & 14 & 0 \\ 0 & 0 & 14 \end{bmatrix} = 14I$$

Since $(\text{adj } A)A = 14I$, Theorem 8 shows that det $A = 14$ and

$$A^{-1} = \frac{1}{14} \begin{bmatrix} -2 & 14 & 4 \\ 3 & -7 & 1 \\ 5 & -7 & -3 \end{bmatrix} = \begin{bmatrix} -1/7 & 1 & 2/7 \\ 3/14 & -1/2 & 1/14 \\ 5/14 & -1/2 & -3/14 \end{bmatrix} \quad \blacksquare$$

---

NUMERICAL NOTES

Theorem 8 is useful mainly for theoretical calculations. The formula for $A^{-1}$ permits one to deduce properties of the inverse without actually calculating it. Except for special cases, the algorithm in Section 2.2 gives a much better way to compute $A^{-1}$, if the inverse is really needed.

Cramer's rule is also a theoretical tool. It can be used to study how sensitive the solution of $A\mathbf{x} = \mathbf{b}$ is to changes in an entry in $\mathbf{b}$ or in $A$ (perhaps due to experimental error when acquiring the entries for $\mathbf{b}$ or $A$). When $A$ is a $3 \times 3$ matrix with *complex* entries, Cramer's rule is sometimes selected for hand computation because row reduction of $[\,A \quad \mathbf{b}\,]$ with complex arithmetic can be messy, and the determinants are fairly easy to compute. For a larger $n \times n$ matrix (real or complex), Cramer's rule is hopelessly inefficient. Computing just *one* determinant takes about as much work as solving $A\mathbf{x} = \mathbf{b}$ by row reduction.

---

## Determinants as Area or Volume

In the next application, we verify the geometric interpretation of determinants described in the chapter introduction. Although a general discussion of length and distance in $\mathbb{R}^n$. We assume here that the usual Euclidean concepts of lenght, area, andvolume are already understood for $\mathbb{R}^2$ and $\mathbb{R}^3$.

**THEOREM 9**

If $A$ is a $2 \times 2$ matrix, the area of the parallelogram determined by the columns of $A$ is $|\det A|$. If $A$ is a $3 \times 3$ matrix, the volume of the parallelepiped determined by the columns of $A$ is $|\det A|$.

SG   A Geometric Proof 3-12

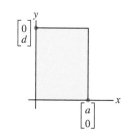

**FIGURE 1**

Area $= |ad|$.

**PROOF**  The theorem is obviously true for any $2 \times 2$ diagonal matrix:

$$\left| \det \begin{bmatrix} a & 0 \\ 0 & d \end{bmatrix} \right| = |ad| = \left\{ \begin{array}{c} \text{area of} \\ \text{rectangle} \end{array} \right\}$$

See Figure 1. It will suffice to show that any $2 \times 2$ matrix $A = [\, \mathbf{a}_1 \quad \mathbf{a}_2 \,]$ can be transformed into a diagonal matrix in a way that changes neither the area of the associated parallelogram nor $|\det A|$. From Section 3.2, we know that the absolute value of the determinant is unchanged when two columns are interchanged or a multiple of one column is added to another. And it is easy to see that such operations suffice to transform $A$ into a diagonal matrix. Column interchanges do not change the parallelogram at all. So it suffices to prove the following simple geometric observation that applies to vectors in $\mathbb{R}^2$ or $\mathbb{R}^3$:

Let $\mathbf{a}_1$ and $\mathbf{a}_2$ be nonzero vectors. Then for any scalar $c$, the area of the parallelogram determined by $\mathbf{a}_1$ and $\mathbf{a}_2$ equals the area of the parallelogram determined by $\mathbf{a}_1$ and $\mathbf{a}_2 + c\mathbf{a}_1$.

To prove this statement, we may assume that $\mathbf{a}_2$ is not a multiple of $\mathbf{a}_1$, for otherwise the two parallelograms would be degenerate and have zero area. If $L$ is the line through $\mathbf{0}$ and $\mathbf{a}_1$, then $\mathbf{a}_2 + L$ is the line through $\mathbf{a}_2$ parallel to $L$, and $\mathbf{a}_2 + c\mathbf{a}_1$ is on this line. See Figure 2. The points $\mathbf{a}_2$ and $\mathbf{a}_2 + c\mathbf{a}_1$ have the same perpendicular distance to $L$. Hence the two parallelograms in Figure 2 have the same area, since they share the base from $\mathbf{0}$ to $\mathbf{a}_1$. This completes the proof for $\mathbb{R}^2$.

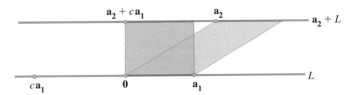

**FIGURE 2** Two parallelograms of equal area.

The proof for $\mathbb{R}^3$ is similar. The theorem is obviously true for a $3 \times 3$ diagonal matrix. See Figure 3. And any $3 \times 3$ matrix $A$ can be transformed into a diagonal matrix using column operations that do not change $|\det A|$. (Think about doing row operations on $A^T$.) So it suffices to show that these operations do not affect the volume of the parallelepiped determined by the columns of $A$.

A parallelepiped is shown in Figure 4 as a shaded box with two sloping sides. Its volume is the area of the base in the plane Span$\{\mathbf{a}_1, \mathbf{a}_3\}$ times the altitude of $\mathbf{a}_2$ above Span$\{\mathbf{a}_1, \mathbf{a}_3\}$. Any vector $\mathbf{a}_2 + c\mathbf{a}_1$ has the same altitude because $\mathbf{a}_2 + c\mathbf{a}_1$ lies in the plane $\mathbf{a}_2 + $ Span$\{\mathbf{a}_1, \mathbf{a}_3\}$, which is parallel to Span$\{\mathbf{a}_1, \mathbf{a}_3\}$. Hence the volume of the parallelepiped is unchanged when $[\,\mathbf{a}_1 \quad \mathbf{a}_2 \quad \mathbf{a}_3\,]$ is changed to $[\,\mathbf{a}_1 \quad \mathbf{a}_2 + c\mathbf{a}_1 \quad \mathbf{a}_3\,]$. Thus a column replacement operation does not affect the volume of the parallelepiped. Since column interchanges have no effect on the volume, the proof is complete. ∎

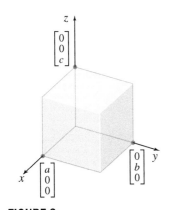

**FIGURE 3**

Volume $= |abc|$.

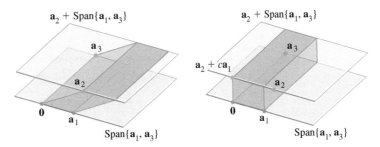

**FIGURE 4** Two parallelepipeds of equal volume.

**EXAMPLE 4**   Calculate the area of the parallelogram determined by the points $(-2, -2), (0, 3), (4, -1)$, and $(6, 4)$. See Figure 5(a).

**SOLUTION** First translate the parallelogram to one having the origin as a vertex. For example, subtract the vertex $(-2, -2)$ from each of the four vertices. The new parallelogram has the same area, and its vertices are $(0, 0), (2, 5), (6, 1)$, and $(8, 6)$. See

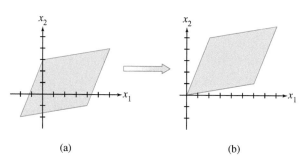

**FIGURE 5** Translating a parallelogram does not change its area.

Figure 5(b). This parallelogram is determined by the columns of

$$A = \begin{bmatrix} 2 & 6 \\ 5 & 1 \end{bmatrix}$$

Since $|\det A| = |-28|$, the area of the parallelogram is 28.    ∎

## Linear Transformations

Determinants can be used to describe an important geometric property of linear transformations in the plane and in $\mathbb{R}^3$. If $T$ is a linear transformation and $S$ is a set in the domain of $T$, let $T(S)$ denote the set of images of points in $S$. We are interested in how the area (or volume) of $T(S)$ compares with the area (or volume) of the original set $S$. For convenience, when $S$ is a region bounded by a parallelogram, we also refer to $S$ as a parallelogram.

**THEOREM 10**

Let $T : \mathbb{R}^2 \to \mathbb{R}^2$ be the linear transformation determined by a $2 \times 2$ matrix $A$. If $S$ is a parallelogram in $\mathbb{R}^2$, then

$$\{\text{area of } T(S)\} = |\det A| \cdot \{\text{area of } S\} \tag{5}$$

If $T$ is determined by a $3 \times 3$ matrix $A$, and if $S$ is a parallelepiped in $\mathbb{R}^3$, then

$$\{\text{volume of } T(S)\} = |\det A| \cdot \{\text{volume of } S\} \tag{6}$$

**PROOF** Consider the $2 \times 2$ case, with $A = [\,\mathbf{a}_1 \quad \mathbf{a}_2\,]$. A parallelogram at the origin in $\mathbb{R}^2$ determined by vectors $\mathbf{b}_1$ and $\mathbf{b}_2$ has the form

$$S = \{s_1\mathbf{b}_1 + s_2\mathbf{b}_2 : 0 \le s_1 \le 1,\ 0 \le s_2 \le 1\}$$

The image of $S$ under $T$ consists of points of the form

$$T(s_1\mathbf{b}_1 + s_2\mathbf{b}_2) = s_1 T(\mathbf{b}_1) + s_2 T(\mathbf{b}_2)$$
$$= s_1 A\mathbf{b}_1 + s_2 A\mathbf{b}_2$$

where $0 \le s_1 \le 1, 0 \le s_2 \le 1$. It follows that $T(S)$ is the parallelogram determined by the columns of the matrix $[\,A\mathbf{b}_1 \quad A\mathbf{b}_2\,]$. This matrix can be written as $AB$, where $B = [\,\mathbf{b}_1 \quad \mathbf{b}_2\,]$. By Theorem 9 and the product theorem for determinants,

$$\{\text{area of } T(S)\} = |\det AB| = |\det A| \cdot |\det B|$$
$$= |\det A| \cdot \{\text{area of } S\} \tag{7}$$

An arbitrary parallelogram has the form $\mathbf{p} + S$, where $\mathbf{p}$ is a vector and $S$ is a parallelogram at the origin, as above. It is easy to see that $T$ transforms $\mathbf{p} + S$ into $T(\mathbf{p}) + T(S)$. (See Exercise 26.) Since translation does not affect the area of a set,

$$\{\text{area of } T(\mathbf{p} + S)\} = \{\text{area of } T(\mathbf{p}) + T(S)\}$$
$$= \{\text{area of } T(S)\} \qquad \text{Translation}$$
$$= |\det A| \cdot \{\text{area of } S\} \qquad \text{By equation (7)}$$
$$= |\det A| \cdot \{\text{area of } \mathbf{p} + S\} \qquad \text{Translation}$$

This shows that (5) holds for all parallelograms in $\mathbb{R}^2$. The proof of (6) for the $3 \times 3$ case is analogous. ∎

When we attempt to generalize Theorem 10 to a region in $\mathbb{R}^2$ or $\mathbb{R}^3$ that is not bounded by straight lines or planes, we must face the problem of how to define and compute its area or volume. This is a question studied in calculus, and we shall only outline the basic idea for $\mathbb{R}^2$. If $R$ is a planar region that has a finite area, then $R$ can be approximated by a grid of small squares that lie inside $R$. By making the squares sufficiently small, the area of $R$ may be approximated as closely as desired by the sum of the areas of the small squares. See Figure 6.

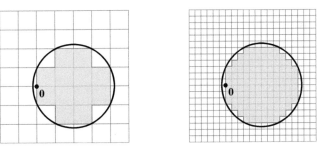

**FIGURE 6** Approximating a planar region by a union of squares. The approximation improves as the grid becomes finer.

If $T$ is a linear transformation associated with a $2 \times 2$ matrix $A$, then the image of a planar region $R$ under $T$ is approximated by the images of the small squares inside $R$. The proof of Theorem 10 shows that each such image is a parallelogram whose area is $|\det A|$ times the area of the square. If $R'$ is the union of the squares inside $R$, then the area of $T(R')$ is $|\det A|$ times the area of $R'$. See Figure 7. Also, the area of $T(R')$ is close to the area of $T(R)$. An argument involving a limiting process may be given to justify the following generalization of Theorem 10.

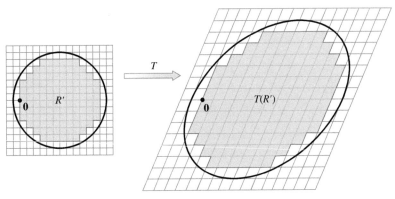

**FIGURE 7** Approximating $T(R)$ by a union of parallelograms.

The conclusions of Theorem 10 hold whenever $S$ is a region in $\mathbb{R}^2$ with finite area or a region in $\mathbb{R}^3$ with finite volume.

**EXAMPLE 5**   Let $a$ and $b$ be positive numbers. Find the area of the region $E$ bounded by the ellipse whose equation is

$$\frac{x_1^2}{a^2} + \frac{x_2^2}{b^2} = 1$$

**SOLUTION** We claim that $E$ is the image of the unit disk $D$ under the linear transformation $T$ determined by the matrix $A = \begin{bmatrix} a & 0 \\ 0 & b \end{bmatrix}$, because if $\mathbf{u} = \begin{bmatrix} u_1 \\ u_2 \end{bmatrix}$, $\mathbf{x} = \begin{bmatrix} x_1 \\ x_2 \end{bmatrix}$, and $\mathbf{x} = A\mathbf{u}$, then

$$u_1 = \frac{x_1}{a} \quad \text{and} \quad u_2 = \frac{x_2}{b}$$

It follows that $\mathbf{u}$ is in the unit disk, with $u_1^2 + u_2^2 \le 1$, if and only if $\mathbf{x}$ is in $E$, with $(x_1/a)^2 + (x_2/b)^2 \le 1$. By the generalization of Theorem 10,

$$\{\text{area of ellipse}\} = \{\text{area of } T(D)\}$$
$$= |\det A| \cdot \{\text{area of } D\}$$
$$= ab \cdot \pi(1)^2 = \pi ab \quad \blacksquare$$

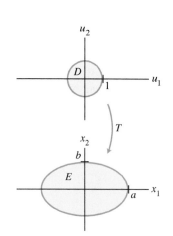

---

| PRACTICE PROBLEM

Let $S$ be the parallelogram determined by the vectors $\mathbf{b}_1 = \begin{bmatrix} 1 \\ 3 \end{bmatrix}$ and $\mathbf{b}_2 = \begin{bmatrix} 5 \\ 1 \end{bmatrix}$, and let $A = \begin{bmatrix} 1 & -.1 \\ 0 & 2 \end{bmatrix}$. Compute the area of the image of $S$ under the mapping $\mathbf{x} \mapsto A\mathbf{x}$.

# 3.3 EXERCISES

Use Cramer's rule to compute the solutions of the systems in Exercises 1–6.

**1.** $5x_1 + 7x_2 = 3$
$\phantom{5}2x_1 + 4x_2 = 1$

**2.** $4x_1 + \phantom{2}x_2 = 6$
$\phantom{4}3x_1 + 2x_2 = 7$

**3.** $3x_1 - 2x_2 = \phantom{-}3$
$-4x_1 + 6x_2 = -5$

**4.** $-5x_1 + 2x_2 = \phantom{-}9$
$\phantom{-}3x_1 - \phantom{2}x_2 = -4$

**5.** $\phantom{-}x_1 + x_2 \phantom{+ 2x_3} = 3$
$-3x_1 \phantom{+ x_2} + 2x_3 = 0$
$\phantom{-3x_1 +} x_2 - 2x_3 = 2$

**6.** $x_1 + 3x_2 + \phantom{2}x_3 = 4$
$-x_1 + \phantom{3x_2 +} 2x_3 = 2$
$3x_1 + \phantom{3}x_2 \phantom{+ 2x_3} = 2$

In Exercises 7–10, determine the values of the parameter $s$ for which the system has a unique solution, and describe the solution.

**7.** $6sx_1 + \phantom{2}4x_2 = \phantom{-}5$
$\phantom{6s}9x_1 + 2sx_2 = -2$

**8.** $3sx_1 + \phantom{5}5x_2 = 3$
$\phantom{3s}12x_1 + 5sx_2 = 2$

**9.** $sx_1 + 2sx_2 = -1$
$\phantom{s}3x_1 + 6sx_2 = \phantom{-}4$

**10.** $sx_1 - \phantom{4}2x_2 = 1$
$4sx_1 + 4sx_2 = 2$

In Exercises 11–16, compute the adjugate of the given matrix, and then use Theorem 8 to give the inverse of the matrix.

**11.** $\begin{bmatrix} 0 & -2 & -1 \\ 5 & 0 & 0 \\ -1 & 1 & 1 \end{bmatrix}$

**12.** $\begin{bmatrix} 1 & 1 & 3 \\ -2 & 2 & 1 \\ 0 & 1 & 1 \end{bmatrix}$

**13.** $\begin{bmatrix} 3 & 5 & 4 \\ 1 & 0 & 1 \\ 2 & 1 & 1 \end{bmatrix}$

**14.** $\begin{bmatrix} 1 & -1 & 2 \\ 0 & 2 & 1 \\ 2 & 0 & 4 \end{bmatrix}$

**15.** $\begin{bmatrix} 5 & 0 & 0 \\ -1 & 1 & 0 \\ -2 & 3 & -1 \end{bmatrix}$

**16.** $\begin{bmatrix} 1 & 2 & 4 \\ 0 & -3 & 1 \\ 0 & 0 & -2 \end{bmatrix}$

**17.** Show that if $A$ is $2 \times 2$, then Theorem 8 gives the same formula for $A^{-1}$ as that given by Theorem 4 in Section 2.2.

**18.** Suppose that all the entries in $A$ are integers and $\det A = 1$. Explain why all the entries in $A^{-1}$ are integers.

In Exercises 19–22, find the area of the parallelogram whose vertices are listed.

19. $(0, 0), (5, 2), (6, 4), (11, 6)$

20. $(0, 0), (-2, 4), (4, -5), (2, -1)$

21. $(-2, 0), (0, 3), (1, 3), (-1, 0)$

22. $(0, -2), (5, -2), (-3, 1), (2, 1)$

23. Find the volume of the parallelepiped with one vertex at the origin and adjacent vertices at $(1, 0, -3)$, $(1, 2, 4)$, and $(5, 1, 0)$.

24. Find the volume of the parallelepiped with one vertex at the origin and adjacent vertices at $(1, 3, 0)$, $(-2, 0, 2)$, and $(-1, 3, -1)$.

25. Use the concept of volume to explain why the determinant of a $3 \times 3$ matrix $A$ is zero if and only if $A$ is not invertible. Do not appeal to Theorem 4 in Section 3.2. [*Hint:* Think about the columns of $A$.]

26. Let $T : \mathbb{R}^m \to \mathbb{R}^n$ be a linear transformation, and let $\mathbf{p}$ be a vector and $S$ a set in $\mathbb{R}^m$. Show that the image of $\mathbf{p} + S$ under $T$ is the translated set $T(\mathbf{p}) + T(S)$ in $\mathbb{R}^n$.

27. Let $S$ be the parallelogram determined by the vectors $\mathbf{b}_1 = \begin{bmatrix} -2 \\ 3 \end{bmatrix}$ and $\mathbf{b}_2 = \begin{bmatrix} -2 \\ 5 \end{bmatrix}$, and let $A = \begin{bmatrix} 6 & -3 \\ -3 & 2 \end{bmatrix}$. Compute the area of the image of $S$ under the mapping $\mathbf{x} \mapsto A\mathbf{x}$.

28. Repeat Exercise 27 with $\mathbf{b}_1 = \begin{bmatrix} 4 \\ -7 \end{bmatrix}$, $\mathbf{b}_2 = \begin{bmatrix} 0 \\ 1 \end{bmatrix}$, and $A = \begin{bmatrix} 5 & 2 \\ 1 & 1 \end{bmatrix}$.

29. Find a formula for the area of the triangle whose vertices are $\mathbf{0}$, $\mathbf{v}_1$, and $\mathbf{v}_2$ in $\mathbb{R}^2$.

30. Let $R$ be the triangle with vertices at $(x_1, y_1)$, $(x_2, y_2)$, and $(x_3, y_3)$. Show that

$$\{\text{area of triangle}\} = \frac{1}{2} \det \begin{bmatrix} x_1 & y_1 & 1 \\ x_2 & y_2 & 1 \\ x_3 & y_3 & 1 \end{bmatrix}$$

[*Hint:* Translate $R$ to the origin by subtracting one of the vertices, and use Exercise 29.]

31. Let $T : \mathbb{R}^3 \to \mathbb{R}^3$ be the linear transformation determined by the matrix $A = \begin{bmatrix} a & 0 & 0 \\ 0 & b & 0 \\ 0 & 0 & c \end{bmatrix}$, where $a$, $b$, and $c$ are

positive numbers. Let $S$ be the unit ball, whose bounding surface has the equation $x_1^2 + x_2^2 + x_3^2 = 1$.

a. Show that $T(S)$ is bounded by the ellipsoid with the equation $\dfrac{x_1^2}{a^2} + \dfrac{x_2^2}{b^2} + \dfrac{x_3^2}{c^2} = 1$.

b. Use the fact that the volume of the unit ball is $4\pi/3$ to determine the volume of the region bounded by the ellipsoid in part (a).

32. Let $S$ be the tetrahedron in $\mathbb{R}^3$ with vertices at the vectors $\mathbf{0}$, $\mathbf{e}_1$, $\mathbf{e}_2$, and $\mathbf{e}_3$, and let $S'$ be the tetrahedron with vertices at vectors $\mathbf{0}$, $\mathbf{v}_1$, $\mathbf{v}_2$, and $\mathbf{v}_3$. See the figure.

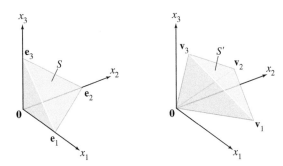

a. Describe a linear transformation that maps $S$ onto $S'$.

b. Find a formula for the volume of the tetrahedron $S'$ using the fact that

$\{\text{volume of } S\} = (1/3) \cdot \{\text{area of base}\} \cdot \{\text{height}\}$

33. [M] Test the inverse formula of Theorem 8 for a random $4 \times 4$ matrix $A$. Use your matrix program to compute the cofactors of the $3 \times 3$ submatrices, construct the adjugate, and set $B = (\text{adj } A)/(\det A)$. Then compute $B - \text{inv}(A)$, where $\text{inv}(A)$ is the inverse of $A$ as computed by the matrix program. Use floating point arithmetic with the maximum possible number of decimal places. Report your results.

34. [M] Test Cramer's rule for a random $4 \times 4$ matrix $A$ and a random $4 \times 1$ vector $\mathbf{b}$. Compute each entry in the solution of $A\mathbf{x} = \mathbf{b}$, and compare these entries with the entries in $A^{-1}\mathbf{b}$. Write the command (or keystrokes) for your matrix program that uses Cramer's rule to produce the second entry of $\mathbf{x}$.

35. [M] If your version of MATLAB has the `flops` command, use it to count the number of floating point operations to compute $A^{-1}$ for a random $30 \times 30$ matrix. Compare this number with the number of flops needed to form $(\text{adj } A)/(\det A)$.

---

SOLUTION TO PRACTICE PROBLEM

The area of $S$ is $\left| \det \begin{bmatrix} 1 & 5 \\ 3 & 1 \end{bmatrix} \right| = 14$, and $\det A = 2$. By Theorem 10, the area of the image of $S$ under the mapping $\mathbf{x} \mapsto A\mathbf{x}$ is

$$|\det A| \cdot \{\text{area of } S\} = 2 \cdot 14 = 28$$

# CHAPTER 4

# Preliminaries

## 4.1 Real Numbers and the Real Line

Calculus depends on properties of the real number system. **Real numbers** are numbers that can be expressed as decimals, for example,

$$5 = 5.00000\ldots$$
$$-\tfrac{3}{4} = -0.750000\ldots$$
$$\tfrac{1}{3} = 0.3333\ldots$$
$$\sqrt{2} = 1.4142\ldots$$
$$\pi = 3.14159\ldots$$

In each case the three dots ($\ldots$) indicate that the sequence of decimal digits goes on forever. For the first three numbers above, the patterns of the digits are obvious; we know what all the subsequent digits are. For $\sqrt{2}$ and $\pi$ there are no obvious patterns.

The real numbers can be represented geometrically as points on a number line, which we call the **real line**, shown in Figure 4.1. The symbol $\mathbb{R}$ is used to denote either the real number system or, equivalently, the real line.

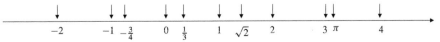

**Figure 4.1**    The real line

The properties of the real number system fall into three categories: algebraic properties, order properties, and completeness. You are already familiar with the *algebraic properties*; roughly speaking, they assert that real numbers can be added, subtracted, multiplied, and divided (except by zero) to produce more real numbers and that the usual rules of arithmetic are valid.

The *order properties* of the real numbers refer to the order in which the numbers appear on the real line. If $x$ lies to the left of $y$, then we say that "$x$ is less than $y$" or "$y$ is greater than $x$." These statements are written symbolically as $x < y$ and $y > x$, respectively. The inequality $x \leq y$ means that either $x < y$ or $x = y$. The order properties of the real numbers are summarized in the following *rules for inequalities*:

---

**Rules for inequalities**

If $a$, $b$, and $c$ are real numbers, then:

1. $a < b \quad\implies\quad a + c < b + c$
2. $a < b \quad\implies\quad a - c < b - c$
3. $a < b$ and $c > 0 \quad\implies\quad ac < bc$
4. $a < b$ and $c < 0 \quad\implies\quad ac > bc$; in particular, $-a > -b$
5. $a > 0 \quad\implies\quad \dfrac{1}{a} > 0$
6. $0 < a < b \quad\implies\quad \dfrac{1}{b} < \dfrac{1}{a}$

Rules 1–4 and 6 (for $a > 0$) also hold if $<$ and $>$ are replaced by $\leq$ and $\geq$.

---

The symbol $\implies$ means "implies."

Note especially the rules for multiplying (or dividing) an inequality by a number. If the number is positive, the inequality is preserved; if the number is negative, the inequality is reversed.

The *completeness* property of the real number system is more subtle and difficult to understand. One way to state it is as follows: if $A$ is any set of real numbers having at least one number in it, and if there exists a real number $y$ with the property that $x \leq y$ for every $x$ in $A$ (such a number $y$ is called an **upper bound** for $A$), then there exists a *smallest* such number, called the **least upper bound** or **supremum** of $A$, and denoted $\sup(A)$. Roughly speaking, this says that there can be no holes or gaps on the real line—every point corresponds to a real number. We will not need to deal much with completeness in our study of calculus. It is typically used to prove certain important results—in particular. (These proofs are given in Appendix III but are not usually included in elementary calculus courses; they are studied in more advanced courses in mathematical analysis.) However, when we study infinite sequences we will make direct use of completeness.

The set of real numbers has some important special subsets:

(i) the **natural numbers** or **positive integers**, namely, the numbers 1, 2, 3, 4, ...

(ii) the **integers**, namely, the numbers 0, $\pm 1$, $\pm 2$, $\pm 3$, ...

(iii) the **rational numbers**, that is, numbers that can be expressed in the form of a fraction $m/n$, where $m$ and $n$ are integers, and $n \neq 0$.

The rational numbers are precisely those real numbers with decimal expansions that are either:

(a) terminating, that is, ending with an infinite string of zeros, for example, $3/4 = 0.750000\ldots$, or

(b) repeating, that is, ending with a string of digits that repeats over and over, for example, $23/11 = 2.090909\ldots = 2.\overline{09}$. (The bar indicates the pattern of repeating digits.)

Real numbers that are not rational are called *irrational numbers*.

**EXAMPLE 1**    Show that each of the numbers   (a)   $1.323232\cdots = 1.\overline{32}$   and   (b)   $0.3405405405\ldots = 0.3\overline{405}$   is a rational number by expressing it as a quotient of two integers.

*Solution*

(a) Let $x = 1.323232\ldots$   Then $x - 1 = 0.323232\ldots$ and

$$100x = 132.323232\ldots = 132 + 0.323232\ldots = 132 + x - 1.$$

Therefore, $99x = 131$ and $x = 131/99$.

(b) Let $y = 0.3405405405\ldots$   Then $10y = 3.405405405\ldots$   and
$10y - 3 = 0.405405405\ldots$   Also,

$$10,000y = 3,405.405405405\ldots = 3,405 + 10y - 3.$$

Therefore, $9,990y = 3,402$ and $y = 3,402/9,990 = 63/185$.

The set of rational numbers possesses all the algebraic and order properties of the real numbers but not the completeness property. There is, for example, no rational number whose square is 2. Hence, there is a "hole" on the "rational line" where $\sqrt{2}$ should be.[1] Because the real line has no such "holes," it is the appropriate setting for studying limits and therefore calculus.

## Intervals

A subset of the real line is called an **interval** if it contains at least two numbers and also contains all real numbers between any two of its elements. For example, the set of real numbers $x$ such that $x > 6$ is an interval, but the set of real numbers $y$ such that $y \neq 0$ is not an interval. (Why?) It consists of two intervals.

If $a$ and $b$ are real numbers and $a < b$, we often refer to

(i) the **open interval** from $a$ to $b$, denoted by $(a, b)$, consisting of all real numbers $x$ satisfying $a < x < b$.

(ii) the **closed interval** from $a$ to $b$, denoted by $[a, b]$, consisting of all real numbers $x$ satisfying $a \leq x \leq b$.

(iii) the **half-open interval** $[a, b)$, consisting of all real numbers $x$ satisfying the inequalities $a \leq x < b$.

(iv) the **half-open interval** $(a, b]$, consisting of all real numbers $x$ satisfying the inequalities $a < x \leq b$.

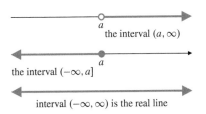

open interval $(a, b)$

closed interval $[a, b]$

half-open interval $[a, b)$

half-open interval $(a, b]$

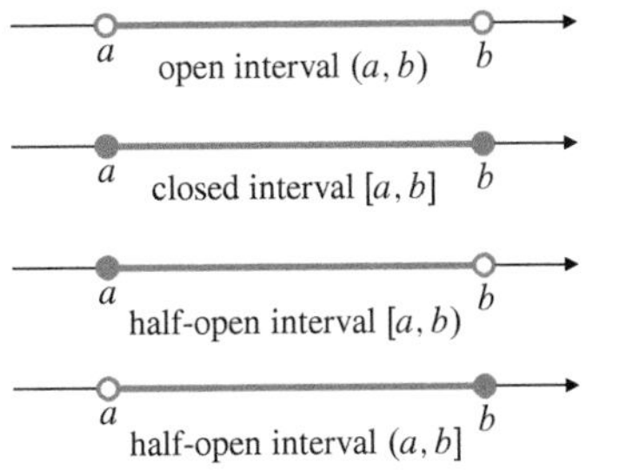

**Figure 4.2**    Finite intervals

These are illustrated in Figure 4.2. Note the use of hollow dots to indicate endpoints of intervals that are not included in the intervals, and solid dots to indicate endpoints that are included. The endpoints of an interval are also called **boundary points**.

The intervals in Figure 4.2 are **finite intervals**; each of them has finite length $b - a$. Intervals can also have infinite length, in which case they are called **infinite intervals**. Figure 4.3 shows some examples of infinite intervals. Note that the whole real line $\mathbb{R}$ is an interval, denoted by $(-\infty, \infty)$. The symbol $\infty$ ("infinity") does *not* denote a real number, so we never allow $\infty$ to belong to an interval.

the interval $(a, \infty)$

the interval $(-\infty, a]$

interval $(-\infty, \infty)$ is the real line

**Figure 4.3**    Infinite intervals

---

[1]   How do we know that $\sqrt{2}$ is an irrational number? Suppose, to the contrary, that $\sqrt{2}$ is rational. Then $\sqrt{2} = m/n$, where $m$ and $n$ are integers and $n \neq 0$. We can assume that the fraction $m/n$ has been "reduced to lowest terms"; any common factors have been cancelled out. Now $m^2/n^2 = 2$, so $m^2 = 2n^2$, which is an even integer. Hence, $m$ must also be even. (The square of an odd integer is always odd.) Since $m$ is even, we can write $m = 2k$, where $k$ is an integer. Thus $4k^2 = 2n^2$ and $n^2 = 2k^2$, which is even. Thus $n$ is also even. This contradicts the assumption that $\sqrt{2}$ could be written as a fraction $m/n$ in lowest terms; $m$ and $n$ cannot both be even. Accordingly, there can be no rational number whose square is 2.

<hr/>

**EXAMPLE 2**    Solve the following inequalities. Express the solution sets in terms of intervals and graph them.

(a)   $2x - 1 > x + 3$          (b)   $-\dfrac{x}{3} \geq 2x - 1$          (c)   $\dfrac{2}{x - 1} \geq 5$

*Solution*

(a)   $2x - 1 > x + 3$          Add 1 to both sides.

$\qquad 2x > x + 4$          Subtract $x$ from both sides.

$\qquad\quad x > 4$          The solution set is the interval $(4, \infty)$.

(b)   $-\dfrac{x}{3} \geq 2x - 1$          Multiply both sides by $-3$.

$\qquad x \leq -6x + 3$          Add $6x$ to both sides.

$\qquad 7x \leq 3$          Divide both sides by 7.

$\qquad\quad x \leq \dfrac{3}{7}$          The solution set is the interval $(-\infty, 3/7]$.

(c)   We transpose the 5 to the left side and simplify to rewrite the given inequality in an equivalent form:

$$\frac{2}{x - 1} - 5 \geq 0 \quad \Longleftrightarrow \quad \frac{2 - 5(x - 1)}{x - 1} \geq 0 \quad \Longleftrightarrow \quad \frac{7 - 5x}{x - 1} \geq 0.$$

The fraction $\dfrac{7 - 5x}{x - 1}$ is undefined at $x = 1$ and is 0 at $x = 7/5$. Between these numbers it is positive if the numerator and denominator have the same sign, and negative if they have opposite sign. It is easiest to organize this sign information in a chart:

| $x$ | | 1 | | 7/5 | |
|---|---|---|---|---|---|
| $7 - 5x$ | $+$ | $+$ | $+$ | $0$ | $-$ |
| $x - 1$ | $-$ | $0$ | $+$ | $+$ | $+$ |
| $(7 - 5x)/(x - 1)$ | $-$ | undef | $+$ | $0$ | $-$ |

Thus the solution set of the given inequality is the interval $(1, 7/5]$.

See Figure 4.4 for graphs of the solutions.

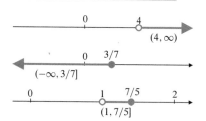

**Figure 4.4**    The intervals for Example 2

<hr/>

Sometimes we will need to solve systems of two or more inequalities that must be satisfied simultaneously. We still solve the inequalities individually and look for numbers in the intersection of the solution sets.

<hr/>

**EXAMPLE 3**    Solve the systems of inequalities:

(a)   $3 \leq 2x + 1 \leq 5$      (b)   $3x - 1 < 5x + 3 \leq 2x + 15$.

*Solution*

(a)   Using the technique of Example 2, we can solve the inequality $3 \leq 2x + 1$ to get $2 \leq 2x$, so $x \geq 1$. Similarly, the inequality $2x + 1 \leq 5$ leads to $2x \leq 4$, so $x \leq 2$. The solution set of system (a) is therefore the closed interval $[1, 2]$.

(b)   We solve both inequalities as follows:

$$\left.\begin{array}{c} 3x - 1 < 5x + 3 \\ -1 - 3 < 5x - 3x \\ -4 < 2x \\ -2 < x \end{array}\right\} \quad \text{and} \quad \left\{\begin{array}{c} 5x + 3 \leq 2x + 15 \\ 5x - 2x \leq 15 - 3 \\ 3x \leq 12 \\ x \leq 4 \end{array}\right.$$

The solution set is the interval $(-2, 4]$.

Solving quadratic inequalities depends on solving the corresponding quadratic equations.

___

**EXAMPLE 4**    **Quadratic inequalities**
Solve:    (a)   $x^2 - 5x + 6 < 0$    (b)   $2x^2 + 1 > 4x$.

*Solution*

(a) The trinomial $x^2 - 5x + 6$ factors into the product $(x - 2)(x - 3)$, which is negative if and only if exactly one of the factors is negative. Since $x - 3 < x - 2$, this happens when $x - 3 < 0$ and $x - 2 > 0$. Thus we need $x < 3$ and $x > 2$; the solution set is the open interval $(2, 3)$.

(b) The inequality $2x^2 + 1 > 4x$ is equivalent to $2x^2 - 4x + 1 > 0$. The corresponding quadratic equation $2x^2 - 4x + 1 = 0$, which is of the form $Ax^2 + Bx + C = 0$, can be solved by the quadratic formula:

$$x = \frac{-B \pm \sqrt{B^2 - 4AC}}{2A} = \frac{4 \pm \sqrt{16 - 8}}{4} = 1 \pm \frac{\sqrt{2}}{2},$$

so the given inequality can be expressed in the form

$$\left(x - 1 + \tfrac{1}{2}\sqrt{2}\right)\left(x - 1 - \tfrac{1}{2}\sqrt{2}\right) > 0.$$

This is satisfied if both factors on the left side are positive or if both are negative. Therefore, we require that either $x < 1 - \tfrac{1}{2}\sqrt{2}$ or $x > 1 + \tfrac{1}{2}\sqrt{2}$. The solution set is the *union* of intervals $\left(-\infty, 1 - \tfrac{1}{2}\sqrt{2}\right) \cup \left(1 + \tfrac{1}{2}\sqrt{2}, \infty\right)$.

___

Note the use of the symbol $\cup$ to denote the **union** of intervals. A real number is in the union of intervals if it is in at least one of the intervals. We will also need to consider the **intersection** of intervals from time to time. A real number belongs to the intersection of intervals if it belongs to *every one* of the intervals. We will use $\cap$ to denote intersection. For example,

$$[1, 3) \cap [2, 4] = [2, 3) \quad \text{while} \quad [1, 3) \cup [2, 4] = [1, 4].$$

___

**EXAMPLE 5**    Solve the inequality $\dfrac{3}{x - 1} < -\dfrac{2}{x}$ and graph the solution set.

*Solution*    We would like to multiply by $x(x - 1)$ to clear the inequality of fractions, but this would require considering three cases separately. (What are they?) Instead, we will transpose and combine the two fractions into a single one:

$$\frac{3}{x - 1} < -\frac{2}{x} \quad \Longleftrightarrow \quad \frac{3}{x - 1} + \frac{2}{x} < 0 \quad \Longleftrightarrow \quad \frac{5x - 2}{x(x - 1)} < 0.$$

We examine the signs of the three factors in the left fraction to determine where that fraction is negative:

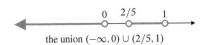

the union $(-\infty, 0) \cup (2/5, 1)$

**Figure 4.5**    The solution set for Example 5

| $x$ | | 0 | | 2/5 | | 1 | |
|---|---|---|---|---|---|---|---|
| $5x - 2$ | $-$ | $-$ | $-$ | 0 | $+$ | $+$ | $+$ |
| $x$ | $-$ | 0 | $+$ | $+$ | $+$ | $+$ | $+$ |
| $x - 1$ | $-$ | $-$ | $-$ | $-$ | $-$ | 0 | $+$ |
| $\dfrac{5x - 2}{x(x - 1)}$ | $-$ | undef | $+$ | 0 | $-$ | undef | $+$ |

The solution set of the given inequality is the union of these two intervals, namely, $(-\infty, 0) \cup (2/5, 1)$. See Figure 4.5.

## The Absolute Value

The **absolute value**, or **magnitude**, of a number $x$, denoted $|x|$ (read "the absolute value of $x$"), is defined by the formula

$$|x| = \begin{cases} x & \text{if } x \geq 0 \\ -x & \text{if } x < 0 \end{cases}$$

The vertical lines in the symbol $|x|$ are called **absolute value bars**.

| EXAMPLE 6 | $|3| = 3, \quad |0| = 0, \quad |-5| = 5.$ |
|---|---|

Note that $|x| \geq 0$ for every real number $x$, and $|x| = 0$ only if $x = 0$. People sometimes find it confusing to say that $|x| = -x$ when $x$ is negative, but this is correct since $-x$ is positive in that case. The symbol $\sqrt{a}$ always denotes the *nonnegative* square root of $a$, so an alternative definition of $|x|$ is $|x| = \sqrt{x^2}$.

Geometrically, $|x|$ represents the (nonnegative) distance from $x$ to 0 on the real line. More generally, $|x - y|$ represents the (nonnegative) distance between the points $x$ and $y$ on the real line, since this distance is the same as that from the point $x - y$ to 0 (see Figure 4.6):

$$|x - y| = \begin{cases} x - y, & \text{if } x \geq y \\ y - x, & \text{if } x < y. \end{cases}$$

> It is important to remember that $\sqrt{a^2} = |a|$. Do not write $\sqrt{a^2} = a$ unless you already know that $a \geq 0$.

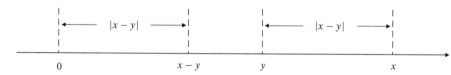

**Figure 4.6**
$|x - y|$ = distance from $x$ to $y$

The absolute value function has the following properties:

> **Properties of absolute values**
>
> 1. $|-a| = |a|$. A number and its negative have the same absolute value.
> 2. $|ab| = |a||b|$ and $\left|\dfrac{a}{b}\right| = \dfrac{|a|}{|b|}$. The absolute value of a product (or quotient) of two numbers is the product (or quotient) of their absolute values.
> 3. $|a \pm b| \leq |a| + |b|$ (the **triangle inequality**). The absolute value of a sum of or difference between numbers is less than or equal to the sum of their absolute values.

The first two of these properties can be checked by considering the cases where either of $a$ or $b$ is either positive or negative. The third property follows from the first two because $\pm 2ab \leq |2ab| = 2|a||b|$. Therefore, we have

$$|a \pm b|^2 = (a \pm b)^2 = a^2 \pm 2ab + b^2$$
$$\leq |a|^2 + 2|a||b| + |b|^2 = (|a| + |b|)^2,$$

and taking the (positive) square roots of both sides, we obtain $|a \pm b| \leq |a| + |b|$. This result is called the "triangle inequality" because it follows from the geometric fact that the length of any side of a triangle cannot exceed the sum of the lengths of the other two sides. For instance, if we regard the points 0, $a$, and $b$ on the number line as the vertices of a degenerate "triangle," then the sides of the triangle have lengths $|a|$, $|b|$, and $|a - b|$. The triangle is degenerate since all three of its vertices lie on a straight line.

## Equations and Inequalities Involving Absolute Values

The equation $|x| = D$ (where $D > 0$) has two solutions, $x = D$ and $x = -D$: the two points on the real line that lie at distance $D$ from the origin. Equations and inequalities involving absolute values can be solved algebraically by breaking them into cases according to the definition of absolute value, but often they can also be solved geometrically by interpreting absolute values as distances. For example, the inequality $|x - a| < D$ says that the distance from $x$ to $a$ is less than $D$, so $x$ must lie between $a - D$ and $a + D$. (Or, equivalently, $a$ must lie between $x - D$ and $x + D$.) If $D$ is a positive number, then

$$
\begin{aligned}
|x| = D &\iff \text{either } x = -D \text{ or } x = D \\
|x| < D &\iff -D < x < D \\
|x| \leq D &\iff -D \leq x \leq D \\
|x| > D &\iff \text{either } x < -D \text{ or } x > D
\end{aligned}
$$

More generally,

$$
\begin{aligned}
|x - a| = D &\iff \text{either } x = a - D \text{ or } x = a + D \\
|x - a| < D &\iff a - D < x < a + D \\
|x - a| \leq D &\iff a - D \leq x \leq a + D \\
|x - a| > D &\iff \text{either } x < a - D \text{ or } x > a + D
\end{aligned}
$$

**EXAMPLE 7**    Solve:    (a)  $|2x + 5| = 3$    (b)  $|3x - 2| \leq 1$.

**Solution**

(a) $|2x + 5| = 3 \iff 2x + 5 = \pm 3$. Thus, either $2x = -3 - 5 = -8$ or $2x = 3 - 5 = -2$. The solutions are $x = -4$ and $x = -1$.

(b) $|3x - 2| \leq 1 \iff -1 \leq 3x - 2 \leq 1$. We solve this pair of inequalities:

$$
\left\{
\begin{aligned}
-1 &\leq 3x - 2 \\
-1 + 2 &\leq 3x \\
1/3 &\leq x
\end{aligned}
\right\}
\quad \text{and} \quad
\left\{
\begin{aligned}
3x - 2 &\leq 1 \\
3x &\leq 1 + 2 \\
x &\leq 1
\end{aligned}
\right\}.
$$

Thus the solutions lie in the interval $[1/3, 1]$.

**Remark**    Here is how part (b) of Example 7 could have been solved geometrically, by interpreting the absolute value as a distance:

$$
|3x - 2| = \left| 3 \left( x - \frac{2}{3} \right) \right| = 3 \left| x - \frac{2}{3} \right|.
$$

Thus, the given inequality says that

$$
3 \left| x - \frac{2}{3} \right| \leq 1 \quad \text{or} \quad \left| x - \frac{2}{3} \right| \leq \frac{1}{3}.
$$

This says that the distance from $x$ to $2/3$ does not exceed $1/3$. The solutions for $x$ therefore lie between $1/3$ and $1$, including both of these endpoints. (See Figure 4.7.)

**Figure 4.7**    The solution set for Example 7(b)

EXAMPLE 8    Solve the equation $|x + 1| = |x - 3|$.

*Solution*    The equation says that $x$ is equidistant from $-1$ and $3$. Therefore, $x$ is the point halfway between $-1$ and $3$; $x = (-1 + 3)/2 = 1$. Alternatively, the given equation says that either $x + 1 = x - 3$ or $x + 1 = -(x - 3)$. The first of these equations has no solutions; the second has the solution $x = 1$.

EXAMPLE 9    What values of $x$ satisfy the inequality $\left|5 - \dfrac{2}{x}\right| < 3$?

*Solution*    We have

$$\left|5 - \frac{2}{x}\right| < 3 \quad \Longleftrightarrow \quad -3 < 5 - \frac{2}{x} < 3 \qquad \text{Subtract 5 from each member.}$$

$$-8 < -\frac{2}{x} < -2 \qquad \text{Divide each member by } -2.$$

$$4 > \frac{1}{x} > 1 \qquad \text{Take reciprocals.}$$

$$\frac{1}{4} < x < 1.$$

In this calculation we manipulated a system of two inequalities simultaneously, rather than split it up into separate inequalities as we have done in previous examples. Note how the various rules for inequalities were used here. Multiplying an inequality by a negative number reverses the inequality. So does taking reciprocals of an inequality in which both sides are positive. The given inequality holds for all $x$ in the open interval $(1/4, 1)$.

## EXERCISES 4.1

In Exercises 1–2, express the given rational number as a repeating decimal. Use a bar to indicate the repeating digits.

**1.** $\dfrac{2}{9}$

**2.** $\dfrac{1}{11}$

In Exercises 3–4, express the given repeating decimal as a quotient of integers in lowest terms.

**3.** $0.\overline{12}$

**4.** $3.2\overline{7}$

**5.** Express the rational numbers $1/7$, $2/7$, $3/7$, and $4/7$ as repeating decimals. (Use a calculator to give as many decimal digits as possible.) Do you see a pattern? Guess the decimal expansions of $5/7$ and $6/7$ and check your guesses.

**6.** Can two different decimals represent the same number? What number is represented by $0.999\ldots = 0.\overline{9}$?

In Exercises 7–12, express the set of all real numbers $x$ satisfying the given conditions as an interval or a union of intervals.

**7.** $x \geq 0$  and  $x \leq 5$

**8.** $x < 2$  and  $x \geq -3$

**9.** $x > -5$  or  $x < -6$

**10.** $x \leq -1$

**11.** $x > -2$

**12.** $x < 4$  or  $x \geq 2$

In Exercises 13–26, solve the given inequality, giving the solution set as an interval or union of intervals.

**13.** $-2x > 4$

**14.** $3x + 5 \leq 8$

**15.** $5x - 3 \leq 7 - 3x$

**16.** $\dfrac{6 - x}{4} \geq \dfrac{3x - 4}{2}$

**17.** $3(2 - x) < 2(3 + x)$

**18.** $x^2 < 9$

**19.** $\dfrac{1}{2 - x} < 3$

**20.** $\dfrac{x + 1}{x} \geq 2$

**21.** $x^2 - 2x \leq 0$

**22.** $6x^2 - 5x \leq -1$

**23.** $x^3 > 4x$

**24.** $x^2 - x \leq 2$

**25.** $\dfrac{x}{2} \geq 1 + \dfrac{4}{x}$

**26.** $\dfrac{3}{x - 1} < \dfrac{2}{x + 1}$

Solve the equations in Exercises 27–32.

**27.** $|x| = 3$

**28.** $|x - 3| = 7$

**29.** $|2t + 5| = 4$

**30.** $|1 - t| = 1$

**31.** $|8 - 3s| = 9$

**32.** $\left|\dfrac{s}{2} - 1\right| = 1$

In Exercises 33–40, write the interval defined by the given inequality.

**33.** $|x| < 2$

**34.** $|x| \leq 2$

**35.** $|s - 1| \leq 2$

**36.** $|t + 2| < 1$

**37.** $|3x - 7| < 2$    **38.** $|2x + 5| < 1$

**39.** $\left|\dfrac{x}{2} - 1\right| \le 1$    **40.** $\left|2 - \dfrac{x}{2}\right| < \dfrac{1}{2}$

In Exercises 41–42, solve the given inequality by interpreting it as a statement about distances on the real line.

**41.** $|x + 1| > |x - 3|$    **42.** $|x - 3| < 2|x|$

**❷ 43.** Do not fall into the trap $|-a| = a$. For what real numbers $a$ is

this equation true? For what numbers is it false?

**44.** Solve the equation $|x - 1| = 1 - x$.

**❷ 45.** Show that the inequality

$$|a - b| \ge \Big||a| - |b|\Big|$$

holds for all real numbers $a$ and $b$.

## 4.2  Cartesian Coordinates in the Plane

The positions of all points in a plane can be measured with respect to two perpendicular real lines in the plane intersecting at the 0-point of each. These lines are called **coordinate axes** in the plane. Usually (but not always) we call one of these axes the $x$-axis and draw it horizontally with numbers $x$ on it increasing to the right; then we call the other the $y$-axis, and draw it vertically with numbers $y$ on it increasing upward. The point of intersection of the coordinate axes (the point where $x$ and $y$ are both zero) is called the **origin** and is often denoted by the letter $O$.

If $P$ is any point in the plane, we can draw a line through $P$ perpendicular to the $x$-axis. If $a$ is the value of $x$ where that line intersects the $x$-axis, we call $a$ the **$x$-coordinate** of $P$. Similarly, the **$y$-coordinate** of $P$ is the value of $y$ where a line through $P$ perpendicular to the $y$-axis meets the $y$-axis. The **ordered pair** $(a, b)$ is called the **coordinate pair**, or the **Cartesian coordinates**, of the point $P$. We refer to the point as $P(a, b)$ to indicate both the name $P$ of the point and its coordinates $(a, b)$. (See Figure 4.8.) Note that the $x$-coordinate appears first in a coordinate pair. Coordinate pairs are in one-to-one correspondence with points in the plane; each point has a unique coordinate pair, and each coordinate pair determines a unique point. We call such a set of coordinate axes and the coordinate pairs they determine a **Cartesian coordinate system** in the plane, after the seventeenth-century philosopher René Descartes, who created analytic (coordinate) geometry. When equipped with such a coordinate system, a plane is called a **Cartesian plane**. Note that we are using the same notation $(a, b)$ for the Cartesian coordinates of a point in the plane as we use for an open interval on the real line. However, this should not cause any confusion because the intended meaning will be clear from the context.

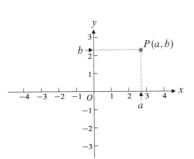

**Figure 4.8**    The coordinate axes and the point $P$ with coordinates $(a, b)$

Figure 4.9 shows the coordinates of some points in the plane. Note that all points on the $x$-axis have $y$-coordinate 0. We usually just write the $x$-coordinates to label such points. Similarly, points on the $y$-axis have $x = 0$, and we can label such points using their $y$-coordinates only.

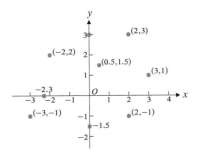

**Figure 4.9**    Some points with their coordinates

The coordinate axes divide the plane into four regions called **quadrants**. These quadrants are numbered I to IV, as shown in Figure 4.10. The **first quadrant** is the upper right one; both coordinates of any point in that quadrant are positive numbers. Both coordinates are negative in quadrant III; only $y$ is positive in quadrant II; only $x$ is positive in quadrant IV.

### Axis Scales

When we plot data in the coordinate plane or graph formulas whose variables have different units of measure, we do not need to use the same scale on the two axes. If, for example, we plot height versus time for a falling rock, there is no reason to place the mark that shows 1 m on the height axis the same distance from the origin as the mark that shows 1 s on the time axis.

When we graph functions whose variables do not represent physical measurements and when we draw figures in the coordinate plane to study their geometry or

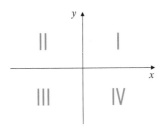

**Figure 4.10**    The four quadrants

trigonometry, we usually make the scales identical. A vertical unit of distance then looks the same as a horizontal unit. As on a surveyor's map or a scale drawing, line segments that are supposed to have the same length will look as if they do, and angles that are supposed to be equal will look equal. Some of the geometric results we obtain later, such as the relationship between the slopes of perpendicular lines, are valid only if equal scales are used on the two axes.

Computer and calculator displays are another matter. The vertical and horizontal scales on machine-generated graphs usually differ, with resulting distortions in distances, slopes, and angles. Circles may appear elliptical, and squares may appear rectangular or even as parallelograms. Right angles may appear as acute or obtuse. Circumstances like these require us to take extra care in interpreting what we see. High-quality computer software for drawing Cartesian graphs usually allows the user to compensate for such scale problems by adjusting the *aspect ratio* (the ratio of vertical to horizontal scale). Some computer screens also allow adjustment within a narrow range. When using graphing software, try to adjust your particular software/hardware configuration so that the horizontal and vertical diameters of a drawn circle appear to be equal.

## Increments and Distances

When a particle moves from one point to another, the net changes in its coordinates are called increments. They are calculated by subtracting the coordinates of the starting point from the coordinates of the ending point. An **increment** in a variable is the net change in the value of the variable. If $x$ changes from $x_1$ to $x_2$, then the increment in $x$ is $\Delta x = x_2 - x_1$. (Here $\Delta$ is the upper case Greek letter delta.)

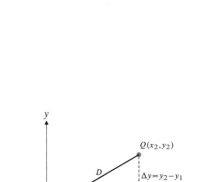

**Figure 4.11**    Increments in $x$ and $y$

**EXAMPLE 1**    Find the increments in the coordinates of a particle that moves from $A(3, -3)$ to $B(-1, 2)$.

*Solution*    The increments (see Figure 4.11) are:

$$\Delta x = -1 - 3 = -4 \quad \text{and} \quad \Delta y = 2 - (-3) = 5.$$

If $P(x_1, y_1)$ and $Q(x_2, y_2)$ are two points in the plane, the straight line segment $PQ$ is the hypotenuse of a right triangle $PCQ$, as shown in Figure 4.12. The sides $PC$ and $CQ$ of the triangle have lengths

$$|\Delta x| = |x_2 - x_1| \quad \text{and} \quad |\Delta y| = |y_2 - y_1|.$$

These are the *horizontal distance* and *vertical distance* between $P$ and $Q$. By the Pythagorean Theorem, the length of $PQ$ is the square root of the sum of the squares of these lengths.

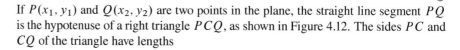

**Figure 4.12**    The distance from $P$ to $Q$ is $D = \sqrt{(x_2 - x_1)^2 + (y_2 - y_1)^2}$

**Distance formula for points in the plane**

The distance $D$ between $P(x_1, y_1)$ and $Q(x_2, y_2)$ is

$$D = \sqrt{(\Delta x)^2 + (\Delta y)^2} = \sqrt{(x_2 - x_1)^2 + (y_2 - y_1)^2}.$$

**EXAMPLE 2**    The distance between $A(3, -3)$ and $B(-1, 2)$ in Figure 4.11 is

$$\sqrt{(-1 - 3)^2 + (2 - (-3))^2} = \sqrt{(-4)^2 + 5^2} = \sqrt{41} \text{ units.}$$

**EXAMPLE 3**    The distance from the origin $O(0,0)$ to a point $P(x, y)$ is

$$\sqrt{(x-0)^2 + (y-0)^2} = \sqrt{x^2 + y^2}.$$

## Graphs

The **graph** of an equation (or inequality) involving the variables $x$ and $y$ is the set of all points $P(x, y)$ whose coordinates satisfy the equation (or inequality).

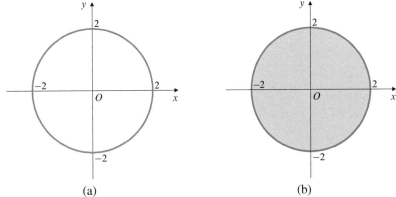

**Figure 4.13**

(a) The circle $x^2 + y^2 = 4$

(b) The disk $x^2 + y^2 \le 4$

(a)    (b)

**EXAMPLE 4**    The equation $x^2 + y^2 = 4$ represents all points $P(x, y)$ whose distance from the origin is $\sqrt{x^2 + y^2} = \sqrt{4} = 2$. These points lie on the **circle** of radius 2 centred at the origin. This circle is the graph of the equation $x^2 + y^2 = 4$. (See Figure 4.13(a).)

**EXAMPLE 5**    Points $(x, y)$ whose coordinates satisfy the inequality $x^2 + y^2 \le 4$ all have distance $\le 2$ from the origin. The graph of the inequality is therefore the disk of radius 2 centred at the origin. (See Figure 4.13(b).)

**EXAMPLE 6**    Consider the equation $y = x^2$. Some points whose coordinates satisfy this equation are $(0, 0)$, $(1, 1)$, $(-1, 1)$, $(2, 4)$, and $(-2, 4)$. These points (and all others satisfying the equation) lie on a smooth curve called a **parabola**. (See Figure 4.14.)

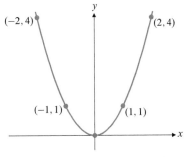

**Figure 4.14**    The parabola $y = x^2$

## Straight Lines

Given two points $P_1(x_1, y_1)$ and $P_2(x_2, y_2)$ in the plane, we call the increments $\Delta x = x_2 - x_1$ and $\Delta y = y_2 - y_1$, respectively, the **run** and the **rise** between $P_1$ and $P_2$. Two such points always determine a unique **straight line** (usually called simply a **line**) passing through them both. We call the line $P_1 P_2$.

Any nonvertical line in the plane has the property that the ratio

$$m = \frac{\text{rise}}{\text{run}} = \frac{\Delta y}{\Delta x} = \frac{y_2 - y_1}{x_2 - x_1}$$

has the *same value* for every choice of two distinct points $P_1(x_1, y_1)$ and $P_2(x_2, y_2)$ on the line. (See Figure 4.15.) The constant $m = \Delta y/\Delta x$ is called the **slope** of the nonvertical line.

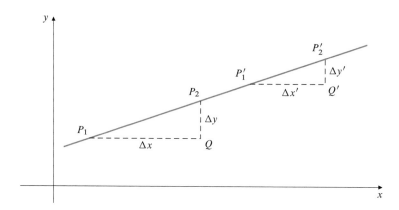

**Figure 4.15** $\Delta y/\Delta x = \Delta y'/\Delta x'$ because triangles $P_1QP_2$ and $P_1'Q'P_2'$ are similar

**EXAMPLE 7** The slope of the line joining $A\,(3,-3)$ and $B\,(-1,2)$ is

$$m = \frac{\Delta y}{\Delta x} = \frac{2-(-3)}{-1-3} = \frac{5}{-4} = -\frac{5}{4}.$$

The slope tells us the direction and steepness of a line. A line with positive slope rises uphill to the right; one with negative slope falls downhill to the right. The greater the absolute value of the slope, the steeper the rise or fall. Since the run $\Delta x$ is zero for a vertical line, we cannot form the ratio $m$; the slope of a vertical line is *undefined*.

The direction of a line can also be measured by an angle. The **inclination** of a line is the smallest counterclockwise angle from the positive direction of the $x$-axis to the line. In Figure 4.16 the angle $\phi$ (the Greek letter "phi") is the inclination of the line $L$. The inclination $\phi$ of any line satisfies $0° \le \phi < 180°$. The inclination of a horizontal line is $0°$ and that of a vertical line is $90°$.

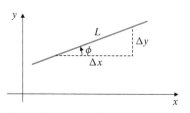

**Figure 4.16** Line $L$ has inclination $\phi$

Provided equal scales are used on the coordinate axes, the relationship between the slope $m$ of a nonvertical line and its inclination $\phi$ is shown in Figure 4.16:

$$m = \frac{\Delta y}{\Delta x} = \tan\phi.$$

Parallel lines have the same inclination. If they are not vertical, they must therefore have the same slope. Conversely, lines with equal slopes have the same inclination and so are parallel.

If two nonvertical lines, $L_1$ and $L_2$, are perpendicular, their slopes $m_1$ and $m_2$ satisfy $m_1 m_2 = -1$, so each slope is the *negative reciprocal* of the other:

$$m_1 = -\frac{1}{m_2} \qquad \text{and} \qquad m_2 = -\frac{1}{m_1}.$$

(This result also assumes equal scales on the two coordinate axes.) To see this, observe in Figure 4.17 that

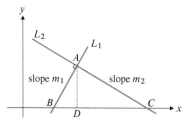

**Figure 4.17** $\triangle ABD$ is similar to $\triangle CAD$

$$m_1 = \frac{AD}{BD} \qquad \text{and} \qquad m_2 = -\frac{AD}{DC}.$$

Since $\triangle ABD$ is similar to $\triangle CAD$, we have $\dfrac{AD}{BD} = \dfrac{DC}{AD}$, and so

$$m_1 m_2 = \left(\frac{DC}{AD}\right)\left(-\frac{AD}{DC}\right) = -1.$$

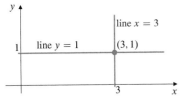

**Figure 4.18**   The lines $y = 1$ and $x = 3$

## Equations of Lines

Straight lines are particularly simple graphs, and their corresponding equations are also simple. All points on the vertical line through the point $a$ on the $x$-axis have their $x$-coordinates equal to $a$. Thus $x = a$ is the equation of the line. Similarly, $y = b$ is the equation of the horizontal line meeting the $y$-axis at $b$.

---

**EXAMPLE 8**   The horizontal and vertical lines passing through the point $(3, 1)$ (Figure 4.18) have equations $y = 1$ and $x = 3$, respectively.

---

To write an equation for a nonvertical straight line $L$, it is enough to know its slope $m$ and the coordinates of one point $P_1(x_1, y_1)$ on it. If $P(x, y)$ is any other point on $L$, then

$$\frac{y - y_1}{x - x_1} = m,$$

so that

$$y - y_1 = m(x - x_1) \qquad \text{or} \qquad y = m(x - x_1) + y_1.$$

The equation

$$y = m(x - x_1) + y_1$$

is the **point-slope equation** of the line that passes through the point $(x_1, y_1)$ and has slope $m$.

---

**EXAMPLE 9**   Find an equation of the line that has slope $-2$ and passes through the point $(1, 4)$ .

**Solution**   We substitute $x_1 = 1$, $y_1 = 4$, and $m = -2$ into the point-slope form of the equation and obtain

$$y = -2(x - 1) + 4 \qquad \text{or} \qquad y = -2x + 6.$$

---

**EXAMPLE 10**   Find an equation of the line through the points $(1, -1)$ and $(3, 5)$.

**Solution**   The slope of the line is $m = \dfrac{5 - (-1)}{3 - 1} = 3$. We can use this slope with either of the two points to write an equation of the line. If we use $(1, -1)$ we get

$$y = 3(x - 1) - 1, \qquad \text{which simplifies to} \quad y = 3x - 4.$$

If we use $(3, 5)$ we get

$$y = 3(x - 3) + 5, \qquad \text{which also simplifies to} \quad y = 3x - 4.$$

Either way, $y = 3x - 4$ is an equation of the line.

---

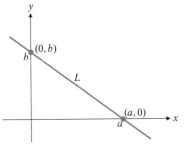

**Figure 4.19**   Line $L$ has $x$-intercept $a$ and $y$-intercept $b$

The $y$-coordinate of the point where a nonvertical line intersects the $y$-axis is called the **$y$-intercept** of the line. (See Figure 4.19.) Similarly, the **$x$-intercept** of a non-horizontal line is the $x$-coordinate of the point where it crosses the $x$-axis. A line with slope $m$ and $y$-intercept $b$ passes through the point $(0, b)$, so its equation is

$$y = m(x - 0) + b \qquad \text{or, more simply,} \quad y = mx + b.$$

A line with slope $m$ and $x$-intercept $a$ passes through $(a, 0)$, and so its equation is

$$y = m(x - a).$$

---

The equation $y = mx + b$ is called the **slope–$y$-intercept equation** of the line with slope $m$ and $y$-intercept $b$.

The equation $y = m(x - a)$ is called the **slope–$x$-intercept equation** of the line with slope $m$ and $x$-intercept $a$.

---

**EXAMPLE 11**    Find the slope and the two intercepts of the line with equation $8x + 5y = 20$.

*Solution*    Solving the equation for $y$ we get

$$y = \frac{20 - 8x}{5} = -\frac{8}{5}x + 4.$$

Comparing this with the general form $y = mx + b$ of the slope–$y$-intercept equation, we see that the slope of the line is $m = -8/5$, and the $y$-intercept is $b = 4$. To find the $x$-intercept, put $y = 0$ and solve for $x$, obtaining $8x = 20$, or $x = 5/2$. The $x$-intercept is $a = 5/2$.

---

The equation $Ax + By = C$ (where $A$ and $B$ are not both zero) is called the **general linear equation** in $x$ and $y$ because its graph always represents a straight line, and every line has an equation in this form.

Many important quantities are related by linear equations. Once we know that a relationship between two variables is linear, we can find it from any two pairs of corresponding values, just as we find the equation of a line from the coordinates of two points.

---

**EXAMPLE 12**    The relationship between Fahrenheit temperature ($F$) and Celsius temperature ($C$) is given by a linear equation of the form $F = mC + b$. The freezing point of water is $F = 32°$ or $C = 0°$, while the boiling point is $F = 212°$ or $C = 100°$. Thus,

$$32 = 0m + b \quad \text{and} \quad 212 = 100m + b,$$

so $b = 32$ and $m = (212 - 32)/100 = 9/5$. The relationship is given by the linear equation

$$F = \frac{9}{5}C + 32 \quad \text{or} \quad C = \frac{5}{9}(F - 32).$$

---

## EXERCISES 4.2

In Exercises 1–4, a particle moves from $A$ to $B$. Find the net increments $\Delta x$ and $\Delta y$ in the particle's coordinates. Also find the distance from $A$ to $B$.

**1.** $A(0, 3)$, $B(4, 0)$

**2.** $A(-1, 2)$, $B(4, -10)$

**3.** $A(3, 2)$, $B(-1, -2)$

**4.** $A(0.5, 3)$, $B(2, 3)$

**5.** A particle starts at $A(-2, 3)$ and its coordinates change by $\Delta x = 4$ and $\Delta y = -7$. Find its new position.

**6.** A particle arrives at the point $(-2, -2)$ after its coordinates experience increments $\Delta x = -5$ and $\Delta y = 1$. From where did it start?

Describe the graphs of the equations and inequalities in Exercises 7–12.

**7.** $x^2 + y^2 = 1$

**8.** $x^2 + y^2 = 2$

**9.** $x^2 + y^2 \leq 1$

**10.** $x^2 + y^2 = 0$

**11.** $y \geq x^2$

**12.** $y < x^2$

In Exercises 13–14, find an equation for (a) the vertical line and (b) the horizontal line through the given point.

**13.** $(-2, 5/3)$    **14.** $(\sqrt{2}, -1.3)$

In Exercises 15–18, write an equation for the line through $P$ with slope $m$.

**15.** $P(-1, 1), \quad m = 1$    **16.** $P(-2, 2), \quad m = 1/2$

**17.** $P(0, b), \quad m = 2$    **18.** $P(a, 0), \quad m = -2$

In Exercises 19–20, does the given point $P$ lie on, above, or below the given line?

**19.** $P(2, 1), \quad 2x + 3y = 6$    **20.** $P(3, -1), \quad x - 4y = 7$

In Exercises 21–24, write an equation for the line through the two points.

**21.** $(0, 0), \quad (2, 3)$    **22.** $(-2, 1), \quad (2, -2)$

**23.** $(4, 1), \quad (-2, 3)$    **24.** $(-2, 0), \quad (0, 2)$

In Exercises 25–26, write an equation for the line with slope $m$ and $y$-intercept $b$.

**25.** $m = -2, \quad b = \sqrt{2}$    **26.** $m = -1/2, \quad b = -3$

In Exercises 27–30, determine the $x$- and $y$-intercepts and the slope of the given lines, and sketch their graphs.

**27.** $3x + 4y = 12$    **28.** $x + 2y = -4$

**29.** $\sqrt{2}x - \sqrt{3}y = 2$    **30.** $1.5x - 2y = -3$

In Exercises 31–32, find equations for the lines through $P$ that are (a) parallel to and (b) perpendicular to the given line.

**31.** $P(2, 1), \quad y = x + 2$    **32.** $P(-2, 2), \quad 2x + y = 4$

**33.** Find the point of intersection of the lines $3x + 4y = -6$ and $2x - 3y = 13$.

**34.** Find the point of intersection of the lines $2x + y = 8$ and $5x - 7y = 1$.

**35.** **(Two-intercept equations)** If a line is neither horizontal nor vertical and does not pass through the origin, show that its equation can be written in the form $\dfrac{x}{a} + \dfrac{y}{b} = 1$, where $a$ is its $x$-intercept and $b$ is its $y$-intercept.

**36.** Determine the intercepts and sketch the graph of the line $\dfrac{x}{2} - \dfrac{y}{3} = 1$.

**37.** Find the $y$-intercept of the line through the points $(2, 1)$ and $(3, -1)$.

**38.** A line passes through $(-2, 5)$ and $(k, 1)$ and has $x$-intercept 3. Find $k$.

**39.** The cost of printing $x$ copies of a pamphlet is $\$C$, where $C = Ax + B$ for certain constants $A$ and $B$. If it costs $\$5{,}000$ to print 10,000 copies and $\$6{,}000$ to print 15,000 copies, how much will it cost to print 100,000 copies?

**40.** **(Fahrenheit versus Celsius)** In the $FC$-plane, sketch the graph of the equation $C = \dfrac{5}{9}(F - 32)$ linking Fahrenheit and Celsius temperatures found in Example 12. On the same graph sketch the line with equation $C = F$. Is there a temperature at which a Celsius thermometer gives the same numerical reading as a Fahrenheit thermometer? If so, find that temperature.

**Geometry**

**41.** By calculating the lengths of its three sides, show that the triangle with vertices at the points $A(2, 1)$, $B(6, 4)$, and $C(5, -3)$ is isosceles.

**42.** Show that the triangle with vertices $A(0, 0)$, $B(1, \sqrt{3})$, and $C(2, 0)$ is equilateral.

**43.** Show that the points $A(2, -1)$, $B(1, 3)$, and $C(-3, 2)$ are three vertices of a square and find the fourth vertex.

**44.** Find the coordinates of the midpoint on the line segment $P_1 P_2$ joining the points $P_1(x_1, y_1)$ and $P_2(x_2, y_2)$.

**45.** Find the coordinates of the point of the line segment joining the points $P_1(x_1, y_1)$ and $P_2(x_2, y_2)$ that is two-thirds of the way from $P_1$ to $P_2$.

**46.** The point $P$ lies on the $x$-axis and the point $Q$ lies on the line $y = -2x$. The point $(2, 1)$ is the midpoint of $PQ$. Find the coordinates of $P$.

In Exercises 47–48, interpret the equation as a statement about distances, and hence determine the graph of the equation.

**47.** $\sqrt{(x - 2)^2 + y^2} = 4$

**48.** $\sqrt{(x - 2)^2 + y^2} = \sqrt{x^2 + (y - 2)^2}$

**49.** For what value of $k$ is the line $2x + ky = 3$ perpendicular to the line $4x + y = 1$? For what value of $k$ are the lines parallel?

**50.** Find the line that passes through the point $(1, 2)$ and through the point of intersection of the two lines $x + 2y = 3$ and $2x - 3y = -1$.

# Differentiation

## Introduction

Two fundamental problems are considered in calculus. The **problem of slopes** is concerned with finding the slope of (the tangent line to) a given curve at a given point on the curve. The **problem of areas** is concerned with finding the area of a plane region bounded by curves and straight lines. The solution of the problem of slopes is the subject of **differential calculus**. As we will see, it has many applications in mathematics and other disciplines. The problem of areas is the subject of **integral calculus**, which we begin in Chapter 8.

## 5.1 Tangent Lines and Their Slopes

This section deals with the problem of finding a straight line $L$ that is tangent to a curve $C$ at a point $P$. As is often the case in mathematics, the most important step in the solution of such a fundamental problem is making a suitable definition.

For simplicity, and to avoid certain problems best postponed until later, we will not deal with the most general kinds of curves now, but only with those that are the *graphs of continuous functions*. Let $C$ be the graph of $y = f(x)$ and let $P$ be the point $(x_0, y_0)$ on $C$, so that $y_0 = f(x_0)$. We assume that $P$ is not an endpoint of $C$. Therefore, $C$ extends some distance on both sides of $P$. (See Figure 5.1.)

What do we mean when we say that the line $L$ is tangent to $C$ at $P$? Past experience with tangent lines to circles does not help us to define tangency for more general curves. A tangent line to a circle at $P$ has the following properties (see Figure 5.2):

(i) It meets the circle at only the one point $P$.

(ii) The circle lies on only one side of the line.

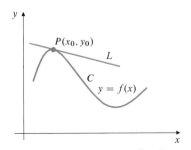

**Figure 5.1**   $L$ is tangent to $C$ at $P$

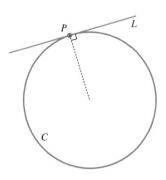

**Figure 5.2**     $L$ is tangent to $C$ at $P$

**Figure 5.3**

(a) $L$ meets $C$ only at $P$ but is not tangent to $C$

(b) $L$ meets $C$ at several points but is tangent to $C$ at $P$

(c) $L$ is tangent to $C$ at $P$ but crosses $C$ at $P$

(d) Many lines meet $C$ only at $P$ but none of them is tangent to $C$ at $P$

(iii) The tangent is perpendicular to the line joining the centre of the circle to $P$.

Most curves do not have obvious *centres*, so (iii) is useless for characterizing tangents to them. The curves in Figure 5.3 show that (i) and (ii) cannot be used to define tangency either. In particular, the curve in Figure 5.3(d) is not "smooth" at $P$, so that curve should not have any tangent line there. A tangent line should have the "same direction" as the curve does at the point of tangency.

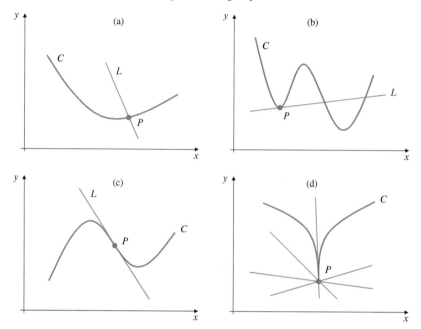

A reasonable definition of tangency can be stated in terms of limits. If $Q$ is a point on $C$ different from $P$, then the line through $P$ and $Q$ is called a **secant line** to the curve. This line rotates around $P$ as $Q$ moves along the curve. If $L$ is a line through $P$ whose slope is the limit of the slopes of these secant lines $PQ$ as $Q$ approaches $P$ along $C$ (Figure 5.4), then we will say that $L$ is tangent to $C$ at $P$.

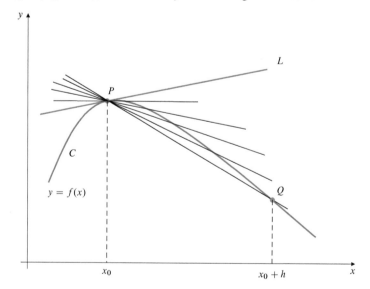

**Figure 5.4**     Secant lines $PQ$ approach tangent line $L$ as $Q$ approaches $P$ along the curve $C$

Since $C$ is the graph of the *function* $y = f(x)$, then vertical lines can meet $C$ only once. Since $P = (x_0, f(x_0))$, a different point $Q$ on the graph must have a different $x$-coordinate, say $x_0 + h$, where $h \neq 0$. Thus $Q = (x_0 + h, f(x_0 + h))$, and the slope of the line $PQ$ is

$$\frac{f(x_0 + h) - f(x_0)}{h}.$$

This expression is called the **Newton quotient** or **difference quotient** for $f$ at $x_0$. Note that $h$ can be positive or negative, depending on whether $Q$ is to the right or left of $P$.

**DEFINITION**

**1**

**Nonvertical tangent lines**

Suppose that the function $f$ is continuous at $x = x_0$ and that

$$\lim_{h \to 0} \frac{f(x_0 + h) - f(x_0)}{h} = m$$

exists. Then the straight line having slope $m$ and passing through the point $P = (x_0, f(x_0))$ is called the **tangent line** (or simply the **tangent**) to the graph of $y = f(x)$ at $P$. An equation of this tangent is

$$y = m(x - x_0) + y_0.$$

**EXAMPLE 1**    Find an equation of the tangent line to the curve $y = x^2$ at the point $(1, 1)$.

**Solution**    Here $f(x) = x^2$, $x_0 = 1$, and $y_0 = f(1) = 1$. The slope of the required tangent is

$$\begin{aligned} m &= \lim_{h \to 0} \frac{f(1 + h) - f(1)}{h} = \lim_{h \to 0} \frac{(1 + h)^2 - 1}{h} \\ &= \lim_{h \to 0} \frac{1 + 2h + h^2 - 1}{h} \\ &= \lim_{h \to 0} \frac{2h + h^2}{h} = \lim_{h \to 0} (2 + h) = 2. \end{aligned}$$

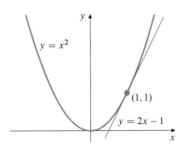

**Figure 5.5**    The tangent to $y = x^2$ at $(1, 1)$

Accordingly, the equation of the tangent line at $(1, 1)$ is $y = 2(x-1)+1$, or $y = 2x-1$. See Figure 5.5.

Definition 1 deals only with tangents that have finite slopes and are, therefore, not vertical. It is also possible for the graph of a continuous function to have a *vertical* tangent line.

**EXAMPLE 2**    Consider the graph of the function $f(x) = \sqrt[3]{x} = x^{1/3}$, which is shown in Figure 5.6. The graph is a smooth curve, and it seems evident that the $y$-axis is tangent to this curve at the origin. Let us try to calculate the limit of the Newton quotient for $f$ at $x = 0$:

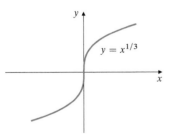

**Figure 5.6**    The $y$-axis is tangent to $y = x^{1/3}$ at the origin

$$\lim_{h \to 0} \frac{f(0 + h) - f(0)}{h} = \lim_{h \to 0} \frac{h^{1/3}}{h} = \lim_{h \to 0} \frac{1}{h^{2/3}} = \infty.$$

Although the limit does not exist, the slope of the secant line joining the origin to another point $Q$ on the curve approaches infinity as $Q$ approaches the origin from either side.

EXAMPLE 3    On the other hand, the function $f(x) = x^{2/3}$, whose graph is shown in Figure 5.7, does not have a tangent line at the origin because it is not "smooth" there. In this case the Newton quotient is

$$\frac{f(0+h) - f(0)}{h} = \frac{h^{2/3}}{h} = \frac{1}{h^{1/3}},$$

which has no limit as $h$ approaches zero. (The right limit is $\infty$; the left limit is $-\infty$.) We say this curve has a **cusp** at the origin. A cusp is an infinitely sharp point; if you were travelling along the curve, you would have to stop and turn 180° at the origin.

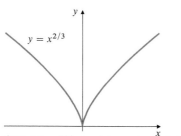

**Figure 5.7**    This graph has no tangent at the origin

In the light of the two preceding examples, we extend the definition of tangent line to allow for vertical tangents as follows:

DEFINITION

2

**Vertical tangents**

If $f$ is continuous at $P = (x_0, y_0)$, where $y_0 = f(x_0)$, and if either

$$\lim_{h \to 0} \frac{f(x_0 + h) - f(x_0)}{h} = \infty \quad \text{or} \quad \lim_{h \to 0} \frac{f(x_0 + h) - f(x_0)}{h} = -\infty,$$

then the vertical line $x = x_0$ is tangent to the graph $y = f(x)$ at $P$. If the limit of the Newton quotient fails to exist in any other way than by being $\infty$ or $-\infty$, the graph $y = f(x)$ has no tangent line at $P$.

EXAMPLE 4    Does the graph of $y = |x|$ have a tangent line at $x = 0$?

*Solution*    The Newton quotient here is

$$\frac{|0+h| - |0|}{h} = \frac{|h|}{h} = \operatorname{sgn} h = \begin{cases} 1, & \text{if } h > 0 \\ -1, & \text{if } h < 0. \end{cases}$$

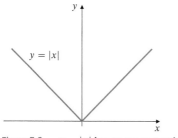

**Figure 5.8**    $y = |x|$ has no tangent at the origin

Since $\operatorname{sgn} h$ has different right and left limits at 0 (namely, 1 and $-1$), the Newton quotient has no limit as $h \to 0$, so $y = |x|$ has no tangent line at $(0, 0)$. (See Figure 5.8.) The graph does not have a cusp at the origin, but it is kinked at that point; *it suddenly changes direction and is not smooth*. Curves have tangents only at points where they are smooth. The graphs of $y = x^{2/3}$ and $y = |x|$ have tangent lines everywhere except at the origin, where they are not smooth.

DEFINITION

3

**The slope of a curve**

The **slope** of a curve $C$ at a point $P$ is the slope of the tangent line to $C$ at $P$ if such a tangent line exists. In particular, the slope of the graph of $y = f(x)$ at the point $x_0$ is

$$\lim_{h \to 0} \frac{f(x_0 + h) - f(x_0)}{h}.$$

**EXAMPLE 5**    Find the slope of the curve $y = x/(3x + 2)$ at the point $x = -2$.

**Solution**    If $x = -2$, then $y = 1/2$, so the required slope is

$$
\begin{aligned}
m &= \lim_{h \to 0} \frac{\dfrac{-2+h}{3(-2+h)+2} - \dfrac{1}{2}}{h} \\
&= \lim_{h \to 0} \frac{-4+2h-(-6+3h+2)}{2(-6+3h+2)h} \\
&= \lim_{h \to 0} \frac{-h}{2h(-4+3h)} = \lim_{h \to 0} \frac{-1}{2(-4+3h)} = \frac{1}{8}.
\end{aligned}
$$

## Normals

If a curve $C$ has a tangent line $L$ at point $P$, then the straight line $N$ through $P$ perpendicular to $L$ is called the **normal** to $C$ at $P$. If $L$ is horizontal, then $N$ is vertical; if $L$ is vertical, then $N$ is horizontal. If $L$ is neither horizontal nor vertical, then, as shown in Section 4.2, the slope of $N$ is the negative reciprocal of the slope of $L$; that is,

$$
\text{slope of the normal} = \frac{-1}{\text{slope of the tangent}}.
$$

**EXAMPLE 6**    Find an equation of the normal to $y = x^2$ at $(1, 1)$.

**Solution**    By Example 1, the tangent to $y = x^2$ at $(1, 1)$ has slope 2. Hence, the normal has slope $-1/2$, and its equation is

$$
y = -\frac{1}{2}(x - 1) + 1 \qquad \text{or} \qquad y = -\frac{x}{2} + \frac{3}{2}.
$$

**EXAMPLE 7**    Find equations of the straight lines that are tangent and normal to the curve $y = \sqrt{x}$ at the point $(4, 2)$.

**Solution**    The slope of the tangent at $(4, 2)$ (Figure 5.9) is

$$
\begin{aligned}
m &= \lim_{h \to 0} \frac{\sqrt{4+h} - 2}{h} = \lim_{h \to 0} \frac{(\sqrt{4+h} - 2)(\sqrt{4+h} + 2)}{h(\sqrt{4+h} + 2)} \\
&= \lim_{h \to 0} \frac{4+h-4}{h(\sqrt{4+h} + 2)} \\
&= \lim_{h \to 0} \frac{1}{\sqrt{4+h} + 2} = \frac{1}{4}.
\end{aligned}
$$

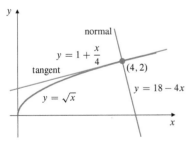

**Figure 5.9**    The tangent (blue) and normal (green) to $y = \sqrt{x}$ at $(4, 2)$

The tangent line has equation

$$
y = \frac{1}{4}(x - 4) + 2 \qquad \text{or} \qquad x - 4y + 4 = 0,
$$

and the normal has slope $-4$ and, therefore, equation

$$
y = -4(x - 4) + 2 \qquad \text{or} \qquad y = -4x + 18.
$$

## EXERCISES 5.1

In Exercises 1–12, find an equation of the straight line tangent to the given curve at the point indicated.

**1.** $y = 3x - 1$ at $(1, 2)$   **2.** $y = x/2$ at $(a, a/2)$

**3.** $y = 2x^2 - 5$ at $(2, 3)$   **4.** $y = 6 - x - x^2$ at $x = -2$

**5.** $y = x^3 + 8$ at $x = -2$   **6.** $y = \dfrac{1}{x^2 + 1}$ at $(0, 1)$

**7.** $y = \sqrt{x + 1}$ at $x = 3$   **8.** $y = \dfrac{1}{\sqrt{x}}$ at $x = 9$

**9.** $y = \dfrac{2x}{x + 2}$ at $x = 2$   **10.** $y = \sqrt{5 - x^2}$ at $x = 1$

**11.** $y = x^2$ at $x = x_0$   **12.** $y = \dfrac{1}{x}$ at $\left(a, \dfrac{1}{a}\right)$

Do the graphs of the functions $f$ in Exercises 13–17 have tangent lines at the given points? If yes, what is the tangent line?

**13.** $f(x) = \sqrt{|x|}$ at $x = 0$   **14.** $f(x) = (x - 1)^{4/3}$ at $x = 1$

**15.** $f(x) = (x + 2)^{3/5}$ at $x = -2$

**16.** $f(x) = |x^2 - 1|$ at $x = 1$

**17.** $f(x) = \begin{cases} \sqrt{x} & \text{if } x \geq 0 \\ -\sqrt{-x} & \text{if } x < 0 \end{cases}$ at $x = 0$

**18.** Find the slope of the curve $y = x^2 - 1$ at the point $x = x_0$. What is the equation of the tangent line to $y = x^2 - 1$ that has slope $-3$?

**19.** (a) Find the slope of $y = x^3$ at the point $x = a$.

   (b) Find the equations of the straight lines having slope 3 that are tangent to $y = x^3$.

**20.** Find all points on the curve $y = x^3 - 3x$ where the tangent line is parallel to the $x$-axis.

**21.** Find all points on the curve $y = x^3 - x + 1$ where the tangent line is parallel to the line $y = 2x + 5$.

**22.** Find all points on the curve $y = 1/x$ where the tangent line is perpendicular to the line $y = 4x - 3$.

**23.** For what value of the constant $k$ is the line $x + y = k$ normal to the curve $y = x^2$?

**24.** For what value of the constant $k$ do the curves $y = kx^2$ and $y = k(x - 2)^2$ intersect at right angles? *Hint:* Where do the curves intersect? What are their slopes there?

Use a graphics utility to plot the following curves. Where does the curve have a horizontal tangent? Does the curve fail to have a tangent line anywhere?

**25.** $y = x^3(5 - x)^2$   **26.** $y = 2x^3 - 3x^2 - 12x + 1$

**27.** $y = |x^2 - 1| - x$   **28.** $y = |x + 1| - |x - 1|$

**29.** $y = (x^2 - 1)^{1/3}$   **30.** $y = ((x^2 - 1)^2)^{1/3}$

**31.** If line $L$ is tangent to curve $C$ at point $P$, then the smaller angle between $L$ and the secant line $PQ$ joining $P$ to another point $Q$ on $C$ approaches 0 as $Q$ approaches $P$ along $C$. Is the converse true: if the angle between $PQ$ and line $L$ (which passes through $P$) approaches 0, must $L$ be tangent to $C$?

**32.** Let $P(x)$ be a polynomial. If $a$ is a real number, then $P(x)$ can be expressed in the form

$$P(x) = a_0 + a_1(x - a) + a_2(x - a)^2 + \cdots + a_n(x - a)^n$$

for some $n \geq 0$. If $\ell(x) = m(x - a) + b$, show that the straight line $y = \ell(x)$ is tangent to the graph of $y = P(x)$ at $x = a$ provided $P(x) - \ell(x) = (x - a)^2 Q(x)$, where $Q(x)$ is a polynomial.

## 5.2   The Derivative

A straight line has the property that its slope is the same at all points. For any other graph, however, the slope may vary from point to point. Thus, the slope of the graph of $y = f(x)$ at the point $x$ is itself a function of $x$. At any point $x$ where the graph has a finite slope, we say that $f$ is differentiable, and we call the slope the derivative of $f$. The derivative is therefore the limit of the Newton quotient.

**DEFINITION**

**4**

The **derivative** of a function $f$ is another function $f'$ defined by

$$f'(x) = \lim_{h \to 0} \frac{f(x + h) - f(x)}{h}$$

at all points $x$ for which the limit exists (i.e., is a finite real number). If $f'(x)$ exists, we say that $f$ is **differentiable** at $x$.

The domain of the derivative $f'$ (read "$f$ prime") is the set of numbers $x$ in the domain of $f$ where the graph of $f$ has a *nonvertical* tangent line, and the value $f'(x_0)$ of $f'$ at such a point $x_0$ is the slope of the tangent line to $y = f(x)$ there. Thus, the equation of the tangent line to $y = f(x)$ at $(x_0, f(x_0))$ is

$$y = f(x_0) + f'(x_0)(x - x_0).$$

The domain $\mathcal{D}(f')$ of $f'$ may be smaller than the domain $\mathcal{D}(f)$ of $f$ because it contains only those points in $\mathcal{D}(f)$ at which $f$ is differentiable. Values of $x$ in $\mathcal{D}(f)$ where $f$ is not differentiable and that are not endpoints of $\mathcal{D}(f)$ are **singular points** of $f$.

*Remark* The value of the derivative of $f$ at a particular point $x_0$ can be expressed as a limit in either of two ways:

$$f'(x_0) = \lim_{h \to 0} \frac{f(x_0 + h) - f(x_0)}{h} = \lim_{x \to x_0} \frac{f(x) - f(x_0)}{x - x_0}.$$

In the second limit $x_0 + h$ is replaced by $x$, so that $h = x - x_0$ and $h \to 0$ is equivalent to $x \to x_0$.

The process of calculating the derivative $f'$ of a given function $f$ is called **differentiation**. The graph of $f'$ can often be sketched directly from that of $f$ by visualizing slopes, a procedure called **graphical differentiation**. In Figure 5.10 the graphs of $f'$ and $g'$ were obtained by measuring the slopes at the corresponding points in the graphs of $f$ and $g$ lying above them. The height of the graph $y = f'(x)$ at $x$ is the slope of the graph of $y = f(x)$ at $x$. Note that $-1$ and $1$ are singular points of $f$. Although $f(-1)$ and $f(1)$ are defined, $f'(-1)$ and $f'(1)$ are not defined; the graph of $f$ has no tangent at $-1$ or at $1$.

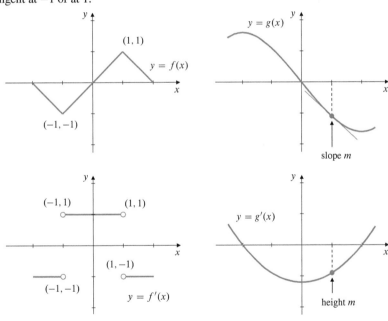

**Figure 5.10** Graphical differentiation

A function is differentiable on a set $S$ if it is differentiable at every point $x$ in $S$. Typically, the functions we encounter are defined on intervals or unions of intervals. If $f$ is defined on a closed interval $[a, b]$, Definition 4 does not allow for the existence of a derivative at the endpoints $x = a$ or $x = b$. (Why?) As we did for continuity, we extend the definition to allow for a **right derivative** at $x = a$ and a **left derivative** at $x = b$:

$$f'_+(a) = \lim_{h \to 0+} \frac{f(a + h) - f(a)}{h}, \qquad f'_-(b) = \lim_{h \to 0-} \frac{f(b + h) - f(b)}{h}.$$

We now say that $f$ is **differentiable** on $[a, b]$ if $f'(x)$ exists for all $x$ in $(a, b)$ and $f'_+(a)$ and $f'_-(b)$ both exist.

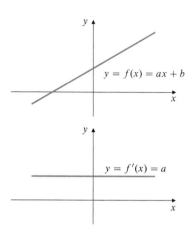

**Figure 5.11**    The derivative of the linear function $f(x) = ax + b$ is the constant function $f'(x) = a$

## Some Important Derivatives

We now give several examples of the calculation of derivatives algebraically from the definition of derivative. Some of these are the basic building blocks from which more complicated derivatives can be calculated later. They are collected in Table 1 later in this section and should be memorized.

**EXAMPLE 1**    **(The derivative of a linear function)** Show that if $f(x) = ax + b$, then $f'(x) = a$.

*Solution*    The result is apparent from the graph of $f$ (Figure 5.11), but we will do the calculation using the definition:

$$f'(x) = \lim_{h \to 0} \frac{f(x + h) - f(x)}{h}$$
$$= \lim_{h \to 0} \frac{a(x + h) + b - (ax + b)}{h}$$
$$= \lim_{h \to 0} \frac{ah}{h} = a.$$

An important special case of Example 1 says that the derivative of a constant function is the zero function:

If $g(x) = c$ (constant),    then    $g'(x) = 0$.

**EXAMPLE 2**    Use the definition of the derivative to calculate the derivatives of the functions

(a) $f(x) = x^2$,    (b) $g(x) = \dfrac{1}{x}$,    and    (c) $k(x) = \sqrt{x}$.

*Solution*    Figures 5.12–5.14 show the graphs of these functions and their derivatives.

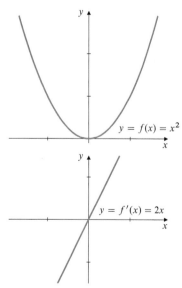

**Figure 5.12**    The derivative of $f(x) = x^2$ is $f'(x) = 2x$

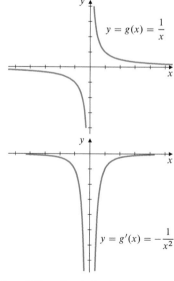

**Figure 5.13**    The derivative of $g(x) = 1/x$ is $g'(x) = -1/x^2$

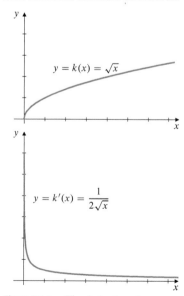

**Figure 5.14**    The derivative of $k(x) = \sqrt{x}$ is $k'(x) = 1/(2\sqrt{x})$

(a)  $f'(x) = \lim\limits_{h \to 0} \dfrac{f(x+h) - f(x)}{h}$

$= \lim\limits_{h \to 0} \dfrac{(x+h)^2 - x^2}{h}$

$= \lim\limits_{h \to 0} \dfrac{2hx + h^2}{h} = \lim\limits_{h \to 0} (2x + h) = 2x.$

(b)  $g'(x) = \lim\limits_{h \to 0} \dfrac{g(x+h) - g(x)}{h}$

$= \lim\limits_{h \to 0} \dfrac{\dfrac{1}{x+h} - \dfrac{1}{x}}{h}$

$= \lim\limits_{h \to 0} \dfrac{x - (x+h)}{h(x+h)x} = \lim\limits_{h \to 0} -\dfrac{1}{(x+h)x} = -\dfrac{1}{x^2}.$

(c)  $k'(x) = \lim\limits_{h \to 0} \dfrac{k(x+h) - k(x)}{h}$

$= \lim\limits_{h \to 0} \dfrac{\sqrt{x+h} - \sqrt{x}}{h}$

$= \lim\limits_{h \to 0} \dfrac{\sqrt{x+h} - \sqrt{x}}{h} \times \dfrac{\sqrt{x+h} + \sqrt{x}}{\sqrt{x+h} + \sqrt{x}}$

$= \lim\limits_{h \to 0} \dfrac{x + h - x}{h(\sqrt{x+h} + \sqrt{x})} = \lim\limits_{h \to 0} \dfrac{1}{\sqrt{x+h} + \sqrt{x}} = \dfrac{1}{2\sqrt{x}}.$

Note that $k$ is not differentiable at the endpoint $x = 0$.

⬤

The three derivative formulas calculated in Example 2 are special cases of the following **General Power Rule**:

If $f(x) = x^r$,   then   $f'(x) = r\,x^{r-1}$.

This formula, which we will verify in Section 6.3, is valid for *all values of r and x for which $x^{r-1}$ makes sense as a real number.*

**EXAMPLE 3**    **(Differentiating powers)**

If $f(x) = x^{5/3}$, then $f'(x) = \dfrac{5}{3}x^{(5/3)-1} = \dfrac{5}{3}x^{2/3}$ for all real $x$.

If $g(t) = \dfrac{1}{\sqrt{t}} = t^{-1/2}$, then $g'(t) = -\dfrac{1}{2}t^{-(1/2)-1} = -\dfrac{1}{2}t^{-3/2}$ for $t > 0$.

⬤

Eventually, we will prove all appropriate cases of the General Power Rule. For the time being, here is a proof of the case $r = n$, a positive integer, based on the *factoring of a difference of nth powers:*

$$a^n - b^n = (a - b)(a^{n-1} + a^{n-2}b + a^{n-3}b^2 + \cdots + ab^{n-2} + b^{n-1}).$$

(Check that this formula is correct by multiplying the two factors on the right-hand side.) If $f(x) = x^n$, $a = x + h$, and $b = x$, then $a - b = h$ and

$f'(x) = \lim\limits_{h \to 0} \dfrac{(x+h)^n - x^n}{h}$

$= \lim\limits_{h \to 0} \dfrac{h\,\overbrace{[(x+h)^{n-1} + (x+h)^{n-2}x + (x+h)^{n-3}x^2 + \cdots + x^{n-1}]}^{n \text{ terms}}}{h}$

$= nx^{n-1}.$

An alternative proof based on the product rule and mathematical induction will be given in Section 5.3. The factorization method used above can also be used to demonstrate the General Power Rule for negative integers, $r = -n$, and reciprocals of integers, $r = 1/n$. (See Exercises 52 and 54 at the end of this section.)

---

**EXAMPLE 4**    **(Differentiating the absolute value function)**  Verify that:

$$\text{If } f(x) = |x|, \quad \text{then} \quad f'(x) = \frac{x}{|x|} = \operatorname{sgn} x.$$

*Solution*   We have

$$f(x) = \begin{cases} x, & \text{if } x \geq 0 \\ -x, & \text{if } x < 0 \end{cases}.$$

Thus, from Example 1 above, $f'(x) = 1$ if $x > 0$ and $f'(x) = -1$ if $x < 0$. Also, Example 4 of Section 5.1 shows that $f$ is not differentiable at $x = 0$, which is a singular point of $f$. Therefore (see Figure 5.15),

$$f'(x) = \begin{cases} 1, & \text{if } x > 0 \\ -1, & \text{if } x < 0 \end{cases} = \frac{x}{|x|} = \operatorname{sgn} x.$$

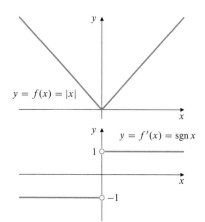

**Figure 5.15**    The derivative of $|x|$ is $\operatorname{sgn} x = x/|x|$

---

Table 1 lists the elementary derivatives calculated above. Beginning in Section 5.3 we will develop general rules for calculating the derivatives of functions obtained by combining simpler functions. Thereafter, we will seldom have to revert to the definition of the derivative and to the calculation of limits to evaluate derivatives. It is important, therefore, to remember the derivatives of some elementary functions. Memorize those in Table 1.

**Table 1.**   Some elementary functions and their derivatives

| $f(x)$ | $f'(x)$ |
|:---:|:---:|
| $c$ (constant) | $0$ |
| $x$ | $1$ |
| $x^2$ | $2x$ |
| $\dfrac{1}{x}$ | $-\dfrac{1}{x^2}$   $(x \neq 0)$ |
| $\sqrt{x}$ | $\dfrac{1}{2\sqrt{x}}$   $(x > 0)$ |
| $x^r$ | $r\,x^{r-1}$   $(x^{r-1}$ real$)$ |
| $|x|$ | $\dfrac{x}{|x|} = \operatorname{sgn} x$ |

## Leibniz Notation

Because functions can be written in different ways, it is useful to have more than one notation for derivatives. If $y = f(x)$, we can use the dependent variable $y$ to represent the function, and we can denote the derivative of the function with respect to $x$ in any of the following ways:

$$D_x y = y' = \frac{dy}{dx} = \frac{d}{dx}f(x) = f'(x) = D_x f(x) = Df(x).$$

(In the forms using "$D_x$," we can omit the subscript $x$ if the variable of differentiation is obvious.) Often the most convenient way of referring to the derivative of a function given explicitly as an expression in the variable $x$ is to write $\frac{d}{dx}$ in front of that expression. The symbol $\frac{d}{dx}$ is a *differential operator* and should be read "the derivative with respect to $x$ of ..." For example,

$$\frac{d}{dx}x^2 = 2x \quad \text{(the derivative with respect to } x \text{ of } x^2 \text{ is } 2x)$$

$$\frac{d}{dx}\sqrt{x} = \frac{1}{2\sqrt{x}}$$

$$\frac{d}{dt}t^{100} = 100\,t^{99}$$

$$\text{if } y = u^3, \text{ then } \frac{dy}{du} = 3u^2.$$

The value of the derivative of a function at a particular number $x_0$ in its domain can also be expressed in several ways:

---

Do not confuse the expressions

$$\frac{d}{dx}\,f(x) \text{ and } \frac{d}{dx}\,f(x)\bigg|_{x=x_0}.$$

The first expression represents a *function*, $f'(x)$. The second represents a *number*, $f'(x_0)$.

---

$$D_x y\bigg|_{x=x_0} = y'\bigg|_{x=x_0} = \frac{dy}{dx}\bigg|_{x=x_0} = \frac{d}{dx}f(x)\bigg|_{x=x_0} = f'(x_0) = D_x f(x_0).$$

The symbol $\bigg|_{x=x_0}$ is called an **evaluation symbol**. It signifies that the expression preceding it should be evaluated at $x = x_0$. Thus,

$$\frac{d}{dx}x^4\bigg|_{x=-1} = 4x^3\bigg|_{x=-1} = 4(-1)^3 = -4.$$

Here is another example in which a derivative is computed from the definition, this time for a somewhat more complicated function.

---

**EXAMPLE 5**    Use the definition of derivative to calculate $\dfrac{d}{dx}\left(\dfrac{x}{x^2+1}\right)\bigg|_{x=2}$.

***Solution***    We could calculate $\dfrac{d}{dx}\left(\dfrac{x}{x^2+1}\right)$ and then substitute $x = 2$, but it is easier to put $x = 2$ in the expression for the Newton quotient before taking the limit:

$$\frac{d}{dx}\left(\frac{x}{x^2+1}\right)\bigg|_{x=2} = \lim_{h\to 0}\frac{\dfrac{2+h}{(2+h)^2+1} - \dfrac{2}{2^2+1}}{h}$$

$$= \lim_{h\to 0}\frac{\dfrac{2+h}{5+4h+h^2} - \dfrac{2}{5}}{h}$$

$$= \lim_{h\to 0}\frac{5(2+h) - 2(5+4h+h^2)}{5(5+4h+h^2)h}$$

$$= \lim_{h\to 0}\frac{-3h - 2h^2}{5(5+4h+h^2)h}$$

$$= \lim_{h\to 0}\frac{-3 - 2h}{5(5+4h+h^2)} = -\frac{3}{25}.$$

---

The notations $dy/dx$ and $\frac{d}{dx}f(x)$ are called **Leibniz notations** for the derivative, after Gottfried Wilhelm Leibniz (1646–1716), one of the creators of calculus, who used such notations. The main ideas of calculus were developed independently by Leibniz and Isaac Newton (1642–1727); Newton used notations similar to the prime ($y'$) notations we use here.

The Leibniz notation is suggested by the definition of derivative. The Newton quotient $[f(x + h) - f(x)]/h$, whose limit we take to find the derivative $dy/dx$, can be written in the form $\Delta y/\Delta x$, where $\Delta y = f(x + h) - f(x)$ is the increment in $y$, and $\Delta x = (x + h) - x = h$ is the corresponding increment in $x$ as we pass from the point $(x, f(x))$ to the point $(x + h, f(x + h))$ on the graph of $f$. (See Figure 5.16.) $\Delta$ is the uppercase Greek letter Delta. Using symbols:

$$\frac{dy}{dx} = \lim_{\Delta x \to 0} \frac{\Delta y}{\Delta x}.$$

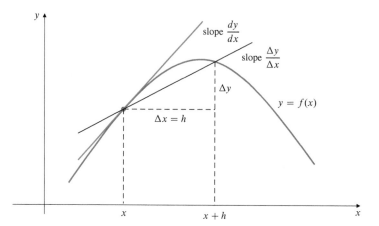

Figure 5.16    $\dfrac{dy}{dx} = \lim\limits_{\Delta x \to 0} \dfrac{\Delta y}{\Delta x}$

## Differentials

The Newton quotient $\Delta y/\Delta x$ is actually the quotient of two quantities, $\Delta y$ and $\Delta x$. It is not at all clear, however, that the derivative $dy/dx$, the limit of $\Delta y/\Delta x$ as $\Delta x$ approaches zero, can be regarded as a quotient. If $y$ is a continuous function of $x$, then $\Delta y$ approaches zero when $\Delta x$ approaches zero, so $dy/dx$ appears to be the meaningless quantity $0/0$. Nevertheless, it is sometimes useful to be able to refer to quantities $dy$ and $dx$ in such a way that their quotient is the derivative $dy/dx$. We can justify this by regarding $dx$ as a new *independent* variable (called **the differential of $x$**) and defining a new *dependent* variable $dy$ (**the differential of $y$**) as a function of $x$ and $dx$ by

$$dy = \frac{dy}{dx}\, dx = f'(x)\, dx.$$

For example, if $y = x^2$, we can write $dy = 2x\, dx$ to mean the same thing as $dy/dx = 2x$. Similarly, if $f(x) = 1/x$, we can write $df(x) = -(1/x^2)\, dx$ as the equivalent differential form of the assertion that $(d/dx)f(x) = f'(x) = -1/x^2$. This *differential notation* is useful in applications (see Sections 5.7), and especially for the interpretation and manipulation of integrals beginning in Chapter 5.

Note that, defined as above, differentials are merely variables that may or may not be small in absolute value. The differentials $dy$ and $dx$ were originally regarded (by Leibniz and his successors) as "infinitesimals" (infinitely small but nonzero) quantities whose quotient $dy/dx$ gave the slope of the tangent line (a secant line meeting the graph of $y = f(x)$ at two points infinitely close together). It can be shown that such "infinitesimal" quantities cannot exist (as real numbers). It is possible to extend the number system to contain infinitesimals and use these to develop calculus, but we will not consider this approach here.

## Derivatives Have the Intermediate-Value Property

Is a function $f$ defined on an interval $I$ necessarily the derivative of some other function defined on $I$? The answer is no; some functions are derivatives and some are not. Although a derivative need not be a continuous function (see Exercise 28 in Section 5.8), it must, like a continuous function, have the intermediate-value property: on an interval $[a, b]$, a derivative $f'(x)$ takes on every value between $f'(a)$ and $f'(b)$. (See Exercise 29 in Section 5.8 for a proof of this fact.) An everywhere-defined step function such as the Heaviside function $H(x)$ considered (see Figure 5 17) does not have this property on, say, the interval $[-1, 1]$, so cannot be the derivative of a function on that interval This argument does not apply to the signum function, which is the derivative of the absolute value function on any interval where it is defined. (See Example 4.) Such an interval cannot contain the origin, as sgn $(x)$ is not defined at $x = 0$.

If $g(x)$ is continuous on an interval $I$, then $g(x) = f'(x)$ for some function $f$ that is differentiable on $I$. We will discuss this fact further in Chapter 8.

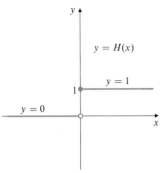

**Figure 5.17** This function is not a derivative on $[-1, 1]$; it does not have the intermediate-value property.

---

## EXERCISES 5.2

Make rough sketches of the graphs of the derivatives of the functions in Exercises 1–4.

1. The function $f$ graphed in Figure 5.18(a).

2. The function $g$ graphed in Figure 5.18(b).

3. The function $h$ graphed in Figure 5.18(c).

4. The function $k$ graphed in Figure 5.18(d).

5. Where is the function $f$ graphed in Figure 5.18(a) differentiable?

6. Where is the function $g$ graphed in Figure 5.18(b) differentiable?

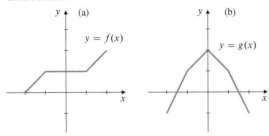

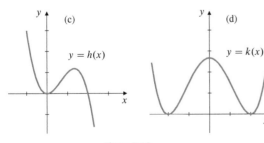

**Figure 5.18**

Use a graphics utility with differentiation capabilities to plot the graphs of the following functions and their derivatives. Observe the relationships between the graph of $y$ and that of $y'$ in each case. What features of the graph of $y$ can you infer from the graph of $y'$?

7. $y = 3x - x^2 - 1$

8. $y = x^3 - 3x^2 + 2x + 1$

9. $y = |x^3 - x|$

10. $y = |x^2 - 1| - |x^2 - 4|$

In Exercises 11–24, (a) calculate the derivative of the given function directly from the definition of derivative, and (b) express the result of (a) using differentials.

11. $y = x^2 - 3x$

12. $f(x) = 1 + 4x - 5x^2$

13. $f(x) = x^3$

14. $s = \dfrac{1}{3 + 4t}$

15. $g(x) = \dfrac{2 - x}{2 + x}$

16. $y = \dfrac{1}{3}x^3 - x$

17. $F(t) = \sqrt{2t + 1}$

18. $f(x) = \dfrac{3}{4}\sqrt{2 - x}$

19. $y = x + \dfrac{1}{x}$

20. $z = \dfrac{s}{1 + s}$

21. $F(x) = \dfrac{1}{\sqrt{1 + x^2}}$

22. $y = \dfrac{1}{x^2}$

23. $y = \dfrac{1}{\sqrt{1 + x}}$

24. $f(t) = \dfrac{t^2 - 3}{t^2 + 3}$

25. How should the function $f(x) = x\,\text{sgn}\,x$ be defined at $x = 0$ so that it is continuous there? Is it then differentiable there?

26. How should the function $g(x) = x^2\text{sgn}\,x$ be defined at $x = 0$ so that it is continuous there? Is it then differentiable there?

27. Where does $h(x) = |x^2 + 3x + 2|$ fail to be differentiable?

28. Using a calculator, find the slope of the secant line to $y = x^3 - 2x$ passing through the points corresponding to $x = 1$ and $x = 1 + \Delta x$, for several values of $\Delta x$ of decreasing size, say $\Delta x = \pm 0.1, \pm 0.01, \pm 0.001, \pm 0.0001$. (Make a table.) Also, calculate $\dfrac{d}{dx}\left(x^3 - 2x\right)\Big|_{x=1}$ using the definition of derivative.

29. Repeat Exercise 28 for the function $f(x) = \dfrac{1}{x}$ and the points $x = 2$ and $x = 2 + \Delta x$.

Using the definition of derivative, find equations for the tangent lines to the curves in Exercises 30–33 at the points indicated.

**30.** $y = 5 + 4x - x^2$ at the point where $x = 2$

**31.** $y = \sqrt{x + 6}$ at the point $(3, 3)$

**32.** $y = \dfrac{t}{t^2 - 2}$ at the point where $t = -2$

**33.** $y = \dfrac{2}{t^2 + t}$ at the point where $t = a$

Calculate the derivatives of the functions in Exercises 34–39 using the General Power Rule. Where is each derivative valid?

**34.** $f(x) = x^{-17}$    **35.** $g(t) = t^{22}$

**36.** $y = x^{1/3}$    **37.** $y = x^{-1/3}$

**38.** $t^{-2.25}$    **39.** $s^{119/4}$

In Exercises 40–50, you may use the formulas for derivatives established in this section.

**40.** Calculate $\left.\dfrac{d}{ds}\sqrt{s}\right|_{s=9}$ .    **41.** Find $F'(\frac{1}{4})$ if $F(x) = \dfrac{1}{x}$.

**42.** Find $f'(8)$ if $f(x) = x^{-2/3}$.

**43.** Find $\left.dy/dt\right|_{t=4}$ if $y = t^{1/4}$.

**44.** Find an equation of the straight line tangent to the curve $y = \sqrt{x}$ at $x = x_0$.

**45.** Find an equation of the straight line normal to the curve $y = 1/x$ at the point where $x = a$.

**46.** Show that the curve $y = x^2$ and the straight line $x + 4y = 18$ intersect at right angles at one of their two intersection points. *Hint:* Find the product of their slopes at their intersection points.

**47.** There are two distinct straight lines that pass through the point $(1, -3)$ and are tangent to the curve $y = x^2$. Find their equations. *Hint:* Draw a sketch. The points of tangency are not given; let them be denoted $(a, a^2)$.

**48.** Find equations of two straight lines that have slope $-2$ and are tangent to the graph of $y = 1/x$.

**49.** Find the slope of a straight line that passes through the point $(-2, 0)$ and is tangent to the curve $y = \sqrt{x}$.

**50.** Show that there are two distinct tangent lines to the curve $y = x^2$ passing through the point $(a, b)$ provided $b < a^2$. How many tangent lines to $y = x^2$ pass through $(a, b)$ if $b = a^2$? if $b > a^2$?

**51.** Show that the derivative of an odd differentiable function is even and that the derivative of an even differentiable function is odd.

**52.** Prove the case $r = -n$ ($n$ is a positive integer) of the General Power Rule; that is, prove that

$$\frac{d}{dx} x^{-n} = -n\, x^{-n-1}.$$

Use the factorization of a difference of $n$th powers given in this section.

**53.** Use the factoring of a difference of cubes:

$$a^3 - b^3 = (a - b)(a^2 + ab + b^2),$$

to help you calculate the derivative of $f(x) = x^{1/3}$ directly from the definition of derivative.

**54.** Prove the General Power Rule for $\frac{d}{dx}x^r$, where $r = 1/n$, $n$ being a positive integer. (*Hint:*

$$\frac{d}{dx}x^{1/n} = \lim_{h \to 0} \frac{(x + h)^{1/n} - x^{1/n}}{h}$$

$$= \lim_{h \to 0} \frac{(x + h)^{1/n} - x^{1/n}}{((x + h)^{1/n})^n - (x^{1/n})^n}.$$

Apply the factorization of the difference of $n$th powers to the denominator of the latter quotient.)

**55.** Give a proof of the power rule $\frac{d}{dx}x^n = nx^{n-1}$ for positive integers $n$ using the Binomial Theorem:

$$(x + h)^n = x^n + \frac{n}{1}x^{n-1}h + \frac{n(n-1)}{1 \times 2}x^{n-2}h^2$$

$$+ \frac{n(n-1)(n-2)}{1 \times 2 \times 3}x^{n-3}h^3 + \cdots + h^n.$$

**56.** Use right and left derivatives, $f'_+(a)$ and $f'_-(a)$, to define the concept of a half-line starting at $(a, f(a))$ being a right or left tangent to the graph of $f$ at $x = a$. Show that the graph has a tangent line at $x = a$ if and only if it has right and left tangents that are opposite halves of the same straight line. What are the left and right tangents to the graphs of $y = x^{1/3}$, $y = x^{2/3}$, and $y = |x|$ at $x = 0$?

## 5.3  Differentiation Rules

If every derivative had to be calculated directly from the definition of derivative as in the examples of Section 5.2, calculus would indeed be a painful subject. Fortunately, there is an easier way. We will develop several general *differentiation rules* that enable us to calculate the derivatives of complicated combinations of functions easily if we already know the derivatives of the elementary functions from which they are constructed. For instance, we will be able to find the derivative of $\dfrac{x^2}{\sqrt{x^2 + 1}}$ if we know the derivatives of $x^2$ and $\sqrt{x}$. The rules we develop in this section tell us how to differentiate sums, constant multiples, products, and quotients of functions whose derivatives we already know. In Section 5.4 we will learn how to differentiate composite functions.

Before developing these differentiation rules we need to establish one obvious but very important theorem which states, roughly, that the graph of a function cannot possibly have a break at a point where it is smooth.

## THEOREM 1

**Differentiability implies continuity**

If $f$ is differentiable at $x$, then $f$ is continuous at $x$.

**PROOF**   Since $f$ is differentiable at $x$, we know that

$$\lim_{h \to 0} \frac{f(x+h) - f(x)}{h} = f'(x)$$

exists. Using the limit rules, we have

$$\lim_{h \to 0} \left( f(x+h) - f(x) \right) = \lim_{h \to 0} \left( \frac{f(x+h) - f(x)}{h} \right) (h) = \left( f'(x) \right)(0) = 0.$$

This is equivalent to $\lim_{h \to 0} f(x+h) = f(x)$, which says that $f$ is continuous at $x$.

## Sums and Constant Multiples

The derivative of a sum (or difference) of functions is the sum (or difference) of the derivatives of those functions. The derivative of a constant multiple of a function is the same constant multiple of the derivative of the function.

## THEOREM 2

**Differentiation rules for sums, differences, and constant multiples**

If functions $f$ and $g$ are differentiable at $x$, and if $C$ is a constant, then the functions $f + g$, $f - g$, and $Cf$ are all differentiable at $x$ and

$$(f + g)'(x) = f'(x) + g'(x),$$
$$(f - g)'(x) = f'(x) - g'(x),$$
$$(Cf)'(x) = Cf'(x).$$

**PROOF**   The proofs of all three assertions are straightforward, using the corresponding limit rules. For the sum, we have

$$(f + g)'(x) = \lim_{h \to 0} \frac{(f + g)(x+h) - (f + g)(x)}{h}$$
$$= \lim_{h \to 0} \frac{(f(x+h) + g(x+h)) - (f(x) + g(x))}{h}$$
$$= \lim_{h \to 0} \left( \frac{f(x+h) - f(x)}{h} + \frac{g(x+h) - g(x)}{h} \right)$$
$$= f'(x) + g'(x),$$

because the limit of a sum is the sum of the limits. The proof for the difference $f - g$ is similar. For the constant multiple, we have

$$(Cf)'(x) = \lim_{h \to 0} \frac{Cf(x+h) - Cf(x)}{h}$$
$$= C \lim_{h \to 0} \frac{f(x+h) - f(x)}{h} = Cf'(x).$$

The rule for differentiating sums extends to sums of any finite number of terms

$$(f_1 + f_2 + \cdots + f_n)' = f_1' + f_2' + \cdots + f_n'. \qquad (*)$$

To see this we can use a technique called **mathematical induction**. (See the note in the margin.) Theorem 2 shows that the case $n = 2$ is true; this is STEP 1. For STEP 2, we must show that *if* the formula $(*)$ holds for some integer $n = k \geq 2$, *then* it must also hold for $n = k + 1$. Therefore, *assume* that

$$(f_1 + f_2 + \cdots + f_k)' = f_1' + f_2' + \cdots + f_k'.$$

Then we have

$$(f_1 + f_2 + \cdots + f_k + f_{k+1})'$$
$$= \underbrace{\left((f_1 + f_2 + \cdots + f_k)\right.}_{\text{Let this function be } f} + f_{k+1})'$$
$$= (f + f_{k+1})' \qquad \text{(Now use the known case } n = 2.)$$
$$= f' + f_{k+1}'$$
$$= f_1' + f_2' + \cdots + f_k' + f_{k+1}'.$$

With both steps verified, we can claim that $(*)$ holds for any $n \geq 2$ *by induction*. In particular, therefore, the derivative of any polynomial is the sum of the derivatives of its terms.

## Mathematical Induction

Mathematical induction is a technique for proving that a statement about an integer $n$ is true for every integer $n$ greater than or equal to some starting integer $n_0$. The proof requires us to carry out two steps:

STEP 1. Prove that the statement is true for $n = n_0$.

STEP 2. Prove that if the statement is true for some integer $n = k$, where $k \geq n_0$, then it is also true for the next larger integer, $n = k + 1$.

Step 2 prevents there from being a smallest integer greater than $n_0$ for which the statement is false. Being true for $n_0$, the statement must therefore be true for all larger integers.

---

**EXAMPLE 1**    Calculate the derivatives of the functions

(a) $2x^3 - 5x^2 + 4x + 7$,    (b) $f(x) = 5\sqrt{x} + \dfrac{3}{x} - 18$,    (c) $y = \dfrac{1}{7}t^4 - 3t^{7/3}$.

*Solution*    Each of these functions is a sum of constant multiples of functions that we already know how to differentiate.

(a) $\dfrac{d}{dx}(2x^3 - 5x^2 + 4x + 7) = 2(3x^2) - 5(2x) + 4(1) + 0 = 6x^2 - 10x + 4.$

(b) $f'(x) = 5\left(\dfrac{1}{2\sqrt{x}}\right) + 3\left(-\dfrac{1}{x^2}\right) - 0 = \dfrac{5}{2\sqrt{x}} - \dfrac{3}{x^2}.$

(c) $\dfrac{dy}{dt} = \dfrac{1}{7}(4t^3) - 3\left(\dfrac{7}{3}t^{4/3}\right) = \dfrac{4}{7}t^3 - 7t^{4/3}.$

---

**EXAMPLE 2**    Find an equation of the tangent to the curve $y = \dfrac{3x^3 - 4}{x}$ at the point on the curve where $x = -2$.

*Solution*    If $x = -2$, then $y = 14$. The slope of the curve at $(-2, 14)$ is

$$\left.\frac{dy}{dx}\right|_{x=-2} = \left.\frac{d}{dx}\left(3x^2 - \frac{4}{x}\right)\right|_{x=-2} = \left.\left(6x + \frac{4}{x^2}\right)\right|_{x=-2} = -11.$$

An equation of the tangent line is $y = 14 - 11(x + 2)$, or $y = -11x - 8$.

---

## The Product Rule

The rule for differentiating a product of functions is a little more complicated than that for sums. It is *not* true that the derivative of a product is the product of the derivatives.

**The Product Rule**

If functions $f$ and $g$ are differentiable at $x$, then their product $fg$ is also differentiable at $x$, and

$$(fg)'(x) = f'(x)g(x) + f(x)g'(x).$$

*PROOF*    We set up the Newton quotient for $fg$ and then add 0 to the numerator in a way that enables us to involve the Newton quotients for $f$ and $g$ separately:

$$(fg)'(x) = \lim_{h \to 0} \frac{f(x+h)g(x+h) - f(x)g(x)}{h}$$

$$= \lim_{h \to 0} \frac{f(x+h)g(x+h) - f(x)g(x+h) + f(x)g(x+h) - f(x)g(x)}{h}$$

$$= \lim_{h \to 0} \left( \frac{f(x+h) - f(x)}{h} g(x+h) + f(x) \frac{g(x+h) - g(x)}{h} \right)$$

$$= f'(x)g(x) + f(x)g'(x).$$

To get the last line, we have used the fact that $f$ and $g$ are differentiable and the fact that $g$ is therefore continuous (Theorem 1), as well as limit rules. A graphical proof of the Product Rule is suggested by Figure 5.19.

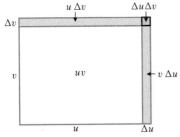

Figure 5.19

**A graphical proof of the Product Rule**

Here $u = f(x)$ and $v = g(x)$, so that the rectangular area $uv$ represents $f(x)g(x)$. If $x$ changes by an amount $\Delta x$, the corresponding increments in $u$ and $v$ are $\Delta u$ and $\Delta v$. The change in the area of the rectangle is

$$\Delta(uv)$$
$$= (u + \Delta u)(v + \Delta v) - uv$$
$$= (\Delta u)v + u(\Delta v) + (\Delta u)(\Delta v),$$

the sum of the three shaded areas. Dividing by $\Delta x$ and taking the limit as $\Delta x \to 0$, we get

$$\frac{d}{dx}(uv) = \left( \frac{du}{dx} \right)v + u\left( \frac{dv}{dx} \right),$$

since

$$\lim_{\Delta x \to 0} \frac{\Delta u}{\Delta x} \Delta v = \frac{du}{dx} \times 0 = 0.$$

EXAMPLE 3    Find the derivative of $(x^2 + 1)(x^3 + 4)$ using and without using the Product Rule.

*Solution*    Using the Product Rule with $f(x) = x^2 + 1$ and $g(x) = x^3 + 4$, we calculate

$$\frac{d}{dx}\left( (x^2 + 1)(x^3 + 4) \right) = 2x(x^3 + 4) + (x^2 + 1)(3x^2) = 5x^4 + 3x^2 + 8x.$$

On the other hand, we can calculate the derivative by first multiplying the two binomials and then differentiating the resulting polynomial:

$$\frac{d}{dx}\left( (x^2 + 1)(x^3 + 4) \right) = \frac{d}{dx}(x^5 + x^3 + 4x^2 + 4) = 5x^4 + 3x^2 + 8x.$$

EXAMPLE 4    Find $\dfrac{dy}{dx}$ if $y = \left( 2\sqrt{x} + \dfrac{3}{x} \right)\left( 3\sqrt{x} - \dfrac{2}{x} \right)$.

*Solution*    Applying the Product Rule with $f$ and $g$ being the two functions enclosed in the large parentheses, we obtain

$$\frac{dy}{dx} = \left( \frac{1}{\sqrt{x}} - \frac{3}{x^2} \right)\left( 3\sqrt{x} - \frac{2}{x} \right) + \left( 2\sqrt{x} + \frac{3}{x} \right)\left( \frac{3}{2\sqrt{x}} + \frac{2}{x^2} \right)$$

$$= 6 - \frac{5}{2x^{3/2}} + \frac{12}{x^3}.$$

EXAMPLE 5    Let $y = uv$ be the product of the functions $u$ and $v$. Find $y'(2)$ if $u(2) = 2$, $u'(2) = -5$, $v(2) = 1$, and $v'(2) = 3$.

*Solution*   From the Product Rule we have
$$y' = (uv)' = u'v + uv'.$$
Therefore,
$$y'(2) = u'(2)v(2) + u(2)v'(2) = (-5)(1) + (2)(3) = -5 + 6 = 1.$$

---

**EXAMPLE 6**   Use mathematical induction to verify the formula $\dfrac{d}{dx}x^n = n\,x^{n-1}$ for all positive integers $n$.

*Solution*   For $n = 1$ the formula says that $\frac{d}{dx}x^1 = 1 = 1x^0$, so the formula is true in this case. We must show that if the formula is true for $n = k \geq 1$, then it is also true for $n = k + 1$. Therefore, assume that
$$\frac{d}{dx}x^k = kx^{k-1}.$$
Using the Product Rule we calculate
$$\frac{d}{dx}x^{k+1} = \frac{d}{dx}(x^k x) = (kx^{k-1})(x) + (x^k)(1) = (k+1)x^k = (k+1)x^{(k+1)-1}.$$
Thus, the formula is true for $n = k + 1$ also. The formula is true for all integers $n \geq 1$ *by induction.*

---

The Product Rule can be extended to products of any number of factors; for instance,
$$(fgh)'(x) = f'(x)(gh)(x) + f(x)(gh)'(x)$$
$$= f'(x)g(x)h(x) + f(x)g'(x)h(x) + f(x)g(x)h'(x).$$
In general, the derivative of a product of $n$ functions will have $n$ terms; each term will be the same product but with one of the factors replaced by its derivative:

$$(f_1 f_2 f_3 \cdots f_n)' = f_1' f_2 f_3 \cdots f_n + f_1 f_2' f_3 \cdots f_n + \cdots + f_1 f_2 f_3 \cdots f_n'.$$

This can be proved by mathematical induction. See Exercise 54 at the end of this section.

## The Reciprocal Rule

**THEOREM**

**4**

**The Reciprocal Rule**

If $f$ is differentiable at $x$ and $f(x) \neq 0$, then $1/f$ is differentiable at $x$, and

$$\left(\frac{1}{f}\right)'(x) = \frac{-f'(x)}{(f(x))^2}.$$

*PROOF*   Using the definition of the derivative, we calculate
$$\frac{d}{dx}\frac{1}{f(x)} = \lim_{h \to 0} \frac{\dfrac{1}{f(x+h)} - \dfrac{1}{f(x)}}{h}$$
$$= \lim_{h \to 0} \frac{f(x) - f(x+h)}{hf(x+h)f(x)}$$
$$= \lim_{h \to 0} \left(\frac{-1}{f(x+h)f(x)}\right) \frac{f(x+h) - f(x)}{h}$$
$$= \frac{-1}{(f(x))^2} f'(x).$$

Again we have to use the continuity of $f$.

---

EXAMPLE 7  Differentiate the functions

(a) $\dfrac{1}{x^2 + 1}$  and  (b) $f(t) = \dfrac{1}{t + \dfrac{1}{t}}$.

*Solution*  Using the Reciprocal Rule:

(a) $\dfrac{d}{dx}\left(\dfrac{1}{x^2 + 1}\right) = \dfrac{-2x}{(x^2 + 1)^2}.$

(b) $f'(t) = \dfrac{-1}{\left(t + \dfrac{1}{t}\right)^2}\left(1 - \dfrac{1}{t^2}\right) = \dfrac{-t^2}{(t^2 + 1)^2}\dfrac{t^2 - 1}{t^2} = \dfrac{1 - t^2}{(t^2 + 1)^2}.$

---

We can use the Reciprocal Rule to confirm the General Power Rule for negative integers:

$$\dfrac{d}{dx}x^{-n} = -n\,x^{-n-1},$$

since we have already proved the rule for positive integers. We have

$$\dfrac{d}{dx}x^{-n} = \dfrac{d}{dx}\dfrac{1}{x^n} = \dfrac{-n\,x^{n-1}}{(x^n)^2} = -n\,x^{-n-1}.$$

EXAMPLE 8  **(Differentiating sums of reciprocals)**

$$\dfrac{d}{dx}\left(\dfrac{x^2 + x + 1}{x^3}\right) = \dfrac{d}{dx}\left(\dfrac{1}{x} + \dfrac{1}{x^2} + \dfrac{1}{x^3}\right)$$

$$= \dfrac{d}{dx}(x^{-1} + x^{-2} + x^{-3})$$

$$= -x^{-2} - 2x^{-3} - 3x^{-4} = -\dfrac{1}{x^2} - \dfrac{2}{x^3} - \dfrac{3}{x^4}.$$

---

## The Quotient Rule

The Product Rule and the Reciprocal Rule can be combined to provide a rule for differentiating a quotient of two functions. Observe that

$$\dfrac{d}{dx}\left(\dfrac{f(x)}{g(x)}\right) = \dfrac{d}{dx}\left(f(x)\dfrac{1}{g(x)}\right) = f'(x)\dfrac{1}{g(x)} + f(x)\left(-\dfrac{g'(x)}{(g(x))^2}\right)$$

$$= \dfrac{g(x)f'(x) - f(x)g'(x)}{(g(x))^2}.$$

Thus, we have proved the following Quotient Rule.

**THEOREM**

**5**

**The Quotient Rule**

If $f$ and $g$ are differentiable at $x$, and if $g(x) \neq 0$, then the quotient $f/g$ is differentiable at $x$ and

$$\left(\frac{f}{g}\right)'(x) = \frac{g(x)f'(x) - f(x)g'(x)}{(g(x))^2}.$$

Sometimes students have trouble remembering this rule. (Getting the order of the terms in the numerator wrong will reverse the sign.) Try to remember (and use) the Quotient Rule in the following form:

(quotient)$'$

$$= \frac{(\text{denominator}) \times (\text{numerator})' - (\text{numerator}) \times (\text{denominator})'}{(\text{denominator})^2}$$

---

**EXAMPLE 9**    Find the derivatives of

(a) $y = \dfrac{1 - x^2}{1 + x^2}$,    (b) $\dfrac{\sqrt{t}}{3 - 5t}$,    and    (c) $f(\theta) = \dfrac{a + b\theta}{m + n\theta}$.

**Solution**    We use the Quotient Rule in each case.

(a) $\dfrac{dy}{dx} = \dfrac{(1 + x^2)(-2x) - (1 - x^2)(2x)}{(1 + x^2)^2} = -\dfrac{4x}{(1 + x^2)^2}.$

(b) $\dfrac{d}{dt}\left(\dfrac{\sqrt{t}}{3 - 5t}\right) = \dfrac{(3 - 5t)\dfrac{1}{2\sqrt{t}} - \sqrt{t}(-5)}{(3 - 5t)^2} = \dfrac{3 + 5t}{2\sqrt{t}(3 - 5t)^2}.$

(c) $f'(\theta) = \dfrac{(m + n\theta)(b) - (a + b\theta)(n)}{(m + n\theta)^2} = \dfrac{mb - na}{(m + n\theta)^2}.$

---

In all three parts of Example 9, the Quotient Rule yielded fractions with numerators that were complicated but could be simplified algebraically. It is advisable to attempt such simplifications when calculating derivatives; the usefulness of derivatives in applications of calculus often depends on such simplifications.

---

**EXAMPLE 10**    Find equations of any lines that pass through the point $(-1, 0)$ and are tangent to the curve $y = (x - 1)/(x + 1)$.

**Solution**    The point $(-1, 0)$ does not lie on the curve, so it is not the point of tangency. Suppose a line is tangent to the curve at $x = a$, so the point of tangency is $(a, (a - 1)/(a + 1))$. Note that $a$ cannot be $-1$. The slope of the line must be

$$\left.\frac{dy}{dx}\right|_{x=a} = \left.\frac{(x + 1)(1) - (x - 1)(1)}{(x + 1)^2}\right|_{x=a} = \frac{2}{(a + 1)^2}.$$

If the line also passes through $(-1, 0)$, its slope must also be given by

$$\frac{\dfrac{a - 1}{a + 1} - 0}{a - (-1)} = \frac{a - 1}{(a + 1)^2}.$$

Equating these two expressions for the slope, we get an equation to solve for $a$:

$$\frac{a - 1}{(a + 1)^2} = \frac{2}{(a + 1)^2} \qquad \Longrightarrow \qquad a - 1 = 2.$$

Thus, $a = 3$, and the slope of the line is $2/4^2 = 1/8$. There is only one line through $(-1, 0)$ tangent to the given curve, and its equation is

$$y = 0 + \frac{1}{8}(x + 1) \qquad \text{or} \qquad x - 8y + 1 = 0.$$

*Remark*   Derivatives of quotients of functions where the denominator is a monomial, such as in Example 8, are usually easier to do by breaking the quotient into a sum of several fractions (as was done in that example) rather than by using the Quotient Rule.

## EXERCISES 5.3

In Exercises 1–32, calculate the derivatives of the given functions. Simplify your answers whenever possible.

**1.** $y = 3x^2 - 5x - 7$

**2.** $y = 4x^{1/2} - \dfrac{5}{x}$

**3.** $f(x) = Ax^2 + Bx + C$

**4.** $f(x) = \dfrac{6}{x^3} + \dfrac{2}{x^2} - 2$

**5.** $z = \dfrac{s^5 - s^3}{15}$

**6.** $y = x^{45} - x^{-45}$

**7.** $g(t) = t^{1/3} + 2t^{1/4} + 3t^{1/5}$

**8.** $y = 3\sqrt[3]{t^2} - \dfrac{2}{\sqrt{t^3}}$

**9.** $u = \dfrac{3}{5}x^{5/3} - \dfrac{5}{3}x^{-3/5}$

**10.** $F(x) = (3x - 2)(1 - 5x)$

**11.** $y = \sqrt{x}\left(5 - x - \dfrac{x^2}{3}\right)$

**12.** $g(t) = \dfrac{1}{2t - 3}$

**13.** $y = \dfrac{1}{x^2 + 5x}$

**14.** $y = \dfrac{4}{3 - x}$

**15.** $f(t) = \dfrac{\pi}{2 - \pi t}$

**16.** $g(y) = \dfrac{2}{1 - y^2}$

**17.** $f(x) = \dfrac{1 - 4x^2}{x^3}$

**18.** $g(u) = \dfrac{u\sqrt{u} - 3}{u^2}$

**19.** $y = \dfrac{2 + t + t^2}{\sqrt{t}}$

**20.** $z = \dfrac{x - 1}{x^{2/3}}$

**21.** $f(x) = \dfrac{3 - 4x}{3 + 4x}$

**22.** $z = \dfrac{t^2 + 2t}{t^2 - 1}$

**23.** $s = \dfrac{1 + \sqrt{t}}{1 - \sqrt{t}}$

**24.** $f(x) = \dfrac{x^3 - 4}{x + 1}$

**25.** $f(x) = \dfrac{ax + b}{cx + d}$

**26.** $F(t) = \dfrac{t^2 + 7t - 8}{t^2 - t + 1}$

**27.** $f(x) = (1 + x)(1 + 2x)(1 + 3x)(1 + 4x)$

**28.** $f(r) = (r^{-2} + r^{-3} - 4)(r^2 + r^3 + 1)$

**29.** $y = (x^2 + 4)(\sqrt{x} + 1)(5x^{2/3} - 2)$

**30.** $y = \dfrac{(x^2 + 1)(x^3 + 2)}{(x^2 + 2)(x^3 + 1)}$

**⚠ 31.** $y = \dfrac{x}{2x + \dfrac{1}{3x + 1}}$

**⚠ 32.** $f(x) = \dfrac{(\sqrt{x} - 1)(2 - x)(1 - x^2)}{\sqrt{x}(3 + 2x)}$

Calculate the derivatives in Exercises 33–36, given that $f(2) = 2$ and $f'(2) = 3$.

**33.** $\left. \dfrac{d}{dx}\left(\dfrac{x^2}{f(x)}\right) \right|_{x=2}$

**34.** $\left. \dfrac{d}{dx}\left(\dfrac{f(x)}{x^2}\right) \right|_{x=2}$

**35.** $\left. \dfrac{d}{dx}\left(x^2 f(x)\right) \right|_{x=2}$

**36.** $\left. \dfrac{d}{dx}\left(\dfrac{f(x)}{x^2 + f(x)}\right) \right|_{x=2}$

**37.** Find $\left. \dfrac{d}{dx}\left(\dfrac{x^2 - 4}{x^2 + 4}\right) \right|_{x=-2}$.   **38.** Find $\left. \dfrac{d}{dt}\left(\dfrac{t(1 + \sqrt{t})}{5 - t}\right) \right|_{t=4}$.

**39.** If $f(x) = \dfrac{\sqrt{x}}{x + 1}$, find $f'(2)$.

**40.** Find $\left. \dfrac{d}{dt}\left((1 + t)(1 + 2t)(1 + 3t)(1 + 4t)\right) \right|_{t=0}$.

**41.** Find an equation of the tangent line to $y = \dfrac{2}{3 - 4\sqrt{x}}$ at the point $(1, -2)$.

**42.** Find equations of the tangent and normal to $y = \dfrac{x + 1}{x - 1}$ at $x = 2$.

**43.** Find the points on the curve $y = x + 1/x$ where the tangent line is horizontal.

**44.** Find the equations of all horizontal lines that are tangent to the curve $y = x^2(4 - x^2)$.

**45.** Find the coordinates of all points where the curve $y = \dfrac{1}{x^2 + x + 1}$ has a horizontal tangent line.

**46.** Find the coordinates of points on the curve $y = \dfrac{x + 1}{x + 2}$ where the tangent line is parallel to the line $y = 4x$.

**47.** Find the equation of the straight line that passes through the point $(0, b)$ and is tangent to the curve $y = 1/x$. Assume $b \neq 0$.

**⚠ 48.** Show that the curve $y = x^2$ intersects the curve $y = 1/\sqrt{x}$ at right angles.

**49.** Find two straight lines that are tangent to $y = x^3$ and pass through the point $(2, 8)$.

**50.** Find two straight lines that are tangent to $y = x^2/(x - 1)$ and pass through the point $(2, 0)$.

**51. (A Square Root Rule)** Show that if $f$ is differentiable at $x$ and $f(x) > 0$, then

$$\frac{d}{dx}\sqrt{f(x)} = \frac{f'(x)}{2\sqrt{f(x)}}.$$

Use this Square Root Rule to find the derivative of $\sqrt{x^2 + 1}$.

**52.** Show that $f(x) = |x^3|$ is differentiable at every real number $x$, and find its derivative.

**Mathematical Induction**

**53.** Use mathematical induction to prove that

$$\frac{d}{dx}x^{n/2} = \frac{n}{2}x^{(n/2)-1}$$ for every positive integer $n$. Then use the Reciprocal Rule to get the same result for every negative integer $n$.

**54.** Use mathematical induction to prove the formula for the derivative of a product of $n$ functions given earlier in this section.

## 5.4 The Chain Rule

Although we can differentiate $\sqrt{x}$ and $x^2 + 1$, we cannot yet differentiate $\sqrt{x^2 + 1}$. To do this, we need a rule that tells us how to differentiate *composites* of functions whose derivatives we already know. This rule is known as the Chain Rule and is the most often used of all the differentiation rules.

---

**EXAMPLE 1** The function $\dfrac{1}{x^2 - 4}$ is the composite $f(g(x))$ of $f(u) = \dfrac{1}{u}$ and $g(x) = x^2 - 4$, which have derivatives

$$f'(u) = \frac{-1}{u^2} \quad \text{and} \quad g'(x) = 2x.$$

According to the Reciprocal Rule (which is a special case of the Chain Rule),

$$\frac{d}{dx}f(g(x)) = \frac{d}{dx}\left(\frac{1}{x^2 - 4}\right) = \frac{-2x}{(x^2 - 4)^2} = \frac{-1}{(x^2 - 4)^2}(2x)$$
$$= f'(g(x))g'(x).$$

---

This example suggests that the derivative of a composite function $f(g(x))$ is the derivative of $f$ evaluated at $g(x)$ multiplied by the derivative of $g$ evaluated at $x$. This is the Chain Rule:

$$\frac{d}{dx}f(g(x)) = f'(g(x))\,g'(x).$$

**THEOREM**

**6**

**The Chain Rule**

If $f(u)$ is differentiable at $u = g(x)$, and $g(x)$ is differentiable at $x$, then the composite function $f \circ g(x) = f(g(x))$ is differentiable at $x$, and

$$(f \circ g)'(x) = f'(g(x))g'(x).$$

In terms of Leibniz notation, if $y = f(u)$ where $u = g(x)$, then $y = f(g(x))$ and:

at $u$, $y$ is changing $\dfrac{dy}{du}$ times as fast as $u$ is changing;

at $x$, $u$ is changing $\dfrac{du}{dx}$ times as fast as $x$ is changing.

Therefore, at $x$, $y = f(u) = f(g(x))$ is changing $\dfrac{dy}{du} \times \dfrac{du}{dx}$ times as fast as $x$ is changing. That is,

$$\frac{dy}{dx} = \frac{dy}{du}\frac{du}{dx}, \qquad \text{where } \frac{dy}{du} \text{ is evaluated at } u = g(x).$$

It appears as though the symbol $du$ cancels from the numerator and denominator, but this is not meaningful because $dy/du$ was not defined as the quotient of two quantities, but rather as a single quantity, the derivative of $y$ with respect to $u$.

We would like to prove Theorem 6 by writing

$$\frac{\Delta y}{\Delta x} = \frac{\Delta y}{\Delta u}\frac{\Delta u}{\Delta x}$$

and taking the limit as $\Delta x \to 0$. Such a proof is valid for most composite functions but not all. (See Exercise 46 at the end of this section.) A correct proof will be given later in this section, but first we do more examples to get a better idea of how the Chain Rule works.

**EXAMPLE 2**    Find the derivative of $y = \sqrt{x^2 + 1}$.

**Solution**    Here $y = f(g(x))$, where $f(u) = \sqrt{u}$ and $g(x) = x^2 + 1$. Since the derivatives of $f$ and $g$ are

$$f'(u) = \frac{1}{2\sqrt{u}} \qquad \text{and} \qquad g'(x) = 2x,$$

the Chain Rule gives

$$\frac{dy}{dx} = \frac{d}{dx}f(g(x)) = f'(g(x)) \cdot g'(x)$$

$$= \frac{1}{2\sqrt{g(x)}} \cdot g'(x) = \frac{1}{2\sqrt{x^2 + 1}} \cdot (2x) = \frac{x}{\sqrt{x^2 + 1}}.$$

**Outside and Inside Functions**

In the composite $f(g(x))$, the function $f$ is "outside," and the function $g$ is "inside." The Chain Rule says that the derivative of the composite is the derivative $f'$ of the outside function evaluated at the inside function $g(x)$, multiplied by the derivative $g'(x)$ of the inside function:

$$\frac{d}{dx}f(g(x)) = f'(g(x)) \times g'(x).$$

Usually, when applying the Chain Rule, we do not introduce symbols to represent the functions being composed, but rather just proceed to calculate the derivative of the "outside" function and then multiply by the derivative of whatever is "inside." You can say to yourself: "the derivative of $f$ of something is $f'$ of that thing, multiplied by the derivative of that thing."

**EXAMPLE 3**    Find derivatives of the following functions:

(a) $(7x - 3)^{10}$,   (b) $f(t) = |t^2 - 1|$,   and   (c) $\left(3x + \frac{1}{(2x+1)^3}\right)^{1/4}$.

**Solution**

(a) Here, the outside function is the 10th power; it must be differentiated first and the result multiplied by the derivative of the expression $7x - 3$:

$$\frac{d}{dx}(7x - 3)^{10} = 10(7x - 3)^9(7) = 70(7x - 3)^9.$$

(b) Here, we are differentiating the absolute value of something. The derivative is signum of that thing, multiplied by the derivative of that thing:

$$f'(t) = \left(\text{sgn}(t^2 - 1)\right)(2t) = \frac{2t(t^2 - 1)}{|t^2 - 1|} = \begin{cases} 2t & \text{if } t < -1 \text{ or } t > 1 \\ -2t & \text{if } -1 < t < 1 \\ \text{undefined} & \text{if } t = \pm 1. \end{cases}$$

(c) Here, we will need to use the Chain Rule twice. We begin by differentiating the $1/4$ power of something, but the something involves the $-3$rd power of $2x + 1$, and the derivative of that will also require the Chain Rule:

$$\frac{d}{dx}\left(3x + \frac{1}{(2x+1)^3}\right)^{1/4} = \frac{1}{4}\left(3x + \frac{1}{(2x+1)^3}\right)^{-3/4}\frac{d}{dx}\left(3x + \frac{1}{(2x+1)^3}\right)$$

$$= \frac{1}{4}\left(3x + \frac{1}{(2x+1)^3}\right)^{-3/4}\left(3 - \frac{3}{(2x+1)^4}\frac{d}{dx}(2x+1)\right)$$

$$= \frac{3}{4}\left(1 - \frac{2}{(2x+1)^4}\right)\left(3x + \frac{1}{(2x+1)^3}\right)^{-3/4}.$$

When you start to feel comfortable with the Chain Rule, you may want to save a line or two by carrying out the whole differentiation in one step:

$$\frac{d}{dx}\left(3x + \frac{1}{(2x+1)^3}\right)^{1/4} = \frac{1}{4}\left(3x + \frac{1}{(2x+1)^3}\right)^{-3/4}\left(3 - \frac{3}{(2x+1)^4}(2)\right)$$

$$= \frac{3}{4}\left(1 - \frac{2}{(2x+1)^4}\right)\left(3x + \frac{1}{(2x+1)^3}\right)^{-3/4}.$$

Use of the Chain Rule produces products of factors that do not usually come out in the order you would naturally write them. Often you will want to rewrite the result with the factors in a different order. This is obvious in parts (a) and (c) of the example above. In monomials (expressions that are products of factors), it is common to write the factors in order of increasing complexity from left to right, with numerical factors coming first. One time when you would *not* waste time doing this, or trying to make any other simplification, is when you are going to evaluate the derivative at a particular number. In this case, substitute the number as soon as you have calculated the derivative, before doing any simplification:

$$\frac{d}{dx}(x^2 - 3)^{10}\bigg|_{x=2} = 10(x^2 - 3)^9(2x)\bigg|_{x=2} = (10)(1^9)(4) = 40.$$

**EXAMPLE 4** Suppose that $f$ is a differentiable function on the real line. In terms of the derivative $f'$ of $f$, express the derivatives of:

(a) $f(3x)$, (b) $f(x^2)$, (c) $f(\pi f(x))$, and (d) $[f(3 - 2f(x))]^4$.

*Solution*

(a) $\dfrac{d}{dx} f(3x) = \left(f'(3x)\right)(3) = 3f'(3x).$

(b) $\dfrac{d}{dx} f(x^2) = \left(f'(x^2)\right)(2x) = 2xf'(x^2).$

(c) $\dfrac{d}{dx} f(\pi f(x)) = \left(f'(\pi f(x))\right)(\pi f'(x)) = \pi f'(x)f'(\pi f(x)).$

(d) $\dfrac{d}{dx}\left[f(3 - 2f(x))\right]^4 = 4\left[f(3 - 2f(x))\right]^3 f'(3 - 2f(x))(-2f'(x))$

$$= -8f'(x)f'(3 - 2f(x))\left[f(3 - 2f(x))\right]^3.$$

As a final example, we illustrate combinations of the Chain Rule with the Product and Quotient Rules.

**EXAMPLE 5** Find and simplify the following derivatives:

(a) $f'(t)$ if $f(t) = \dfrac{t^2 + 1}{\sqrt{t^2 + 2}}$, and (b) $g'(-1)$ if $g(x) = \left(x^2 + 3x + 4\right)^5 \sqrt{3 - 2x}$.

*Solution*

(a)  $f'(t) = \dfrac{\sqrt{t^2 + 2}\,(2t) - (t^2 + 1)\dfrac{2t}{2\sqrt{t^2 + 2}}}{t^2 + 2}$

$= \dfrac{2t}{\sqrt{t^2 + 2}} - \dfrac{t^3 + t}{\left(t^2 + 2\right)^{3/2}} = \dfrac{t^3 + 3t}{\left(t^2 + 2\right)^{3/2}}.$

(b)  $g'(x) = 5\left(x^2 + 3x + 4\right)^4(2x + 3)\sqrt{3 - 2x} + \left(x^2 + 3x + 4\right)^5\dfrac{-2}{2\sqrt{3 - 2x}}$

$g'(-1) = (5)(2^4)(1)(\sqrt{5}) - \dfrac{2^5}{\sqrt{5}} = 80\sqrt{5} - \dfrac{32}{5}\,\sqrt{5} = \dfrac{368\sqrt{5}}{5}.$

## Finding Derivatives with Maple

Computer algebra systems know the derivatives of elementary functions and can calculate the derivatives of combinations of these functions symbolically, using differentiation rules. Maple's D operator can be used to find the derivative function D(f) of a function f of one variable. Alternatively, you can use diff to differentiate an expression with respect to a variable and then use the substitution routine subs to evaluate the result at a particular number.

```
>  f := x -> sqrt(1+2*x^2);
```

$$f := x \rightarrow \sqrt{1 + 2x^2}$$

```
>  fprime := D(f);
```

$$fprime := x \rightarrow 2\frac{x}{\sqrt{1 + 2x^2}}$$

```
>  fprime(2);
```

$$\frac{4}{3}$$

```
>  diff(t^2*sin(3*t),t);
```

$$2t\,\sin(3t) + 3t^2\,\cos(3t)$$

```
>  simplify(subs(t=Pi/12, %));
```

$$\frac{1}{12}\pi\,\sqrt{2} + \frac{1}{96}\pi^2\sqrt{2}$$

## Building the Chain Rule into Differentiation Formulas

If $u$ is a differentiable function of $x$ and $y = u^n$, then the Chain Rule gives

$$\frac{d}{dx}u^n = \frac{dy}{dx} = \frac{dy}{du}\frac{du}{dx} = nu^{n-1}\frac{du}{dx}.$$

The formula

$$\frac{d}{dx}u^n = nu^{n-1}\frac{du}{dx}$$

is just the formula $\frac{d}{dx}x^n = nx^{n-1}$ with an application of the Chain Rule built in, so that it applies to functions of $x$ rather than just to $x$. Some other differentiation rules with built-in Chain Rule applications are:

$$\frac{d}{dx}\left(\frac{1}{u}\right) = \frac{-1}{u^2}\frac{du}{dx} \qquad \text{(the Reciprocal Rule)}$$

$$\frac{d}{dx}\sqrt{u} = \frac{1}{2\sqrt{u}}\frac{du}{dx} \qquad \text{(the Square Root Rule)}$$

$$\frac{d}{dx}u^r = r\,u^{r-1}\frac{du}{dx} \qquad \text{(the General Power Rule)}$$

$$\frac{d}{dx}|u| = \operatorname{sgn}u\,\frac{du}{dx} = \frac{u}{|u|}\frac{du}{dx} \qquad \text{(the Absolute Value Rule)}$$

## Proof of the Chain Rule (Theorem 6)

Suppose that $f$ is differentiable at the point $u = g(x)$ and that $g$ is differentiable at $x$. Let the function $E(k)$ be defined by

$$E(0) = 0,$$

$$E(k) = \frac{f(u+k) - f(u)}{k} - f'(u), \qquad \text{if } k \neq 0.$$

By the definition of derivative, $\lim_{k \to 0} E(k) = f'(u) - f'(u) = 0 = E(0)$, so $E(k)$ is continuous at $k = 0$. Also, whether $k = 0$ or not, we have

$$f(u+k) - f(u) = \big(f'(u) + E(k)\big)k.$$

Now put $u = g(x)$ and $k = g(x+h) - g(x)$, so that $u + k = g(x+h)$, and obtain

$$f(g(x+h)) - f(g(x)) = \big(f'(g(x)) + E(k)\big)(g(x+h) - g(x)).$$

Since $g$ is differentiable at $x$, $\lim_{h \to 0}[g(x+h) - g(x)]/h = g'(x)$. Also, $g$ is continuous at $x$ by Theorem 1, so $\lim_{h \to 0} k = \lim_{h \to 0}(g(x+h) - g(x)) = 0$. Since $E$ is continuous at 0, $\lim_{h \to 0} E(k) = \lim_{k \to 0} E(k) = E(0) = 0$. Hence,

$$\frac{d}{dx}f(g(x)) = \lim_{h \to 0}\frac{f(g(x+h)) - f(g(x))}{h}$$

$$= \lim_{h \to 0}\big(f'(g(x)) + E(k)\big)\frac{g(x+h) - g(x)}{h}$$

$$= \big(f'(g(x)) + 0\big)g'(x) = f'(g(x))g'(x),$$

which was to be proved.

## EXERCISES 5.4

Find the derivatives of the functions in Exercises 1–16.

**1.** $y = (2x + 3)^6$

**2.** $y = \left(1 - \frac{x}{3}\right)^{99}$

**3.** $f(x) = (4 - x^2)^{10}$

**4.** $y = \sqrt{1 - 3x^2}$

**5.** $F(t) = \left(2 + \frac{3}{t}\right)^{-10}$

**6.** $(1 + x^{2/3})^{3/2}$

**7.** $\dfrac{3}{5 - 4x}$

**8.** $(1 - 2t^2)^{-3/2}$

**9.** $y = |1 - x^2|$

**10.** $f(t) = |2 + t^3|$

**11.** $y = 4x + |4x - 1|$

**12.** $y = (2 + |x|^3)^{1/3}$

**13.** $y = \dfrac{1}{2 + \sqrt{3x + 4}}$

**14.** $f(x) = \left(1 + \sqrt{\frac{x-2}{3}}\right)^4$

**15.** $z = \left(u + \dfrac{1}{u-1}\right)^{-5/3}$

**16.** $y = \dfrac{x^5\sqrt{3 + x^6}}{(4 + x^2)^3}$

**17.** Sketch the graph of the function in Exercise 10.

**18.** Sketch the graph of the function in Exercise 11.

Verify that the General Power Rule holds for the functions in Exercises 19–21.

**19.** $x^{1/4} = \sqrt{\sqrt{x}}$        **20.** $x^{3/4} = \sqrt{x\sqrt{x}}$

**21.** $x^{3/2} = \sqrt{(x^3)}$

In Exercises 22–29, express the derivative of the given function in terms of the derivative $f'$ of the differentiable function $f$.

**22.** $f(2t + 3)$        **23.** $f(5x - x^2)$

**24.** $\left[ f\left( \dfrac{2}{x} \right) \right]^3$        **25.** $\sqrt{3 + 2f(x)}$

**26.** $f\left( \sqrt{3 + 2t} \right)$        **27.** $f\left( 3 + 2\sqrt{x} \right)$

**28.** $f\left( 2f(3f(x)) \right)$        **29.** $f\left( 2 - 3f(4 - 5t) \right)$

**30.** Find $\dfrac{d}{dx} \left( \dfrac{\sqrt{x^2 - 1}}{x^2 + 1} \right)\bigg|_{x=-2}$.

**31.** Find $\dfrac{d}{dt} \sqrt{3t - 7}\bigg|_{t=3}$.

**32.** If $f(x) = \dfrac{1}{\sqrt{2x + 1}}$, find $f'(4)$.

**33.** If $y = (x^3 + 9)^{17/2}$, find $y'\bigg|_{x=-2}$.

**34.** Find $F'(0)$ if $F(x) = (1 + x)(2 + x)^2(3 + x)^3(4 + x)^4$.

**⚠ 35.** Calculate $y'$ if $y = (x + ((3x)^5 - 2)^{-1/2})^{-6}$. Try to do it all in one step.

In Exercises 36–39, find an equation of the tangent line to the given curve at the given point.

**36.** $y = \sqrt{1 + 2x^2}$ at $x = 2$

**37.** $y = (1 + x^{2/3})^{3/2}$ at $x = -1$

**38.** $y = (ax + b)^8$ at $x = b/a$

**39.** $y = 1/(x^2 - x + 3)^{3/2}$ at $x = -2$

**40.** Show that the derivative of $f(x) = (x - a)^m(x - b)^n$ vanishes at some point between $a$ and $b$ if $m$ and $n$ are positive integers.

Use Maple or another computer algebra system to evaluate and simplify the derivatives of the functions in Exercises 41–44.

**🖱 41.** $y = \sqrt{x^2 + 1} + \dfrac{1}{(x^2 + 1)^{3/2}}$

**🖱 42.** $y = \dfrac{(x^2 - 1)(x^2 - 4)(x^2 - 9)}{x^6}$

**🖱 43.** $\dfrac{dy}{dt}\bigg|_{t=2}$    if    $y = (t + 1)(t^2 + 2)(t^3 + 3)(t^4 + 4)(t^5 + 5)$

**🖱 44.** $f'(1)$    if    $f(x) = \dfrac{(x^2 + 3)^{1/2}(x^3 + 7)^{1/3}}{(x^4 + 15)^{1/4}}$

**❓ 45.** Does the Chain Rule enable you to calculate the derivatives of $|x|^2$ and $|x^2|$ at $x = 0$? Do these functions have derivatives at $x = 0$? Why?

**❗ 46.** What is wrong with the following "proof" of the Chain Rule? Let $k = g(x + h) - g(x)$. Then $\lim_{h \to 0} k = 0$. Thus,

$$\lim_{h \to 0} \frac{f(g(x + h)) - f(g(x))}{h}$$

$$= \lim_{h \to 0} \frac{f(g(x + h)) - f(g(x))}{g(x + h) - g(x)} \frac{g(x + h) - g(x)}{h}$$

$$= \lim_{h \to 0} \frac{f(g(x) + k) - f(g(x))}{k} \frac{g(x + h) - g(x)}{h}$$

$$= f'(g(x))\, g'(x).$$

---

5.5

## Derivatives of Trigonometric Functions

The trigonometric functions, especially sine and cosine, play a very important role in the mathematical modelling of real-world phenomena. In particular, they arise whenever quantities fluctuate in a periodic way. Elastic motions, vibrations, and waves of all kinds naturally involve the trigonometric functions, and many physical and mechanical laws are formulated as differential equations having these functions as solutions.

In this section we will calculate the derivatives of the six trigonometric functions. We only have to work hard for one of them, sine; the others then follow from known identities and the differentiation rules of Section 5.3.

### Some Special Limits

First, we have to establish some trigonometric limits that we will need to calculate the derivative of sine. It is assumed throughout that the arguments of the trigonometric functions are measured in radians.

**THEOREM**

**7**

The functions $\sin \theta$ and $\cos \theta$ are continuous at every value of $\theta$. In particular, at $\theta = 0$ we have:

$$\lim_{\theta \to 0} \sin \theta = \sin 0 = 0 \quad \text{and} \quad \lim_{\theta \to 0} \cos \theta = \cos 0 = 1.$$

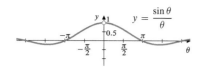

**Figure 5.20** It appears that $\lim_{\theta \to 0}(\sin\theta)/\theta = 1$

This result is obvious from the graphs of sine and cosine, so we will not prove it here. A proof can be based on the Squeeze Theorem. The method is suggested in Exercise 62 at the end of this section.

The graph of the function $y = (\sin\theta)/\theta$ is shown in Figure 5.20. Although it is not defined at $\theta = 0$, this function appears to have limit 1 as $\theta$ approaches 0.

**THEOREM**

**8**

**An important trigonometric limit**

$$\lim_{\theta \to 0} \frac{\sin\theta}{\theta} = 1 \qquad \text{(where } \theta \text{ is in radians).}$$

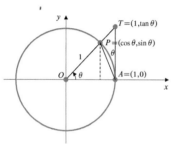

**Figure 5.21**  Area $\triangle\, OAP$
$<$ Area sector $OAP$
$<$ Area $\triangle\, OAT$

**PROOF** Let $0 < \theta < \pi/2$, and represent $\theta$ as shown in Figure 5.21. Points $A(1,0)$ and $P(\cos\theta, \sin\theta)$ lie on the unit circle $x^2 + y^2 = 1$. The area of the circular sector $OAP$ lies between the areas of triangles $OAP$ and $OAT$:

$$\text{Area } \triangle\, OAP < \text{Area sector } OAP < \text{Area } \triangle\, OAT.$$

The area of a circular sector having central angle $\theta$ (radians) and radius 1 is $\theta/2$. The area of a triangle is $(1/2) \times$ base $\times$ height, so

$$\text{Area } \triangle\, OAP = \frac{1}{2}(1)(\sin\theta) = \frac{\sin\theta}{2},$$

$$\text{Area } \triangle\, OAT = \frac{1}{2}(1)(\tan\theta) = \frac{\sin\theta}{2\cos\theta}.$$

Thus,

$$\frac{\sin\theta}{2} < \frac{\theta}{2} < \frac{\sin\theta}{2\cos\theta},$$

or, upon multiplication by the positive number $2/\sin\theta$,

$$1 < \frac{\theta}{\sin\theta} < \frac{1}{\cos\theta}.$$

Now take reciprocals, thereby reversing the inequalities:

$$1 > \frac{\sin\theta}{\theta} > \cos\theta.$$

Since $\lim_{\theta \to 0+}\cos\theta = 1$ by Theorem 7, the Squeeze Theorem gives

$$\lim_{\theta \to 0+} \frac{\sin\theta}{\theta} = 1.$$

Finally, note that $\sin\theta$ and $\theta$ are *odd functions*. Therefore, $f(\theta) = (\sin\theta)/\theta$ is an *even function*: $f(-\theta) = f(\theta)$, as shown in Figure 5.20. This symmetry implies that the left limit at 0 must have the same value as the right limit:

$$\lim_{\theta \to 0-} \frac{\sin\theta}{\theta} = 1 = \lim_{\theta \to 0+} \frac{\sin\theta}{\theta},$$

so $\lim_{\theta \to 0}(\sin\theta)/\theta = 1$.

Theorem 8 can be combined with limit rules and known trigonometric identities to yield other trigonometric limits.

---
**EXAMPLE 1**   Show that $\lim\limits_{h \to 0} \dfrac{\cos h - 1}{h} = 0$.

*Solution*   Using the half-angle formula $\cos h = 1 - 2\sin^2(h/2)$, we calculate

$$\lim_{h \to 0} \frac{\cos h - 1}{h} = \lim_{h \to 0} -\frac{2\sin^2(h/2)}{h} \qquad \text{Let } \theta = h/2.$$

$$= -\lim_{\theta \to 0} \frac{\sin \theta}{\theta}\, \sin \theta = -(1)(0) = 0.$$

---

## The Derivatives of Sine and Cosine

To calculate the derivative of $\sin x$, we need the addition formula for sine:

$$\sin(x + h) = \sin x \cos h + \cos x \sin h.$$

**THEOREM**

**9**

**The derivative of the sine function is the cosine function.**

$$\frac{d}{dx} \sin x = \cos x.$$

**PROOF**   We use the definition of derivative, the addition formula for sine, the rules for combining limits, Theorem 8, and the result of Example 1:

$$\frac{d}{dx} \sin x = \lim_{h \to 0} \frac{\sin(x + h) - \sin x}{h}$$

$$= \lim_{h \to 0} \frac{\sin x \cos h + \cos x \sin h - \sin x}{h}$$

$$= \lim_{h \to 0} \frac{\sin x (\cos h - 1) + \cos x \sin h}{h}$$

$$= \lim_{h \to 0} \sin x \cdot \lim_{h \to 0} \frac{\cos h - 1}{h} + \lim_{h \to 0} \cos x \cdot \lim_{h \to 0} \frac{\sin h}{h}$$

$$= (\sin x) \cdot (0) + (\cos x) \cdot (1) = \cos x.$$

**THEOREM**

**10**

**The derivative of the cosine function is the negative of the sine function.**

$$\frac{d}{dx} \cos x = -\sin x.$$

**PROOF**   We could mimic the proof for sine above, using the addition rule for cosine, $\cos(x + h) = \cos x \cos h - \sin x \sin h$. An easier way is to make use of the complementary angle identities, $\sin((\pi/2) - x) = \cos x$ and $\cos((\pi/2) - x) = \sin x$, and the Chain Rule from Section 5.4:

$$\frac{d}{dx} \cos x = \frac{d}{dx} \sin\left(\frac{\pi}{2} - x\right) = (-1)\cos\left(\frac{\pi}{2} - x\right) = -\sin x.$$

Notice the minus sign in the derivative of cosine. The derivative of the sine is the cosine, but the derivative of the cosine is *minus* the sine. This is shown graphically in Figure 5.22.

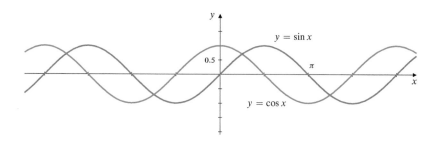

**Figure 5.22**    The sine (red) and cosine (blue) plotted together. The slope of the sine curve at $x$ is $\cos x$; the slope of the cosine curve at $x$ is $-\sin x$

---

**EXAMPLE 2**    Evaluate the derivatives of the following functions:

(a) $\sin(\pi x) + \cos(3x)$,    (b) $x^2 \sin \sqrt{x}$,    and    (c) $\dfrac{\cos x}{1 - \sin x}$.

*Solution*

(a) By the Sum Rule and the Chain Rule:

$$\frac{d}{dx}(\sin(\pi x) + \cos(3x)) = \cos(\pi x)(\pi) - \sin(3x)(3)$$
$$= \pi \cos(\pi x) - 3 \sin(3x).$$

(b) By the Product and Chain Rules:

$$\frac{d}{dx}(x^2 \sin \sqrt{x}) = 2x \sin \sqrt{x} + x^2 \left(\cos \sqrt{x}\right) \frac{1}{2\sqrt{x}}$$
$$= 2x \sin \sqrt{x} + \frac{1}{2}x^{3/2} \cos \sqrt{x}.$$

(c) By the Quotient Rule:

$$\frac{d}{dx}\left(\frac{\cos x}{1 - \sin x}\right) = \frac{(1 - \sin x)(-\sin x) - (\cos x)(0 - \cos x)}{(1 - \sin x)^2}$$
$$= \frac{-\sin x + \sin^2 x + \cos^2 x}{(1 - \sin x)^2}$$
$$= \frac{1 - \sin x}{(1 - \sin x)^2} = \frac{1}{1 - \sin x}.$$

We used the identity $\sin^2 x + \cos^2 x = 1$ to simplify the middle line.

---

Using trigonometric identities can sometimes change the way a derivative is calculated. Carrying out a differentiation in different ways can lead to different-looking answers, but they should be equal if no errors have been made.

---

**EXAMPLE 3**    Use two different methods to find the derivative of the function $f(t) = \sin t \cos t$.

*Solution*   By the Product Rule:

$$f'(t) = (\cos t)(\cos t) + (\sin t)(-\sin t) = \cos^2 t - \sin^2 t.$$

On the other hand, since $\sin(2t) = 2\sin t \cos t$, we have

$$f'(t) = \frac{d}{dt}\left(\frac{1}{2}\sin(2t)\right) = \left(\frac{1}{2}\right)(2)\cos(2t) = \cos(2t).$$

The two answers are really the same, since $\cos(2t) = \cos^2 t - \sin^2 t.$

It is very important to remember that the formulas for the derivatives of $\sin x$ and $\cos x$ were obtained under the assumption that $x$ is measured in *radians*. Since we know that $180° = \pi$ radians, $x° = \pi x/180$ radians. By the Chain Rule,

$$\frac{d}{dx}\sin(x°) = \frac{d}{dx}\sin\left(\frac{\pi x}{180}\right) = \frac{\pi}{180}\cos\left(\frac{\pi x}{180}\right) = \frac{\pi}{180}\cos(x°).$$

(See Figure 2.23.) Similarly, the derivative of $\cos(x°)$ is $-(\pi/180)\sin(x°)$.

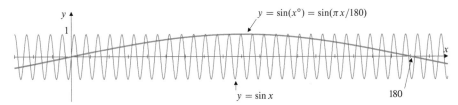

**Figure 5.23**   $\sin(x°)$ (blue) oscillates much more slowly than $\sin x$ (red). Its maximum slope is $\pi/180$

## The Derivatives of the Other Trigonometric Functions

Because $\sin x$ and $\cos x$ are differentiable everywhere, the functions

$$\tan x = \frac{\sin x}{\cos x} \qquad \sec x = \frac{1}{\cos x}$$

$$\cot x = \frac{\cos x}{\sin x} \qquad \csc x = \frac{1}{\sin x}$$

are differentiable at every value of $x$ at which they are defined (i.e., where their denominators are not zero). Their derivatives can be calculated by the Quotient and Reciprocal Rules and are as follows:

$$\frac{d}{dx}\tan x = \sec^2 x \qquad \frac{d}{dx}\sec x = \sec x \tan x$$

$$\frac{d}{dx}\cot x = -\csc^2 x \qquad \frac{d}{dx}\csc x = -\csc x \cot x.$$

**EXAMPLE 4**  Verify the derivative formulas for $\tan x$ and $\sec x$.

**Solution**  We use the Quotient Rule for tangent and the Reciprocal Rule for secant:

$$\frac{d}{dx}\tan x = \frac{d}{dx}\left(\frac{\sin x}{\cos x}\right) = \frac{\cos x \frac{d}{dx}(\sin x) - \sin x \frac{d}{dx}(\cos x)}{\cos^2 x}$$

$$= \frac{\cos x \cos x - \sin x(-\sin x)}{\cos^2 x} = \frac{\cos^2 x + \sin^2 x}{\cos^2 x}$$

$$= \frac{1}{\cos^2 x} = \sec^2 x.$$

$$\frac{d}{dx}\sec x = \frac{d}{dx}\left(\frac{1}{\cos x}\right) = \frac{-1}{\cos^2 x}\frac{d}{dx}(\cos x)$$

$$= \frac{-1}{\cos^2 x}(-\sin x) = \frac{1}{\cos x} \cdot \frac{\sin x}{\cos x}$$

$$= \sec x \tan x.$$

---

**EXAMPLE 5**  (a) $\dfrac{d}{dx}\left[3x + \cot\left(\dfrac{x}{2}\right)\right] = 3 + \left[-\csc^2\left(\dfrac{x}{2}\right)\right]\dfrac{1}{2} = 3 - \dfrac{1}{2}\csc^2\left(\dfrac{x}{2}\right)$

(b) $\dfrac{d}{dx}\left(\dfrac{3}{\sin(2x)}\right) = \dfrac{d}{dx}(3\csc(2x))$

$$= 3(-\csc(2x)\cot(2x))(2) = -6\csc(2x)\cot(2x).$$

---

**EXAMPLE 6**  Find the tangent and normal lines to the curve $y = \tan(\pi x/4)$ at the point $(1, 1)$.

**Solution**  The slope of the tangent to $y = \tan(\pi x/4)$ at $(1, 1)$ is

$$\left.\frac{dy}{dx}\right|_{x=1} = \frac{\pi}{4}\sec^2(\pi x/4)\bigg|_{x=1} = \frac{\pi}{4}\sec^2\left(\frac{\pi}{4}\right) = \frac{\pi}{4}\left(\sqrt{2}\right)^2 = \frac{\pi}{2}.$$

The tangent is the line

$$y = 1 + \frac{\pi}{2}(x - 1), \qquad \text{or} \qquad y = \frac{\pi x}{2} - \frac{\pi}{2} + 1.$$

The normal has slope $m = -2/\pi$, so its point-slope equation is

$$y = 1 - \frac{2}{\pi}(x - 1), \qquad \text{or} \qquad y = -\frac{2x}{\pi} + \frac{2}{\pi} + 1.$$

---

## EXERCISES 5.5

**1.** Verify the formula for the derivative of $\csc x = 1/(\sin x)$.

**2.** Verify the formula for the derivative of $\cot x = (\cos x)/(\sin x)$.

Find the derivatives of the functions in Exercises 3–36. Simplify your answers whenever possible. Also be on the lookout for ways you might simplify the given expression before differentiating it.

**3.** $y = \cos 3x$

**4.** $y = \sin\dfrac{x}{5}$

**5.** $y = \tan \pi x$

**6.** $y = \sec ax$

**7.** $y = \cot(4 - 3x)$

**8.** $y = \sin((\pi - x)/3)$

**9.** $f(x) = \cos(s - rx)$

**10.** $y = \sin(Ax + B)$

**11.** $\sin(\pi x^2)$

**12.** $\cos(\sqrt{x})$

**13.** $y = \sqrt{1 + \cos x}$

**14.** $\sin(2\cos x)$

**15.** $f(x) = \cos(x + \sin x)$

**16.** $g(\theta) = \tan(\theta \sin \theta)$

**17.** $u = \sin^3(\pi x/2)$

**18.** $y = \sec(1/x)$

**19.** $F(t) = \sin at \cos at$

**20.** $G(\theta) = \dfrac{\sin a\theta}{\cos b\theta}$

**21.** $\sin(2x) - \cos(2x)$

**22.** $\cos^2 x - \sin^2 x$

**23.** $\tan x + \cot x$

**24.** $\sec x - \csc x$

**25.** $\tan x - x$

**26.** $\tan(3x)\cot(3x)$

**27.** $t \cos t - \sin t$

**28.** $t \sin t + \cos t$

**29.** $\dfrac{\sin x}{1 + \cos x}$

**30.** $\dfrac{\cos x}{1 + \sin x}$

**31.** $x^2 \cos(3x)$

**32.** $g(t) = \sqrt{(\sin t)/t}$

**33.** $v = \sec(x^2)\tan(x^2)$

**34.** $z = \dfrac{\sin \sqrt{x}}{1 + \cos \sqrt{x}}$

**35.** $\sin(\cos(\tan t))$

**36.** $f(s) = \cos(s + \cos(s + \cos s))$

**37.** Given that $\sin 2x = 2 \sin x \cos x$, deduce that $\cos 2x = \cos^2 x - \sin^2 x$.

**38.** Given that $\cos 2x = \cos^2 x - \sin^2 x$, deduce that $\sin 2x = 2 \sin x \cos x$.

In Exercises 39–42, find equations for the lines that are tangent and normal to the curve $y = f(x)$ at the given point.

**39.** $y = \sin x$, $(\pi, 0)$

**40.** $y = \tan(2x)$, $(0, 0)$

**41.** $y = \sqrt{2} \cos(x/4)$, $(\pi, 1)$

**42.** $y = \cos^2 x$, $\left(\dfrac{\pi}{3}, \dfrac{1}{4}\right)$

**43.** Find an equation of the line tangent to the curve $y = \sin(x°)$ at the point where $x = 45$.

**44.** Find an equation of the straight line normal to $y = \sec(x°)$ at the point where $x = 60$.

**45.** Find the points on the curve $y = \tan x$, $-\pi/2 < x < \pi/2$, where the tangent is parallel to the line $y = 2x$.

**46.** Find the points on the curve $y = \tan(2x)$, $-\pi/4 < x < \pi/4$, where the normal is parallel to the line $y = -x/8$.

**47.** Show that the graphs of $y = \sin x$, $y = \cos x$, $y = \sec x$, and $y = \csc x$ have horizontal tangents.

**48.** Show that the graphs of $y = \tan x$ and $y = \cot x$ never have horizontal tangents.

Do the graphs of the functions in Exercises 49–52 have any horizontal tangents in the interval $0 \le x \le 2\pi$? If so, where? If not, why not?

**49.** $y = x + \sin x$

**50.** $y = 2x + \sin x$

**51.** $y = x + 2 \sin x$

**52.** $y = x + 2 \cos x$

Find the limits in Exercises 53–56.

**53.** $\lim\limits_{x \to 0} \dfrac{\tan(2x)}{x}$

**54.** $\lim\limits_{x \to \pi} \sec(1 + \cos x)$

**55.** $\lim\limits_{x \to 0} (x^2 \csc x \cot x)$

**56.** $\lim\limits_{x \to 0} \cos\left(\dfrac{\pi - \pi \cos^2 x}{x^2}\right)$

**57.** Use the method of Example 1 to evaluate $\lim\limits_{h \to 0} \dfrac{1 - \cos h}{h^2}$.

**58.** Find values of $a$ and $b$ that make

$$f(x) = \begin{cases} ax + b, & x < 0 \\ 2\sin x + 3\cos x, & x \ge 0 \end{cases}$$

differentiable at $x = 0$.

**59.** How many straight lines that pass through the origin are tangent to $y = \cos x$? Find (to 6 decimal places) the slopes of the two such lines that have the largest positive slopes.

Use Maple or another computer algebra system to evaluate and simplify the derivatives of the functions in Exercises 60–61.

**60.** $\dfrac{d}{dx} \left. \dfrac{x \cos(x \sin x)}{x + \cos(x \cos x)} \right|_{x=0}$

**61.** $\dfrac{d}{dx} \left( \sqrt{2x^2 + 3} \sin(x^2) - \dfrac{(2x^2 + 3)^{3/2} \cos(x^2)}{x} \right) \Big|_{x = \sqrt{\pi}}$

**62.** **(The continuity of sine and cosine)**

(a) Prove that

$$\lim\limits_{\theta \to 0} \sin \theta = 0 \quad \text{and} \quad \lim\limits_{\theta \to 0} \cos \theta = 1$$

as follows: Use the fact that the length of chord $AP$ is less than the length of arc $AP$ in Figure 5.24 to show that

$$\sin^2 \theta + (1 - \cos \theta)^2 < \theta^2.$$

Then deduce that $0 \le |\sin \theta| < |\theta|$ and $0 \le |1 - \cos \theta| < |\theta|$. Then use the Squeeze Theorem.

(b) Part (a) says that $\sin \theta$ and $\cos \theta$ are continuous at $\theta = 0$. Use the addition formulas to prove that they are therefore continuous at every $\theta$.

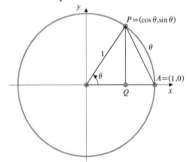

Figure 2.24

---

5.6   # Higher-Order Derivatives

If the derivative $y' = f'(x)$ of a function $y = f(x)$ is itself differentiable at $x$, we can calculate *its* derivative, which we call the **second derivative** of $f$ and denote by $y'' = f''(x)$. As is the case for first derivatives, second derivatives can be denoted by various notations depending on the context. Some of the more common ones are

$$y'' = f''(x) = \frac{d^2y}{dx^2} = \frac{d}{dx}\frac{d}{dx}f(x) = \frac{d^2}{dx^2}f(x) = D_x^2 y = D_x^2 f(x).$$

Similarly, you can consider third-, fourth-, and in general $n$th-order derivatives. The prime notation is inconvenient for derivatives of high order, so we denote the order by a superscript in parentheses (to distinguish it from an exponent): the $n$th derivative of $y = f(x)$ is

$$y^{(n)} = f^{(n)}(x) = \frac{d^n y}{dx^n} = \frac{d^n}{dx^n}f(x) = D_x^n y = D_x^n f(x),$$

and it is defined to be the derivative of the $(n-1)$st derivative. For $n = 1$, 2, and 3, primes are still normally used: $f^{(2)}(x) = f''(x)$, $f^{(3)}(x) = f'''(x)$. It is sometimes convenient to denote $f^{(0)}(x) = f(x)$, that is, to regard a function as its own zeroth-order derivative.

---

**EXAMPLE 1**    The **velocity** of a moving object is the (instantaneous) rate of change of the position of the object with respect to time; if the object moves along the $x$-axis and is at position $x = f(t)$ at time $t$, then its velocity at that time is

$$v = \frac{dx}{dt} = f'(t).$$

Similarly, the **acceleration** of the object is the rate of change of the velocity. Thus, the acceleration is the *second derivative* of the position:

$$a = \frac{dv}{dt} = \frac{d^2x}{dt^2} = f''(t).$$

We will investigate the relationships between position, velocity, and acceleration further in Section 5.11.

---

**EXAMPLE 2**    If $y = x^3$, then $y' = 3x^2$, $y'' = 6x$, $y''' = 6$, $y^{(4)} = 0$, and all higher derivatives are zero.

---

In general, if $f(x) = x^n$ (where $n$ is a positive integer), then

$$f^{(k)}(x) = n(n-1)(n-2)\cdots(n-(k-1))\,x^{n-k}$$

$$= \begin{cases} \dfrac{n!}{(n-k)!}\,x^{n-k} & \text{if } 0 \le k \le n \\ 0 & \text{if } k > n, \end{cases}$$

where $n!$ (called $n$ **factorial**) is defined by:

$$0! = 1$$
$$1! = 0! \times 1 = 1 \times 1 = 1$$
$$2! = 1! \times 2 = 1 \times 2 = 2$$
$$3! = 2! \times 3 = 1 \times 2 \times 3 = 6$$
$$4! = 3! \times 4 = 1 \times 2 \times 3 \times 4 = 24$$
$$\vdots$$
$$n! = (n-1)! \times n = 1 \times 2 \times 3 \times \cdots \times (n-1) \times n.$$

It follows that if $P$ is a polynomial of degree $n$,

$$P(x) = a_n x^n + a_{n-1} x^{n-1} + \cdots + a_1 x + a_0,$$

where $a_n$, $a_{n-1}$, $\ldots$ , $a_1$, $a_0$ are constants, then $P^{(k)}(x) = 0$ for $k > n$. For $k \leq n$, $P^{(k)}$ is a polynomial of degree $n - k$; in particular, $P^{(n)}(x) = n!a_n$, a constant function.

---

**EXAMPLE 3**   Show that if $A$, $B$, and $k$ are constants, then the function $y = A\cos(kt) + B\sin(kt)$ is a solution of the *second-order* **differential equation of simple harmonic motion** (see Section 6.7):

$$\frac{d^2 y}{dt^2} + k^2 y = 0.$$

*Solution*   To be a solution, the function $y(t)$ must satisfy the differential equation *identically*; that is,

$$\frac{d^2}{dt^2} y(t) + k^2 y(t) = 0$$

must hold for every real number $t$. We verify this by calculating the first two derivatives of the given function $y(t) = A\cos(kt) + B\sin(kt)$ and observing that the second derivative plus $k^2 y(t)$ is, in fact, zero everywhere:

$$\frac{dy}{dt} = -Ak\sin(kt) + Bk\cos(kt)$$

$$\frac{d^2 y}{dt^2} = -Ak^2\cos(kt) - Bk^2\sin(kt) = -k^2 y(t),$$

$$\frac{d^2 y}{dt^2} + k^2 y(t) = 0.$$

---

**EXAMPLE 4**   Find the $n$th derivative, $y^{(n)}$, of $y = \dfrac{1}{1+x} = (1+x)^{-1}$.

*Solution*   Begin by calculating the first few derivatives:

$$y' = -(1+x)^{-2}$$
$$y'' = -(-2)(1+x)^{-3} = 2(1+x)^{-3}$$
$$y''' = 2(-3)(1+x)^{-4} = -3!(1+x)^{-4}$$
$$y^{(4)} = -3!(-4)(1+x)^{-5} = 4!(1+x)^{-5}$$

The pattern here is becoming obvious. It seems that

$$y^{(n)} = (-1)^n n!(1+x)^{-n-1}.$$

We have not yet actually proved that the above formula is correct for every $n$, although it is clearly correct for $n = 1$, 2, 3, and 4. To complete the proof we use mathematical induction (Section 5.3). Suppose that the formula is valid for $n = k$, where $k$ is some positive integer. Consider $y^{(k+1)}$:

$$y^{(k+1)} = \frac{d}{dx} y^{(k)} = \frac{d}{dx}\left((-1)^k k!(1+x)^{-k-1}\right)$$
$$= (-1)^k k!(-k-1)(1+x)^{-k-2} = (-1)^{k+1}(k+1)!(1+x)^{-(k+1)-1}.$$

This is what the formula predicts for the $(k+1)$st derivative. Therefore, if the formula for $y^{(n)}$ is correct for $n = k$, then it is also correct for $n = k + 1$. Since the formula is known to be true for $n = 1$, it must therefore be true for every integer $n \geq 1$ *by induction*.

Note the use of $(-1)^n$ to denote a positive sign if $n$ is even and a negative sign if $n$ is odd.

**EXAMPLE 5**    Find a formula for $f^{(n)}(x)$, given that $f(x) = \sin(ax + b)$.

*Solution*    Begin by calculating several derivatives:

$$f'(x) = a \, \cos(ax + b)$$
$$f''(x) = -a^2 \, \sin(ax + b) = -a^2 f(x)$$
$$f'''(x) = -a^3 \, \cos(ax + b) = -a^2 f'(x)$$
$$f^{(4)}(x) = a^4 \, \sin(ax + b) = a^4 f(x)$$
$$f^{(5)}(x) = a^5 \, \cos(ax + b) = a^4 f'(x)$$
$$\vdots$$

The pattern is pretty obvious here. Each new derivative is $-a^2$ times the second previous one. A formula that gives all the derivatives is

$$f^{(n)}(x) = \begin{cases} (-1)^k \, a^n \, \sin(ax + b) & \text{if } n = 2k \\ (-1)^k \, a^n \, \cos(ax + b) & \text{if } n = 2k + 1 \end{cases} \qquad (k = 0, \, 1, \, 2, \, \ldots),$$

which can also be verified by induction on $k$.

Our final example shows that it is not always easy to obtain a formula for the $n$th derivative of a function.

**EXAMPLE 6**    Calculate $f'$, $f''$, and $f'''$ for $f(x) = \sqrt{x^2 + 1}$. Can you see enough of a pattern to predict $f^{(4)}$?

*Solution*    Since $f(x) = (x^2 + 1)^{1/2}$, we have

$$f'(x) = \tfrac{1}{2}(x^2 + 1)^{-1/2}(2x) = x(x^2 + 1)^{-1/2},$$
$$f''(x) = (x^2 + 1)^{-1/2} + x\left(-\tfrac{1}{2}\right)(x^2 + 1)^{-3/2}(2x)$$
$$= (x^2 + 1)^{-3/2}(x^2 + 1 - x^2) = (x^2 + 1)^{-3/2},$$
$$f'''(x) = -\tfrac{3}{2}(x^2 + 1)^{-5/2}(2x) = -3x(x^2 + 1)^{-5/2}.$$

Although the expression obtained from each differentiation simplified somewhat, the pattern of these derivatives is not (yet) obvious enough to enable us to predict the formula for $f^{(4)}(x)$ without having to calculate it. In fact,

$$f^{(4)}(x) = 3(4x^2 - 1)(x^2 + 1)^{-7/2},$$

so the pattern (if there is one) doesn't become any clearer at this stage.

**Remark**    Computing higher-order derivatives may be useful in applications involving Taylor polynomials. As taking derivatives can be automated with a known algorithm, it makes sense to use a computer to calculate higher-order ones. However, depending on the function, the amount of memory and processor time needed may severely restrict the order of derivatives calculated in this way. Higher-order derivatives can be indicated in Maple by repeating the variable of differentiation or indicating the order by using the $ operator:

```
> diff(x^5,x,x) + diff(sin(2*x),x$3);
```

$$20\,x^3 - 8\,\cos(2x)$$

The `D` operator can also be used for higher-order derivatives of a function (as distinct from an expression) by composing it explicitly or using the `@@` operator:

```
>  f := x -> x^5; fpp := D(D(f)); (D@@3)(f)(a);
```

$$f := x \to x^5$$
$$fpp := x \to 20\,x^3$$
$$60\,a^2$$

## EXERCISES 5.6

Find $y'$, $y''$, and $y'''$ for the functions in Exercises 1–12.

**1.** $y = (3 - 2x)^7$

**2.** $y = x^2 - \dfrac{1}{x}$

**3.** $y = \dfrac{6}{(x-1)^2}$

**4.** $y = \sqrt{ax+b}$

**5.** $y = x^{1/3} - x^{-1/3}$

**6.** $y = x^{10} + 2x^8$

**7.** $y = (x^2 + 3)\sqrt{x}$

**8.** $y = \dfrac{x-1}{x+1}$

**9.** $y = \tan x$

**10.** $y = \sec x$

**11.** $y = \cos(x^2)$

**12.** $y = \dfrac{\sin x}{x}$

In Exercises 13–23, calculate enough derivatives of the given function to enable you to guess the general formula for $f^{(n)}(x)$. Then verify your guess using mathematical induction.

**13.** $f(x) = \dfrac{1}{x}$

**14.** $f(x) = \dfrac{1}{x^2}$

**15.** $f(x) = \dfrac{1}{2-x}$

**16.** $f(x) = \sqrt{x}$

**17.** $f(x) = \dfrac{1}{a+bx}$

**18.** $f(x) = x^{2/3}$

**19.** $f(x) = \cos(ax)$

**20.** $f(x) = x \cos x$

**21.** $f(x) = x \sin(ax)$

**22.** $f(x) = \dfrac{1}{|x|}$

**23.** $f(x) = \sqrt{1-3x}$

**24.** If $y = \tan kx$, show that $y'' = 2k^2 y(1 + y^2)$.

**25.** If $y = \sec kx$, show that $y'' = k^2 y(2y^2 - 1)$.

**26.** Use mathematical induction to prove that the $n$th derivative of $y = \sin(ax + b)$ is given by the formula asserted at the end of Example 5.

**27.** Use mathematical induction to prove that the $n$th derivative of $y = \tan x$ is of the form $P_{n+1}(\tan x)$, where $P_{n+1}$ is a polynomial of degree $n + 1$.

**28.** If $f$ and $g$ are twice-differentiable functions, show that $(fg)'' = f''g + 2f'g' + fg''$.

**29.** State and prove the results analogous to that of Exercise 28 but for $(fg)^{(3)}$ and $(fg)^{(4)}$. Can you guess the formula for $(fg)^{(n)}$?

## 5.7 Using Differentials and Derivatives

In this section we will look at some examples of ways in which derivatives are used to represent and interpret changes and rates of change in the world around us. It is natural to think of change in terms of dependence on time, such as the velocity of a moving object, but there is no need to be so restrictive. Change with respect to variables other than time can be treated in the same way. For example, a physician may want to know how small changes in dosage can affect the body's response to a drug. An economist may want to study how foreign investment changes with respect to variations in a country's interest rates. These questions can all be formulated in terms of rate of change of a function with respect to a variable.

### Approximating Small Changes

If one quantity, say $y$, is a function of another quantity $x$, that is,

$$y = f(x),$$

we sometimes want to know how a change in the value of $x$ by an amount $\Delta x$ will affect the value of $y$. The exact change $\Delta y$ in $y$ is given by

$$\Delta y = f(x + \Delta x) - f(x),$$

but if the change $\Delta x$ is small, then we can get a good approximation to $\Delta y$ by using the fact that $\Delta y / \Delta x$ is approximately the derivative $dy/dx$. Thus,

$$\Delta y = \frac{\Delta y}{\Delta x} \Delta x \approx \frac{dy}{dx} \Delta x = f'(x) \Delta x.$$

It is often convenient to represent this approximation in terms of differentials; if we denote the change in $x$ by $dx$ instead of $\Delta x$, then the change $\Delta y$ in $y$ is approximated by the differential $dy$, that is (see Figure 5.25),

$$\Delta y \approx dy = f'(x)\, dx.$$

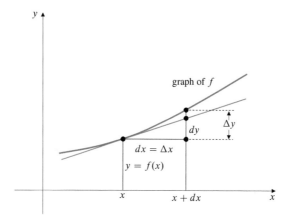

**Figure 5.25**    $dy$, the change in height to the tangent line, approximates $\Delta y$, the change in height to the graph of $f$

**EXAMPLE 1**    Without using a scientific calculator, determine by approximately how much the value of $\sin x$ increases as $x$ increases from $\pi/3$ to $(\pi/3) + 0.006$. To 3 decimal places, what is the value of $\sin\big((\pi/3) + 0.006\big)$?

*Solution*   If $y = \sin x$, $x = \pi/3 \approx 1.0472$, and $dx = 0.006$, then

$$dy = \cos(x)\, dx = \cos\left(\frac{\pi}{3}\right) dx = \frac{1}{2}(0.006) = 0.003.$$

Thus, the change in the value of $\sin x$ is approximately 0.003, and

$$\sin\left(\frac{\pi}{3} + 0.006\right) \approx \sin\frac{\pi}{3} + 0.003 = \frac{\sqrt{3}}{2} + 0.003 = 0.869$$

rounded to 3 decimal places.

Whenever one makes an approximation it is wise to try and estimate how big the error might be. We will have more to say about such approximations and their error estimates in Section 7.9.

Sometimes changes in a quantity are measured with respect to the size of the quantity. The **relative change** in $x$ is the ratio $dx/x$ if $x$ changes by amount $dx$. The **percentage change** in $x$ is the relative change expressed as a percentage:

$$\text{relative change in } x = \frac{dx}{x}$$

$$\text{percentage change in } x = 100\,\frac{dx}{x}.$$

EXAMPLE 2    By approximately what percentage does the area of a circle increase if the radius increases by 2%?

*Solution*    The area $A$ of a circle is given in terms of the radius $r$ by $A = \pi r^2$. Thus,

$$\Delta A \approx dA = \frac{dA}{dr} \, dr = 2\pi r \, dr.$$

We divide this approximation by $A = \pi r^2$ to get an approximation that links the relative changes in $A$ and $r$:

$$\frac{\Delta A}{A} \approx \frac{dA}{A} = \frac{2\pi r \, dr}{\pi r^2} = 2 \frac{dr}{r}.$$

If $r$ increases by 2%, then $dr = \frac{2}{100} r$, so

$$\frac{\Delta A}{A} \approx 2 \times \frac{2}{100} = \frac{4}{100}.$$

Thus, $A$ increases by approximately 4%.

## Average and Instantaneous Rates of Change

Recall the concept of average rate of change of a function over an interval. The derivative of the function is the limit of this average rate as the length of the interval goes to zero and so represents the rate of change of the function at a given value of its variable.

DEFINITION

**5**

> The **average rate of change** of a function $f(x)$ with respect to $x$ over the interval from $a$ to $a + h$ is
>
> $$\frac{f(a+h) - f(a)}{h}.$$
>
> The **(instantaneous) rate of change** of $f$ with respect to $x$ at $x = a$ is the derivative
>
> $$f'(a) = \lim_{h \to 0} \frac{f(a+h) - f(a)}{h},$$
>
> provided the limit exists.

It is conventional to use the word *instantaneous* even when $x$ does not represent time, although the word is frequently omitted. When we say *rate of change*, we mean *instantaneous rate of change*.

EXAMPLE 3    How fast is area $A$ of a circle increasing with respect to its radius
when the radius is 5 m?

*Solution*    The rate of change of the area with respect to the radius is

$$\frac{dA}{dr} = \frac{d}{dr} (\pi r^2) = 2\pi r.$$

When $r = 5$ m, the area is changing at the rate $2\pi \times 5 = 10\pi$ m²/m. This means that a small change $\Delta r$ m in the radius when the radius is 5 m would result in a change of about $10\pi \Delta r$ m² in the area of the circle.

The above example suggests that the appropriate units for the rate of change of a quantity $y$ with respect to another quantity $x$ are units of $y$ per unit of $x$.

If $f'(x_0) = 0$, we say that $f$ is **stationary** at $x_0$ and call $x_0$ a **critical point** of $f$. The corresponding point $(x_0, f(x_0))$ on the graph of $f$ is also called a **critical point** of the graph. The graph has a horizontal tangent at a critical point, and $f$ may or may not have a maximum or minimum value there. (See Figure 5.26.) It is still possible for $f$ to be increasing or decreasing on an open interval containing a critical point. (See point $a$ in Figure 5.26.) We will revisit these ideas in the next section.

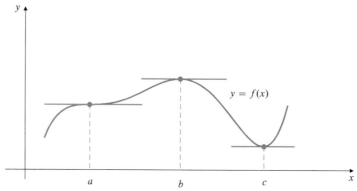

Figure 5.26    Critical points of $f$

**EXAMPLE 4**    Suppose the temperature at a certain location $t$ hours after noon on a certain day is $T$ °C ($T$ degrees Celsius), where

$$T = \frac{1}{3}t^3 - 3t^2 + 8t + 10 \qquad \text{(for } 0 \le t \le 5\text{).}$$

How fast is the temperature rising or falling at 1:00 p.m.? At 3:00 p.m.? At what instants is the temperature stationary?

*Solution*    The rate of change of the temperature is given by

$$\frac{dT}{dt} = t^2 - 6t + 8 = (t - 2)(t - 4).$$

If $t = 1$, then $\dfrac{dT}{dt} = 3$, so the temperature is *rising* at rate 3 °C/h at 1:00 p.m.

If $t = 3$, then $\dfrac{dT}{dt} = -1$, so the temperature is *falling* at a rate of 1 °C/h at 3:00 p.m.

The temperature is stationary when $\dfrac{dT}{dt} = 0$, that is, at 2:00 p.m. and 4:00 p.m.

## Sensitivity to Change

When a small change in $x$ produces a large change in the value of a function $f(x)$, we say that the function is very **sensitive** to changes in $x$. The derivative $f'(x)$ is a measure of the sensitivity of the dependence of $f$ on $x$.

**EXAMPLE 5**    (**Dosage of a medicine**)  A pharmacologist studying a drug that has been developed to lower blood pressure determines experimentally that the average reduction $R$ in blood pressure resulting from a daily dosage of $x$ mg of the drug is

$$R = 24.2 \left(1 + \frac{x - 13}{\sqrt{x^2 - 26x + 529}}\right) \text{ mm Hg.}$$

(The units are millimetres of mercury (Hg).) Determine the sensitivity of $R$ to dosage $x$ at dosage levels of 5 mg, 15 mg, and 35 mg. At which of these dosage levels would an increase in the dosage have the greatest effect?

*Solution*  The sensitivity of $R$ to $x$ is $dR/dx$. We have

$$\frac{dR}{dx} = 24.2\left(\frac{\sqrt{x^2 - 26x + 529}(1) - (x - 13)\dfrac{x - 13}{\sqrt{x^2 - 26x + 529}}}{x^2 - 26x + 529}\right)$$

$$= 24.2\left(\frac{x^2 - 26x + 529 - (x^2 - 26x + 169)}{(x^2 - 26x + 529)^{3/2}}\right)$$

$$= \frac{8{,}712}{(x^2 - 26x + 529)^{3/2}}.$$

At dosages $x = 5$ mg, 15 mg, and 35 mg, we have sensitivities of

$$\left.\frac{dR}{dx}\right|_{x=5} = 0.998 \text{ mm Hg/mg}, \qquad \left.\frac{dR}{dx}\right|_{x=15} = 1.254 \text{ mm Hg/mg},$$

$$\left.\frac{dR}{dx}\right|_{x=35} = 0.355 \text{ mm Hg/mg}.$$

Among these three levels, the greatest sensitivity is at 15 mg. Increasing the dosage from 15 to 16 mg/day could be expected to further reduce average blood pressure by about 1.25 mm Hg.

## Derivatives in Economics

Just as physicists use terms such as *velocity* and *acceleration* to refer to derivatives of certain quantities, economists also have their own specialized vocabulary for derivatives. They call them marginals. In economics the term **marginal** denotes the rate of change of a quantity with respect to a variable on which it depends. For example, the **cost of production** $C(x)$ in a manufacturing operation is a function of $x$, the number of units of product produced. The **marginal cost of production** is the rate of change of $C$ with respect to $x$, so it is $dC/dx$. Sometimes the marginal cost of production is loosely defined to be the extra cost of producing one more unit; that is,

$$\Delta C = C(x + 1) - C(x).$$

To see why this is approximately correct, observe from Figure 5.27 that if the slope of $C = C(x)$ does not change quickly near $x$, then the difference quotient $\Delta C/\Delta x$ will be close to its limit, the derivative $dC/dx$, even if $\Delta x = 1$.

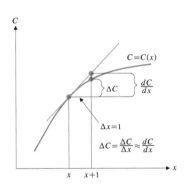

**Figure 5.27**  The marginal cost $dC/dx$ is approximately the extra cost $\Delta C$ of producing $\Delta x = 1$ more unit

---

**EXAMPLE 6**  **(Marginal tax rates)**  If your marginal income tax rate is 35% and your income increases by $1,000, you can expect to have to pay an extra $350 in income taxes. This does not mean that you pay 35% of your entire income in taxes. It just means that at your current income level $I$, the rate of increase of taxes $T$ with respect to income is $dT/dI = 0.35$. You will pay $0.35 out of every extra dollar you earn in taxes. Of course, if your income increases greatly, you may land in a higher tax bracket and your marginal rate will increase.

---

**EXAMPLE 7**  **(Marginal cost of production)**  The cost of producing $x$ tonnes of coal per day in a mine is $\$C(x)$, where

$$C(x) = 4{,}200 + 5.40x - 0.001x^2 + 0.000\,002x^3.$$

(a) What is the average cost of producing each tonne if the daily production level is 1,000 tonnes? 2,000 tonnes?

(b) Find the marginal cost of production if the daily production level is 1,000 tonnes. 2,000 tonnes.

(c) If the production level increases slightly from 1,000 tonnes or from 2,000 tonnes, what will happen to the average cost per tonne?

*Solution*

(a) The average cost per tonne of coal is

$$\frac{C(x)}{x} = \frac{4,200}{x} + 5.40 - 0.001x + 0.000\,002x^2.$$

If $x = 1{,}000$, the average cost per tonne is $C(1{,}000)/1{,}000 = \$10.60$/tonne. If $x = 2{,}000$, the average cost per tonne is $C(2{,}000)/2{,}000 = \$13.50$/tonne.

(b) The marginal cost of production is

$$C'(x) = 5.40 - 0.002x + 0.000\,006x^2.$$

If $x = 1{,}000$, the marginal cost is $C'(1{,}000) = \$9.40$/tonne. If $x = 2{,}000$, the marginal cost is $C'(2{,}000) = \$25.40$/tonne.

(c) If the production level $x$ is increased slightly from $x = 1{,}000$, then the average cost per tonne will drop because the cost is increasing at a rate lower than the average cost. At $x = 2{,}000$ the opposite is true; an increase in production will increase the average cost per tonne.

---

Economists sometimes prefer to measure relative rates of change that do not depend on the units used to measure the quantities involved. They use the term **elasticity** for such relative rates.

---

**EXAMPLE 8**   **(Elasticity of demand)** The demand $y$ for a certain product (i.e., the amount that can be sold) typically depends on the price $p$ charged for the product: $y = f(p)$. The marginal demand $dy/dp = f'(p)$ (which is typically negative) depends on the units used to measure $y$ and $p$. The *elasticity of the demand* is the quantity

$$-\frac{p}{y}\frac{dy}{dp} \qquad \text{(the ``$-$'' sign ensures elasticity is positive),}$$

which is independent of units and provides a good measure of the sensitivity of demand to changes in price. To see this, suppose that new units of demand and price are introduced, which are multiples of the old units. In terms of the new units the demand and price are now $Y$ and $P$, where

$$Y = k_1 y \qquad \text{and} \qquad P = k_2 p.$$

Thus, $Y = k_1 f(P/k_2)$ and $dY/dP = (k_1/k_2)f'(P/k_2) = (k_1/k_2)f'(p)$ by the Chain Rule. It follows that the elasticity has the same value:

$$-\frac{P}{Y}\frac{dY}{dP} = -\frac{k_2 p}{k_1 y}\frac{k_1}{k_2}f'(p) = -\frac{p}{y}\frac{dy}{dp}.$$

---

## EXERCISES 5.7

In Exercises 1–4, use differentials to determine the approximate change in the value of the given function as its argument changes from the given value by the given amount. What is the approximate value of the function after the change?

**1.** $y = 1/x$, as $x$ increases from 2 to 2.01.

**2.** $f(x) = \sqrt{3x + 1}$, as $x$ increases from 1 to 1.08.

**3.** $h(t) = \cos(\pi t/4)$, as $t$ increases from 2 to $2 + (1/10\pi)$.

**4.** $u = \tan(s/4)$ as $s$ decreases from $\pi$ to $\pi - 0.04$.

In Exercises 5–10, find the approximate percentage changes in the given function $y = f(x)$ that will result from an increase of 2% in the value of $x$.

**5.** $y = x^2$

**6.** $y = 1/x$

**7.** $y = 1/x^2$

**8.** $y = x^3$

**9.** $y = \sqrt{x}$

**10.** $y = x^{-2/3}$

**11.** By approximately what percentage will the volume $(V = \frac{4}{3}\pi r^3)$ of a ball of radius $r$ increase if the radius increases by 2%?

**12.** By about what percentage will the edge length of an ice cube decrease if the cube loses 6% of its volume by melting?

**13.** Find the rate of change of the area of a square with respect to the length of its side when the side is 4 ft.

**14.** Find the rate of change of the side of a square with respect to the area of the square when the area is $16 \text{ m}^2$.

**15.** Find the rate of change of the diameter of a circle with respect to its area.

**16.** Find the rate of change of the area of a circle with respect to its diameter.

**17.** Find the rate of change of the volume of a sphere (given by $V = \frac{4}{3}\pi r^3$) with respect to its radius $r$ when the radius is 2 m.

**18.** What is the rate of change of the area $A$ of a square with respect to the length $L$ of the diagonal of the square?

**19.** What is the rate of change of the circumference $C$ of a circle with respect to the area $A$ of the circle?

**20.** Find the rate of change of the side $s$ of a cube with respect to the volume $V$ of the cube.

**21.** The volume of water in a tank $t$ min after it starts draining is

$$V(t) = 350(20 - t)^2 \text{ L}.$$

(a) How fast is the water draining out after 5 min? after 15 min?

(b) What is the average rate at which water is draining out during the time interval from 5 to 15 min?

**22. (Poiseuille's Law)** The flow rate $F$ (in litres per minute) of a liquid through a pipe is proportional to the fourth power of the radius of the pipe:

$$F = kr^4.$$

Approximately what percentage increase is needed in the radius of the pipe to increase the flow rate by 10%?

**23. (Gravitational force)** The gravitational force $F$ with which the earth attracts an object in space is given by $F = k/r^2$, where $k$ is a constant and $r$ is the distance from the object to the centre of the earth. If $F$ decreases with respect to $r$ at rate 1 pound/mile when $r = 4,000$ mi, how fast does $F$ change with respect to $r$ when $r = 8,000$ mi?

**24. (Sensitivity of revenue to price)** The sales revenue $\$R$ from a software product depends on the price $\$p$ charged by the distributor according to the formula

$$R = 4,000p - 10p^2.$$

(a) How sensitive is $R$ to $p$ when $p = \$100$? $p = \$200$? $p = \$300$?

(b) Which of these three is the most reasonable price for the distributor to charge? Why?

**25. (Marginal cost)** The cost of manufacturing $x$ refrigerators is $\$C(x)$, where

$$C(x) = 8,000 + 400x - 0.5x^2.$$

(a) Find the marginal cost if 100 refrigerators are manufactured.

(b) Show that the marginal cost is approximately the difference in cost of manufacturing 101 refrigerators instead of 100.

**26. (Marginal profit)** If a plywood factory produces $x$ sheets of plywood per day, its profit per day will be $\$P(x)$, where

$$P(x) = 8x - 0.005x^2 - 1,000.$$

(a) Find the marginal profit. For what values of $x$ is the marginal profit positive? negative?

(b) How many sheets should be produced each day to generate maximum profits?

**27.** The cost $C$ (in dollars) of producing $n$ widgets per month in a widget factory is given by

$$C = \frac{80,000}{n} + 4n + \frac{n^2}{100}.$$

Find the marginal cost of production if the number of widgets manufactured each month is (a) 100 and (b) 300.

**! 28.** In a mining operation the cost $C$ (in dollars) of extracting each tonne of ore is given by

$$C = 10 + \frac{20}{x} + \frac{x}{1,000},$$

where $x$ is the number of tonnes extracted each day. (For small $x$, $C$ decreases as $x$ increases because of economies of scale, but for large $x$, $C$ increases with $x$ because of overloaded equipment and labour overtime.) If each tonne of ore can be sold for $13, how many tonnes should be extracted each day to maximize the daily profit of the mine?

**! 29. (Average cost and marginal cost)** If it costs a manufacturer $C(x)$ dollars to produce $x$ items, then his average cost of production is $C(x)/x$ dollars per item. Typically the average cost is a decreasing function of $x$ for small $x$ and an increasing function of $x$ for large $x$. (Why?)

Show that the value of $x$ that minimizes the average cost makes the average cost equal to the marginal cost.

**30. (Constant elasticity)** Show that if demand $y$ is related to price $p$ by the equation $y = Cp^{-r}$, where $C$ and $r$ are positive constants, then the elasticity of demand (see Example 8) is the constant $r$.

---

 5.8     The Mean-Value Theorem

If you set out in a car at 1:00 p.m. and arrive in a town 150 km away from your starting point at 3:00 p.m., then you have travelled at an average speed of $150/2 = 75$ km/h. Although you may not have travelled at constant speed, you must have been going 75 km/h at *at least one instant* during your journey, for if your speed was always less than 75 km/h you would have gone less than 150 km in 2 h, and if your speed was always more than 75 km/h, you would have gone more than 150 km in 2 h. In order to get from a value less than 75 km/h to a value greater than 75 km/h, your speed, which is a continuous function of time, must pass through the value 75 km/h at some intermediate time.

The conclusion that the average speed over a time interval must be equal to the instantaneous speed at some time in that interval is an instance of an important mathematical principle. In geometric terms it says that if $A$ and $B$ are two points on a smooth curve, then there is at least one point $C$ on the curve between $A$ and $B$ where the tangent line is parallel to the chord line $AB$. See Figure 5.28.

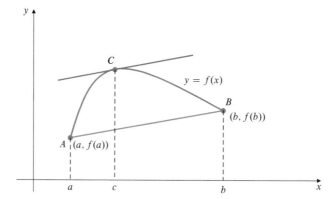

**Figure 5.28**     There is a point $C$ on the curve where the tangent (green) is parallel to the chord $AB$ (blue)

This principle is stated more precisely in the following theorem.

**T H E O R E M**

**11**

**The Mean-Value Theorem**

Suppose that the function $f$ is continuous on the closed, finite interval $[a, b]$ and that it is differentiable on the open interval $(a, b)$. Then there exists a point $c$ in the open interval $(a, b)$ such that

$$\frac{f(b) - f(a)}{b - a} = f'(c).$$

This says that the slope of the chord line joining the points $(a, f(a))$ and $(b, f(b))$ is equal to the slope of the tangent line to the curve $y = f(x)$ at the point $(c, f(c))$, so the two lines are parallel.

We will prove the Mean-Value Theorem later in this section. For now we make several observations:

1. The hypotheses of the Mean-Value Theorem are all necessary for the conclusion; if $f$ fails to be continuous at even one point of $[a, b]$ or fails to be differentiable

at even one point of $(a,b)$, then there may be no point where the tangent line is parallel to the secant line $AB$. (See Figure 5.29.)

2. The Mean-Value Theorem gives no indication of how many points $C$ there may be on the curve between $A$ and $B$ where the tangent is parallel to $AB$. If the curve is itself the straight line $AB$, then every point on the line between $A$ and $B$ has the required property. In general, there may be more than one point (see Figure 5.30); the Mean-Value Theorem asserts only that there must be at least one.

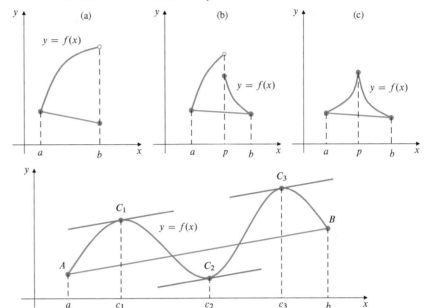

**Figure 5.29** Functions that fail to satisfy the hypotheses of the Mean-Value Theorem and for which the conclusion is false:

(a) $f$ is discontinuous at endpoint $b$

(b) $f$ is discontinuous at $p$

(c) $f$ is not differentiable at $p$

**Figure 5.30** For this curve there are three points $C$ where the tangent (green) is parallel to the chord $AB$ (blue)

3. The Mean-Value Theorem gives us no information on how to find the point $c$, which it says must exist. For some simple functions it is possible to calculate $c$ (see the following example), but doing so is usually of no practical value. As we shall see, the importance of the Mean-Value Theorem lies in its use as a theoretical tool. It belongs to a class of theorems called *existence theorems*, as do the Max-Min Theorem and the Intermediate-Value Theorem.

**EXAMPLE 1** Verify the conclusion of the Mean-Value Theorem for $f(x) = \sqrt{x}$ on the interval $[a,b]$, where $0 \le a < b$.

**Solution** The theorem says that there must be a number $c$ in the interval $(a,b)$ such that

$$f'(c) = \frac{f(b)-f(a)}{b-a}$$

$$\frac{1}{2\sqrt{c}} = \frac{\sqrt{b}-\sqrt{a}}{b-a} = \frac{\sqrt{b}-\sqrt{a}}{(\sqrt{b}-\sqrt{a})(\sqrt{b}+\sqrt{a})} = \frac{1}{\sqrt{b}+\sqrt{a}}.$$

Thus, $2\sqrt{c} = \sqrt{a}+\sqrt{b}$ and $c = \left(\dfrac{\sqrt{b}+\sqrt{a}}{2}\right)^2$. Since $a < b$, we have

$$a = \left(\frac{\sqrt{a}+\sqrt{a}}{2}\right)^2 < c < \left(\frac{\sqrt{b}+\sqrt{b}}{2}\right)^2 = b,$$

so $c$ lies in the interval $(a,b)$.

The following two examples are more representative of how the Mean-Value Theorem is actually used.

**EXAMPLE 2**    Show that $\sin x < x$ for all $x > 0$.

**Solution**  If $x > 2\pi$, then $\sin x \leq 1 < 2\pi < x$. If $0 < x \leq 2\pi$, then, by the Mean-Value Theorem, there exists $c$ in the open interval $(0, 2\pi)$ such that

$$\frac{\sin x}{x} = \frac{\sin x - \sin 0}{x - 0} = \frac{d}{dx}\sin x\Big|_{x=c} = \cos c < 1.$$

Thus, $\sin x < x$ in this case too.

**EXAMPLE 3**    Show that $\sqrt{1+x} < 1 + \frac{x}{2}$ for $x > 0$ and for $-1 \leq x < 0$.

**Solution**  If $x > 0$, apply the Mean-Value Theorem to $f(x) = \sqrt{1+x}$ on the interval $[0, x]$. There exists $c$ in $(0, x)$ such that

$$\frac{\sqrt{1+x} - 1}{x} = \frac{f(x) - f(0)}{x - 0} = f'(c) = \frac{1}{2\sqrt{1+c}} < \frac{1}{2}.$$

The last inequality holds because $c > 0$. Multiplying by the positive number $x$ and transposing the $-1$ gives $\sqrt{1+x} < 1 + \frac{x}{2}$.

If $-1 \leq x < 0$, we apply the Mean-Value Theorem to $f(x) = \sqrt{1+x}$ on the interval $[x, 0]$. There exists $c$ in $(x, 0)$ such that

$$\frac{\sqrt{1+x} - 1}{x} = \frac{1 - \sqrt{1+x}}{-x} = \frac{f(0) - f(x)}{0 - x} = f'(c) = \frac{1}{2\sqrt{1+c}} > \frac{1}{2}$$

(because $0 < 1 + c < 1$). Now we must multiply by the negative number $x$, which reverses the inequality, $\sqrt{1+x} - 1 < \frac{x}{2}$, and the required inequality again follows by transposing the $-1$.

## Increasing and Decreasing Functions

Intervals on which the graph of a function $f$ has positive or negative slope provide useful information about the behaviour of $f$. The Mean-Value Theorem enables us to determine such intervals by considering the sign of the derivative $f'$.

**DEFINITION**

**6**

**Increasing and decreasing functions**

Suppose that the function $f$ is defined on an interval $I$ and that $x_1$ and $x_2$ are two points of $I$.
(a) If $f(x_2) > f(x_1)$ whenever $x_2 > x_1$, we say $f$ is **increasing** on $I$.
(b) If $f(x_2) < f(x_1)$ whenever $x_2 > x_1$, we say $f$ is **decreasing** on $I$.
(c) If $f(x_2) \geq f(x_1)$ whenever $x_2 > x_1$, we say $f$ is **nondecreasing** on $I$.
(d) If $f(x_2) \leq f(x_1)$ whenever $x_2 > x_1$, we say $f$ is **nonincreasing** on $I$.

Figure 5.31 illustrates these terms. Note the distinction between *increasing* and *nondecreasing*. If a function is increasing (or decreasing) on an interval, it must take different values at different points. (Such a function is called **one-to-one**.) A nondecreasing function (or a nonincreasing function) may be constant on a subinterval of its domain, and may therefore not be one-to-one. An increasing function is nondecreasing, but a nondecreasing function is not necessarily increasing.

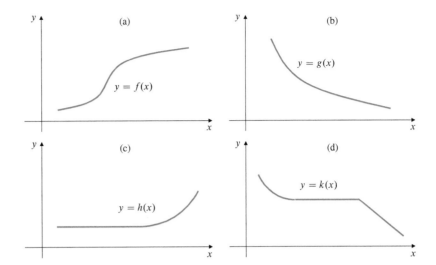

Figure 5.31

(a) Function $f$ is increasing

(b) Function $g$ is decreasing

(c) Function $h$ is nondecreasing

(d) Function $k$ is nonincreasing

**THEOREM**

**12**

Let $J$ be an open interval, and let $I$ be an interval consisting of all the points in $J$ and possibly one or both of the endpoints of $J$. Suppose that $f$ is continuous on $I$ and differentiable on $J$.

(a) If $f'(x) > 0$ for all $x$ in $J$, then $f$ is increasing on $I$.

(b) If $f'(x) < 0$ for all $x$ in $J$, then $f$ is decreasing on $I$.

(c) If $f'(x) \geq 0$ for all $x$ in $J$, then $f$ is nondecreasing on $I$.

(d) If $f'(x) \leq 0$ for all $x$ in $J$, then $f$ is nonincreasing on $I$.

**PROOF**    Let $x_1$ and $x_2$ be points in $I$ with $x_2 > x_1$. By the Mean-Value Theorem there exists a point $c$ in $(x_1, x_2)$ (and therefore in $J$) such that

$$\frac{f(x_2) - f(x_1)}{x_2 - x_1} = f'(c);$$

hence, $f(x_2) - f(x_1) = (x_2 - x_1) \, f'(c)$. Since $x_2 - x_1 > 0$, the difference $f(x_2) - f(x_1)$ has the same sign as $f'(c)$ and may be zero if $f'(c)$ is zero. Thus, all four conclusions follow from the corresponding parts of Definition 6. ∎

**Remark**    Despite Theorem 12, $f'(x_0) > 0$ at a single point $x_0$ does *not* imply that $f$ is increasing on *any* interval containing $x_0$. See Exercise 30 at the end of this section for a counterexample.

**EXAMPLE 4**    On what intervals is the function $f(x) = x^3 - 12x + 1$ increasing? On what intervals is it decreasing?

**Solution**    We have $f'(x) = 3x^2 - 12 = 3(x - 2)(x + 2)$. Observe that $f'(x) > 0$ if $x < -2$ or $x > 2$ and $f'(x) < 0$ if $-2 < x < 2$. Therefore, $f$ is increasing on the intervals $(-\infty, -2)$ and $(2, \infty)$ and is decreasing on the interval $(-2, 2)$. See Figure 5.32.

A function $f$ whose derivative satisfies $f'(x) \geq 0$ on an interval can still be increasing there, rather than just nondecreasing as assured by Theorem 12(c). This will happen if $f'(x) = 0$ only at isolated points, so that $f$ is assured to be increasing on intervals to the left and right of these points.

**EXAMPLE 5**    Show that $f(x) = x^3$ is increasing on any interval.

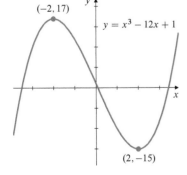

$(-2, 17)$

$y = x^3 - 12x + 1$

$(2, -15)$

Figure 5.32

*Solution* Let $x_1$ and $x_2$ be any two real numbers satsifying $x_1 < x_2$. Since $f'(x) = 3x^2 > 0$ except at $x = 0$, Theorem 12(a) tells us that $f(x_1) < f(x_2)$ if either $x_1 < x_2 \le 0$ or $0 \le x_1 < x_2$. If $x_1 < 0 < x_2$, then $f(x_1) < 0 < f(x_2)$. Thus, $f$ is increasing on every interval.

---

If a function is constant on an interval, then its derivative is zero on that interval. The Mean-Value Theorem provides a converse of this fact.

**THEOREM**

**13**

If $f$ is continuous on an interval $I$, and $f'(x) = 0$ at every interior point of $I$ (i.e., at every point of $I$ that is not an endpoint of $I$), then $f(x) = C$, a constant, on $I$.

*PROOF* Pick a point $x_0$ in $I$ and let $C = f(x_0)$. If $x$ is any other point of $I$, then the Mean-Value Theorem says that there exists a point $c$ between $x_0$ and $x$ such that

$$\frac{f(x) - f(x_0)}{x - x_0} = f'(c).$$

The point $c$ must belong to $I$ because an interval contains all points between any two of its points, and $c$ cannot be an endpoint of $I$ since $c \neq x_0$ and $c \neq x$. Since $f'(c) = 0$ for all such points $c$, we have $f(x) - f(x_0) = 0$ for all $x$ in $I$, and $f(x) = f(x_0) = C$ as claimed.

---

We will see how Theorem 13 can be used to establish identities for new functions encountered in later chapters. We will also use it when finding antiderivatives in Section 5.10.

## Proof of the Mean-Value Theorem

The Mean-Value Theorem is one of those deep results that is based on the completeness of the real number system via the fact that a continuous function on a closed, finite interval takes on a maximum and minimum value. Before giving the proof, we establish two preliminary results.

**THEOREM**

**14**

If $f$ is defined on an open interval $(a, b)$ and achieves a maximum (or minimum) value at the point $c$ in $(a, b)$, and if $f'(c)$ exists, then $f'(c) = 0$. (Values of $x$ where $f'(x) = 0$ are called **critical points** of the function $f$.)

*PROOF* Suppose that $f$ has a maximum value at $c$. Then $f(x) - f(c) \le 0$ whenever $x$ is in $(a, b)$. If $c < x < b$, then

$$\frac{f(x) - f(c)}{x - c} \le 0, \qquad \text{so} \quad f'(c) = \lim_{x \to c+} \frac{f(x) - f(c)}{x - c} \le 0.$$

Similarly, if $a < x < c$, then

$$\frac{f(x) - f(c)}{x - c} \ge 0, \qquad \text{so} \quad f'(c) = \lim_{x \to c-} \frac{f(x) - f(c)}{x - c} \ge 0.$$

Thus $f'(c) = 0$. The proof for a minimum value at $c$ is similar.

---

**THEOREM**

**15**

**Rolle's Theorem**

Suppose that the function $g$ is continuous on the closed, finite interval $[a, b]$ and that it is differentiable on the open interval $(a, b)$. If $g(a) = g(b)$, then there exists a point $c$ in the open interval $(a, b)$ such that $g'(c) = 0$.

***PROOF***  If $g(x) = g(a)$ for every $x$ in $[a, b]$, then $g$ is a constant function, so $g'(c) = 0$ for every $c$ in $(a, b)$. Therefore, suppose there exists $x$ in $(a, b)$ such that $g(x) \neq g(a)$. Let us assume that $g(x) > g(a)$. (If $g(x) < g(a)$, the proof is similar.) By the Max-Min Theorem, being continuous on $[a, b]$, $g$ must have a maximum value at some point $c$ in $[a, b]$. Since $g(c) \geq g(x) > g(a) = g(b)$, $c$ cannot be either $a$ or $b$. Therefore, $c$ is in the open interval $(a, b)$, so $g$ is differentiable at $c$. By Theorem 14, $c$ must be a critical point of $g$: $g'(c) = 0$.

***Remark***  Rolle's Theorem is a special case of the Mean-Value Theorem in which the chord line has slope 0, so the corresponding parallel tangent line must also have slope 0. We can deduce the Mean-Value Theorem from this special case.

***PROOF of the Mean-Value Theorem***  Suppose $f$ satisfies the conditions of the Mean-Value Theorem. Let

$$g(x) = f(x) - \left( f(a) + \frac{f(b) - f(a)}{b - a}(x - a) \right).$$

(For $a \leq x \leq b$, $g(x)$ is the vertical displacement between the curve $y = f(x)$ and the chord line

$$y = f(a) + \frac{f(b) - f(a)}{b - a}(x - a)$$

joining $(a, f(a))$ and $(b, f(b))$. See Figure 5.33.)

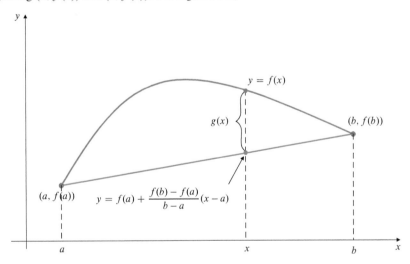

**Figure 5.33**    $g(x)$ is the vertical distance between the graph of $f$ and the chord line

The function $g$ is also continuous on $[a, b]$ and differentiable on $(a, b)$ because $f$ has these properties. In addition, $g(a) = g(b) = 0$. By Rolle's Theorem, there is some point $c$ in $(a, b)$ such that $g'(c) = 0$. Since

$$g'(x) = f'(x) - \frac{f(b) - f(a)}{b - a},$$

it follows that

$$f'(c) = \frac{f(b) - f(a)}{b - a}.$$

Many of the applications we will make of the Mean-Value Theorem in later chapters will actually use the following generalized version of it.

THEOREM

16

**The Generalized Mean-Value Theorem**

If functions $f$ and $g$ are both continuous on $[a, b]$ and differentiable on $(a, b)$, and if $g'(x) \neq 0$ for every $x$ in $(a, b)$, then there exists a number $c$ in $(a, b)$ such that

$$\frac{f(b) - f(a)}{g(b) - g(a)} = \frac{f'(c)}{g'(c)}.$$

*PROOF*   Note that $g(b) \neq g(a)$; otherwise, there would be some number in $(a, b)$ where $g' = 0$. Hence, neither denominator above can be zero. Apply the Mean-Value Theorem to

$$h(x) = \big(f(b) - f(a)\big)\big(g(x) - g(a)\big) - \big(g(b) - g(a)\big)\big(f(x) - f(a)\big).$$

Since $h(a) = h(b) = 0$, there exists $c$ in $(a, b)$ such that $h'(c) = 0$. Thus,

$$\big(f(b) - f(a)\big)g'(c) - \big(g(b) - g(a)\big)f'(c) = 0,$$

and the result follows on division by the $g$ factors.

## EXERCISES 5.8

In Exercises 1–3, illustrate the Mean-Value Theorem by finding any points in the open interval $(a, b)$ where the tangent line to $y = f(x)$ is parallel to the chord line joining $(a, f(a))$ and $(b, f(b))$.

**1.** $f(x) = x^2$ on $[a, b]$

**2.** $f(x) = \dfrac{1}{x}$ on $[1, 2]$

**3.** $f(x) = x^3 - 3x + 1$ on $[-2, 2]$

**4.** By applying the Mean-Value Theorem to $f(x) = \cos x + \dfrac{x^2}{2}$ on the interval $[0, x]$, and using the result of Example 2, show that

$$\cos x > 1 - \frac{x^2}{2}$$

for $x > 0$. This inequality is also true for $x < 0$. Why?

**5.** Show that $\tan x > x$ for $0 < x < \pi/2$.

**6.** Let $r > 1$. If $x > 0$ or $-1 \leq x < 0$, show that $(1 + x)^r > 1 + rx$.

**7.** Let $0 < r < 1$. If $x > 0$ or $-1 \leq x < 0$, show that $(1 + x)^r < 1 + rx$.

Find the intervals of increase and decrease of the functions in Exercises 8–19.

**8.** $f(x) = x^3 - 12x + 1$

**9.** $f(x) = x^2 - 4$

**10.** $y = 1 - x - x^5$

**11.** $y = x^3 + 6x^2$

**12.** $f(x) = x^2 + 2x + 2$

**13.** $f(x) = x^3 - 4x + 1$

**14.** $f(x) = x^3 + 4x + 1$

**15.** $f(x) = (x^2 - 4)^2$

**16.** $f(x) = \dfrac{1}{x^2 + 1}$

**17.** $f(x) = x^3(5 - x)^2$

**18.** $f(x) = x - 2\sin x$

**19.** $f(x) = x + \sin x$

**20.** On what intervals is $f(x) = x + 2\sin x$ increasing?

**21.** Show that $f(x) = x^3$ is increasing on the whole real line even though $f'(x)$ is not positive at every point.

**22.** What is wrong with the following "proof" of the Generalized Mean-Value Theorem? By the Mean-Value Theorem, $f(b) - f(a) = (b - a)f'(c)$ for some $c$ between $a$ and $b$ and, similarly, $g(b) - g(a) = (b - a)g'(c)$ for some such $c$. Hence, $(f(b) - f(a))/(g(b) - g(a)) = f'(c)/g'(c)$, as required.

Use a graphing utility or a computer algebra system to find the critical points of the functions in Exercises 23–26 correct to 6 decimal places.

**23.** $f(x) = \dfrac{x^2 - x}{x^2 - 4}$

**24.** $f(x) = \dfrac{2x + 1}{x^2 + x + 1}$

**25.** $f(x) = x - \sin\left(\dfrac{x}{x^2 + x + 1}\right)$

**26.** $f(x) = \dfrac{\sqrt{1 - x^2}}{\cos(x + 0.1)}$

**27.** If $f(x)$ is differentiable on an interval $I$ and vanishes at $n \geq 2$ distinct points of $I$, prove that $f'(x)$ must vanish at at least $n - 1$ points in $I$.

**28.** Let $f(x) = x^2 \sin(1/x)$ if $x \neq 0$ and $f(0) = 0$. Show that $f'(x)$ exists at every $x$ but $f'$ is not continuous at $x = 0$. This proves the assertion (made at the end of Section 5.2) that a derivative, defined on an interval, need not be continuous there.

**29.** Prove the assertion (made at the end of Section 5.2) that a derivative, defined on an interval, must have the intermediate-value property. (*Hint:* Assume that $f'$ exists on $[a, b]$ and $f'(a) \neq f'(b)$. If $k$ lies between $f'(a)$ and $f'(b)$, show that the function $g$ defined by $g(x) = f(x) - kx$ must have *either* a maximum value *or* a minimum value on $[a, b]$ occurring at an interior point $c$ in $(a, b)$. Deduce that $f'(c) = k$.)

**30.** Let $f(x) = \begin{cases} x + 2x^2 \sin(1/x) & \text{if } x \neq 0, \\ 0 & \text{if } x = 0. \end{cases}$

(a) Show that $f'(0) = 1$. (*Hint:* Use the definition of derivative.)

(b) Show that any interval containing $x = 0$ also contains points where $f'(x) < 0$, so $f$ cannot be increasing on such an interval.

**31.** If $f''(x)$ exists on an interval $I$ and if $f$ vanishes at at least three distinct points of $I$, prove that $f''$ must vanish at some point in $I$.

**32.** Generalize Exercise 31 to a function for which $f^{(n)}$ exists on $I$ and for which $f$ vanishes at at least $n + 1$ distinct points in $I$.

**33.** Suppose $f$ is twice differentiable on an interval $I$ (i.e., $f''$ exists on $I$). Suppose that the points 0 and 2 belong to $I$ and that $f(0) = f(1) = 0$ and $f(2) = 1$. Prove that

(a) $f'(a) = \dfrac{1}{2}$ for some point $a$ in $I$.

(b) $f''(b) > \dfrac{1}{2}$ for some point $b$ in $I$.

(c) $f'(c) = \dfrac{1}{7}$ for some point $c$ in $I$.

## 5.9  Implicit Differentiation

We know how to find the slope of a curve that is the graph of a function $y = f(x)$ by calculating the derivative of $f$. But not all curves are the graphs of such functions. To be the graph of a function $f(x)$, the curve must not intersect any vertical lines at more than one point.

Curves are generally the graphs of *equations* in two variables. Such equations can be written in the form

$$F(x, y) = 0,$$

where $F(x, y)$ denotes an expression involving the two variables $x$ and $y$. For example, a circle with centre at the origin and radius 5 has equation

$$x^2 + y^2 - 25 = 0,$$

so $F(x, y) = x^2 + y^2 - 25$ for that circle.

Sometimes we can solve an equation $F(x, y) = 0$ for $y$ and so find explicit formulas for one or more functions $y = f(x)$ defined by the equation. Usually, however, we are not able to solve the equation. However, we can still regard it as defining $y$ as one or more functions of $x$ *implicitly*, even it we cannot solve for these functions *explicitly*. Moreover, we still find the derivative $dy/dx$ of these implicit solutions by a technique called **implicit differentiation**. The idea is to differentiate the given equation with respect to $x$, regarding $y$ as a function of $x$ having derivative $dy/dx$, or $y'$.

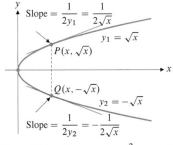

**Figure 5.34**   The equation $y^2 = x$ defines two differentiable functions of $x$ on the interval $x \geq 0$

**EXAMPLE 1**   Find $dy/dx$ if $y^2 = x$.

**Solution**   The equation $y^2 = x$ defines two differentiable functions of $x$; in this case we know them explicitly. They are $y_1 = \sqrt{x}$ and $y_2 = -\sqrt{x}$ (see Figure 5.34), having derivatives defined for $x > 0$ by

$$\frac{dy_1}{dx} = \frac{1}{2\sqrt{x}} \qquad \text{and} \qquad \frac{dy_2}{dx} = -\frac{1}{2\sqrt{x}}.$$

However, we can find the slope of the curve $y^2 = x$ at any point $(x, y)$ satisfying that equation without first solving the equation for $y$. To find $dy/dx$, we simply differentiate both sides of the equation $y^2 = x$ with respect to $x$, treating $y$ as a differentiable function of $x$ and using the Chain Rule to differentiate $y^2$:

$$\frac{d}{dx}(y^2) = \frac{d}{dx}(x) \qquad \left(\text{The Chain Rule gives } \frac{d}{dx}\, y^2 = 2y\frac{dy}{dx}.\right)$$

$$2y\frac{dy}{dx} = 1$$

$$\frac{dy}{dx} = \frac{1}{2y}.$$

Observe that this agrees with the derivatives we calculated above for *both* of the explicit solutions $y_1 = \sqrt{x}$ and $y_2 = -\sqrt{x}$:

$$\frac{dy_1}{dx} = \frac{1}{2y_1} = \frac{1}{2\sqrt{x}} \qquad \text{and} \qquad \frac{dy_2}{dx} = \frac{1}{2y_2} = \frac{1}{2(-\sqrt{x})} = -\frac{1}{2\sqrt{x}}.$$

---

**EXAMPLE 2**    Find the slope of circle $x^2 + y^2 = 25$ at the point $(3, -4)$.

*Solution*    The circle is not the graph of a single function of $x$. Again, it combines the graphs of two functions, $y_1 = \sqrt{25 - x^2}$ and $y_2 = -\sqrt{25 - x^2}$ (Figure 5.35). The point $(3, -4)$ lies on the graph of $y_2$, so we can find the slope by calculating explicitly:

$$\frac{dy_2}{dx}\bigg|_{x=3} = -\frac{-2x}{2\sqrt{25 - x^2}}\bigg|_{x=3} = -\frac{-6}{2\sqrt{25 - 9}} = \frac{3}{4}.$$

But we can also solve the problem more easily by differentiating the given equation of the circle implicitly with respect to $x$:

$$\frac{d}{dx}(x^2) + \frac{d}{dx}(y^2) = \frac{d}{dx}(25)$$

$$2x + 2y\frac{dy}{dx} = 0$$

$$\frac{dy}{dx} = -\frac{x}{y}.$$

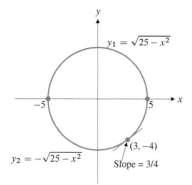

$y_1 = \sqrt{25 - x^2}$

$y_2 = -\sqrt{25 - x^2}$

$(3, -4)$

Slope = 3/4

**Figure 5.35**    The circle combines the graphs of two functions. The graph of $y_2$ is the lower semicircle and passes through $(3, -4)$

The slope at $(3, -4)$ is $-\dfrac{x}{y}\bigg|_{(3,-4)} = -\dfrac{3}{-4} = \dfrac{3}{4}.$

---

**EXAMPLE 3**    Find $\dfrac{dy}{dx}$ if $y\sin x = x^3 + \cos y$.

*Solution*    This time we cannot solve the equation for $y$ as an explicit function of $x$, so we *must* use implicit differentiation:

$$\frac{d}{dx}(y\sin x) = \frac{d}{dx}(x^3) + \frac{d}{dx}(\cos y) \qquad \left(\begin{array}{l}\text{Use the Product Rule}\\ \text{on the left side.}\end{array}\right)$$

$$(\sin x)\frac{dy}{dx} + y\cos x = 3x^2 - (\sin y)\frac{dy}{dx}$$

$$(\sin x + \sin y)\frac{dy}{dx} = 3x^2 - y\cos x$$

$$\frac{dy}{dx} = \frac{3x^2 - y\cos x}{\sin x + \sin y}.$$

To find $dy/dx$ by implicit differentiation:

1. Differentiate both sides of the equation with respect to $x$, regarding $y$ as a function of $x$ and using the Chain Rule to differentiate functions of $y$.

2. Collect terms with $dy/dx$ on one side of the equation and solve for $dy/dx$ by dividing by its coefficient.

In the examples above, the derivatives $dy/dx$ calculated by implicit differentiation depend on $y$, or on both $y$ and $x$, rather than just on $x$. This is to be expected because an equation in $x$ and $y$ can define more than one function of $x$, and the implicitly calculated derivative must apply to each of the solutions. For example, in Example 2, the derivative $dy/dx = -x/y$ also gives the slope $-3/4$ at the point $(3, 4)$ on the circle. When you use implicit differentiation to find the slope of a curve at a point, you will usually have to know both coordinates of the point.

There are subtle dangers involved in calculating derivatives implicitly. When you use the Chain Rule to differentiate an equation involving $y$ with respect to $x$, you are automatically assuming that the equation defines $y$ as a differentiable function of $x$. This need not be the case. To see what can happen, consider the problem of finding $y' = dy/dx$ from the equation

$$x^2 + y^2 = K, \qquad\qquad (*)$$

where $K$ is a constant. As in Example 2 (where $K = 25$), implicit differentiation gives

$$2x + 2yy' = 0 \qquad \text{or} \qquad y' = -\frac{x}{y}.$$

This formula will give the slope of the curve $(*)$ at any point on the curve where $y \neq 0$. For $K > 0$, $(*)$ represents a circle centred at the origin and having radius $\sqrt{K}$. This circle has a finite slope, except at the two points where it crosses the $x$-axis (where $y = 0$). If $K = 0$, the equation represents only a single point, the origin. The concept of slope of a point is meaningless. For $K < 0$, there are no real points whose coordinates satisfy equation $(*)$, so $y'$ is meaningless here too. The point of this is that being able to calculate $y'$ from a given equation by implicit differentiation does not guarantee that $y'$ actually represents the slope of anything.

If $(x_0, y_0)$ is a point on the graph of the equation $F(x, y) = 0$, there is a theorem that can justify our use of implicit differentiation to find the slope of the graph there. We cannot give a careful statement or proof of this **implicit function theorem** yet, but roughly speaking, it says that part of the graph of $F(x, y) = 0$ near $(x_0, y_0)$ is the graph of a function of $x$ that is differentiable at $x_0$, provided that $F(x, y)$ is a "smooth" function, and that the derivative

$$\frac{d}{dy} F(x_0, y)\bigg|_{y=y_0} \neq 0.$$

For the circle $x^2 + y^2 - K = 0$ (where $K > 0$) this condition says that $2y_0 \neq 0$, which is the condition that the derivative $y' = -x/y$ should exist at $(x_0, y_0)$.

---

**EXAMPLE 4**    Find an equation of the tangent to $x^2 + xy + 2y^3 = 4$ at $(-2, 1)$.

---

*Solution*    Note that $(-2, 1)$ does lie on the given curve. To find the slope of the tangent we differentiate the given equation implicitly with respect to $x$. Use the Product Rule to differentiate the $xy$ term:

$$2x + y + xy' + 6y^2 y' = 0.$$

Substitute the coordinates $x = -2$, $y = 1$, and solve the resulting equation for $y'$:

$$-4 + 1 - 2y' + 6y' = 0 \qquad \Rightarrow \qquad y' = \frac{3}{4}.$$

The slope of the tangent at $(-2, 1)$ is $3/4$, and its equation is

$$y = \frac{3}{4}(x + 2) + 1 \qquad \text{or} \qquad 3x - 4y = -10.$$

**A useful strategy**

When you use implicit differentiation to find the value of a derivative at a particular point, it is best to substitute the coordinates of the point immediately after you carry out the differentiation and before you solve for the derivative $dy/dx$. It is easier to solve an equation involving numbers than one with algebraic expressions.

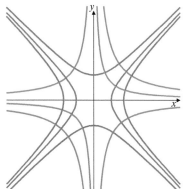

Figure 5.36    Some hyperbolas in the family $x^2 - y^2 = a$ (red) intersecting some hyperbolas in the family $xy = b$ (blue) at right angles

EXAMPLE 5    Show that for any constants $a$ and $b$, the curves $x^2 - y^2 = a$ and $xy = b$ intersect at right angles, that is, at any point where they intersect their tangents are perpendicular.

**Solution**    The slope at any point on $x^2 - y^2 = a$ is given by $2x - 2yy' = 0$, or $y' = x/y$. The slope at any point on $xy = b$ is given by $y + xy' = 0$, or $y' = -y/x$. If the two curves (they are both hyperbolas if $a \neq 0$ and $b \neq 0$) intersect at $(x_0, y_0)$, then their slopes at that point are $x_0/y_0$ and $-y_0/x_0$, respectively. Clearly, these slopes are negative reciprocals, so the tangent line to one curve is the normal line to the other at that point. Hence, the curves intersect at right angles. (See Figure 5.36.)

## Higher-Order Derivatives

EXAMPLE 6    Find $y'' = \dfrac{d^2 y}{dx^2}$ if $xy + y^2 = 2x$.

**Solution**    Twice differentiate both sides of the given equation with respect to $x$:

$$y + xy' + 2yy' = 2$$
$$y' + y' + xy'' + 2(y')^2 + 2yy'' = 0.$$

Now solve these equations for $y'$ and $y''$.

$$y' = \frac{2 - y}{x + 2y}$$

$$y'' = -\frac{2y' + 2(y')^2}{x + 2y} = -2\,\frac{2 - y}{x + 2y}\,\frac{1 + \dfrac{2 - y}{x + 2y}}{x + 2y}$$
$$= -2\,\frac{(2 - y)(x + y + 2)}{(x + 2y)^3}$$
$$= -2\,\frac{2x - xy + 2y - y^2 + 4 - 2y}{(x + 2y)^3} = -\frac{8}{(x + 2y)^3}.$$

(We used the given equation to simplify the numerator in the last line.)

**Remark**    We can use Maple to calculate derivatives implicitly provided we show explicitly which variable depends on which. For example, we can calculate the value of $y''$ for the curve $xy + y^3 = 3$ at the point $(2, 1)$ as follows. First, we differentiate the equation with respect to $x$, writing $y(x)$ for $y$ to indicate to Maple that it depends on $x$.

```
>  deq := diff(x*y(x)+(y(x))^3=3, x);
```

$$deq := y(x) + x\left(\frac{\partial}{\partial x} y(x)\right) + 3y(x)^2 \left(\frac{\partial}{\partial x} y(x)\right) = 0$$

Now we solve the resulting equation for $y'$:

```
>  yp := solve(deq, diff(y(x),x));
```

$$yp := -\frac{y(x)}{x + 3y(x)^2}$$

We can now differentiate $yp$ with respect to $x$ to get $y''$:

```
>  ypp := diff(yp,x);
```

Note that Maple uses the symbol $\partial$ instead of $d$ when expressing the derivative in Leibniz form. This is because the expression it is differentiating can involve more than one variable; $(\partial/\partial x)y$ denotes the derivative of $y$ with respect to the specific variable $x$ rather than any other variables on which $y$ may depend. It is called a **partial derivative**. For the time being, just regard $\partial$ as a $d$.

$$ypp := -\dfrac{\dfrac{\partial}{\partial x} y(x)}{x + 3y(x)^2} + \dfrac{y(x)\left(1 + 6y(x)\left(\dfrac{\partial}{\partial x} y(x)\right)\right)}{(x + 3y(x)^2)^2}$$

To get an expression depending only on $x$ and $y$, we need to substitute the expression obtained for the first derivative into this result. Since the result of this substitution will involve compound fractions, let us simplify the result as well.

```
>   ypp := simplify(subs(diff(y(x),x)=yp, ypp);
```

$$ypp := 2\,\dfrac{x\,y(x)}{(x + 3y(x)^2)^3}$$

This is $y''$ expressed as a function of $x$ and $y$. Now we want to substitute the coordinates $x = 2$, $y(x) = 1$ to get the value of $y''$ at $(2, 1)$. However, the order of the substitutions is important. *First* we must replace $y(x)$ with 1 and *then* replace $x$ with 2. (If we replace $x$ first, we would have to then replace $y(2)$ rather than $y(x)$ with 1.) Maple's `subs` command makes the substitutions in the order they are written.

```
>   subs(y(x)=1, x=2, ypp);
```

$$\dfrac{4}{125}$$

## The General Power Rule

Until now, we have only proven the General Power Rule

$$\dfrac{d}{dx} x^r = r\,x^{r-1}$$

for integer exponents $r$ and a few special rational exponents such as $r = 1/2$. Using implicit differentiation, we can give the proof for any rational exponent $r = m/n$, where $m$ and $n$ are integers, and $n \neq 0$.

If $y = x^{m/n}$, then $y^n = x^m$. Differentiating implicitly with respect to $x$, we obtain

$$n\,y^{n-1}\dfrac{dy}{dx} = m\,x^{m-1}, \qquad \text{so}$$

$$\dfrac{dy}{dx} = \dfrac{m}{n}x^{m-1}\,y^{1-n} = \dfrac{m}{n}x^{m-1}\,x^{(m/n)(1-n)} = \dfrac{m}{n}x^{m-1+(m/n)-m} = \dfrac{m}{n}x^{(m/n)-1}.$$

## EXERCISES 5.9

In Exercises 1–8, find $dy/dx$ in terms of $x$ and $y$.

**1.** $xy - x + 2y = 1$

**2.** $x^3 + y^3 = 1$

**3.** $x^2 + xy = y^3$

**4.** $x^3y + xy^5 = 2$

**5.** $x^2y^3 = 2x - y$

**6.** $x^2 + 4(y - 1)^2 = 4$

**7.** $\dfrac{x - y}{x + y} = \dfrac{x^2}{y} + 1$

**8.** $x\sqrt{x + y} = 8 - xy$

In Exercises 9–16, find an equation of the tangent to the given curve at the given point.

**9.** $2x^2 + 3y^2 = 5$ at $(1, 1)$

**10.** $x^2y^3 - x^3y^2 = 12$ at $(-1, 2)$

**11.** $\dfrac{x}{y} + \left(\dfrac{y}{x}\right)^3 = 2$ at $(-1, -1)$

**12.** $x + 2y + 1 = \dfrac{y^2}{x - 1}$ at $(2, -1)$

**13.** $2x + y - \sqrt{2}\sin(xy) = \pi/2$ at $\left(\dfrac{\pi}{4}, 1\right)$

**14.** $\tan(xy^2) = \dfrac{2xy}{\pi}$ at $\left(-\pi, \dfrac{1}{2}\right)$

**15.** $x\sin(xy - y^2) = x^2 - 1$ at $(1, 1)$

**16.** $\cos\left(\dfrac{\pi y}{x}\right) = \dfrac{x^2}{y} - \dfrac{17}{2}$ at $(3, 1)$

In Exercises 17–20, find $y''$ in terms of $x$ and $y$.

**17.** $xy = x + y$

**18.** $x^2 + 4y^2 = 4$

**19.** $x^3 - y^2 + y^3 = x$

**20.** $x^3 - 3xy + y^3 = 1$

**21.** For $x^2 + y^2 = a^2$ show that $y'' = -\dfrac{a^2}{y^3}$.

**22.** For $Ax^2 + By^2 = C$ show that $y'' = -\dfrac{AC}{B^2 y^3}$.

Use Maple or another computer algebra program to find the values requested in Exercises 23–26.

**23.** Find the slope of $x + y^2 + y \sin x = y^3 + \pi$ at $(\pi, 1)$.

**24.** Find the slope of $\dfrac{x + \sqrt{y}}{y + \sqrt{x}} = \dfrac{3y - 9x}{x + y}$ at the point $(1, 4)$.

**25.** If $x + y^5 + 1 = y + x^4 + xy^2$, find $d^2y/dx^2$ at $(1, 1)$.

**26.** If $x^3 y + xy^3 = 11$, find $d^3y/dx^3$ at $(1, 2)$.

**27.** Show that the ellipse $x^2 + 2y^2 = 2$ and the hyperbola

$2x^2 - 2y^2 = 1$ intersect at right angles.

**28.** Show that the ellipse $x^2/a^2 + y^2/b^2 = 1$ and the hyperbola $x^2/A^2 - y^2/B^2 = 1$ intersect at right angles if $A^2 \le a^2$ and $a^2 - b^2 = A^2 + B^2$. (This says that the ellipse and the hyperbola have the same foci.)

**29.** If $z = \tan \dfrac{x}{2}$, show that

$$\frac{dx}{dz} = \frac{2}{1 + z^2}, \quad \sin x = \frac{2z}{1 + z^2}, \quad \text{and} \quad \cos x = \frac{1 - z^2}{1 + z^2}.$$

**30.** Use implicit differentiation to find $y'$ if $y$ is defined by $(x - y)/(x + y) = x/y + 1$. Now show that there are, in fact, no points on that curve, so the derivative you calculated is meaningless. This is another example that demonstrates the dangers of calculating something when you don't know whether or not it exists.

---

## 5.10   Antiderivatives and Initial-Value Problems

Throughout this chapter we have been concerned with the problem of finding the derivative $f'$ of a given function $f$. The reverse problem—given the derivative $f'$, find $f$—is also interesting and important. It is the problem studied in *integral calculus* and is generally more difficult to solve than the problem of finding a derivative. We will take a preliminary look at this problem in this section and will return to it in more detail in Chapter 8.

### Antiderivatives

We begin by defining an antiderivative of a function $f$ to be a function $F$ whose derivative is $f$. It is appropriate to require that $F'(x) = f(x)$ on an *interval*.

**DEFINITION**

**7**

An **antiderivative** of a function $f$ on an interval $I$ is another function $F$ satisfying

$$F'(x) = f(x) \quad \text{for } x \text{ in } I.$$

---

### EXAMPLE 1

(a) $F(x) = x$ is an antiderivative of the function $f(x) = 1$ on any interval because $F'(x) = 1 = f(x)$ everywhere.

(b) $G(x) = \frac{1}{2} x^2$ is an antiderivative of the function $g(x) = x$ on any interval because $G'(x) = \frac{1}{2}(2x) = x = g(x)$ everywhere.

(c) $R(x) = -\frac{1}{3} \cos(3x)$ is an antiderivative of $r(x) = \sin(3x)$ on any interval because $R'(x) = -\frac{1}{3}(-3 \sin(3x)) = \sin(3x) = r(x)$ everywhere.

(d) $F(x) = -1/x$ is an antiderivative of $f(x) = 1/x^2$ on any interval not containing $x = 0$ because $F'(x) = 1/x^2 = f(x)$ everywhere except at $x = 0$.

---

Antiderivatives are not unique; since a constant has derivative zero, you can always add any constant to an antiderivative $F$ of a function $f$ on an interval and get another antiderivative of $f$ on that interval. More importantly, *all* antiderivatives of $f$ on an interval can be obtained by adding constants to any particular one. If $F$ and $G$ are both antiderivatives of $f$ on an interval $I$, then

$$\frac{d}{dx}\big(G(x) - F(x)\big) = f(x) - f(x) = 0$$

on $I$, so $G(x) - F(x) = C$ (a constant) on $I$ by Theorem 13 of Section 5.8. Thus, $G(x) = F(x) + C$ on $I$.

Note that neither this conclusion nor Theorem 13 is valid over a set that is not an interval. For example, the derivative of

$$\mathrm{sgn}\, x = \begin{cases} -1 & \text{if } x < 0 \\ 1 & \text{if } x > 0 \end{cases}$$

is 0 for all $x \neq 0$, but $\mathrm{sgn}\, x$ is not constant for all $x \neq 0$. $\mathrm{sgn}\, x$ has *different* constant values on the two intervals $(-\infty, 0)$ and $(0, \infty)$ comprising its domain.

## The Indefinite Integral

The *general antiderivative* of a function $f(x)$ on an interval $I$ is $F(x) + C$, where $F(x)$ is any particular antiderivative of $f(x)$ on $I$ and $C$ is a constant. This general antiderivative is called the indefinite integral of $f(x)$ on $I$ and is denoted $\int f(x)\,dx$.

**DEFINITION**

**8**

The **indefinite integral** of $f(x)$ on interval $I$ is

$$\int f(x)\,dx = F(x) + C \qquad \text{on } I,$$

provided $F'(x) = f(x)$ for all $x$ in $I$.

The symbol $\int$ is called an **integral sign**. It is shaped like an elongated "S" for reasons that will only become apparent when we study the *definite integral* in Chapter 8. Just as you regard $dy/dx$ as a single symbol representing the derivative of $y$ with respect to $x$, so you should regard $\int f(x)\,dx$ as a single symbol representing the indefinite integral (general antiderivative) of $f$ with respect to $x$. The constant $C$ is called a **constant of integration**.

---

### EXAMPLE 2

(a) $\displaystyle\int x\,dx = \frac{1}{2}x^2 + C$ on any interval.

(b) $\displaystyle\int (x^3 - 5x^2 + 7)\,dx = \frac{1}{4}x^4 - \frac{5}{3}x^3 + 7x + C$ on any interval.

(c) $\displaystyle\int \left(\frac{1}{x^2} + \frac{2}{\sqrt{x}}\right) dx = -\frac{1}{x} + 4\sqrt{x} + C$ on any interval to the right of $x = 0$.

All three formulas above can be checked by differentiating the right-hand sides.

---

Finding antiderivatives is generally more difficult than finding derivatives; many functions do not have antiderivatives that can be expressed as combinations of finitely many elementary functions. However, *every formula for a derivative can be rephrased as a formula for an antiderivative*. For instance,

$$\frac{d}{dx}\sin x = \cos x; \qquad \text{therefore,} \qquad \int \cos x\,dx = \sin x + C.$$

We will develop several techniques for finding antiderivatives in later chapters. Until then, we must content ourselves with being able to write a few simple antiderivatives based on the known derivatives of elementary functions:

(a) $\displaystyle\int dx = \int 1\,dx = x + C$    (b) $\displaystyle\int x\,dx = \frac{x^2}{2} + C$

(c) $\displaystyle\int x^2\,dx = \frac{x^3}{3} + C$    (d) $\displaystyle\int \frac{1}{x^2}\,dx = \int \frac{dx}{x^2} = -\frac{1}{x} + C$

(e) $\displaystyle\int \frac{1}{\sqrt{x}}\,dx = 2\sqrt{x} + C$    (f) $\displaystyle\int x^r\,dx = \frac{x^{r+1}}{r+1} + C \;\; (r \neq -1)$

(g) $\displaystyle\int \sin x\,dx = -\cos x + C$    (h) $\displaystyle\int \cos x\,dx = \sin x + C$

(i) $\displaystyle\int \sec^2 x\,dx = \tan x + C$    (j) $\displaystyle\int \csc^2 x\,dx = -\cot x + C$

(k) $\displaystyle\int \sec x \tan x\,dx = \sec x + C$    (l) $\displaystyle\int \csc x \cot x\,dx = -\csc x + C$

Observe that formulas (a)–(e) are special cases of formula (f). For the moment, $r$ must be rational in (f), but this restriction will be removed later.

The rule for differentiating sums and constant multiples of functions translates into a similar rule for antiderivatives, as reflected in parts (b) and (c) of Example 2 above.

The graphs of the different antiderivatives of the same function on the same interval are vertically displaced versions of the same curve, as shown in Figure 5.37. In general, only one of these curves will pass through any given point, so we can obtain a unique antiderivative of a given function on an interval by requiring the antiderivative to take a prescribed value at a particular point $x$.

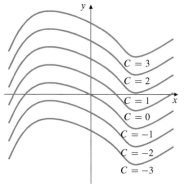

**Figure 5.37**   Graphs of various antiderivatives of the same function

**EXAMPLE 3**   Find the function $f(x)$ whose derivative is $f'(x) = 6x^2 - 1$ for all real $x$ and for which $f(2) = 10$.

*Solution*   Since $f'(x) = 6x^2 - 1$, we have

$$f(x) = \int (6x^2 - 1)\,dx = 2x^3 - x + C$$

for some constant $C$. Since $f(2) = 10$, we have

$$10 = f(2) = 16 - 2 + C.$$

Thus, $C = -4$ and $f(x) = 2x^3 - x - 4$. (By direct calculation we can verify that $f'(x) = 6x^2 - 1$ and $f(2) = 10$.)

**EXAMPLE 4**   Find the function $g(t)$ whose derivative is $\dfrac{t+5}{t^{3/2}}$ and whose graph passes through the point $(4, 1)$.

*Solution*   We have

$$g(t) = \int \frac{t+5}{t^{3/2}}\,dt$$

$$= \int (t^{-1/2} + 5t^{-3/2})\,dt$$

$$= 2t^{1/2} - 10t^{-1/2} + C$$

Since the graph of $y = g(t)$ must pass through $(4, 1)$, we require that

$$1 = g(4) = 4 - 5 + C.$$

Hence, $C = 2$ and

$$g(t) = 2t^{1/2} - 10t^{-1/2} + 2 \qquad \text{for } t > 0.$$

## Differential Equations and Initial-Value Problems

A **differential equation** (DE) is an equation involving one or more derivatives of an unknown function. Any function whose derivatives satisfy the differential equation *identically on an interval* is called a **solution** of the equation on that interval. For instance, the function $y = x^3 - x$ is a solution of the differential equation

$$\frac{dy}{dx} = 3x^2 - 1$$

on the whole real line. This differential equation has more than one solution; in fact, $y = x^3 - x + C$ is a solution for any value of the constant $C$.

---

**EXAMPLE 5**   Show that for any constants $A$ and $B$, the function $y = Ax^3 + B/x$ is a solution of the differential equation $x^2 y'' - xy' - 3y = 0$ on any interval not containing 0.

*Solution*   If $y = Ax^3 + B/x$, then for $x \neq 0$ we have

$$y' = 3Ax^2 - B/x^2 \quad \text{and} \quad y'' = 6Ax + 2B/x^3.$$

Therefore,

$$x^2 y'' - xy' - 3y = 6Ax^3 + \frac{2B}{x} - 3Ax^3 + \frac{B}{x} - 3Ax^3 - \frac{3B}{x} = 0,$$

provided $x \neq 0$. This is what had to be proved.

---

The **order** of a differential equation is the order of the highest-order derivative appearing in the equation. The DE in Example 5 is a *second-order* DE since it involves $y''$ and no higher derivatives of $y$. Note that the solution verified in Example 5 involves two arbitrary constants, $A$ and $B$. This solution is called a **general solution** to the equation, since it can be shown that every solution is of this form for some choice of the constants $A$ and $B$. A **particular solution** of the equation is obtained by assigning specific values to these constants. The general solution of an $n$th-order differential equation typically involves $n$ arbitrary constants.

An **initial-value problem** (IVP) is a problem that consists of:

(i) a differential equation (to be solved for an unknown function) and

(ii) prescribed values for the solution and enough of its derivatives at a particular point (the initial point) to determine values for all the arbitrary constants in the general solution of the DE and so yield a particular solution.

*Remark*   It is common to use the same symbol, say $y$, to denote both the dependent variable and the function that is the solution to a DE or an IVP; that is, we call the solution function $y = y(x)$ rather than $y = f(x)$.

*Remark*   The solution of an IVP is valid in the largest interval containing the initial point where the solution function is defined.

---

**EXAMPLE 6**   Use the result of Example 5 to solve the following initial-value problem.

$$\begin{cases} x^2 y'' - xy' - 3y = 0 & (x > 0) \\ y(1) = 2 \\ y'(1) = -6 \end{cases}$$

*Solution*    As shown in Example 5, the DE $x^2 y'' - xy' - 3y = 0$ has solution $y = Ax^3 + B/x$, which has derivative $y' = 3Ax^2 - B/x^2$. At $x = 1$ we must have $y = 2$ and $y' = -6$. Therefore,

$$A + B = \phantom{-}2$$
$$3A - B = -6.$$

Solving these two linear equations for $A$ and $B$, we get $A = -1$ and $B = 3$. Hence, $y = -x^3 + 3/x$ for $x > 0$ is the solution of the IVP.

One of the simplest kinds of differential equation is the equation

$$\frac{dy}{dx} = f(x),$$

which is to be solved for $y$ as a function of $x$. Evidently the solution is

$$y = \int f(x)\, dx.$$

Our ability to find the unknown function $y(x)$ depends on our ability to find an antiderivative of $f$.

**EXAMPLE 7**    Solve the initial-value problem

$$\begin{cases} y' = \dfrac{3 + 2x^2}{x^2} \\ y(-2) = 1. \end{cases}$$

Where is the solution valid?

*Solution*

$$y = \int \left( \frac{3}{x^2} + 2 \right) dx = -\frac{3}{x} + 2x + C$$
$$1 = y(-2) = \frac{3}{2} - 4 + C$$

Therefore, $C = \frac{7}{2}$ and

$$y = -\frac{3}{x} + 2x + \frac{7}{2}.$$

Although the solution function appears to be defined for all $x$ except 0, it is only a solution of the given IVP for $x < 0$. This is because $(-\infty, 0)$ is the largest interval that contains the initial point $-2$ but not the point $x = 0$, where the solution $y$ is undefined.

**EXAMPLE 8**    Solve the second-order IVP

$$\begin{cases} y'' = \sin x \\ y(\pi) = 2 \\ y'(\pi) = -1. \end{cases}$$

**Solution**   Since $(y')' = y'' = \sin x$, we have

$$y'(x) = \int \sin x \, dx = -\cos x + C_1.$$

The initial condition for $y'$ gives

$$-1 = y'(\pi) = -\cos \pi + C_1 = 1 + C_1,$$

so that $C_1 = -2$ and $y'(x) = -(\cos x + 2)$. Thus,

$$\begin{aligned} y(x) &= -\int (\cos x + 2) \, dx \\ &= -\sin x - 2x + C_2. \end{aligned}$$

The initial condition for $y$ now gives

$$2 = y(\pi) = -\sin \pi - 2\pi + C_2 = -2\pi + C_2,$$

so that $C_2 = 2 + 2\pi$. The solution to the given IVP is

$$y = 2 + 2\pi - \sin x - 2x$$

and is valid for all $x$.

Differential equations and initial-value problems are of great importance in applications of calculus, especially for expressing in mathematical form certain laws of nature that involve rates of change of quantities. A large portion of the total mathematical endeavour of the last two hundred years has been devoted to their study. They are usually treated in separate courses on differential equations, but we will discuss them from time to time in this book when appropriate. Throughout this book, except in sections devoted entirely to differential equations, we will use the symbol ✣ to mark exercises about differential equations and initial-value problems.

## EXERCISES 5.10

In Exercises 1–14, find the given indefinite integrals.

**1.** $\displaystyle\int 5 \, dx$

**2.** $\displaystyle\int x^2 \, dx$

**3.** $\displaystyle\int \sqrt{x} \, dx$

**4.** $\displaystyle\int x^{12} \, dx$

**5.** $\displaystyle\int x^3 \, dx$

**6.** $\displaystyle\int (x + \cos x) \, dx$

**7.** $\displaystyle\int \tan x \cos x \, dx$

**8.** $\displaystyle\int \frac{1 + \cos^3 x}{\cos^2 x} \, dx$

**9.** $\displaystyle\int (a^2 - x^2) \, dx$

**10.** $\displaystyle\int (A + Bx + Cx^2) \, dx$

**11.** $\displaystyle\int (2x^{1/2} + 3x^{1/3}) \, dx$

**12.** $\displaystyle\int \frac{6(x - 1)}{x^{4/3}} \, dx$

**13.** $\displaystyle\int \left( \frac{x^3}{3} - \frac{x^2}{2} + x - 1 \right) dx$

**14.** $105 \displaystyle\int (1 + t^2 + t^4 + t^6) \, dt$

In Exercises 15–22, find the given indefinite integrals. This may require guessing the form of an antiderivative and then checking by differentiation. For instance, you might suspect that $\int \cos(5x - 2) \, dx = k \sin(5x - 2) + C$ for some $k$. Differentiating the answer shows that $k$ must be $1/5$.

**15.** $\displaystyle\int \cos(2x) \, dx$

**16.** $\displaystyle\int \sin \left( \frac{x}{2} \right) dx$

✣ **17.** $\displaystyle\int \frac{dx}{(1 + x)^2}$

✣ **18.** $\displaystyle\int \sec(1 - x) \tan(1 - x) \, dx$

✣ **19.** $\displaystyle\int \sqrt{2x + 3} \, dx$

✣ **20.** $\displaystyle\int \frac{4}{\sqrt{x + 1}} \, dx$

**21.** $\displaystyle\int 2x \sin(x^2) \, dx$

✣ **22.** $\displaystyle\int \frac{2x}{\sqrt{x^2 + 1}} \, dx$

Use known trigonometric identities such as $\sec^2 x = 1 + \tan^2 x$, $\cos(2x) = 2\cos^2 x - 1 = 1 - 2\sin^2 x$, and $\sin(2x) = 2 \sin x \cos x$ to help you evaluate the indefinite integrals in Exercises 23–26.

✣ **23.** $\displaystyle\int \tan^2 x \, dx$

✣ **24.** $\displaystyle\int \sin x \cos x \, dx$

**！ 25.** $\int \cos^2 x \, dx$      **！ 26.** $\int \sin^2 x \, dx$

**Differential equations**

In Exercises 27–42, find the solution $y = y(x)$ to the given initial-value problem. On what interval is the solution valid? (Note that exercises involving differential equations are prefixed with the symbol ✳ .)

**✳ 27.** $\begin{cases} y' = x - 2 \\ y(0) = 3 \end{cases}$     **✳ 28.** $\begin{cases} y' = x^{-2} - x^{-3} \\ y(-1) = 0 \end{cases}$

**✳ 29.** $\begin{cases} y' = 3\sqrt{x} \\ y(4) = 1 \end{cases}$     **✳ 30.** $\begin{cases} y' = x^{1/3} \\ y(0) = 5 \end{cases}$

**✳ 31.** $\begin{cases} y' = Ax^2 + Bx + C \\ y(1) = 1 \end{cases}$     **✳ 32.** $\begin{cases} y' = x^{-9/7} \\ y(1) = -4 \end{cases}$

**✳ 33.** $\begin{cases} y' = \cos x \\ y(\pi/6) = 2 \end{cases}$     **✳ 34.** $\begin{cases} y' = \sin(2x) \\ y(\pi/2) = 1 \end{cases}$

**✳ 35.** $\begin{cases} y' = \sec^2 x \\ y(0) = 1 \end{cases}$     **✳ 36.** $\begin{cases} y' = \sec^2 x \\ y(\pi) = 1 \end{cases}$

**✳ 37.** $\begin{cases} y'' = 2 \\ y'(0) = 5 \\ y(0) = -3 \end{cases}$     **✳ 38.** $\begin{cases} y'' = x^{-4} \\ y'(1) = 2 \\ y(1) = 1 \end{cases}$

**✳ 39.** $\begin{cases} y'' = x^3 - 1 \\ y'(0) = 0 \\ y(0) = 8 \end{cases}$     **✳ 40.** $\begin{cases} y'' = 5x^2 - 3x^{-1/2} \\ y'(1) = 2 \\ y(1) = 0 \end{cases}$

**✳ 41.** $\begin{cases} y'' = \cos x \\ y(0) = 0 \\ y'(0) = 1 \end{cases}$     **✳ 42.** $\begin{cases} y'' = x + \sin x \\ y(0) = 2 \\ y'(0) = 0 \end{cases}$

**✳ 43.** Show that for any constants $A$ and $B$ the function $y = y(x) = Ax + B/x$ satisfies the *second-order differential equation* $x^2 y'' + xy' - y = 0$ for $x \neq 0$. Find a function $y$ satisfying the initial-value problem:

$$\begin{cases} x^2 y'' + xy' - y = 0 & (x > 0) \\ y(1) = 2 \\ y'(1) = 4. \end{cases}$$

**✳ 44.** Show that for any constants $A$ and $B$ the function $y = Ax^{r_1} + Bx^{r_2}$ satisfies, for $x > 0$, the differential equation $ax^2 y'' + bxy' + cy = 0$, provided that $r_1$ and $r_2$ are two distinct rational roots of the quadratic equation $ar(r - 1) + br + c = 0$.

Use the result of Exercise 44 to solve the initial-value problems in Exercises 45–46 on the interval $x > 0$.

**✳ 45.** $\begin{cases} 4x^2 y'' + 4xy' - y \\ \quad\quad = 0 \\ y(4) = 2 \\ y'(4) = -2 \end{cases}$     **✳ 46.** $\begin{cases} x^2 y'' - 6y = 0 \\ y(1) = 1 \\ y'(1) = 1 \end{cases}$

---

## 5.11   Velocity and Acceleration

### Velocity and Speed

Suppose that an object is moving along a straight line (say the $x$-axis) so that its position $x$ is a function of time $t$, say $x = x(t)$. (We are using $x$ to represent both the dependent variable and the function.) Suppose we are measuring $x$ in metres and $t$ in seconds. The **average velocity** of the object over the time interval $[t, t + h]$ is the change in position divided by the change in time, that is, the Newton quotient

$$v_{\text{average}} = \frac{\Delta x}{\Delta t} = \frac{x(t + h) - x(t)}{h} \text{ m/s.}$$

The **velocity** $v(t)$ of the object at time $t$ is the limit of this average velocity as $h \to 0$. Thus, it is the rate of change (the derivative) of position with respect to time:

$$\text{Velocity:} \quad v(t) = \frac{dx}{dt} = x'(t).$$

Besides telling us how fast the object is moving, the velocity also tells us in which direction it is moving. If $v(t) > 0$, then $x$ is increasing, so the object is moving to the right; if $v(t) < 0$, then $x$ is decreasing, so the object is moving to the left. At a critical point of $x$, that is, a time $t$ when $v(t) = 0$, the object is instantaneously at rest—at that instant it is not moving in either direction.

We distinguish between the term *velocity* (which involves direction of motion as well as the rate) and **speed**, which only involves the rate and not the direction. The speed is the absolute value of the velocity:

$$\text{Speed:} \quad s(t) = |v(t)| = \left| \frac{dx}{dt} \right|.$$

A speedometer gives us the speed a vehicle is moving; it does not give the velocity. The speedometer does not start to show negative values if the vehicle turns around and heads in the opposite direction.

### EXAMPLE 1

(a) Determine the velocity $v(t)$ at time $t$ of an object moving along the $x$-axis so that at time $t$ its position is given by

$$x = v_0 t + \frac{1}{2} a t^2,$$

where $v_0$ and $a$ are constants.

(b) Draw the graph of $v(t)$, and show that the area under the graph and above the $t$-axis, over $[t_1, t_2]$, is equal to the distance the object travels in that time interval.

**Solution**   The velocity is given by

$$v(t) = \frac{dx}{dt} = v_0 + at.$$

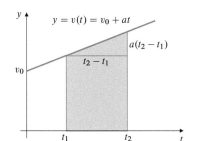

Figure 5.38    The shaded area equals the distance travelled between $t_1$ and $t_2$

Its graph is a straight line with slope $a$ and intercept $v_0$ on the vertical (velocity) axis. The area under the graph (shaded in Figure 5.38) is the sum of the areas of a rectangle and a triangle. Each has base $t_2 - t_1$. The rectangle has height $v(t_1) = v_0 + at_1$, and the triangle has height $a(t_2 - t_1)$. (Why?) Thus, the shaded area is equal to

$$
\begin{aligned}
\text{Area} &= (t_2 - t_1)(v_0 + at_1) + \frac{1}{2}(t_2 - t_1)[a(t_2 - t_1)] \\
&= (t_2 - t_1)\left[ v_0 + at_1 + \frac{a}{2}(t_2 - t_1) \right] \\
&= (t_2 - t_1)\left[ v_0 + \frac{a}{2}(t_2 + t_1) \right] \\
&= v_0(t_2 - t_1) + \frac{a}{2}(t_2^2 - t_1^2) \\
&= x(t_2) - x(t_1),
\end{aligned}
$$

which is the distance travelled by the object between times $t_1$ and $t_2$.

**Remark**   In Example 1 we differentiated the position $x$ to get the velocity $v$ and then used the area under the velocity graph to recover information about the position. It appears that there is a connection between finding areas and finding functions that have given derivatives (i.e., finding antiderivatives). This connection, which we will explore in Chapter 8, is perhaps the most important idea in calculus!

## Acceleration

The derivative of the velocity also has a useful interpretation. The rate of change of the velocity with respect to time is the **acceleration** of the moving object. It is measured in units of distance/time². The value of the acceleration at time $t$ is

$$\text{Acceleration:} \quad a(t) = v'(t) = \frac{dv}{dt} = \frac{d^2 x}{dt^2}.$$

The acceleration is the *second derivative* of the position. If $a(t) > 0$, the velocity is increasing. This does not necessarily mean that the speed is increasing; if the object is moving to the left ($v(t) < 0$) and accelerating to the right ($a(t) > 0$), then it is actually slowing down. The object is speeding up only when the velocity and acceleration have the same sign. (See Table 2.)

Table 2. Velocity, acceleration, and speed

| If velocity is | and acceleration is | then object is | and its speed is |
|---|---|---|---|
| positive | positive | moving right | increasing |
| positive | negative | moving right | decreasing |
| negative | positive | moving left | decreasing |
| negative | negative | moving left | increasing |

If $a(t_0) = 0$, then the velocity and the speed are stationary at $t_0$. If $a(t) = 0$ during an interval of time, then the velocity is unchanging and, therefore, constant over that interval.

---

**EXAMPLE 2**   A point $P$ moves along the $x$-axis in such a way that its position at time $t$ s is given by

$$x = 2t^3 - 15t^2 + 24t \text{ ft.}$$

(a) Find the velocity and acceleration of $P$ at time $t$.

(b) In which direction and how fast is $P$ moving at $t = 2$ s? Is it speeding up or slowing down at that time?

(c) When is $P$ instantaneously at rest? When is its speed instantaneously not changing?

(d) When is $P$ moving to the left? to the right?

(e) When is $P$ speeding up? slowing down?

*Solution*

(a) The velocity and acceleration of $P$ at time $t$ are

$$v = \frac{dx}{dt} = 6t^2 - 30t + 24 = 6(t-1)(t-4) \text{ ft/s} \quad \text{and}$$
$$a = \frac{dv}{dt} = 12t - 30 = 6(2t-5) \text{ ft/s}^2.$$

(b) At $t = 2$ we have $v = -12$ and $a = -6$. Thus, $P$ is moving to the left with speed 12 ft/s, and, since the velocity and acceleration are both negative, its speed is increasing.

(c) $P$ is at rest when $v = 0$, that is, when $t = 1$ s or $t = 4$ s. Its speed is unchanging when $a = 0$, that is, at $t = 5/2$ s.

(d) The velocity is continuous for all $t$ so, by the Intermediate-Value Theorem, has a constant sign on the intervals between the points where it is 0. By examining the values of $v(t)$ at $t = 0, 2$, and 5 (or by analyzing the signs of the factors $(t-1)$ and $(t-4)$ in the expression for $v(t)$), we conclude that $v(t) < 0$ (and $P$ is moving to the left) on time interval $(1, 4)$. $v(t) > 0$ (and $P$ is moving to the right) on time intervals $(-\infty, 1)$ and $(4, \infty)$.

(e) The acceleration $a$ is negative for $t < 5/2$ and positive for $t > 5/2$. Table 3 combines this information with information about $v$ to show where $P$ is speeding up and slowing down.

Table 3.    Data for Example 2

| Interval | $v(t)$ is | $a(t)$ is | $P$ is |
|---|---|---|---|
| $(-\infty, 1)$ | positive | negative | slowing down |
| $(1, 5/2)$ | negative | negative | speeding up |
| $(5/2, 4)$ | negative | positive | slowing down |
| $(4, \infty)$ | positive | positive | speeding up |

The motion of $P$ is shown in Figure 5.39.

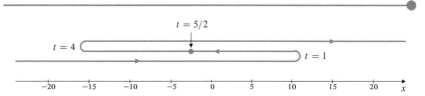

**Figure 5.39**    The motion of the point $P$ in Example 2

---

**EXAMPLE 3**    An object is hurled upward from the roof of a building 10 m high. It rises and then falls back; its height above ground $t$ s after it is thrown is

$$y = -4.9t^2 + 8t + 10 \text{ m},$$

until it strikes the ground. What is the greatest height above the ground that the object attains? With what speed does the object strike the ground?

***Solution***    Refer to Figure 5.40. The vertical velocity at time $t$ during flight is

$$v(t) = -2(4.9)t + 8 = -9.8t + 8 \text{ m/s}.$$

The object is rising when $v > 0$, that is, when $0 < t < 8/9.8$, and is falling for $t > 8/9.8$. Thus, the object is at its maximum height at time $t = 8/9.8 \approx 0.8163$ s, and this maximum height is

$$y_{\max} = -4.9 \left(\frac{8}{9.8}\right)^2 + 8 \left(\frac{8}{9.8}\right) + 10 \approx 13.27 \text{ m}.$$

The time $t$ at which the object strikes the ground is the positive root of the quadratic equation obtained by setting $y = 0$,

$$-4.9t^2 + 8t + 10 = 0,$$

namely,

$$t = \frac{-8 - \sqrt{64 + 196}}{-9.8} \approx 2.462 \text{ s}.$$

The velocity at this time is $v = -(9.8)(2.462) + 8 \approx -16.12$. Thus, the object strikes the ground with a speed of about 16.12 m/s.

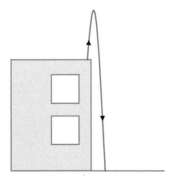

**Figure 5.40**

## Falling under Gravity

According to Newton's Second Law of Motion, a rock of mass $m$ acted on by an unbalanced force $F$ will experience an acceleration $a$ proportional to and in the same direction as $F$; with appropriate units of force, $F = ma$. If the rock is sitting on the ground, it is acted on by two forces: the force of gravity acting downward and the reaction of the ground acting upward. These forces balance, so there is no resulting acceleration. On the other hand, if the rock is up in the air and is unsupported, the gravitational force on it will be unbalanced and the rock will experience downward acceleration. It will fall.

According to Newton's Universal Law of Gravitation, the force by which the earth attracts the rock is proportional to the mass $m$ of the rock and inversely proportional to the square of its distance $r$ from the centre of the earth: $F = km/r^2$. If the relative change $\Delta r/r$ is small, as will be the case if the rock remains near the surface of the earth, then $F = mg$, where $g = k/r^2$ is approximately constant. It follows that $ma = F = mg$, and the rock experiences *constant* downward acceleration $g$. Since $g$ does not depend on $m$, all objects experience the same acceleration when falling near the surface of the earth, provided we ignore air resistance and any other forces that may be acting on them. Newton's laws therefore imply that if the height of such an object at time $t$ is $y(t)$, then

$$\frac{d^2y}{dt^2} = -g.$$

The negative sign is needed because the gravitational acceleration is downward, the opposite direction to that of increasing $y$. Physical experiments give the following approximate values for $g$ at the surface of the earth:

$$g = 32 \text{ ft/s}^2 \quad \text{or} \quad g = 9.8 \text{ m/s}^2.$$

**EXAMPLE 4** A rock falling freely near the surface of the earth is subject to a constant downward acceleration $g$, if the effect of air resistance is neglected. If the height and velocity of the rock are $y_0$ and $v_0$ at time $t = 0$, find the height $y(t)$ of the rock at any later time $t$ until the rock strikes the ground.

*Solution* This example asks for a solution $y(t)$ to the second-order initial-value problem:

$$\begin{cases} y''(t) = -g \\ y(0) = y_0 \\ y'(0) = v_0. \end{cases}$$

We have

$$y'(t) = -\int g\, dt = -gt + C_1$$
$$v_0 = y'(0) = 0 + C_1.$$

Thus, $C_1 = v_0$.

$$y'(t) = -gt + v_0$$
$$y(t) = \int (-gt + v_0)dt = -\frac{1}{2}gt^2 + v_0 t + C_2$$
$$y_0 = y(0) = 0 + 0 + C_2.$$

Thus, $C_2 = y_0$. Finally, therefore,

$$y(t) = -\frac{1}{2}gt^2 + v_0 t + y_0.$$

---

**EXAMPLE 5**     A ball is thrown down with an initial speed of 20 ft/s from the top of a cliff, and it strikes the ground at the bottom of the cliff after 5 s. How high is the cliff?

*Solution*   We will apply the result of Example 4. Here we have $g = 32$ ft/s$^2$, $v_0 = -20$ ft/s, and $y_0$ is the unknown height of the cliff. The height of the ball $t$ s after it is thrown down is

$$y(t) = -16t^2 - 20t + y_0 \text{ ft.}$$

At $t = 5$ the ball reaches the ground, so $y(5) = 0$:

$$0 = -16(25) - 20(5) + y_0 \qquad \Rightarrow \qquad y_0 = 500.$$

The cliff is 500 ft high.

---

**EXAMPLE 6**     **(Stopping distance)**  A car is travelling at 72 km/h. At a certain instant its brakes are applied to produce a constant deceleration of $0.8$ m/s$^2$. How far does the car travel before coming to a stop?

*Solution*   Let $s(t)$ be the distance the car travels in the $t$ seconds after the brakes are applied. Then $s''(t) = -0.8$ (m/s$^2$), so the velocity at time $t$ is given by

$$s'(t) = \int -0.8\, dt = -0.8t + C_1 \quad \text{m/s.}$$

Since $s'(0) = 72$ km/h $= 72 \times 1,000/3,600 = 20$ m/s, we have $C_1 = 20$. Thus,

$$s'(t) = 20 - 0.8t$$

and

$$s(t) = \int (20 - 0.8t)\, dt = 20t - 0.4t^2 + C_2.$$

Since $s(0) = 0$, we have $C_2 = 0$ and $s(t) = 20t - 0.4t^2$. When the car has stopped, its velocity will be 0. Hence, the stopping time is the solution $t$ of the equation

$$0 = s'(t) = 20 - 0.8t,$$

that is, $t = 25$ s. The distance travelled during deceleration is $s(25) = 250$ m.

## EXERCISES 5.11

In Exercises 1–4, a particle moves along the $x$-axis so that its position $x$ at time $t$ is specified by the given function. In each case determine the following:

(a) the time intervals on which the particle is moving to the right and (b) to the left;

(c) the time intervals on which the particle is accelerating to the right and (d) to the left;

(e) the time intervals when the particle is speeding up and (f) slowing down;

(g) the acceleration at times when the velocity is zero;

(h) the average velocity over the time interval $[0, 4]$.

**1.** $x = t^2 - 4t + 3$    **2.** $x = 4 + 5t - t^2$

**3.** $x = t^3 - 4t + 1$    **4.** $x = \dfrac{t}{t^2 + 1}$

**5.** A ball is thrown upward from ground level with an initial speed of 9.8 m/s so that its height in metres after $t$ s is given by $y = 9.8t - 4.9t^2$. What is the acceleration of the ball at any time $t$? How high does the ball go? How fast is it moving when it strikes the ground?

**6.** A ball is thrown downward from the top of a 100-metre-high tower with an initial speed of 2 m/s. Its height in metres above the ground $t$ s later is $y = 100 - 2t - 4.9t^2$. How long does it take to reach the ground? What is its average velocity during the fall? At what instant is its velocity equal to its average velocity?

**7.** (**Takeoff distance**) The distance an aircraft travels along a runway before takeoff is given by $D = t^2$, where $D$ is measured in metres from the starting point, and $t$ is measured in seconds from the time the brake is released. If the aircraft will become airborne when its speed reaches 200 km/h, how long will it take to become airborne, and what distance will it travel in that time?

**8.** (**Projectiles on Mars**) A projectile fired upward from the surface of the earth falls back to the ground after 10 s. How long would it take to fall back to the surface if it is fired upward on Mars with the same initial velocity? $g_{\text{Mars}} = 3.72$ m/s$^2$.

**9.** A ball is thrown upward with initial velocity $v_0$ m/s and reaches a maximum height of $h$ m. How high would it have gone if its initial velocity was $2v_0$? How fast must it be thrown upward to achieve a maximum height of $2h$ m?

**10.** How fast would the ball in Exercise 9 have to be thrown upward on Mars in order to achieve a maximum height of $3h$ m?

**11.** A rock falls from the top of a cliff and hits the ground at the base of the cliff at a speed of 160 ft/s. How high is the cliff?

**12.** A rock is thrown down from the top of a cliff with the initial speed of 32 ft/s and hits the ground at the base of the cliff at a speed of 160 ft/s. How high is the cliff?

**13.** (**Distance travelled while braking**) With full brakes applied, a freight train can decelerate at a constant rate of $1/6$ m/s$^2$. How far will the train travel while braking to a full stop from an initial speed of 60 km/h?

**14.** Show that if the position $x$ of a moving point is given by a quadratic function of $t$, $x = At^2 + Bt + C$, then the average velocity over any time interval $[t_1, t_2]$ is equal to the instantaneous velocity at the midpoint of that time interval.

**15.** (**Piecewise motion**) The position of an object moving along the $s$-axis is given at time $t$ by

$$s = \begin{cases} t^2 & \text{if } 0 \le t \le 2 \\ 4t - 4 & \text{if } 2 < t < 8 \\ -68 + 20t - t^2 & \text{if } 8 \le t \le 10. \end{cases}$$

Determine the velocity and acceleration at any time $t$. Is the velocity continuous? Is the acceleration continuous? What is the maximum velocity and when is it attained?

(**Rocket flight with limited fuel**) Figure 5.41 shows the velocity $v$ in feet per second of a small rocket that was fired from the top of a tower at time $t = 0$ ($t$ in seconds), accelerated with constant upward acceleration until its fuel was used up, then fell back to the ground at the foot of the tower. The whole flight lasted 14 s. Exercises 16–19 refer to this rocket.

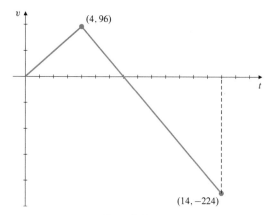

**Figure 5.41**

**16.** What was the acceleration of the rocket while its fuel lasted?

**17.** How long was the rocket rising?

**18.** What is the maximum height above ground that the rocket reached?

**19.** How high was the tower from which the rocket was fired?

**20.** Redo Example 6 using instead a nonconstant deceleration, $s''(t) = -t$ m/s$^2$.

# CHAPTER REVIEW

## Key Ideas

- **What do the following statements and phrases mean?**

  ◇ Line $L$ is tangent to curve $C$ at point $P$.

  ◇ the Newton quotient of $f(x)$ at $x = a$

  ◇ the derivative $f'(x)$ of the function $f(x)$

  ◇ $f$ is differentiable at $x = a$.

  ◇ the slope of the graph $y = f(x)$ at $x = a$

  ◇ $f$ is increasing (or decreasing) on interval $I$.

  ◇ $f$ is nondecreasing (or nonincreasing) on interval $I$.

  ◇ the average rate of change of $f(x)$ on $[a, b]$

  ◇ the rate of change of $f(x)$ at $x = a$

  ◇ $c$ is a critical point of $f(x)$.

  ◇ the second derivative of $f(x)$ at $x = a$

  ◇ an antiderivative of $f$ on interval $I$

  ◇ the indefinite integral of $f$ on interval $I$

  ◇ differential equation        ◇ initial-value problem

  ◇ velocity        ◇ speed        ◇ acceleration

- **State the following differentiation rules:**

  ◇ the rule for differentiating a sum of functions

  ◇ the rule for differentiating a constant multiple of a function

  ◇ the Product Rule        ◇ the Reciprocal Rule

  ◇ the Quotient Rule        ◇ the Chain Rule

- **State the Mean-Value Theorem.**

- **State the Generalized Mean-Value Theorem.**

- **State the derivatives of the following functions:**

  ◇ $x$        ◇ $x^2$        ◇ $1/x$        ◇ $\sqrt{x}$

  ◇ $x^n$        ◇ $|x|$        ◇ $\sin x$        ◇ $\cos x$

  ◇ $\tan x$        ◇ $\cot x$        ◇ $\sec x$        ◇ $\csc x$

- **What is a proof by mathematical induction?**

## Review Exercises

Use the definition of derivative to calculate the derivatives in Exercises 1–4.

**1.** $\dfrac{dy}{dx}$ if $y = (3x + 1)^2$

**2.** $\dfrac{d}{dx}\sqrt{1 - x^2}$

**3.** $f'(2)$ if $f(x) = \dfrac{4}{x^2}$

**4.** $g'(9)$ if $g(t) = \dfrac{t - 5}{1 + \sqrt{t}}$

**5.** Find the tangent to $y = \cos(\pi x)$ at $x = 1/6$.

**6.** Find the normal to $y = \tan(x/4)$ at $x = \pi$.

Calculate the derivatives of the functions in Exercises 7–12.

**7.** $\dfrac{1}{x - \sin x}$

**8.** $\dfrac{1 + x + x^2 + x^3}{x^4}$

**9.** $(4 - x^{2/5})^{-5/2}$

**10.** $\sqrt{2 + \cos^2 x}$

**11.** $\tan \theta - \theta \sec^2 \theta$

**12.** $\dfrac{\sqrt{1 + t^2} - 1}{\sqrt{1 + t^2} + 1}$

Evaluate the limits in Exercises 13–16 by interpreting each as a derivative.

**13.** $\displaystyle\lim_{h \to 0} \dfrac{(x + h)^{20} - x^{20}}{h}$

**14.** $\displaystyle\lim_{x \to 2} \dfrac{\sqrt{4x + 1} - 3}{x - 2}$

**15.** $\displaystyle\lim_{x \to \pi/6} \dfrac{\cos(2x) - (1/2)}{x - \pi/6}$

**16.** $\displaystyle\lim_{x \to -a} \dfrac{(1/x^2) - (1/a^2)}{x + a}$

In Exercises 17–24, express the derivatives of the given functions in terms of the derivatives $f'$ and $g'$ of the differentiable functions $f$ and $g$.

**17.** $f(3 - x^2)$

**18.** $[f(\sqrt{x})]^2$

**19.** $f(2x)\,\sqrt{g(x/2)}$

**20.** $\dfrac{f(x) - g(x)}{f(x) + g(x)}$

**21.** $f(x + (g(x))^2)$

**22.** $f\left(\dfrac{g(x^2)}{x}\right)$

**23.** $f(\sin x)\, g(\cos x)$

**24.** $\sqrt{\dfrac{\cos f(x)}{\sin g(x)}}$

**25.** Find the tangent to the curve $x^3 y + 2xy^3 = 12$ at the point $(2, 1)$.

**26.** Find the slope of the curve $3\sqrt{2}x \sin(\pi y) + 8y \cos(\pi x) = 2$ at the point $\left(\frac{1}{3}, \frac{1}{4}\right)$.

Find the indefinite integrals in Exercises 27–30.

**27.** $\displaystyle\int \dfrac{1 + x^4}{x^2}\, dx$

**28.** $\displaystyle\int \dfrac{1 + x}{\sqrt{x}}\, dx$

**29.** $\displaystyle\int \dfrac{2 + 3\sin x}{\cos^2 x}\, dx$

**30.** $\displaystyle\int (2x + 1)^4\, dx$

**31.** Find $f(x)$ given that $f'(x) = 12x^2 + 12x^3$ and $f(1) = 0$.

**32.** Find $g(x)$ if $g'(x) = \sin(x/3) + \cos(x/6)$ and the graph of $g$ passes through the point $(\pi, 2)$.

**33.** Differentiate $x \sin x + \cos x$ and $x \cos x - \sin x$, and use the results to find the indefinite integrals

$$I_1 = \int x \cos x\, dx \quad \text{and} \quad I_2 = \int x \sin x\, dx.$$

**34.** Suppose that $f'(x) = f(x)$ for every $x$. Let $g(x) = x\, f(x)$. Calculate the first several derivatives of $g$ and guess a formula for the $n$th-order derivative $g^{(n)}(x)$. Verify your guess by induction.

**35.** Find an equation of the straight line that passes through the origin and is tangent to the curve $y = x^3 + 2$.

**36.** Find an equation of the straight lines that pass through the point $(0, 1)$ and are tangent to the curve $y = \sqrt{2 + x^2}$.

**37.** Show that $\dfrac{d}{dx}\left(\sin^n x \sin(nx)\right) = n \sin^{n-1} x \sin((n + 1)x)$. At what points $x$ in $[0, \pi]$ does the graph of $y = \sin^n x \sin(nx)$ have a horizontal tangent? Assume that $n \geq 2$.

**38.** Find differentiation formulas for $y = \sin^n x \cos(nx)$, $y = \cos^n x \sin(nx)$, and $y = \cos^n x \cos(nx)$ analogous to the one given for $y = \sin^n x \sin(nx)$ in Exercise 37.

**39.** Let $Q$ be the point $(0, 1)$. Find all points $P$ on the curve $y = x^2$ such that the line $PQ$ is normal to $y = x^2$ at $P$. What is the shortest distance from $Q$ to the curve $y = x^2$?

40. **(Average and marginal profit)** Figure 5.42 shows the graph of the profit $\$P(x)$ realized by a grain exporter from its sale of $x$ tonnes of wheat. Thus, the average profit per tonne is $\$P(x)/x$. Show that the maximum average profit occurs when the average profit equals the marginal profit. What is the geometric significance of this fact in the figure?

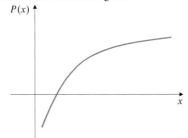

**Figure 5.42**

41. **(Gravitational attraction)** The gravitational attraction of the earth on a mass $m$ at distance $r$ from the centre of the earth is a continuous function $F(r)$ given for $r \geq 0$ by

$$F(r) = \begin{cases} \dfrac{mgR^2}{r^2} & \text{if } r \geq R \\ mkr & \text{if } 0 \leq r < R \end{cases}$$

where $R$ is the radius of the earth, and $g$ is the acceleration due to gravity at the surface of the earth.

   (a) Find the constant $k$ in terms of $g$ and $R$.

   (b) $F$ decreases as $m$ moves away from the surface of the earth, either upward or downward. Show that $F$ decreases as $r$ increases from $R$ at twice the rate at which $F$ decreases as $r$ decreases from $R$.

42. **(Compressibility of a gas)** The isothermal compressibility of a gas is the relative rate of change of the volume $V$ with respect to the pressure $P$ at a constant temperature $T$, that is, $(1/V)\,dV/dP$. For a sample of an ideal gas, the temperature, pressure, and volume satisfy the equation $PV = kT$, where $k$ is a constant related to the number of molecules of gas present in the sample. Show that the isothermal compressibility of such a gas is the negative reciprocal of the pressure:

$$\frac{1}{V}\frac{dV}{dP} = -\frac{1}{P}.$$

43. A ball is thrown upward with an initial speed of 10 m/s from the top of a building. A second ball is thrown upward with an initial speed of 20 m/s from the ground. Both balls achieve the same maximum height above the ground. How tall is the building?

44. A ball is dropped from the top of a 60 m high tower at the same instant that a second ball is thrown upward from the ground at the base of the tower. The balls collide at a height of 30 m above the ground. With what initial velocity was the second ball thrown? How fast is each ball moving when they collide?

45. **(Braking distance)** A car's brakes can decelerate the car at 20 ft/s². How fast can the car travel if it must be able to stop in a distance of 160 ft?

46. **(Measuring variations in $g$)** The period $P$ of a pendulum of length $L$ is given by $P = 2\pi\sqrt{L/g}$, where $g$ is the acceleration of gravity.

   (a) Assuming that $L$ remains fixed, show that a 1% increase in $g$ results in approximately a 1/2% decrease in the period $P$. (Variations in the period of a pendulum can be used to detect small variations in $g$ from place to place on the earth's surface.)

   (b) For fixed $g$, what percentage change in $L$ will produce a 1% increase in $P$?

## Challenging Problems

1. René Descartes, the inventor of analytic geometry, calculated the tangent to a parabola (or a circle or other quadratic curve) at a given point $(x_0, y_0)$ on the curve by looking for a straight line through $(x_0, y_0)$ having only one intersection with the given curve. Illustrate his method by writing the equation of a line through $(a, a^2)$, having arbitrary slope $m$, and then finding the value of $m$ for which the line has only one intersection with the parabola $y = x^2$. Why does the method not work for more general curves?

2. Given that $f'(x) = 1/x$ and $f(2) = 9$, find:

   (a) $\displaystyle\lim_{x\to 2}\frac{f(x^2 + 5) - f(9)}{x - 2}$   (b) $\displaystyle\lim_{x\to 2}\frac{\sqrt{f(x)} - 3}{x - 2}$

3. Suppose that $f'(4) = 3$, $g'(4) = 7$, $g(4) = 4$, and $g(x) \neq 4$ for $x \neq 4$. Find:

   (a) $\displaystyle\lim_{x\to 4}\left(f(x) - f(4)\right)$   (b) $\displaystyle\lim_{x\to 4}\frac{f(x) - f(4)}{x^2 - 16}$

   (c) $\displaystyle\lim_{x\to 4}\frac{f(x) - f(4)}{\sqrt{x} - 2}$   (d) $\displaystyle\lim_{x\to 4}\frac{f(x) - f(4)}{(1/x) - (1/4)}$

   (e) $\displaystyle\lim_{x\to 4}\frac{f(x) - f(4)}{g(x) - 4}$   (f) $\displaystyle\lim_{x\to 4}\frac{f(g(x)) - f(4)}{x - 4}$

4. Let $f(x) = \begin{cases} x & \text{if } x = 1,\ 1/2,\ 1/3,\ 1/4,\ \dots \\ x^2 & \text{otherwise.} \end{cases}$

   (a) Find all points at which $f$ is continuous. In particular, is it continuous at $x = 0$?

   (b) Is the following statement true or false? Justify your answer. For any two real numbers $a$ and $b$, there is some $x$ between $a$ and $b$ such that $f(x) = (f(a) + f(b))/2$.

   (c) Find all points at which $f$ is differentiable. In particular, is it differentiable at $x = 0$?

5. Suppose $f(0) = 0$ and $|f(x)| > \sqrt{|x|}$ for all $x$. Show that $f'(0)$ does not exist.

6. Suppose that $f$ is a function satisfying the following conditions: $f'(0) = k$, $f(0) \neq 0$, and $f(x + y) = f(x)f(y)$ for all $x$ and $y$. Show that $f(0) = 1$ and that $f'(x) = k\,f(x)$ for every $x$. (We will study functions with these properties in Chapter 3.)

7. Suppose the function $g$ satisfies the conditions: $g'(0) = k$, and $g(x + y) = g(x) + g(y)$ for all $x$ and $y$. Show that:

   (a) $g(0) = 0$,   (b) $g'(x) = k$ for all $x$,   and

   (c) $g(x) = kx$ for all $x$. *Hint:* Let $h(x) = g(x) - g'(0)x$.

8. (a) If $f$ is differentiable at $x$, show that

   (i) $\displaystyle\lim_{h\to 0}\frac{f(x) - f(x - h)}{h} = f'(x)$

   (ii) $\displaystyle\lim_{h\to 0}\frac{f(x + h) - f(x - h)}{2h} = f'(x)$

   (b) Show that the existence of the limit in (i) guarantees that $f$ is differentiable at $x$.

(c) Show that the existence of the limit in (ii) does *not* guarantee that $f$ is differentiable at $x$. *Hint:* Consider the function $f(x) = |x|$ at $x = 0$.

9. Show that there is a line through $(a, 0)$ that is tangent to the curve $y = x^3$ at $x = 3a/2$. If $a \neq 0$, is there any other line through $(a, 0)$ that is tangent to the curve? If $(x_0, y_0)$ is an arbitrary point, what is the maximum number of lines through $(x_0, y_0)$ that can be tangent to $y = x^3$? the minimum number?

10. Make a sketch showing that there are two straight lines, each of which is tangent to both of the parabolas $y = x^2 + 4x + 1$ and $y = -x^2 + 4x - 1$. Find equations of the two lines.

11. Show that if $b > 1/2$, there are three straight lines through $(0, b)$, each of which is normal to the curve $y = x^2$. How many such lines are there if $b = 1/2$? if $b < 1/2$?

12. (**Distance from a point to a curve**) Find the point on the curve $y = x^2$ that is closest to the point $(3, 0)$. *Hint:* The line from $(3, 0)$ to the closest point $Q$ on the parabola is normal to the parabola at $Q$.

▣ 13. (**Envelope of a family of lines**) Show that for each value of the parameter $m$, the line $y = mx - (m^2/4)$ is tangent to the parabola $y = x^2$. (The parabola is called the *envelope* of the family of lines $y = mx - (m^2/4)$.) Find $f(m)$ such that the family of lines $y = mx + f(m)$ has envelope the parabola $y = Ax^2 + Bx + C$.

▣ 14. (**Common tangents**) Consider the two parabolas with equations $y = x^2$ and $y = Ax^2 + Bx + C$. We assume that $A \neq 0$, and if $A = 1$, then either $B \neq 0$ or $C \neq 0$, so that the two equations do represent different parabolas. Show that:

   (a) the two parabolas are tangent to each other if $B^2 = 4C(A - 1)$;

   (b) the parabolas have two common tangent lines if and only if $A \neq 1$ and $A\left(B^2 - 4C(A - 1)\right) > 0$;

   (c) the parabolas have exactly one common tangent line if either $A = 1$ and $B \neq 0$, or $A \neq 1$ and $B^2 = 4C(A - 1)$;

   (d) the parabolas have no common tangent lines if either $A = 1$ and $B = 0$, or $A \neq 1$ and $A\left(B^2 - 4C(A-1)\right) < 0$.

   Make sketches illustrating each of the above possibilities.

15. Let $C$ be the graph of $y = x^3$.

   (a) Show that if $a \neq 0$, then the tangent to $C$ at $x = a$ also intersects $C$ at a second point $x = b$.

   (b) Show that the slope of $C$ at $x = b$ is four times its slope at $x = a$.

   (c) Can any line be tangent to $C$ at more than one point?

   (d) Can any line be tangent to the graph of $y = Ax^3 + Bx^2 + Cx + D$ at more than one point?

▣ 16. Let $C$ be the graph of $y = x^4 - 2x^2$.

   (a) Find all horizontal lines that are tangent to $C$.

   (b) One of the lines found in (a) is tangent to $C$ at two different points. Show that there are no other lines with this property.

   (c) Find an equation of a straight line that is tangent to the graph of $y = x^4 - 2x^2 + x$ at two different points. Can there exist more than one such line? Why?

🕑 17. (**Double tangents**) A line tangent to the quartic (fourth-degree polynomial) curve $C$ with equation $y = ax^4 + bx^3 + cx^2 + dx + e$ at $x = p$ may intersect $C$ at zero, one, or two other points. If it meets $C$ at only one other point $x = q$, it must be tangent to $C$ at that point also, and it is thus a "double tangent."

   (a) Find the condition that must be satisfied by the coefficients of the quartic to ensure that there does exist such a double tangent, and show that there cannot be more than one such double tangent. Illustrate this by applying your results to $y = x^4 - 2x^2 + x - 1$.

   (b) If the line $PQ$ is tangent to $C$ at two distinct points $x = p$ and $x = q$, show that $PQ$ is parallel to the line tangent to $C$ at $x = (p + q)/2$.

   (c) If the line $PQ$ is tangent to $C$ at two distinct points $x = p$ and $x = q$, show that $C$ has two distinct inflection points $R$ and $S$ and that $RS$ is parallel to $PQ$.

18. Verify the following formulas for every positive integer $n$:

   (a) $\dfrac{d^n}{dx^n} \cos(ax) = a^n \cos\left(ax + \dfrac{n\pi}{2}\right)$

   (b) $\dfrac{d^n}{dx^n} \sin(ax) = a^n \sin\left(ax + \dfrac{n\pi}{2}\right)$

   (c) $\dfrac{d^n}{dx^n}\left(\cos^4 x + \sin^4 x\right) = 4^{n-1} \cos\left(4x + \dfrac{n\pi}{2}\right)$

19. (**Rocket with a parachute**) A rocket is fired from the top of a tower at time $t = 0$. It experiences constant upward acceleration until its fuel is used up. Thereafter its acceleration is the constant downward acceleration of gravity until, during its fall, it deploys a parachute that gives it a constant upward acceleration again to slow it down. The rocket hits the ground near the base of the tower. The upward velocity $v$ (in metres per second) is graphed against time in Figure 5.43. From information in the figure answer the following questions:

   (a) How long did the fuel last?

   (b) When was the rocket's height maximum?

   (c) When was the parachute deployed?

   (d) What was the rocket's upward acceleration while its motor was firing?

   (e) What was the maximum height achieved by the rocket?

   (f) How high was the tower from which the rocket was fired?

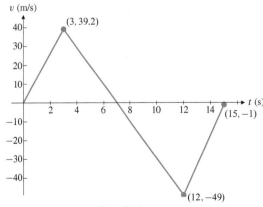

Figure 5.43

# CHAPTER 6

# Transcendental Functions

## Introduction

With the exception of the trigonometric functions, all the functions we have encountered so far have been of three main types: *polynomials, rational functions* (quotients of polynomials), and *algebraic functions* (fractional powers of rational functions). On an interval in its domain, each of these functions can be constructed from real numbers and a single real variable $x$ by using finitely many arithmetic operations (addition, subtraction, multiplication, and division) and by taking finitely many roots (fractional powers). Functions that cannot be so constructed are called **transcendental functions**. The only examples of these that we have seen so far are the trigonometric functions.

Much of the importance of calculus and many of its most useful applications result from its ability to illuminate the behaviour of transcendental functions that arise naturally when we try to model concrete problems in mathematical terms. This chapter is devoted to developing other transcendental functions, including exponential and logarithmic functions and the inverse trigonometric functions.

Some of these functions "undo" what other ones "do" and vice versa. When a pair of functions behaves this way, we call each one the inverse of the other. We begin the chapter by studying inverse functions in general.

## 6.1 Inverse Functions

Consider the function $f(x) = x^3$ whose graph is shown in Figure 6.1. Like any function, $f(x)$ has only one value for each $x$ in its domain (for $x^3$ this is the whole real line $\mathbb{R}$). In geometric terms, this means that any *vertical* line meets the graph of $f$ at only one point. However, for this function $f$, any *horizontal* line also meets the graph at only one point. This means that different values of $x$ always give different values $f(x)$. Such a function is said to be *one-to-one*.

**DEFINITION**

**1**

A function $f$ is **one-to-one** if $f(x_1) \neq f(x_2)$ whenever $x_1$ and $x_2$ belong to the domain of $f$ and $x_1 \neq x_2$, or, equivalently, if

$$f(x_1) = f(x_2) \implies x_1 = x_2.$$

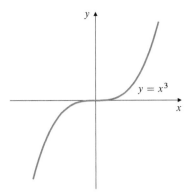

**Figure 6.1**   The graph of $f(x) = x^3$

---

Do not confuse the $-1$ in $f^{-1}$ with an exponent. The inverse $f^{-1}$ is *not* the reciprocal $1/f$. If we want to denote the reciprocal $1/f(x)$ with an exponent we can write it as $\left( f(x) \right)^{-1}$.

---

**Figure 6.2**

(a) $f$ is one-to-one and has an inverse: $y = f(x)$ means the same thing as $x = f^{-1}(y)$

(b) $g$ is not one-to-one

A function is one-to-one if any horizontal line that intersects its graph does so at only one point. If a function defined on a single interval is increasing (or decreasing), then it is one-to-one. (See Section 5.6 for more discussion of this.)

Reconsider the one-to-one function $f(x) = x^3$ (Figure 6.1). Since the equation

$$y = x^3$$

has a unique solution $x$ for every given value of $y$ in the range of $f$, $f$ is one-to-one. Specifically, this solution is given by

$$x = y^{1/3};$$

it defines $x$ as a function of $y$. We call this new function the *inverse of $f$* and denote it $f^{-1}$. Thus,

$$f^{-1}(y) = y^{1/3}.$$

In general, if a function $f$ is one-to-one, then for any number $y$ in its range there will always exist a single number $x$ in its domain such that $y = f(x)$. Since $x$ is determined uniquely by $y$, it is a function of $y$. We write $x = f^{-1}(y)$ and call $f^{-1}$ the inverse of $f$. The function $f$ whose graph is shown in Figure 6.2(a) is one-to-one and has an inverse. The function $g$ whose graph is shown in Figure 6.2(b) is not one-to-one (some horizontal lines meet the graph twice) and so does not have an inverse.

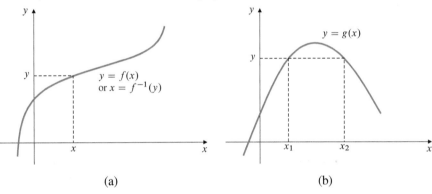

(a)                    (b)

We usually like to write functions with the domain variable called $x$ rather than $y$, so we reverse the roles of $x$ and $y$ and reformulate the above definition as follows.

**DEFINITION**

**2**

If $f$ is one-to-one, then it has an **inverse function** $f^{-1}$. The value of $f^{-1}(x)$ is the unique number $y$ in the domain of $f$ for which $f(y) = x$. Thus,

$$y = f^{-1}(x) \quad \Longleftrightarrow \quad x = f(y).$$

As seen above, $y = f(x) = x^3$ is equivalent to $x = f^{-1}(y) = y^{1/3}$, or, reversing the roles of $x$ and $y$, $y = f^{-1}(x) = x^{1/3}$ is equivalent to $x = f(y) = y^3$.

---

**EXAMPLE 1**

Show that $f(x) = 2x - 1$ is one-to-one, and find its inverse $f^{-1}(x)$.

***Solution***   Since $f'(x) = 2 > 0$ on $\mathbb{R}$, $f$ is increasing and therefore one-to-one there. Let $y = f^{-1}(x)$. Then

$$x = f(y) = 2y - 1.$$

Solving this equation for $y$ gives $y = \dfrac{x+1}{2}$. Thus, $f^{-1}(x) = \dfrac{x+1}{2}$.

There are several things you should remember about the relationship between a function $f$ and its inverse $f^{-1}$. The most important one is that the two equations

$$y = f^{-1}(x) \quad \text{and} \quad x = f(y)$$

*say the same thing.* They are equivalent just as, for example, $y = x + 1$ and $x = y - 1$ are equivalent. Either of the equations can be replaced by the other. This implies that the domain of $f^{-1}$ is the range of $f$ and vice versa.

The inverse of a one-to-one function is itself one-to-one and so also has an inverse. Not surprisingly, the inverse of $f^{-1}$ is $f$:

$$y = (f^{-1})^{-1}(x) \quad \Longleftrightarrow \quad x = f^{-1}(y) \quad \Longleftrightarrow \quad y = f(x).$$

We can substitute either of the equations $y = f^{-1}(x)$ or $x = f(y)$ into the other and obtain the **cancellation identities**:

$$f\big(f^{-1}(x)\big) = x, \qquad f^{-1}\big(f(y)\big) = y.$$

The first of these identities holds for all $x$ in the domain of $f^{-1}$ and the second for all $y$ in the domain of $f$. If $S$ is any set of real numbers and $I_S$ denotes the **identity function** on $S$, defined by

$$I_S(x) = x \quad \text{for all } x \text{ in } S,$$

then the cancellation identities say that if $\mathcal{D}(f)$ is the domain of $f$, then

$$f \circ f^{-1} = I_{\mathcal{D}(f^{-1})} \quad \text{and} \quad f^{-1} \circ f = I_{\mathcal{D}(f)},$$

where $f \circ g(x)$ denotes the composition $f\big(g(x)\big)$.

If the coordinates of a point $P = (a, b)$ are exchanged to give those of a new point $Q = (b, a)$, then each point is the reflection of the other in the line $x = y$. (To see this, note that the line $PQ$ has slope $-1$, so it is perpendicular to $y = x$. Also, the midpoint of $PQ$ is $\left(\frac{a+b}{2}, \frac{b+a}{2}\right)$, which lies on $y = x$.) It follows that the graphs of the equations $x = f(y)$ and $y = f(x)$ are reflections of each other in the line $x = y$. Since the equation $x = f(y)$ is equivalent to $y = f^{-1}(x)$, the graphs of the functions $f^{-1}$ and $f$ are reflections of each other in $y = x$. See Figure 6.3.

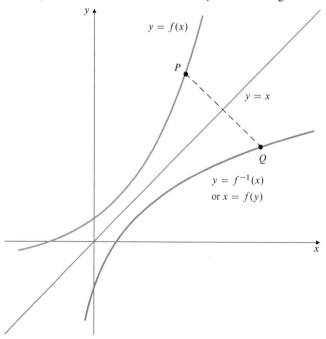

Figure 6.3    The graph of $y = f^{-1}(x)$ (red) is the reflection of the graph of $y = f(x)$ (blue) in the line $y = x$ (green)

Here is a summary of the properties of inverse functions discussed above:

**Properties of inverse functions**

1. $y = f^{-1}(x) \iff x = f(y)$.
2. The domain of $f^{-1}$ is the range of $f$.
3. The range of $f^{-1}$ is the domain of $f$.
4. $f^{-1}(f(x)) = x$ for all $x$ in the domain of $f$.
5. $f(f^{-1}(x)) = x$ for all $x$ in the domain of $f^{-1}$.
6. $(f^{-1})^{-1}(x) = f(x)$ for all $x$ in the domain of $f$.
7. The graph of $f^{-1}$ is the reflection of the graph of $f$ in the line $x = y$.

**EXAMPLE 2**  Show that $g(x) = \sqrt{2x + 1}$ is invertible, and find its inverse.

*Solution*  If $g(x_1) = g(x_2)$, then $\sqrt{2x_1 + 1} = \sqrt{2x_2 + 1}$. Squaring both sides we get $2x_1 + 1 = 2x_2 + 1$, which implies that $x_1 = x_2$. Thus, $g$ is one-to-one and invertible. Let $y = g^{-1}(x)$; then

$$x = g(y) = \sqrt{2y + 1}.$$

It follows that $x \geq 0$ and $x^2 = 2y + 1$. Therefore, $y = \dfrac{x^2 - 1}{2}$ and

$$g^{-1}(x) = \frac{x^2 - 1}{2} \qquad \text{for } x \geq 0.$$

(The restriction $x \geq 0$ applies since the range of $g$ is $[0, \infty)$.) See Figure 6.4(a) for the graphs of $g$ and $g^{-1}$.

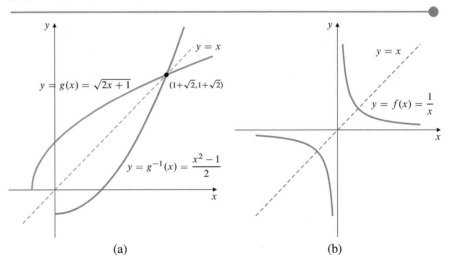

**Figure 6.4**

(a) The graphs of $g(x) = \sqrt{2x + 1}$ and its inverse

(b) The graph of the self-inverse function $f(x) = 1/x$

**DEFINITION**

**3**

A function $f$ is **self-inverse** if $f^{-1} = f$, that is, if $f(f(x)) = x$ for every $x$ in the domain of $f$.

**EXAMPLE 3**  The function $f(x) = 1/x$ is self-inverse. If $y = f^{-1}(x)$, then $x = f(y) = \dfrac{1}{y}$. Therefore, $y = \dfrac{1}{x}$, so $f^{-1}(x) = \dfrac{1}{x} = f(x)$.

See Figure 6.4(b). The graph of any self-inverse function must be its own reflection in the line $x = y$ and must therefore be symmetric about that line.

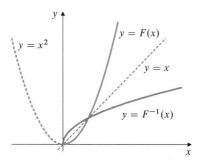

**Figure 6.5**    The restriction $F$ of $x^2$ (blue) to $[0, \infty)$ and its inverse $F^{-1}$ (red)

## Inverting Non–One-to-One Functions

Many important functions, such as the trigonometric functions, are not one-to-one on their whole domains. It is still possible to define an inverse for such a function, but we have to restrict the domain of the function artificially so that the restricted function is one-to-one.

As an example, consider the function $f(x) = x^2$. Unrestricted, its domain is the whole real line and it is not one-to-one since $f(-a) = f(a)$ for any $a$. Let us define a new function $F(x)$ equal to $f(x)$ but having a smaller domain, so that it is one-to-one. We can use the interval $[0, \infty)$ as the domain of $F$:

$$F(x) = x^2 \qquad \text{for} \quad 0 \le x < \infty.$$

The graph of $F$ is shown in Figure 6.5; it is the right half of the parabola $y = x^2$, the graph of $f$. Evidently $F$ is one-to-one, so it has an inverse $F^{-1}$, which we calculate as follows:

Let $y = F^{-1}(x)$, then $x = F(y) = y^2$ and $y \ge 0$. Thus, $y = \sqrt{x}$. Hence $F^{-1}(x) = \sqrt{x}$.

This method of restricting the domain of a non–one-to-one function to make it invertible will be used when we invert the trigonometric functions in Section 6.5.

## Derivatives of Inverse Functions

Suppose that the function $f$ is differentiable on an interval $(a, b)$ and that either $f'(x) > 0$ for $a < x < b$, so that $f$ is increasing on $(a, b)$, or $f'(x) < 0$ for $a < x < b$, so that $f$ is decreasing on $(a, b)$. In either case $f$ is one-to-one on $(a, b)$ and has an inverse, $f^{-1}$ there. Differentiating the cancellation identity

$$f\big(f^{-1}(x)\big) = x$$

with respect to $x$, using the Chain Rule, we obtain

$$f'\big(f^{-1}(x)\big) \frac{d}{dx} f^{-1}(x) = \frac{d}{dx} x = 1.$$

Thus,

$$\frac{d}{dx} f^{-1}(x) = \frac{1}{f'\left(f^{-1}(x)\right)}.$$

In Leibniz notation, if $y = f^{-1}(x)$, we have $\dfrac{dy}{dx}\Big|_x = \dfrac{1}{\dfrac{dx}{dy}\Big|_{y=f^{-1}(x)}}$.

The slope of the graph of $f^{-1}$ at $(x, y)$ is the reciprocal of the slope of the graph of $f$ at $(y, x)$. (See Figure 6.6.)

---

**EXAMPLE 4**    Show that $f(x) = x^3 + x$ is one-to-one on the whole real line, and, noting that $f(2) = 10$, find $\left(f^{-1}\right)'(10)$.

**Solution**    Since $f'(x) = 3x^2 + 1 > 0$ for all real numbers $x$, $f$ is increasing and therefore one-to-one and invertible. If $y = f^{-1}(x)$, then

$$x = f(y) = y^3 + y \quad \Longrightarrow \quad 1 = (3y^2 + 1)y'$$

$$\Longrightarrow \quad y' = \frac{1}{3y^2 + 1}.$$

Now $x = f(2) = 10$ implies $y = f^{-1}(10) = 2$. Thus,

$$\left(f^{-1}\right)'(10) = \frac{1}{3y^2 + 1}\bigg|_{y=2} = \frac{1}{13}.$$

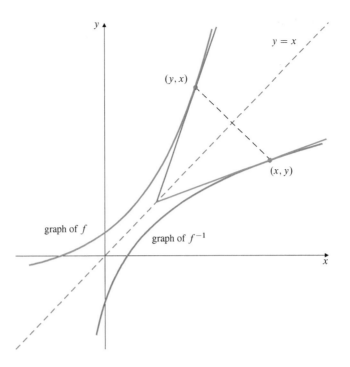

**Figure 6.6**    Tangents to the graphs of $f$ and $f^{-1}$

Show that the functions $f$ in Exercises 1–12 are one-to-one, and calculate the inverse functions $f^{-1}$. Specify the domains and ranges of $f$ and $f^{-1}$.

**1.** $f(x) = x - 1$

**2.** $f(x) = 2x - 1$

**3.** $f(x) = \sqrt{x - 1}$

**4.** $f(x) = -\sqrt{x - 1}$

**5.** $f(x) = x^3$

**6.** $f(x) = 1 + \sqrt[3]{x}$

**7.** $f(x) = x^2, \quad x \leq 0$

**8.** $f(x) = (1 - 2x)^3$

**9.** $f(x) = \dfrac{1}{x + 1}$

**10.** $f(x) = \dfrac{x}{1 + x}$

**11.** $f(x) = \dfrac{1 - 2x}{1 + x}$

**12.** $f(x) = \dfrac{x}{\sqrt{x^2 + 1}}$

In Exercises 13–20, $f$ is a one-to-one function with inverse $f^{-1}$. Calculate the inverses of the given functions in terms of $f^{-1}$.

**13.** $g(x) = f(x) - 2$

**14.** $h(x) = f(2x)$

**15.** $k(x) = -3f(x)$

**16.** $m(x) = f(x - 2)$

**17.** $p(x) = \dfrac{1}{1 + f(x)}$

**18.** $q(x) = \dfrac{f(x) - 3}{2}$

**19.** $r(x) = 1 - 2f(3 - 4x)$

**20.** $s(x) = \dfrac{1 + f(x)}{1 - f(x)}$

In Exercises 21–23, show that the given function is one-to-one and find its inverse.

**21.** $f(x) = \begin{cases} x^2 + 1 & \text{if } x \geq 0 \\ x + 1 & \text{if } x < 0 \end{cases}$

**22.** $g(x) = \begin{cases} x^3 & \text{if } x \geq 0 \\ x^{1/3} & \text{if } x < 0 \end{cases}$

**23.** $h(x) = x|x| + 1$

**24.** Find $f^{-1}(2)$ if $f(x) = x^3 + x$.

**25.** Find $g^{-1}(1)$ if $g(x) = x^3 + x - 9$.

**26.** Find $h^{-1}(-3)$ if $h(x) = x|x| + 1$.

**27.** Assume that the function $f(x)$ satisfies $f'(x) = \dfrac{1}{x}$ and that $f$ is one-to-one. If $y = f^{-1}(x)$, show that $dy/dx = y$.

**28.** Find $\left(f^{-1}\right)'(x)$ if $f(x) = 1 + 2x^3$.

**29.** Show that $f(x) = \dfrac{4x^3}{x^2 + 1}$ has an inverse and find $\left(f^{-1}\right)'(2)$.

**30.** Find $\left(f^{-1}\right)'(-2)$ if $f(x) = x\sqrt{3 + x^2}$.

**31.** If $f(x) = x^2/(1 + \sqrt{x})$, find $f^{-1}(2)$ correct to 5 decimal places.

**32.** If $g(x) = 2x + \sin x$, show that $g$ is invertible, and find $g^{-1}(2)$ and $(g^{-1})'(2)$ correct to 5 decimal places.

**33.** Show that $f(x) = x \sec x$ is one-to-one on $(-\pi/2, \pi/2)$. What is the domain of $f^{-1}(x)$? Find $(f^{-1})'(0)$.

**34.** If functions $f$ and $g$ have respective inverses $f^{-1}$ and $g^{-1}$, show that the composite function $f \circ g$ has inverse $(f \circ g)^{-1} = g^{-1} \circ f^{-1}$.

**35.** For what values of the constants $a$, $b$, and $c$ is the function $f(x) = (x - a)/(bx - c)$ self-inverse?

**36.** Can an even function be self-inverse? an odd function?

**37.** In this section it was claimed that an increasing (or decreasing) function defined on a single interval is necessarily one-to-one. Is the converse of this statement true? Explain.

**38.** Repeat Exercise 37 with the added assumption that $f$ is continuous on the interval where it is defined.

## 6.2    Exponential and Logarithmic Functions

To begin we review exponential and logarithmic functions as you may have encountered them in your previous mathematical studies. In the following sections we will approach these functions from a different point of view and learn how to find their derivatives.

### Exponentials

An **exponential function** is a function of the form $f(x) = a^x$, where the **base** $a$ is a positive constant and the **exponent** $x$ is the variable. Do not confuse such functions with **power** functions such as $f(x) = x^a$, where the base is variable and the exponent is constant. The exponential function $a^x$ can be defined for integer and rational exponents $x$ as follows:

**DEFINITION**

**4**

> **Exponential functions**
>
> If $a > 0$, then
>
> $$a^0 = 1$$
> $$a^n = \underbrace{a \cdot a \cdot a \cdots a}_{n \text{ factors}} \qquad \text{if } n = 1, 2, 3, \ldots$$
> $$a^{-n} = \frac{1}{a^n} \qquad \text{if } n = 1, 2, 3, \ldots$$
> $$a^{m/n} = \sqrt[n]{a^m} \qquad \text{if } n = 1, 2, 3, \ldots \quad \text{and } m = \pm 1, \pm 2, \pm 3, \ldots.$$
>
> In this definition, $\sqrt[n]{a}$ is the number $b > 0$ that satisfies $b^n = a$.

How should we define $a^x$ if $x$ is not rational? For example, what does $2^\pi$ mean? In order to calculate a derivative of $a^x$, we will want the function to be defined for all real numbers $x$, not just rational ones.

In Figure 6.7 we plot points with coordinates $(x, 2^x)$ for many closely spaced rational values of $x$. They appear to lie on a smooth curve. The definition of $a^x$ can be extended to irrational $x$ in such a way that $a^x$ becomes a differentiable function of $x$ on the whole real line. We will do so in the next section. For the moment, if $x$ is irrational we can regard $a^x$ as being the limit of values $a^r$ for rational numbers $r$ approaching $x$:

$$a^x = \lim_{\substack{r \to x \\ r \text{ rational}}} a^r.$$

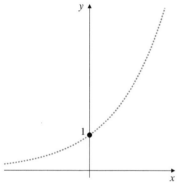

**Figure 6.7**    $y = 2^x$ for rational $x$

**EXAMPLE 1**    Since the irrational number $\pi = 3.141\,592\,653\,59\ldots$ is the limit of the sequence of rational numbers

$$r_1 = 3, \quad r_2 = 3.1, \quad r_3 = 3.14, \quad r_4 = 3.141, \quad r_5 = 3.1415, \quad \ldots,$$

we can calculate $2^\pi$ as the limit of the corresponding sequence

$$2^3 = 8, \quad 2^{3.1} = 8.574\,187\,7\ldots, \quad 2^{3.14} = 8.815\,240\,9\ldots.$$

This gives $2^\pi = \lim_{n \to \infty} 2^{r_n} = 8.824\,977\,827\ldots$.

Exponential functions satisfy several identities called *laws of exponents*:

**Laws of exponents**

If $a > 0$ and $b > 0$, and $x$ and $y$ are any real numbers, then

(i) $\quad a^0 = 1$ 

(ii) $\quad a^{x+y} = a^x \, a^y$

(iii) $\quad a^{-x} = \dfrac{1}{a^x}$ 

(iv) $\quad a^{x-y} = \dfrac{a^x}{a^y}$

(v) $\quad (a^x)^y = a^{xy}$ 

(vi) $\quad (ab)^x = a^x \, b^x$

These identities can be proved for rational exponents using the definitions above. They remain true for irrational exponents, but we can't show that until the next section.

If $a = 1$, then $a^x = 1^x = 1$ for every $x$. If $a > 1$, then $a^x$ is an increasing function of $x$; if $0 < a < 1$, then $a^x$ is decreasing. The graphs of some typical exponential functions are shown in Figure 6.8(a). They all pass through the point $(0,1)$ since $a^0 = 1$ for every $a > 0$. Observe that $a^x > 0$ for all $a > 0$ and all real $x$ and that:

$$\text{If} \quad a > 1, \quad \text{then} \quad \lim_{x \to -\infty} a^x = 0 \quad \text{and} \quad \lim_{x \to \infty} a^x = \infty.$$

$$\text{If} \quad 0 < a < 1, \quad \text{then} \quad \lim_{x \to -\infty} a^x = \infty \quad \text{and} \quad \lim_{x \to \infty} a^x = 0.$$

**Figure 6.8**

(a) Graphs of some exponential functions $y = a^x$

(b) Graphs of some logarithmic functions $y = \log_a(x)$

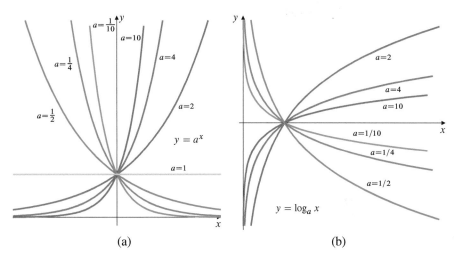

(a)

(b)

The graph of $y = a^x$ has the $x$-axis as a horizontal asymptote if $a \neq 1$. It is asymptotic on the left (as $x \to -\infty$) if $a > 1$ and on the right (as $x \to \infty$) if $0 < a < 1$.

## Logarithms

The function $f(x) = a^x$ is a one-to-one function provided that $a > 0$ and $a \neq 1$. Therefore, $f$ has an inverse which we call a *logarithmic function*.

**DEFINITION**

**5**

If $a > 0$ and $a \neq 1$, the function $\log_a x$, called **the logarithm of $x$ to the base $a$**, is the inverse of the one-to-one function $a^x$:

$$y = \log_a x \iff x = a^y, \quad (a > 0, \quad a \neq 1).$$

Since $a^x$ has domain $(-\infty, \infty)$, $\log_a x$ has range $(-\infty, \infty)$. Since $a^x$ has range $(0, \infty)$, $\log_a x$ has domain $(0, \infty)$. Since $a^x$ and $\log_a x$ are inverse functions, the following **cancellation identities** hold:

$$\log_a (a^x) = x \quad \text{for all real } x \quad \text{and} \quad a^{\log_a x} = x \quad \text{for all} \quad x > 0.$$

The graphs of some typical logarithmic functions are shown in Figure 6.8(b). They all pass through the point $(1, 0)$. Each graph is the reflection in the line $y = x$ of the corresponding exponential graph in Figure 6.8(a).

From the laws of exponents we can derive the following laws of logarithms:

**Laws of logarithms**

If $x > 0$, $y > 0$, $a > 0$, $b > 0$, $a \neq 1$, and $b \neq 1$, then

(i)  $\log_a 1 = 0$                                         (ii)  $\log_a (xy) = \log_a x + \log_a y$

(iii)  $\log_a \left( \dfrac{1}{x} \right) = -\log_a x$      (iv)  $\log_a \left( \dfrac{x}{y} \right) = \log_a x - \log_a y$

(v)  $\log_a (x^y) = y \log_a x$                            (vi)  $\log_a x = \dfrac{\log_b x}{\log_b a}$

**EXAMPLE 2**  If $a > 0$, $x > 0$, and $y > 0$, verify that $\log_a (xy) = \log_a x + \log_a y$, using laws of exponents.

**Solution**  Let $u = \log_a x$ and $v = \log_a y$. By the defining property of inverse functions, $x = a^u$ and $y = a^v$. Thus, $xy = a^u a^v = a^{u+v}$. Inverting again, we get $\log_a (xy) = u + v = \log_a x + \log_a y$.

Logarithm law (vi) presented above shows that if you know logarithms to a particular base $b$, you can calculate logarithms to any other base $a$. Scientific calculators usually have built-in programs for calculating logarithms to base 10 and to base $e$, a special number that we will discover in Section 6.3. Logarithms to any base can be calculated using either of these functions. For example, computer scientists sometimes need to use logarithms to base 2. Using a scientific calculator, you can readily calculate

$$\log_2 13 = \frac{\log_{10} 13}{\log_{10} 2} = \frac{1.113\,943\,352\,31\ldots}{0.301\,029\,995\,664\ldots} = 3.700\,439\,718\,14\ldots \ .$$

The laws of logarithms can sometimes be used to simplify complicated expressions.

**EXAMPLE 3**  Simplify
(a) $\log_2 10 + \log_2 12 - \log_2 15$,   (b) $\log_{a^2} a^3$,   and   (c) $3^{\log_9 4}$.

**Solution**

(a)  $\log_2 10 + \log_2 12 - \log_2 15 = \log_2 \dfrac{10 \times 12}{15}$      (laws (ii) and (iv))

$\qquad\qquad\qquad\qquad\qquad\qquad = \log_2 8$

$\qquad\qquad\qquad\qquad\qquad\qquad = \log_2 2^3 = 3.$      (cancellation identity)

(b)  $\log_{a^2} a^3 = 3 \log_{a^2} a$      (law (v))

$\qquad\qquad = \dfrac{3}{2} \log_{a^2} a^2$      (law (v) again)

$\qquad\qquad = \dfrac{3}{2}.$      (cancellation identity)

(c)  $3^{\log_9 4} = 3^{(\log_3 4)/(\log_3 9)}$      (law (vi))

$\qquad\quad = \left( 3^{\log_3 4} \right)^{1/\log_3 9}$

$\qquad\quad = 4^{1/\log_3 3^2} = 4^{1/2} = 2.$      (cancellation identity)

**EXAMPLE 4**  Solve the equation $3^{x-1} = 2^x$.

*Solution*    We can take logarithms of both sides of the equation to any base $a$ and get

$$(x - 1) \log_a 3 = x \log_a 2$$
$$(\log_a 3 - \log_a 2)x = \log_a 3$$
$$x = \frac{\log_a 3}{\log_a 3 - \log_a 2} = \frac{\log_a 3}{\log_a (3/2)}.$$

The numerical value of $x$ can be found using the "log" function on a scientific calculator. (This function is $\log_{10}$.) The value is $x = 2.7095\ldots$.

Corresponding to the asymptotic behaviour of the exponential functions, the logarithmic functions also exhibit asymptotic behaviour. Their graphs are all asymptotic to the $y$-axis as $x \to 0$ from the right:

If  $a > 1$,    then    $\displaystyle\lim_{x \to 0+} \log_a x = -\infty$ and $\displaystyle\lim_{x \to \infty} \log_a x = \infty$.

If  $0 < a < 1$, then    $\displaystyle\lim_{x \to 0+} \log_a x = \infty$ and $\displaystyle\lim_{x \to \infty} \log_a x = -\infty$.

## EXERCISES 6.2

Simplify the expressions in Exercises 1–18.

**1.** $\dfrac{3^3}{\sqrt{3^5}}$

**2.** $2^{1/2} 8^{1/2}$

**3.** $\left(x^{-3}\right)^{-2}$

**4.** $\left(\dfrac{1}{2}\right)^x 4^{x/2}$

**5.** $\log_5 125$

**6.** $\log_4 \left(\dfrac{1}{8}\right)$

**7.** $\log_{1/3} 3^{2x}$

**8.** $2^{\log_4 8}$

**9.** $10^{-\log_{10}(1/x)}$

**10.** $x^{1/(\log_a x)}$

**11.** $(\log_a b)(\log_b a)$

**12.** $\log_x \left(x(\log_y y^2)\right)$

**13.** $(\log_4 16)(\log_4 2)$

**14.** $\log_{15} 75 + \log_{15} 3$

**15.** $\log_6 9 + \log_6 4$

**16.** $2 \log_3 12 - 4 \log_3 6$

**17.** $\log_a (x^4 + 3x^2 + 2) + \log_a (x^4 + 5x^2 + 6)$
$\qquad - 4 \log_a \sqrt{x^2 + 2}$

**18.** $\log_\pi (1 - \cos x) + \log_\pi (1 + \cos x) - 2 \log_\pi \sin x$

Use the base 10 exponential and logarithm functions $10^x$ and $\log x$ (that is, $\log_{10} x$) on a scientific calculator to evaluate the expressions or solve the equations in Exercises 19–24.

**19.** $3^{\sqrt{2}}$

**20.** $\log_3 5$

**21.** $2^{2x} = 5^{x+1}$

**22.** $x^{\sqrt{2}} = 3$

**23.** $\log_x 3 = 5$

**24.** $\log_3 x = 5$

Use the laws of exponents to prove the laws of logarithms in Exercises 25–28.

**25.** $\log_a \left(\dfrac{1}{x}\right) = -\log_a x$

**26.** $\log_a \left(\dfrac{x}{y}\right) = \log_a x - \log_a y$

**27.** $\log_a (x^y) = y \log_a x$

**28.** $\log_a x = (\log_b x)/(\log_b a)$

**29.** Solve $\log_4 (x + 4) - 2 \log_4 (x + 1) = \dfrac{1}{2}$ for $x$.

**30.** Solve $2 \log_3 x + \log_9 x = 10$ for $x$.

Evaluate the limits in Exercises 31–34.

**31.** $\displaystyle\lim_{x \to \infty} \log_x 2$

**32.** $\displaystyle\lim_{x \to 0+} \log_x (1/2)$

**33.** $\displaystyle\lim_{x \to 1+} \log_x 2$

**34.** $\displaystyle\lim_{x \to 1-} \log_x 2$

**35.** Suppose that $f(x) = a^x$ is differentiable at $x = 0$ and that $f'(0) = k$, where $k \neq 0$. Prove that $f$ is differentiable at any real number $x$ and that

$$f'(x) = k\, a^x = k\, f(x).$$

**36.** Continuing Exercise 35, prove that $f^{-1}(x) = \log_a x$ is differentiable at any $x > 0$ and that

$$(f^{-1})'(x) = \frac{1}{kx}.$$

# 6.3    The Natural Logarithm and Exponential Functions

Regard this paragraph as describing a game we are going to play in this section. The result of the game will be that we will acquire two new classes of functions, logarithms, and exponentials, to which the rules of calculus will apply.

In this section we are going to define a function $\ln x$, called the *natural* logarithm of $x$, in a way that does not at first seem to have anything to do with the logarithms considered in Section 6.2. We will show, however, that it has the same properties as those logarithms, and in the end we will see that $\ln x = \log_e x$, the logarithm of $x$ to a certain specific base $e$. We will show that $\ln x$ is a one-to-one function, defined for all positive real numbers. It must therefore have an inverse, $e^x$, that we will call *the* exponential function. Our final goal is to arrive at a definition of the exponential functions $a^x$ (for any $a > 0$) that is valid for any real number $x$ instead of just rational numbers, and that is known to be continuous and even differentiable without our having to assume those properties as we did in Section 6.2.

Table 1.    Derivatives of integer powers

| $f(x)$ | $f'(x)$ |
|--------|---------|
| $\vdots$ | $\vdots$ |
| $x^4$ | $4x^3$ |
| $x^3$ | $3x^2$ |
| $x^2$ | $2x$ |
| $x^1$ | $1x^0 = 1$ |
| $x^0$ | $0$ |
| $x^{-1}$ | $-x^{-2}$ |
| $x^{-2}$ | $-2x^{-3}$ |
| $x^{-3}$ | $-3x^{-4}$ |
| $\vdots$ | $\vdots$ |

## The Natural Logarithm

Table 1 lists the derivatives of integer powers of $x$. Those derivatives are multiples of integer powers of $x$, but one integer power, $x^{-1}$, is conspicuously absent from the list of derivatives; we do not yet know a function whose derivative is $x^{-1} = 1/x$. We are going to remedy this situation by defining a function $\ln x$ in such a way that it will have derivative $1/x$.

To get a hint as to how this can be done, review Example 1 of Section 5.11. In that example we showed that the area under the graph of the velocity of a moving object in a time interval is equal to the distance travelled by the object in that time interval. Since the derivative of distance is velocity, measuring the area provided a way of finding a function (the distance) that had a given derivative (the velocity). This relationship between area and derivatives is one of the most important ideas in calculus. It is called the **Fundamental Theorem of Calculus**. We will explore it fully in Chapter 8, but we will make use of the idea now to define $\ln x$, which we want to have derivative $1/x$.

DEFINITION

6

**The natural logarithm**

For $x > 0$, let $A_x$ be the area of the plane region bounded by the curve $y = 1/t$, the $t$-axis, and the vertical lines $t = 1$ and $t = x$. The function $\ln x$ is defined by

$$\ln x = \begin{cases} A_x & \text{if } x \geq 1, \\ -A_x & \text{if } 0 < x < 1, \end{cases}$$

as shown in Figure 6.9.

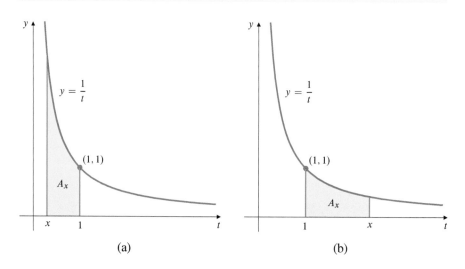

Figure 6.9

(a) $\ln x = -\text{area } A_x$ if $0 < x < 1$

(b) $\ln x = \text{area } A_x$ if $x \geq 1$

(a)

(b)

The definition implies that $\ln 1 = 0$, that $\ln x > 0$ if $x > 1$, that $\ln x < 0$ if $0 < x < 1$, and that ln is a one-to-one function. We now show that if $y = \ln x$, then $y' = 1/x$. The proof of this result is similar to the proof we will give for the Fundamental Theorem of Calculus in Section 8.5.

**THEOREM**

**1**

If $x > 0$, then

$$\frac{d}{dx} \ln x = \frac{1}{x}.$$

**PROOF** For $x > 0$ and $h > 0$, $\ln(x+h) - \ln x$ is the area of the plane region bounded by $y = 1/t$, $y = 0$, and the vertical lines $t = x$ and $t = x + h$; it is the shaded area in Figure 6.10. Comparing this area with that of two rectangles, we see that

$$\frac{h}{x+h} < \text{shaded area} = \ln(x+h) - \ln x < \frac{h}{x}.$$

Hence, the Newton quotient for $\ln x$ satisfies

$$\frac{1}{x+h} < \frac{\ln(x+h) - \ln x}{h} < \frac{1}{x}.$$

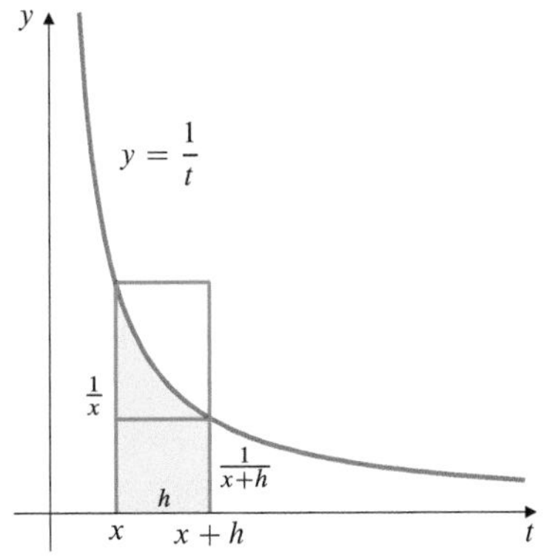

Letting $h$ approach 0 from the right, we obtain (by the Squeeze Theorem applied to one-sided limits)

$$\lim_{h \to 0+} \frac{\ln(x+h) - \ln x}{h} = \frac{1}{x}.$$

A similar argument shows that if $0 < x + h < x$, then

$$\frac{1}{x} < \frac{\ln(x+h) - \ln x}{h} < \frac{1}{x+h},$$

so that

$$\lim_{h \to 0-} \frac{\ln(x+h) - \ln x}{h} = \frac{1}{x}.$$

Combining these two one-sided limits we get the desired result:

$$\frac{d}{dx} \ln x = \lim_{h \to 0} \frac{\ln(x+h) - \ln x}{h} = \frac{1}{x}.$$

$y = \frac{1}{t}$

Figure 6.10

The two properties $(d/dx) \ln x = 1/x$ and $\ln 1 = 0$ are sufficient to determine the function $\ln x$ completely. (This follows from Theorem 13 in Section 2.8.) We can deduce from these two properties that $\ln x$ satisfies the appropriate laws of logarithms:

**THEOREM**

**2**

**Properties of the natural logarithm**

(i)   $\ln(xy) = \ln x + \ln y$        (ii)  $\ln\left(\frac{1}{x}\right) = -\ln x$

(iii)  $\ln\left(\frac{x}{y}\right) = \ln x - \ln y$        (iv)  $\ln(x^r) = r \ln x$

Because we do not want to *assume* that exponentials are continuous (as we did in Section 6.2), we should regard (iv) for the moment as only valid for exponents $r$ that are rational numbers.

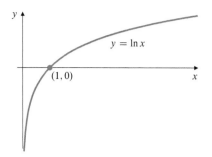

**Figure 6.11**    The graph of $\ln x$

**PROOF**    We will only prove part (i) because the other parts are proved by the same method. If $y > 0$ is a constant, then by the Chain Rule,

$$\frac{d}{dx}\big(\ln(xy) - \ln x\big) = \frac{y}{xy} - \frac{1}{x} = 0 \quad \text{for all } x > 0.$$

Theorem 13 of Section 5.8 now tells us that $\ln(xy) - \ln x = C$ (a constant) for $x > 0$. Putting $x = 1$ we get $C = \ln y$ and identity (i) follows.

Part (iv) of Theorem 2 shows that $\ln(2^n) = n \ln 2 \to \infty$ as $n \to \infty$. Therefore, we also have $\ln(1/2)^n = -n \ln 2 \to -\infty$ as $n \to \infty$. Since $(d/dx)\ln x = 1/x > 0$ for $x > 0$, it follows that $\ln x$ is increasing, so we must have (see Figure 6.11)

$$\lim_{x \to \infty} \ln x = \infty, \qquad\qquad \lim_{x \to 0+} \ln x = -\infty.$$

---

**EXAMPLE 1**    Show that $\dfrac{d}{dx} \ln|x| = \dfrac{1}{x}$ for any $x \ne 0$. Hence find $\displaystyle\int \frac{1}{x}\,dx$.

**Solution**    If $x > 0$, then

$$\frac{d}{dx} \ln|x| = \frac{d}{dx} \ln x = \frac{1}{x}$$

by Theorem 1. If $x < 0$, then, using the Chain Rule,

$$\frac{d}{dx} \ln|x| = \frac{d}{dx} \ln(-x) = \frac{1}{-x}(-1) = \frac{1}{x}.$$

Therefore, $\dfrac{d}{dx} \ln|x| = \dfrac{1}{x}$, and on any interval not containing $x = 0$,

$$\int \frac{1}{x}\,dx = \ln|x| + C.$$

---

**EXAMPLE 2**    Find the derivatives of (a) $\ln|\cos x|$ and (b) $\ln\big(x + \sqrt{x^2 + 1}\big)$. Simplify your answers as much as possible.

**Solution**

(a) Using the result of Example 1 and the Chain Rule, we have

$$\frac{d}{dx} \ln|\cos x| = \frac{1}{\cos x}(-\sin x) = -\tan x.$$

(b) $\dfrac{d}{dx} \ln\big(x + \sqrt{x^2 + 1}\big) = \dfrac{1}{x + \sqrt{x^2 + 1}}\left(1 + \dfrac{2x}{2\sqrt{x^2 + 1}}\right)$

$$= \frac{1}{x + \sqrt{x^2 + 1}} \cdot \frac{\sqrt{x^2 + 1} + x}{\sqrt{x^2 + 1}}$$

$$= \frac{1}{\sqrt{x^2 + 1}}.$$

## The Exponential Function

The function $\ln x$ is one-to-one on its domain, the interval $(0, \infty)$, so it has an inverse there. For the moment, let us call this inverse $\exp x$. Thus,

$$y = \exp x \iff x = \ln y \quad (y > 0).$$

Since $\ln 1 = 0$, we have $\exp 0 = 1$. The domain of $\exp$ is $(-\infty, \infty)$, the range of $\ln$. The range of $\exp$ is $(0, \infty)$, the domain of $\ln$. We have cancellation identities

$$\ln(\exp x) = x \quad \text{for all real } x \quad \text{and} \quad \exp(\ln x) = x \quad \text{for } x > 0.$$

We can deduce various properties of $\exp$ from corresponding properties of $\ln$. Not surprisingly, they are properties we would expect an exponential function to have.

**THEOREM**

**3**

**Properties of the exponential function**

$$\text{(i)} \quad (\exp x)^r = \exp(rx) \qquad \text{(ii)} \quad \exp(x+y) = (\exp x)(\exp y)$$

$$\text{(iii)} \quad \exp(-x) = \frac{1}{\exp(x)} \qquad \text{(iv)} \quad \exp(x - y) = \frac{\exp x}{\exp y}$$

For the moment, identity (i) is asserted only for rational numbers $r$.

**PROOF** We prove only identity (i); the rest are done similarly. If $u = (\exp x)^r$, then, by Theorem 2(iv), $\ln u = r \ln(\exp x) = rx$. Therefore, $u = \exp(rx)$. ∎

Now we make an important definition!

Let $e = \exp(1)$.

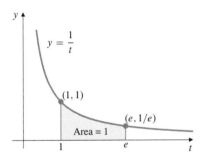

$y = \frac{1}{t}$

$(1, 1)$

$(e, 1/e)$

Area = 1

**Figure 6.12** The definition of $e$

The number $e$ satisfies $\ln e = 1$, so the area bounded by the curve $y = 1/t$, the $t$-axis, and the vertical lines $t = 1$ and $t = e$ must be equal to 1 square unit. See Figure 6.12. The number $e$ is one of the most important numbers in mathematics. Like $\pi$, it is irrational and not a zero of any polynomial with rational coefficients. (Such numbers are called **transcendental**.) Its value is between 2 and 3 and begins

$$e = 2.7\ 1828\ 1828\ 45\ 90\ 45 \ldots.$$

Later on we will learn that

$$e = 1 + \frac{1}{1!} + \frac{1}{2!} + \frac{1}{3!} + \frac{1}{4!} + \cdots,$$

a formula from which the value of $e$ can be calculated to any desired precision.

Theorem 3(i) shows that $\exp r = \exp(1r) = (\exp 1)^r = e^r$ holds for any rational number $r$. Now here is a crucial observation. We only know what $e^r$ means if $r$ is a rational number (if $r = m/n$, then $e^r = \sqrt[n]{e^m}$). But $\exp x$ is defined for all *real x*, rational or not. Since $e^r = \exp r$ when $r$ is rational, we can use $\exp x$ as a *definition* of what $e^x$ means for any real number $x$, and there will be no contradiction if $x$ happens to be rational.

$$e^x = \exp x \quad \text{for all real } x.$$

Theorem 3 can now be restated in terms of $e^x$:

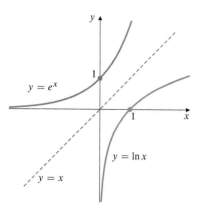

**Figure 6.13**    The graphs of $e^x$ and $\ln x$

> (i)  $(e^x)^y = e^{xy}$          (ii)  $e^{x+y} = e^x e^y$
>
> (iii)  $e^{-x} = \dfrac{1}{e^x}$          (iv)  $e^{x-y} = \dfrac{e^x}{e^y}$

The graph of $e^x$ is the reflection of the graph of its inverse, $\ln x$, in the line $y = x$. Both graphs are shown for comparison in Figure 6.13. Observe that the $x$-axis is a horizontal asymptote of the graph of $y = e^x$ as $x \to -\infty$. We have

$$\lim_{x \to -\infty} e^x = 0, \qquad \lim_{x \to \infty} e^x = \infty.$$

Since $\exp x = e^x$ actually *is* an exponential function, its inverse must actually *be* a logarithm:

$$\ln x = \log_e x.$$

The derivative of $y = e^x$ is calculated by implicit differentiation:

$$y = e^x \implies x = \ln y$$
$$\implies 1 = \frac{1}{y}\frac{dy}{dx}$$
$$\implies \frac{dy}{dx} = y = e^x.$$

Thus, the exponential function has the remarkable property that it is its own derivative and, therefore, also its own antiderivative:

$$\frac{d}{dx} e^x = e^x, \qquad \int e^x\, dx = e^x + C.$$

---

**EXAMPLE 3**    Find the derivatives of
(a) $e^{x^2-3x}$,  (b) $\sqrt{1+e^{2x}}$,  and  (c) $\dfrac{e^x - e^{-x}}{e^x + e^{-x}}$.

**Solution**

(a) $\dfrac{d}{dx} e^{x^2-3x} = e^{x^2-3x}(2x-3) = (2x-3)e^{x^2-3x}$.

(b) $\dfrac{d}{dx}\sqrt{1+e^{2x}} = \dfrac{1}{2\sqrt{1+e^{2x}}}\left(e^{2x}(2)\right) = \dfrac{e^{2x}}{\sqrt{1+e^{2x}}}$.

(c) $\dfrac{d}{dx}\dfrac{e^x-e^{-x}}{e^x+e^{-x}} = \dfrac{(e^x+e^{-x})(e^x-(-e^{-x})) - (e^x-e^{-x})(e^x+(-e^{-x}))}{(e^x+e^{-x})^2}$

$\qquad = \dfrac{(e^x)^2 + 2e^x e^{-x} + (e^{-x})^2 - [(e^x)^2 - 2e^x e^{-x} + (e^{-x})^2]}{(e^x+e^{-x})^2}$

$\qquad = \dfrac{4e^{x-x}}{(e^x+e^{-x})^2} = \dfrac{4}{(e^x+e^{-x})^2}$.

---

**EXAMPLE 4**    Let $f(t) = e^{at}$. Find  (a) $f^{(n)}(t)$  and  (b) $\int f(t)\, dt$.

*Solution*   (a)   We have   $f'(t) = a\,e^{at}$

$$f''(t) = a^2\,e^{at}$$
$$f'''(t) = a^3\,e^{at}$$
$$\vdots$$
$$f^{(n)}(t) = a^n\,e^{at}.$$

(b)  Also, $\displaystyle\int f(t)\,dt = \int e^{at}\,dt = \frac{1}{a}\,e^{at} + C$, since $\dfrac{d}{dt}\dfrac{1}{a}e^{at} = e^{at}$.

## General Exponentials and Logarithms

We can use the fact that $e^x$ is now defined for *all* real $x$ to define the arbitrary exponential $a^x$ (where $a > 0$) for all real $x$. If $r$ is rational, then $\ln(a^r) = r\ln a$; therefore, $a^r = e^{r\ln a}$. However, $e^{x\ln a}$ is defined for all real $x$, so we can use it as a definition of $a^x$ with no possibility of contradiction arising if $x$ is rational.

**DEFINITION**

**7**

> **The general exponential $a^x$**
>
> $$a^x = e^{x\ln a}, \qquad (a > 0, \quad x \text{ real}).$$

**EXAMPLE 5**   Evaluate $2^\pi$, using the natural logarithm (ln) and exponential (exp or $e^x$) keys on a scientific calculator, but not using the $y^x$ or $\wedge$ keys.

*Solution*   $2^\pi = e^{\pi\ln 2} = 8.824\,977\,8\cdots$. If your calculator has a $\wedge$ key, or an $x^y$ or $y^x$ key, chances are that it is implemented in terms of the exp and ln functions.

The laws of exponents for $a^x$ as presented in Section 6.2 can now be obtained from those for $e^x$, as can the derivative:

$$\frac{d}{dx}\,a^x = \frac{d}{dx}e^{x\ln a} = e^{x\ln a}\ln a = a^x\ln a.$$

We can also verify the General Power Rule for $x^a$, where $a$ is any real number, provided $x > 0$:

$$\frac{d}{dx}x^a = \frac{d}{dx}e^{a\ln x} = e^{a\ln x}\,\frac{a}{x} = \frac{a\,x^a}{x} = a\,x^{a-1}.$$

**EXAMPLE 6**   Show that the graph of $f(x) = x^\pi - \pi^x$ has a negative slope at $x = \pi$.

Do not confuse $x^\pi$, which is a power function of $x$, and $\pi^x$, which is an exponential function of $x$.

*Solution*   $f'(x) = \pi\,x^{\pi-1} - \pi^x\,\ln\pi$

$$f'(\pi) = \pi\,\pi^{\pi-1} - \pi^\pi\,\ln\pi = \pi^\pi(1 - \ln\pi).$$

Since $\pi > 3 > e$, we have $\ln\pi > \ln e = 1$, so $1 - \ln\pi < 0$. Since $\pi^\pi = e^{\pi\ln\pi} > 0$, we have $f'(\pi) < 0$. Thus, the graph $y = f(x)$ has negative slope at $x = \pi$.

**EXAMPLE 7**   Find the critical point of $y = x^x$.

*Solution*   We can't differentiate $x^x$ by treating it as a power (like $x^a$) because the exponent varies. We can't treat it as an exponential (like $a^x$) because the base varies. We can differentiate it if we first write it in terms of the exponential function,

$x^x = e^{x \ln x}$, and then use the Chain Rule and the Product Rule:

$$\frac{dy}{dx} = \frac{d}{dx} e^{x \ln x} = e^{x \ln x} \left( \ln x + x \left( \frac{1}{x} \right) \right) = x^x (1 + \ln x).$$

Now $x^x$ is defined only for $x > 0$ and is itself never 0. (Why?) Therefore, the critical point occurs where $1 + \ln x = 0$; that is, $\ln x = -1$, or $x = 1/e$.

Finally, observe that $(d/dx)a^x = a^x \ln a$ is negative for all $x$ if $0 < a < 1$ and is positive for all $x$ if $a > 1$. Thus, $a^x$ is one-to-one and has an inverse function, $\log_a x$, provided $a > 0$ and $a \neq 1$. Its properties follow in the same way as in Section 6.2. If $y = \log_a x$, then $x = a^y$ and, differentiating implicitly with respect to $x$, we get

$$1 = a^y \ln a \frac{dy}{dx} = x \ln a \frac{dy}{dx}.$$

Thus, the derivative of $\log_a x$ is given by

$$\frac{d}{dx} \log_a x = \frac{1}{x \ln a}.$$

Since $\log_a x$ can be expressed in terms of logarithms to any other base, say $e$,

$$\log_a x = \frac{\ln x}{\ln a},$$

we normally use only natural logarithms. Exceptions are found in chemistry, acoustics, and other sciences where "logarithmic scales" are used to measure quantities for which a one-unit increase in the measure corresponds to a tenfold increase in the quantity. Logarithms to base 10 are used in defining such scales. In computer science, where powers of 2 play a central role, logarithms to base 2 are often encountered.

## Logarithmic Differentiation

Suppose we want to differentiate a function of the form

$$y = (f(x))^{g(x)} \qquad \text{(for } f(x) > 0\text{)}.$$

Since the variable appears in both the base and the exponent, neither the general power rule, $(d/dx)x^a = ax^{a-1}$, nor the exponential rule, $(d/dx)a^x = a^x \ln a$, can be directly applied. One method for finding the derivative of such a function is to express it in the form

$$y = e^{g(x) \ln f(x)}$$

and then differentiate, using the Product Rule to handle the exponent. This is the method used in Example 7.

The derivative in Example 7 can also be obtained by taking natural logarithms of both sides of the equation $y = x^x$ and differentiating implicitly:

$$\ln y = x \ln x$$
$$\frac{1}{y} \frac{dy}{dx} = \ln x + \frac{x}{x} = 1 + \ln x$$
$$\frac{dy}{dx} = y(1 + \ln x) = x^x (1 + \ln x).$$

This latter technique is called **logarithmic differentiation**.

**EXAMPLE 8**   Find $dy/dt$ if $y = (\sin t)^{\ln t}$, where $0 < t < \pi$.

*Solution*   We have $\ln y = \ln t \ln \sin t$. Thus,

$$\frac{1}{y}\frac{dy}{dt} = \frac{1}{t}\ln \sin t + \ln t \frac{\cos t}{\sin t}$$

$$\frac{dy}{dt} = y\left(\frac{\ln \sin t}{t} + \ln t \cot t\right) = (\sin t)^{\ln t}\left(\frac{\ln \sin t}{t} + \ln t \cot t\right).$$

Logarithmic differentiation is also useful for finding the derivatives of functions expressed as products and quotients of many factors. Taking logarithms reduces these products and quotients to sums and differences. This usually makes the calculation easier than it would be using the Product and Quotient Rules, especially if the derivative is to be evaluated at a specific point.

**EXAMPLE 9**   Differentiate $y = [(x + 1)(x + 2)(x + 3)]/(x + 4)$.

*Solution*   $\ln |y| = \ln |x + 1| + \ln |x + 2| + \ln |x + 3| - \ln |x + 4|$. Thus,

$$\frac{1}{y}y' = \frac{1}{x+1} + \frac{1}{x+2} + \frac{1}{x+3} - \frac{1}{x+4}$$

$$y' = \frac{(x+1)(x+2)(x+3)}{x+4}\left(\frac{1}{x+1} + \frac{1}{x+2} + \frac{1}{x+3} - \frac{1}{x+4}\right)$$

$$= \frac{(x+2)(x+3)}{x+4} + \frac{(x+1)(x+3)}{x+4} + \frac{(x+1)(x+2)}{x+4}$$

$$- \frac{(x+1)(x+2)(x+3)}{(x+4)^2}.$$

**EXAMPLE 10**   Find $\left.\dfrac{du}{dx}\right|_{x=1}$ if $u = \sqrt{(x+1)(x^2+1)(x^3+1)}$.

*Solution*

$$\ln u = \frac{1}{2}\left(\ln(x+1) + \ln(x^2+1) + \ln(x^3+1)\right)$$

$$\frac{1}{u}\frac{du}{dx} = \frac{1}{2}\left(\frac{1}{x+1} + \frac{2x}{x^2+1} + \frac{3x^2}{x^3+1}\right).$$

At $x = 1$ we have $u = \sqrt{8} = 2\sqrt{2}$. Hence,

$$\left.\frac{du}{dx}\right|_{x=1} = \sqrt{2}\left(\frac{1}{2} + 1 + \frac{3}{2}\right) = 3\sqrt{2}.$$

## EXERCISES 6.3

Simplify the expressions given in Exercises 1–10.

**1.** $e^3/\sqrt{e^5}$

**2.** $\ln\left(e^{1/2}e^{2/3}\right)$

**3.** $e^{5\ln x}$

**4.** $e^{(3\ln 9)/2}$

**5.** $\ln \dfrac{1}{e^{3x}}$

**6.** $e^{2\ln\cos x} + \left(\ln e^{\sin x}\right)^2$

**7.** $3\ln 4 - 4\ln 3$

**8.** $4\ln \sqrt{x} + 6\ln(x^{1/3})$

**9.** $2\ln x + 5\ln(x - 2)$

**10.** $\ln(x^2 + 6x + 9)$

Solve the equations in Exercises 11–14 for $x$.

**11.** $2^{x+1} = 3^x$ 

**12.** $3^x = 9^{1-x}$

**13.** $\dfrac{1}{2^x} = \dfrac{5}{8^{x+3}}$ 

**14.** $2^{x^2-3} = 4^x$

Find the domains of the functions in Exercises 15–16.

**15.** $\ln \dfrac{x}{2-x}$ 

**16.** $\ln(x^2 - x - 2)$

Solve the inequalities in Exercises 17–18.

**17.** $\ln(2x - 5) > \ln(7 - 2x)$ **18.** $\ln(x^2 - 2) \le \ln x$

In Exercises 19–48, differentiate the given functions. If possible, simplify your answers.

**19.** $y = e^{5x}$ 

**20.** $y = xe^x - x$

**21.** $y = \dfrac{x}{e^{2x}}$ 

**22.** $y = x^2 e^{x/2}$

**23.** $y = \ln(3x - 2)$ 

**24.** $y = \ln|3x - 2|$

**25.** $y = \ln(1 + e^x)$ 

**26.** $f(x) = e^{(x^2)}$

**27.** $y = \dfrac{e^x + e^{-x}}{2}$ 

**28.** $x = e^{3t} \ln t$

**29.** $y = e^{(e^x)}$ 

**30.** $y = \dfrac{e^x}{1 + e^x}$

**31.** $y = e^x \sin x$ 

**32.** $y = e^{-x} \cos x$

**33.** $y = \ln \ln x$ 

**34.** $y = x \ln x - x$

**35.** $y = x^2 \ln x - \dfrac{x^2}{2}$ 

**36.** $y = \ln|\sin x|$

**37.** $y = 5^{2x+1}$ 

**38.** $y = 2^{(x^2 - 3x + 8)}$

**39.** $g(x) = t^x x^t$ 

**40.** $h(t) = t^x - x^t$

**41.** $f(s) = \log_a(bs + c)$ 

**42.** $g(x) = \log_x(2x + 3)$

**43.** $y = x^{\sqrt{x}}$ 

**44.** $y = (1/x)^{\ln x}$

**45.** $y = \ln|\sec x + \tan x|$ 

**46.** $y = \ln|x + \sqrt{x^2 - a^2}|$

**47.** $y = \ln\left(\sqrt{x^2 + a^2} - x\right)$ 

**48.** $y = (\cos x)^x - x^{\cos x}$

**49.** Find the $n$th derivative of $f(x) = xe^{ax}$.

**50.** Show that the $n$th derivative of $(ax^2 + bx + c)e^x$ is a function of the same form but with different constants.

**51.** Find the first four derivatives of $e^{x^2}$.

**52.** Find the $n$th derivative of $\ln(2x + 1)$.

**53.** Differentiate (a) $f(x) = (x^x)^x$ and (b) $g(x) = x^{(x^x)}$. Which function grows more rapidly as $x$ grows large?

**! 54.** Solve the equation $x^{x^{x^{\cdots}}} = a$, where $a > 0$. The exponent tower goes on forever.

Use logarithmic differentiation to find the required derivatives in Exercises 55–57.

**55.** $f(x) = (x - 1)(x - 2)(x - 3)(x - 4)$. Find $f'(x)$.

**56.** $F(x) = \dfrac{\sqrt{1+x}(1-x)^{1/3}}{(1+5x)^{4/5}}$. Find $F'(0)$.

**57.** $f(x) = \dfrac{(x^2 - 1)(x^2 - 2)(x^2 - 3)}{(x^2 + 1)(x^2 + 2)(x^2 + 3)}$. Find $f'(2)$. Also find $f'(1)$.

**58.** At what points does the graph $y = x^2 e^{-x^2}$ have a horizontal tangent line?

**59.** Let $f(x) = xe^{-x}$. Determine where $f$ is increasing and where it is decreasing. Sketch the graph of $f$.

**60.** Find the equation of a straight line of slope 4 that is tangent to the graph of $y = \ln x$.

**61.** Find an equation of the straight line tangent to the curve $y = e^x$ and passing through the origin.

**62.** Find an equation of the straight line tangent to the curve $y = \ln x$ and passing through the origin.

**63.** Find an equation of the straight line that is tangent to $y = 2^x$ and that passes through the point $(1, 0)$.

**64.** For what values of $a > 0$ does the curve $y = a^x$ intersect the straight line $y = x$?

**65.** Find the slope of the curve $e^{xy} \ln \dfrac{x}{y} = x + \dfrac{1}{y}$ at $(e, 1/e)$.

**66.** Find an equation of the straight line tangent to the curve $xe^y + y - 2x = \ln 2$ at the point $(1, \ln 2)$.

**67.** Find the derivative of $f(x) = Ax \cos \ln x + Bx \sin \ln x$. Use the result to help you find the indefinite integrals

$$\int \cos \ln x \, dx \quad \text{and} \quad \int \sin \ln x \, dx.$$

**! 68.** Let $F_{A,B}(x) = Ae^x \cos x + Be^x \sin x$. Show that $(d/dx)F_{A,B}(x) = F_{A+B, B-A}(x)$.

**! 69.** Using the results of Exercise 68, find
(a) $(d^2/dx^2)F_{A,B}(x)$ and (b) $(d^3/dx^3)e^x \cos x$.

**! 70.** Find $\dfrac{d}{dx}(Ae^{ax} \cos bx + Be^{ax} \sin bx)$ and use the answer to help you evaluate

(a) $\displaystyle\int e^{ax} \cos bx \, dx$ and (b) $\displaystyle\int e^{ax} \sin bx \, dx$.

**? 71.** Prove identity (ii) of Theorem 2 by examining the derivative of the left side minus the right side, as was done in the proof of identity (i).

**? 72.** Deduce identity (iii) of Theorem 2 from identities (i) and (ii).

**? 73.** Prove identity (iv) of Theorem 2 for rational exponents $r$ by the same method used for Exercise 71.

**! 74.** Let $x > 0$, and let $F(x)$ be the area bounded by the curve $y = t^2$, the $t$-axis, and the vertical lines $t = 0$ and $t = x$. Using the method of the proof of Theorem 1, show that $F'(x) = x^2$. Hence, find an explicit formula for $F(x)$. What is the area of the region bounded by $y = t^2$, $y = 0$, $t = 0$, and $t = 2$?

**! 75.** Carry out the following steps to show that $2 < e < 3$. Let $f(t) = 1/t$ for $t > 0$.
(a) Show that the area under $y = f(t)$, above $y = 0$, and between $t = 1$ and $t = 2$ is less than 1 square unit. Deduce that $e > 2$.
(b) Show that all tangent lines to the graph of $f$ lie below the graph. *Hint:* $f''(t) = 2/t^3 > 0$.
(c) Find the lines $T_2$ and $T_3$ that are tangent to $y = f(t)$ at $t = 2$ and $t = 3$, respectively.
(d) Find the area $A_2$ under $T_2$, above $y = 0$, and between $t = 1$ and $t = 2$. Also find the area $A_3$ under $T_3$, above $y = 0$, and between $t = 2$ and $t = 3$.
(e) Show that $A_2 + A_3 > 1$ square unit. Deduce that $e < 3$.

## 6.4    Growth and Decay

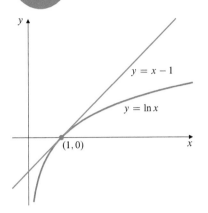

**Figure 6.14**    $\ln x \le x - 1$ for $x > 0$

In this section we will study the use of exponential functions to model the growth rates of quantities whose rate of growth is directly related to their size. The growth of such quantities is typically governed by differential equations whose solutions involve exponential functions. Before delving into this topic, we prepare the way by examining the growth behaviour of exponential and logarithmic functions.

### The Growth of Exponentials and Logarithms

In Section 6.3 we showed that both $e^x$ and $\ln x$ grow large (approach infinity) as $x$ grows large. However, $e^x$ increases very rapidly as $x$ increases, and $\ln x$ increases very slowly. In fact, $e^x$ increases faster than any positive power of $x$ (no matter how large the power), while $\ln x$ increases more slowly than any positive power of $x$ (no matter how small the power). To verify this behaviour we start with an inequality satisfied by $\ln x$. The straight line $y = x - 1$ is tangent to the curve $y = \ln x$ at the point $(1, 0)$. The following theorem asserts that the curve lies below that line. (See Figure 6.14.)

**THEOREM**

**4**

If $x > 0$, then $\ln x \le x - 1$.

**PROOF**    Let $g(x) = \ln x - (x - 1)$ for $x > 0$. Then $g(1) = 0$ and

$$g'(x) = \frac{1}{x} - 1 \quad \begin{cases} > 0 & \text{if } 0 < x < 1 \\ < 0 & \text{if } x > 1. \end{cases}$$

As observed in Section 5.8, these inequalities imply that $g$ is increasing on $(0, 1)$ and decreasing on $(1, \infty)$. Thus, $g(x) \le g(1) = 0$ for all $x > 0$ and $\ln x \le x - 1$ for all such $x$.

**THEOREM**

**5**

**The growth properties of exp and ln**

If $a > 0$, then

(a)    $\displaystyle \lim_{x \to \infty} \frac{x^a}{e^x} = 0,$    (b)    $\displaystyle \lim_{x \to \infty} \frac{\ln x}{x^a} = 0,$

(c)    $\displaystyle \lim_{x \to -\infty} |x|^a e^x = 0,$    (d)    $\displaystyle \lim_{x \to 0+} x^a \ln x = 0.$

Each of these limits makes a statement about who "wins" in a contest between an exponential or logarithm and a power. For example, in part (a), the denominator $e^x$ grows large as $x \to \infty$, so it tries to make the fraction $x^a/e^x$ approach 0. On the other hand, if $a$ is a large positive number, the numerator $x^a$ also grows large and tries to make the fraction approach infinity. The assertion of (a) is that in this contest between the exponential and the power, the exponential is stronger and wins; the fraction approaches 0. The content of Theorem 5 can be paraphrased as follows:

> In a struggle between a power and an exponential, the exponential wins.
> In a struggle between a power and a logarithm, the power wins.

**PROOF**    First, we prove part (b). Let $x > 1$, $a > 0$, and let $s = a/2$. Since $\ln(x^s) = s \ln x$, we have, using Theorem 4,

$$0 < s \ln x = \ln(x^s) \le x^s - 1 < x^s.$$

Thus, $0 < \ln x < \dfrac{1}{s} x^s$ and, dividing by $x^a = x^{2s}$,

$$0 < \frac{\ln x}{x^a} < \frac{1}{s} \frac{x^s}{x^{2s}} = \frac{1}{s\, x^s}.$$

Now $1/(s\, x^s) \to 0$ as $x \to \infty$ (since $s > 0$); therefore, by the Squeeze Theorem,

$$\lim_{x \to \infty} \frac{\ln x}{x^a} = 0.$$

Next, we deduce part (d) from part (b) by substituting $x = 1/t$. As $x \to 0+$, we have $t \to \infty$, so

$$\lim_{x \to 0+} x^a \ln x = \lim_{t \to \infty} \frac{\ln(1/t)}{t^a} = \lim_{t \to \infty} \frac{-\ln t}{t^a} = -0 = 0.$$

Now we deduce (a) from (b). If $x = \ln t$, then $t \to \infty$ as $x \to \infty$, so

$$\lim_{x \to \infty} \frac{x^a}{e^x} = \lim_{t \to \infty} \frac{(\ln t)^a}{t} = \lim_{t \to \infty} \left( \frac{\ln t}{t^{1/a}} \right)^a = 0^a = 0.$$

Finally, (c) follows from (a) via the substitution $x = -t$:

$$\lim_{x \to -\infty} |x|^a\, e^x = \lim_{t \to \infty} |-t|^a\, e^{-t} = \lim_{t \to \infty} \frac{t^a}{e^t} = 0.$$

## Exponential Growth and Decay Models

Many natural processes involve quantities that increase or decrease at a rate proportional to their size. For example, the mass of a culture of bacteria growing in a medium supplying adequate nourishment will increase at a rate proportional to that mass. The value of an investment bearing interest that is continuously compounding increases at a rate proportional to that value. The mass of undecayed radioactive material in a sample decreases at a rate proportional to that mass.

All of these phenomena, and others exhibiting similar behaviour, can be modelled mathematically in the same way. If $y = y(t)$ denotes the value of a quantity $y$ at time $t$, and if $y$ changes at a rate proportional to its size, then

$$\frac{dy}{dt} = ky,$$

where $k$ is the constant of proportionality. The above equation is called the **differential equation of exponential growth or decay** because, for any value of the constant $C$, the function $y = Ce^{kt}$ satisfies the equation. In fact, if $y(t)$ is any solution of the differential equation $y' = ky$, then

$$\frac{d}{dt} \left( \frac{y(t)}{e^{kt}} \right) = \frac{e^{kt} y'(t) - k e^{kt} y(t)}{e^{2kt}} = \frac{y'(t) - k y(t)}{e^{kt}} = 0 \quad \text{for all } t.$$

Thus, $y(t)/e^{kt} = C$, a constant, and $y(t) = Ce^{kt}$. Since $y(0) = Ce^0 = C$,

The initial-value problem $\begin{cases} \dfrac{dy}{dt} = ky \\ y(0) = y_0 \end{cases}$ has unique solution $y = y_0 e^{kt}$.

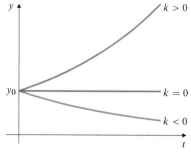

**Figure 6.15** Solutions of the initial-value problem $dy/dt = ky$, $y(0) = y_0$, for $k > 0$, $k = 0$, and $k < 0$

If $y_0 > 0$, then $y(t)$ is an increasing function of $t$ if $k > 0$ and a decreasing function of $t$ if $k < 0$. We say that the quantity $y$ exhibits **exponential growth** if $k > 0$ and **exponential decay** if $k < 0$. (See Figure 6.15.)

EXAMPLE 1    (**Growth of a cell culture**)  A certain cell culture grows at a rate proportional to the number of cells present. If the culture contains 500 cells initially and 800 after 24 h, how many cells will there be after a further 12 h?

*Solution*  Let $y(t)$ be the number of cells present $t$ hours after there were 500 cells. Thus, $y(0) = 500$ and $y(24) = 800$. Because $dy/dt = ky$, we have

$$y(t) = y(0)e^{kt} = 500e^{kt}.$$

Therefore, $800 = y(24) = 500e^{24k}$, so $24k = \ln \frac{800}{500} = \ln(1.6)$. It follows that $k = (1/24)\ln(1.6)$ and

$$y(t) = 500e^{(t/24)\ln(1.6)} = 500(1.6)^{t/24}.$$

We want to know $y$ when $t = 36$: $y(36) = 500e^{(36/24)\ln(1.6)} = 500(1.6)^{3/2} \approx 1012$. The cell count grew to about 1,012 in the 12 h after it was 800.

Exponential growth is characterized by a **fixed doubling time**. If $T$ is the time at which $y$ has doubled from its size at $t = 0$, then $2y(0) = y(T) = y(0)e^{kT}$. Therefore, $e^{kT} = 2$. Since $y(t) = y(0)e^{kt}$, we have

$$y(t + T) = y(0)e^{k(t+T)} = e^{kT}y(0)e^{kt} = 2y(t);$$

that is, $T$ units of time are required for $y$ to double from any value. Similarly, exponential decay involves a fixed halving time (usually called the **half-life**). If $y(T) = \frac{1}{2}y(0)$, then $e^{kT} = \frac{1}{2}$ and

$$y(t + T) = y(0)e^{k(t+T)} = \frac{1}{2}y(t).$$

EXAMPLE 2    (**Radioactive decay**)  A radioactive material has a half-life of 1,200 years. What percentage of the original radioactivity of a sample is left after 10 years? How many years are required to reduce the radioactivity by 10%?

*Solution*  Let $p(t)$ be the percentage of the original radioactivity left after $t$ years. Thus $p(0) = 100$ and $p(1,200) = 50$. Since the radioactivity decreases at a rate proportional to itself, $dp/dt = kp$ and

$$p(t) = 100e^{kt}.$$

Now $50 = p(1,200) = 100e^{1,200k}$, so

$$k = \frac{1}{1,200} \ln \frac{50}{100} = -\frac{\ln 2}{1,200}.$$

The percentage left after 10 years is

$$p(10) = 100e^{10k} = 100e^{-10(\ln 2)/1,200} \approx 99.424.$$

If after $t$ years 90% of the radioactivity is left, then

$$90 = 100e^{kt},$$
$$kt = \ln \frac{90}{100},$$
$$t = \frac{1}{k} \ln(0.9) = -\frac{1,200}{\ln 2} \ln(0.9) \approx 182.4,$$

so it will take a little over 182 years to reduce the radioactivity by 10%.

Sometimes an exponential growth or decay problem will involve a quantity that changes at a rate proportional to the difference between itself and a fixed value:

$$\frac{dy}{dt} = k(y - a).$$

In this case, the change of dependent variable $u(t) = y(t) - a$ should be used to convert the differential equation to the standard form. Observe that $u(t)$ changes at the same rate as $y(t)$ (i.e., $du/dt = dy/dt$), so it satisfies

$$\frac{du}{dt} = ku.$$

**EXAMPLE 3**   **(Newton's law of cooling)**  A hot object introduced into a cooler environment will cool at a rate proportional to the excess of its temperature above that of its environment. If a cup of coffee sitting in a room maintained at a temperature of $20\,°C$ cools from $80\,°C$ to $50\,°C$ in 5 minutes, how much longer will it take to cool to $40\,°C$?

*Solution*   Let $y(t)$ be the temperature of the coffee $t$ min after it was $80\,°C$. Thus, $y(0) = 80$ and $y(5) = 50$. Newton's law says that $dy/dt = k(y - 20)$ in this case, so let $u(t) = y(t) - 20$. Thus, $u(0) = 60$ and $u(5) = 30$. We have

$$\frac{du}{dt} = \frac{dy}{dt} = k(y - 20) = ku.$$

Thus,

$$u(t) = 60e^{kt},$$
$$30 = u(5) = 60e^{5k},$$
$$5k = \ln \tfrac{1}{2} = -\ln 2.$$

We want to know $t$ such that $y(t) = 40$, that is, $u(t) = 20$:

$$20 = u(t) = 60e^{-(t/5)\ln 2}$$
$$-\frac{t}{5}\ln 2 = \ln \frac{20}{60} = -\ln 3,$$
$$t = 5\frac{\ln 3}{\ln 2} \approx 7.92.$$

The coffee will take about $7.92 - 5 = 2.92$ min to cool from $50\,°C$ to $40\,°C$.

## Interest on Investments

Suppose that \$10,000 is invested at an annual rate of interest of 8%. Thus, the value of the investment at the end of one year will be \$10,000(1.08) = \$10,800. If this amount remains invested for a second year at the same rate, it will grow to \$10,000(1.08)² = \$11,664; in general, $n$ years after the original investment was made, it will be worth \$10,000(1.08)$^n$.

Now suppose that the 8% rate is *compounded semiannually* so that the interest is actually paid at a rate of 4% per 6-month period. After one year (two interest periods) the \$10,000 will grow to \$10,000(1.04)² = \$10,816. This is \$16 more than was obtained when the 8% was compounded only once per year. The extra \$16 is the interest paid in the second 6-month period on the \$400 interest earned in the first 6-month period. Continuing in this way, if the 8% interest is compounded *monthly* (12 periods per year and $\frac{8}{12}$% paid per period) or *daily* (365 periods per year and $\frac{8}{365}$% paid per period), then the original \$10,000 would grow in one year to $\$10{,}000\left(1 + \frac{8}{1{,}200}\right)^{12} = \$10{,}830$ or $\$10{,}000\left(1 + \frac{8}{36{,}500}\right)^{365} = \$10{,}832.78$, respectively.

For any given *nominal* interest rate, the investment grows more if the compounding period is shorter. In general, an original investment of $A invested at $r\%$ per annum compounded $n$ times per year grows in one year to

$$\$A\left(1+\frac{r}{100n}\right)^n.$$

It is natural to ask how well we can do with our investment if we let the number of periods in a year approach infinity, that is, we compound the interest *continuously*. The answer is that in 1 year the $A will grow to

$$\$A\lim_{n\to\infty}\left(1+\frac{r}{100n}\right)^n=\$Ae^{r/100}.$$

For example, at 8% per annum compounded continuously, our $10,000 will grow in one year to $10,000e^{0.08}\approx\$10,832.87$. (Note that this is just a few cents more than we get by compounding daily.) To justify this result we need the following theorem.

**THEOREM**

**6**

For every real number $x$,

$$e^x=\lim_{n\to\infty}\left(1+\frac{x}{n}\right)^n.$$

**PROOF**  If $x=0$, there is nothing to prove; both sides of the identity are 1. If $x\neq 0$, let $h=x/n$. As $n$ tends to infinity, $h$ approaches 0. Thus,

$$\lim_{n\to\infty}\ln\left(1+\frac{x}{n}\right)^n=\lim_{n\to\infty}n\ln\left(1+\frac{x}{n}\right)$$

$$=\lim_{n\to\infty}x\frac{\ln\left(1+\frac{x}{n}\right)}{\frac{x}{n}}$$

$$=x\lim_{h\to 0}\frac{\ln(1+h)}{h}\qquad\text{(where }h=x/n\text{)}$$

$$=x\lim_{h\to 0}\frac{\ln(1+h)-\ln 1}{h}\qquad\text{(since }\ln 1=0\text{)}$$

$$=x\left(\frac{d}{dt}\ln t\right)\Big|_{t=1}\qquad\text{(by the definition of derivative)}$$

$$=x\frac{1}{t}\Big|_{t=1}=x.$$

Since ln is differentiable, it is continuous.

$$\ln\left(\lim_{n\to\infty}\left(1+\frac{x}{n}\right)^n\right)=\lim_{n\to\infty}\ln\left(1+\frac{x}{n}\right)^n=x.$$

Taking exponentials of both sides gives the required formula.

Table 2.

| $n$ | $\left(1+\dfrac{1}{n}\right)^n$ |
|---|---|
| 1 | 2 |
| 10 | $2.593\,74\cdots$ |
| 100 | $2.704\,81\cdots$ |
| 1,000 | $2.716\,92\cdots$ |
| 10,000 | $2.718\,15\cdots$ |
| 100,000 | $2.718\,27\cdots$ |

In the case $x=1$, the formula given in Theorem 6 takes the following form:

$$e=\lim_{n\to\infty}\left(1+\frac{1}{n}\right)^n.$$

We can use this formula to compute approximations to $e$, as shown in Table 2. In a sense we have cheated in obtaining the numbers in this table; they were produced using the $y^x$ function on a scientific calculator. However, this function is actually computed as $e^{x\ln y}$. In any event, the formula in this table is not a very efficient way to calculate $e$ to any great accuracy. Only 4 decimal places are correct for $n=100,000$. A much better way is to use the series

$$e = 1 + \frac{1}{1!} + \frac{1}{2!} + \frac{1}{3!} + \frac{1}{4!} + \cdots = 1 + 1 + \frac{1}{2} + \frac{1}{6} + \frac{1}{24} + \cdots,$$

A final word about interest rates. Financial institutions sometimes quote *effective* rates of interest rather than *nominal* rates. The effective rate tells you what the actual effect of the interest rate will be after one year. Thus, $10,000 invested at an effective rate of 8% will grow to $10,800.00 in one year regardless of the compounding period. A nominal rate of 8% per annum compounded daily is equivalent to an effective rate of about 8.3278%.

## Logistic Growth

Few quantities in nature can sustain exponential growth over extended periods of time; the growth is usually limited by external constraints. For example, suppose a small number of rabbits (of both sexes) is introduced to a small island where there were no rabbits previously, and where there are no predators who eat rabbits. By virtue of natural fertility, the number of rabbits might be expected to grow exponentially, but this growth will eventually be limited by the food supply available to the rabbits. Suppose the island can grow enough food to supply a population of $L$ rabbits indefinitely. If there are $y(t)$ rabbits in the population at time $t$, we would expect $y(t)$ to grow at a rate proportional to $y(t)$ provided $y(t)$ is quite small (much less than $L$). But as the numbers increase, it will be harder for the rabbits to find enough food, and we would expect the rate of increase to approach 0 as $y(t)$ gets closer and closer to $L$. One possible model for such behaviour is the differential equation

$$\frac{dy}{dt} = ky\left(1 - \frac{y}{L}\right),$$

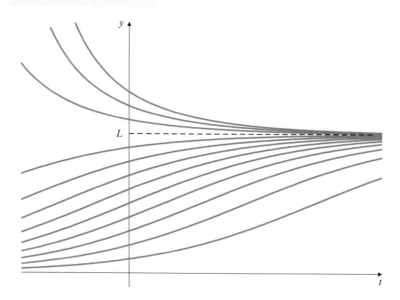

Figure 6.16    Some logistic curves

which is called the **logistic equation** since it models growth that is limited by the *supply* of necessary resources. Observe that $dy/dt > 0$ if $0 < y < L$ and that this rate is small if $y$ is small (there are few rabbits to reproduce) or if $y$ is close to $L$ (there are almost as many rabbits as the available resources can feed). Observe also that $dy/dt < 0$ if $y > L$; there being more animals than the resources can feed, the rabbits die at a greater rate than they are born. Of course, the steady-state populations $y = 0$ and $y = L$ are solutions of the logistic equation; for both of these $dy/dt = 0$. We will examine techniques for solving differential equations like the logistic equation in

Section 10.9. For now, we invite the reader to verify by differentiation that the solution satisfying $y(0) = y_0$ is

$$y = \frac{Ly_0}{y_0 + (L - y_0)e^{-kt}}.$$

Observe that, as expected, if $0 < y_0 < L$, then

$$\lim_{t \to \infty} y(t) = L, \qquad \lim_{t \to -\infty} y(t) = 0.$$

The solution given above also holds for $y_0 > L$. However, the solution does not approach 0 as $t$ approaches $-\infty$ in this case. It has a vertical asymptote at a certain negative value of $t$. (See Exercise 30 below.) The graphs of solutions of the logistic equation for various positive values of $y_0$ are given in Figure 6.16.

## EXERCISES 6.4

Evaluate the limits in Exercises 1–8.

**1.** $\displaystyle\lim_{x \to \infty} x^3 e^{-x}$

**2.** $\displaystyle\lim_{x \to \infty} x^{-3} e^x$

**3.** $\displaystyle\lim_{x \to \infty} \frac{2e^x - 3}{e^x + 5}$

**4.** $\displaystyle\lim_{x \to \infty} \frac{x - 2e^{-x}}{x + 3e^{-x}}$

**5.** $\displaystyle\lim_{x \to 0+} x \ln x$

**6.** $\displaystyle\lim_{x \to 0+} \frac{\ln x}{x}$

**7.** $\displaystyle\lim_{x \to 0} x \left( \ln |x| \right)^2$

**8.** $\displaystyle\lim_{x \to \infty} \frac{(\ln x)^3}{\sqrt{x}}$

**9.** **(Bacterial growth)** Bacteria grow in a certain culture at a rate proportional to the amount present. If there are 100 bacteria present initially and the amount doubles in 1 h, how many will there be after a further $1\frac{1}{2}$ h?

**10.** **(Dissolving sugar)** Sugar dissolves in water at a rate proportional to the amount still undissolved. If there were 50 kg of sugar present initially, and at the end of 5 h only 20 kg are left, how much longer will it take until 90% of the sugar is dissolved?

**11.** **(Radioactive decay)** A radioactive substance decays at a rate proportional to the amount present. If 30% of such a substance decays in 15 years, what is the half-life of the substance?

**12.** **(Half-life of radium)** If the half-life of radium is 1,690 years, what percentage of the amount present now will be remaining after (a) 100 years, (b) 1,000 years?

**13.** Find the half-life of a radioactive substance if after 1 year 99.57% of an initial amount still remains.

**14.** **(Bacterial growth)** In a certain culture where the rate of growth of bacteria is proportional to the number present, the number triples in 3 days. If at the end of 7 days there are 10 million bacteria present in the culture, how many were present initially?

**15.** **(Weight of a newborn)** In the first few weeks after birth, babies gain weight at a rate proportional to their weight. A baby weighing 4 kg at birth weighs 4.4 kg after 2 weeks. How much did the baby weigh 5 days after birth?

**16.** **(Electric current)** When a simple electrical circuit containing inductance and resistance but no capacitance has the electromotive force removed, the rate of decrease of the current is proportional to the current. If the current is $I(t)$ amperes $t$ s after cutoff, and if $I = 40$ when $t = 0$, and $I = 15$ when $t = 0.01$, find a formula for $I(t)$.

**17.** **(Continuously compounding interest)** How much money needs to be invested today at a nominal rate of 4% compounded continuously, in order that it should grow to $10,000 in 7 years?

**18.** **(Continuously compounding interest)** Money invested at compound interest (with instantaneous compounding) accumulates at a rate proportional to the amount present. If an initial investment of $1,000 grows to $1,500 in exactly 5 years, find (a) the doubling time for the investment and (b) the effective annual rate of interest being paid.

**19.** **(Purchasing power)** If the purchasing power of the dollar is decreasing at an effective rate of 9% annually, how long will it take for the purchasing power to be reduced to 25 cents?

**20.** **(Effective interest rate)** A bank claims to pay interest at an effective rate of 9.5% on an investment account. If the interest is actually being compounded monthly, what is the nominal rate of interest being paid on the account?

**21.** Suppose that 1,000 rabbits were introduced onto an island where they had no natural predators. During the next five years, the rabbit population grew exponentially. After the first two years the population was 3,500 rabbits. After the first five years a rabbit virus was sprayed on the island, and after that the rabbit population decayed exponentially. Two years after the virus was introduced (so seven years after rabbits were introduced to the island), the rabbit population had dropped to 3,000 rabbits. How many rabbits will there be on the island 10 years after they were introduced?

**22.** Lab rats are to be used in experiments on an isolated island. Initially $R$ rats are brought to the island and released. Having a plentiful food supply and no natural predators on the island, the rat population grows exponentially and doubles in three months. At the end of the fifth month, and at the end of every five months thereafter, 1,000 of the rats are captured and killed. What is the minimum value of $R$ that ensures that the scientists will never run out of rats?

**Differential equations of the form** $y' = a + by$

✳ **23.** Suppose that $f(x)$ satisfies the differential equation

$$f'(x) = a + bf(x),$$

where $a$ and $b$ are constants.

(a) Solve the differential equation by substituting $u(x) = a + bf(x)$ and solving the simpler differential equation that results for $u(x)$.

(b) Solve the initial-value problem:

$$\begin{cases} \dfrac{dy}{dx} = a + by \\ y(0) = y_0 \end{cases}$$

✳ **24.** **(Drug concentrations in the blood)** A drug is introduced into the bloodstream intravenously at a constant rate and breaks down and is eliminated from the body at a rate proportional to its concentration in the blood. The concentration $x(t)$ of the drug in the blood satisfies the differential equation

$$\frac{dx}{dt} = a - bx,$$

where $a$ and $b$ are positive constants.

(a) What is the limiting concentration $\lim_{t\to\infty} x(t)$ of the drug in the blood?

(b) Find the concentration of the drug in the blood at time $t$, given that the concentration was zero at $t = 0$.

(c) How long after $t = 0$ will it take for the concentration to rise to half its limiting value?

✳ **25.** **(Cooling)** Use Newton's law of cooling to determine the reading on a thermometer five minutes after it is taken from an oven at $72\,°C$ to the outdoors where the temperature is $20\,°C$, if the reading dropped to $48\,°C$ after one minute.

✳ **26.** **(Cooling)** An object is placed in a freezer maintained at a temperature of $-5\,°C$. If the object cools from $45\,°C$ to $20\,°C$ in 40 minutes, how many more minutes will it take to cool to $0\,°C$?

✳ **27.** **(Warming)** If an object in a room warms up from $5\,°C$ to $10\,°C$ in 4 minutes, and if the room is being maintained at $20\,°C$, how much longer will the object take to warm up to $15\,°C$? Assume the object warms at a rate proportional to the difference between its temperature and room temperature.

**The logistic equation**

❗ **28.** Suppose the quantity $y(t)$ exhibits logistic growth. If the values of $y(t)$ at times $t = 0$, $t = 1$, and $t = 2$ are $y_0$, $y_1$, and $y_2$, respectively, find an equation satisfied by the limiting value $L$ of $y(t)$, and solve it for $L$. If $y_0 = 3$, $y_1 = 5$, and $y_2 = 6$, find $L$.

✳ **29.** Show that a solution $y(t)$ of the logistic equation having $0 < y(0) < L$ is increasing most rapidly when its value is $L/2$. (*Hint:* You do not need to use the formula for the solution to see this.)

❗ **30.** If $y_0 > L$, find the interval on which the given solution of the logistic equation is valid. What happens to the solution as $t$ approaches the left endpoint of this interval?

❗ **31.** If $y_0 < 0$, find the interval on which the given solution of the logistic equation is valid. What happens to the solution as $t$ approaches the right endpoint of this interval?

**32.** **(Modelling an epidemic)** The number $y$ of persons infected by a highly contagious virus is modelled by a logistic curve

$$y = \frac{L}{1 + Me^{-kt}},$$

where $t$ is measured in months from the time the outbreak was discovered. At that time there were 200 infected persons, and the number grew to 1,000 after 1 month. Eventually, the number levelled out at 10,000. Find the values of the parameters $L$, $M$, and $k$ of the model.

**33.** Continuing Exercise 32, how many people were infected 3 months after the outbreak was discovered, and how fast was the number growing at that time?

---

**6.5** The Inverse Trigonometric Functions

The six trigonometric functions are periodic and, hence, not one-to-one. However, as we did with the function $x^2$ in Section 6.1, we can restrict their domains in such a way that the restricted functions are one-to-one and invertible.

### The Inverse Sine (or Arcsine) Function

Let us define a function $\operatorname{Sin} x$ (note the capital letter) to be $\sin x$, restricted so that its domain is the interval $-\frac{\pi}{2} \le x \le \frac{\pi}{2}$:

**DEFINITION**

**8**

**The restricted sine function** $\operatorname{Sin} x$

$$\operatorname{Sin} x = \sin x \qquad \text{if } -\frac{\pi}{2} \le x \le \frac{\pi}{2}.$$

Since its derivative $\cos x$ is positive on the interval $\left(-\frac{\pi}{2}, \frac{\pi}{2}\right)$, the function $\operatorname{Sin} x$ is increasing on its domain, so it is a one-to-one function. It has domain $\left[-\frac{\pi}{2}, \frac{\pi}{2}\right]$ and range $[-1, 1]$. (See Figure 6.17.)

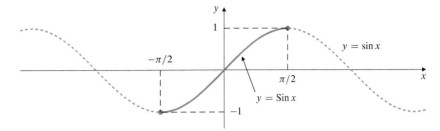

$y = \sin x$

$-\pi/2$

$\pi/2$

$y = \text{Sin } x$

**Figure 6.17**    The graph of Sin $x$ forms part of the graph of sin $x$

Being one-to-one, Sin has an inverse function which is denoted $\sin^{-1}$ (or, in some books and computer programs, by arcsin, Arcsin, or asin) and which is called the **inverse sine** or **arcsine** function.

**DEFINITION**

**9**

> **The inverse sine function $\sin^{-1} x$ or Arcsin $x$**
>
> $$y = \sin^{-1} x \iff x = \text{Sin } y$$
>
> $$\iff x = \sin y \quad \text{and} \quad -\frac{\pi}{2} \le y \le \frac{\pi}{2}$$

The graph of $\sin^{-1}$ is shown in Figure 6.18; it is the reflection of the graph of Sin in the line $y = x$. The domain of $\sin^{-1}$ is $[-1, 1]$ (the range of Sin), and the range of $\sin^{-1}$ is $\left[-\frac{\pi}{2}, \frac{\pi}{2}\right]$ (the domain of Sin). The **cancellation identities** for Sin and $\sin^{-1}$ are

$$\sin^{-1}(\text{Sin } x) = \arcsin(\text{Sin } x) = x \quad \text{for} \quad -\frac{\pi}{2} \le x \le \frac{\pi}{2}$$

$$\text{Sin}(\sin^{-1} x) = \text{Sin}(\arcsin x) = x \quad \text{for} \quad -1 \le x \le 1$$

Since the intervals where they apply are specified, Sin can be replaced by sin in both identities above.

***Remark*** As for the general inverse function $f^{-1}$, be aware that $\sin^{-1} x$ does *not* represent the *reciprocal* $1/\sin x$. (We already have a perfectly good name for the reciprocal of $\sin x$; we call it $\csc x$.) We should think of $\sin^{-1} x$ as "the angle between $-\frac{\pi}{2}$ and $\frac{\pi}{2}$ whose sine is $x$."

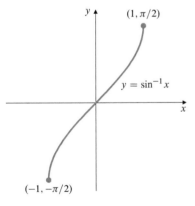

$(1, \pi/2)$

$y = \sin^{-1} x$

$(-1, -\pi/2)$

**Figure 6.18**    The arcsine function

---

**EXAMPLE 1**

(a) $\sin^{-1}\left(\frac{1}{2}\right) = \frac{\pi}{6}$ (because $\sin\frac{\pi}{6} = \frac{1}{2}$ and $-\frac{\pi}{2} < \frac{\pi}{6} < \frac{\pi}{2}$).

(b) $\sin^{-1}\left(-\frac{1}{\sqrt{2}}\right) = -\frac{\pi}{4}$ (because $\sin\left(-\frac{\pi}{4}\right) = -\frac{1}{\sqrt{2}}$ and $-\frac{\pi}{2} < -\frac{\pi}{4} < \frac{\pi}{2}$).

(c) $\sin^{-1}(-1) = -\frac{\pi}{2}$ (because $\sin\left(-\frac{\pi}{2}\right) = -1$).

(d) $\sin^{-1} 2$ is not defined. (2 is not in the range of sine.)

---

**EXAMPLE 2**    Find (a) $\sin\left(\sin^{-1} 0.7\right)$, (b) $\sin^{-1}\left(\sin 0.3\right)$, (c) $\sin^{-1}\left(\sin\frac{4\pi}{5}\right)$, and (d) $\cos\left(\sin^{-1} 0.6\right)$.

***Solution***

(a) $\sin\left(\sin^{-1} 0.7\right) = 0.7$ (cancellation identity).

(b) $\sin^{-1}\left(\sin 0.3\right) = 0.3$ (cancellation identity).

(c) The number $\frac{4\pi}{5}$ does not lie in $\left[-\frac{\pi}{2}, \frac{\pi}{2}\right]$, so we can't apply the cancellation identity directly. However, $\sin\frac{4\pi}{5} = \sin\left(\pi - \frac{\pi}{5}\right) = \sin\frac{\pi}{5}$ by the supplementary angle identity. Therefore, $\sin^{-1}\left(\sin\frac{4\pi}{5}\right) = \sin^{-1}\left(\sin\frac{\pi}{5}\right) = \frac{\pi}{5}$ (by cancellation).

(d) Let $\theta = \sin^{-1} 0.6$, as shown in the right triangle in Figure 6.19, which has hypotenuse 1 and side opposite $\theta$ equal to 0.6. By the Pythagorean Theorem, the side adjacent $\theta$ is $\sqrt{1 - (0.6)^2} = 0.8$. Thus, $\cos\left(\sin^{-1} 0.6\right) = \cos\theta = 0.8$.

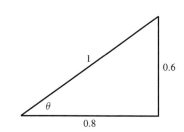

**Figure 6.19**

---

**EXAMPLE 3**   Simplify the expression $\tan(\sin^{-1} x)$.

*Solution*   We want the tangent of an angle whose sine is $x$. Suppose first that $0 \le x < 1$. As in Example 2, we draw a right triangle (Figure 6.20) with one angle $\theta$, and label the sides so that $\theta = \sin^{-1} x$. The side opposite $\theta$ is $x$, and the hypotenuse is 1. The remaining side is $\sqrt{1 - x^2}$, and we have

$$\tan(\sin^{-1} x) = \tan\theta = \frac{x}{\sqrt{1 - x^2}}.$$

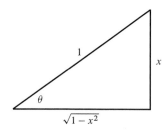

**Figure 6.20**

Because both sides of the above equation are odd functions of $x$, the same result holds for $-1 < x < 0$.

---

Now let us use implicit differentiation to find the derivative of the inverse sine function. If $y = \sin^{-1} x$, then $x = \sin y$ and $-\frac{\pi}{2} \le y \le \frac{\pi}{2}$. Differentiating with respect to $x$, we obtain

$$1 = (\cos y)\frac{dy}{dx}.$$

Since $-\frac{\pi}{2} \le y \le \frac{\pi}{2}$, we know that $\cos y \ge 0$. Therefore,

$$\cos y = \sqrt{1 - \sin^2 y} = \sqrt{1 - x^2},$$

and $dy/dx = 1/\cos y = 1/\sqrt{1 - x^2}$;

$$\frac{d}{dx}\sin^{-1} x = \frac{d}{dx}\arcsin x = \frac{1}{\sqrt{1 - x^2}}.$$

Note that the inverse sine function is differentiable only on the *open* interval $(-1, 1)$; the slope of its graph approaches infinity as $x \to -1+$ or as $x \to 1-$. (See Figure 6.18.)

---

**EXAMPLE 4**   Find the derivative of $\sin^{-1}\left(\frac{x}{a}\right)$ and hence evaluate $\displaystyle\int \frac{dx}{\sqrt{a^2 - x^2}}$, where $a > 0$.

*Solution*   By the Chain Rule,

$$\frac{d}{dx}\sin^{-1}\frac{x}{a} = \frac{1}{\sqrt{1 - \dfrac{x^2}{a^2}}}\frac{1}{a} = \frac{1}{\sqrt{\dfrac{a^2 - x^2}{a^2}}}\frac{1}{a} = \frac{1}{\sqrt{a^2 - x^2}} \qquad \text{if } a > 0.$$

Hence,

$$\int \frac{1}{\sqrt{a^2 - x^2}}\, dx = \sin^{-1}\frac{x}{a} + C \qquad (a > 0).$$

**EXAMPLE 5**    Find the solution $y$ of the following initial-value problem:

$$\begin{cases} y' = \dfrac{4}{\sqrt{2-x^2}} & (-\sqrt{2} < x < \sqrt{2}) \\ y(1) = 2\pi. \end{cases}$$

***Solution***   Using the integral from the previous example, we have

$$y = \int \frac{4}{\sqrt{2-x^2}}\, dx = 4\sin^{-1}\left(\frac{x}{\sqrt{2}}\right) + C$$

for some constant $C$. Also $2\pi = y(1) = 4\sin^{-1}(1/\sqrt{2}) + C = 4\left(\frac{\pi}{4}\right) + C = \pi + C$. Thus, $C = \pi$ and $y = 4\sin^{-1}(x/\sqrt{2}) + \pi$.

---

**EXAMPLE 6**    **(A sawtooth curve)**   Let $f(x) = \sin^{-1}(\sin x)$ for all real numbers $x$.

(a) Calculate and simplify $f'(x)$.

(b) Where is $f$ differentiable? Where is $f$ continuous?

(c) Use your results from (a) and (b) to sketch the graph of $f$.

***Solution***   (a) Using the Chain Rule and the Pythagorean identity we calculate

$$\begin{aligned} f'(x) &= \frac{1}{\sqrt{1-(\sin x)^2}}(\cos x) \\ &= \frac{\cos x}{\sqrt{\cos^2 x}} = \frac{\cos x}{|\cos x|} = \begin{cases} 1 & \text{if } \cos x > 0 \\ -1 & \text{if } \cos x < 0. \end{cases} \end{aligned}$$

(b) $f$ is differentiable at all points where $\cos x \neq 0$, that is, everywhere except at odd multiples of $\pi/2$, namely, $\pm\frac{\pi}{2}, \pm\frac{3\pi}{2}, \pm\frac{5\pi}{2}, \ldots$.
Since sin is continuous everywhere and has values in $[-1, 1]$, and since $\sin^{-1}$ is continuous on $[-1, 1]$, we have that $f$ is continuous on the whole real line.

(c) Since $f$ is continuous, its graph has no breaks. The graph consists of straight line segments of slopes alternating between 1 and $-1$ on intervals between consecutive odd multiples of $\pi/2$. Since $f'(x) = 1$ on the interval $\left[-\frac{\pi}{2}, \frac{\pi}{2}\right]$ (where $\cos x \geq 0$), the graph must be as shown in Figure 6.21.

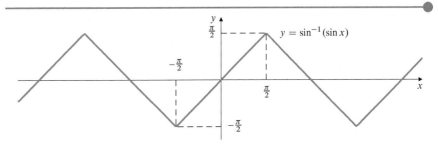

**Figure 6.21**    A sawtooth graph

## The Inverse Tangent (or Arctangent) Function

The inverse tangent function is defined in a manner similar to the inverse sine. We begin by restricting the tangent function to an interval where it is one-to-one; in this case we use the open interval $\left(-\frac{\pi}{2}, \frac{\pi}{2}\right)$. See Figure 6.22(a).

**DEFINITION**

**10**

**The restricted tangent function Tan $x$**

$$\text{Tan } x = \tan x \qquad \text{if } -\frac{\pi}{2} < x < \frac{\pi}{2}.$$

The inverse of the function Tan is called the **inverse tangent** function and is denoted $\tan^{-1}$ (or arctan, Arctan, or atan). The domain of $\tan^{-1}$ is the whole real line (the range of Tan). Its range is the open interval $\left(-\frac{\pi}{2}, \frac{\pi}{2}\right)$.

**DEFINITION**

**The inverse tangent function $\tan^{-1} x$ or Arctan $x$**

$$y = \tan^{-1} x \quad \Longleftrightarrow \quad x = \text{Tan } y$$

$$\Longleftrightarrow \quad x = \tan y \quad \text{and} \quad -\frac{\pi}{2} < y < \frac{\pi}{2}$$

The graph of $\tan^{-1}$ is shown in Figure 6.22(b); it is the reflection of the graph of Tan in the line $y = x$.

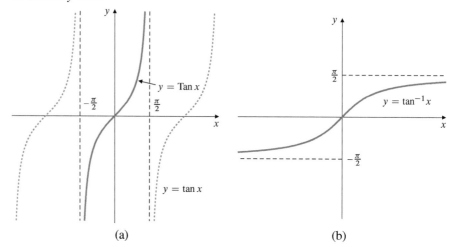

**Figure 6.22**

(a) The graph of Tan $x$

(b) The graph of $\tan^{-1} x$

(a)                    (b)

The cancellation identities for Tan and $\tan^{-1}$ are

$$\tan^{-1}(\text{Tan } x) = \arctan(\text{Tan } x) = x \qquad \text{for } -\frac{\pi}{2} < x < \frac{\pi}{2}$$

$$\text{Tan}(\tan^{-1} x) = \text{Tan}(\arctan x) = x \qquad \text{for } -\infty < x < \infty$$

Again, we can replace Tan with tan above since the intervals are specified.

**EXAMPLE 7** Evaluate: (a) $\tan(\tan^{-1} 3)$, (b) $\tan^{-1}\left(\tan \frac{3\pi}{4}\right)$, and (c) $\cos(\tan^{-1} 2)$.

*Solution*

(a) $\tan(\tan^{-1} 3) = 3$ by cancellation.

(b) $\tan^{-1}\left(\tan \frac{3\pi}{4}\right) = \tan^{-1}(-1) = -\frac{\pi}{4}$.

(c) $\cos(\tan^{-1} 2) = \cos \theta = \frac{1}{\sqrt{5}}$ via the triangle in Figure 6.23. Alternatively, we have $\tan(\tan^{-1} 2) = 2$, so $\sec^2(\tan^{-1} 2) = 1 + 2^2 = 5$. Thus, $\cos^2(\tan^{-1} 2) = \frac{1}{5}$. Since cosine is positive on the range of $\tan^{-1}$, we have $\cos(\tan^{-1} 2) = \frac{1}{\sqrt{5}}$.

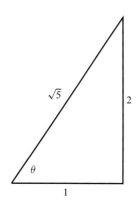

**Figure 6.23**

The derivative of the inverse tangent function is also found by implicit differentiation: if $y = \tan^{-1} x$, then $x = \tan y$ and

$$1 = (\sec^2 y)\frac{dy}{dx} = (1 + \tan^2 y)\frac{dy}{dx} = (1 + x^2)\frac{dy}{dx}.$$

Thus,

$$\frac{d}{dx} \tan^{-1} x = \frac{1}{1 + x^2}.$$

**EXAMPLE 8**   Find $\dfrac{d}{dx}\tan^{-1}\left(\dfrac{x}{a}\right)$, and hence evaluate $\displaystyle\int \dfrac{1}{x^2+a^2}\,dx$.

*Solution*   We have

$$\frac{d}{dx}\tan^{-1}\left(\frac{x}{a}\right) = \frac{1}{1+\dfrac{x^2}{a^2}}\,\frac{1}{a} = \frac{a}{a^2+x^2};$$

hence,

$$\int \frac{dx}{a^2+x^2} = \frac{1}{a}\tan^{-1}\left(\frac{x}{a}\right) + C.$$

**EXAMPLE 9**   Prove that $\tan^{-1}\left(\dfrac{x-1}{x+1}\right) = \tan^{-1}x - \dfrac{\pi}{4}$ for $x > -1$.

*Solution*   Let $f(x) = \tan^{-1}\left(\dfrac{x-1}{x+1}\right) - \tan^{-1}x$. On the interval $(-1,\infty)$ we have, by the Chain Rule and the Quotient Rule,

$$f'(x) = \frac{1}{1+\left(\dfrac{x-1}{x+1}\right)^2}\,\frac{(x+1)-(x-1)}{(x+1)^2} - \frac{1}{1+x^2}$$

$$= \frac{(x+1)^2}{(x^2+2x+1)+(x^2-2x+1)}\,\frac{2}{(x+1)^2} - \frac{1}{1+x^2}$$

$$= \frac{2}{2+2x^2} - \frac{1}{1+x^2} = 0.$$

Hence, $f(x) = C$ (constant) on that interval. We can find $C$ by finding $f(0)$:

$$C = f(0) = \tan^{-1}(-1) - \tan^{-1}0 = -\frac{\pi}{4}.$$

Hence, the given identity holds on $(-1,\infty)$.

*Remark*   Some computer programs, especially spreadsheets, implement two versions of the arctangent function, usually called "atan" and "atan2." The function atan is just the function $\tan^{-1}$ that we have defined; atan$(y/x)$ gives the angle in radians, between the line from the origin to the point $(x, y)$ and the positive $x$-axis, provided $(x, y)$ lies in quadrants I or IV of the plane. The function atan2 is a function of two variables: atan2$(x, y)$ gives that angle for any point $(x, y)$ not on the $y$-axis. See Figure 6.24. Some programs, for instance MATLAB, reverse the order of the variables $x$ and $y$ in their atan2 function. Maple uses `arctan(x)` and `arctan(y,x)` for the one- and two-variable versions of arctangent.

## Other Inverse Trigonometric Functions

The function $\cos x$ is one-to-one on the interval $[0, \pi]$, so we could define the **inverse cosine function**, $\cos^{-1}x$ (or arccos $x$, or Arccos $x$, or acos $x$), so that

$$y = \cos^{-1}x \iff x = \cos y \quad \text{and} \quad 0 \le y \le \pi.$$

However, $\cos y = \sin\left(\dfrac{\pi}{2} - y\right)$ (the complementary angle identity), and $\dfrac{\pi}{2} - y$ is in the interval $\left[-\dfrac{\pi}{2}, \dfrac{\pi}{2}\right]$ when $0 \le y \le \pi$. Thus, the definition above would lead to

$$y = \cos^{-1}x \iff x = \sin\left(\frac{\pi}{2} - y\right) \iff \sin^{-1}x = \frac{\pi}{2} - y = \frac{\pi}{2} - \cos^{-1}x.$$

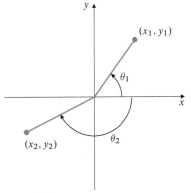

**Figure 6.24**

$\theta_1 = \tan^{-1}(y_1/x_1)$

$\quad = \text{atan}(y_1/x_1)$

$\quad = \text{atan2}(x_1, y_1)$

$\quad = \text{arctan}(y_1/x_1)$   (Maple)

$\quad = \text{arctan}(y_1, x_1)$   (Maple)

$\theta_2 = \text{atan2}(x_2, y_2)$

$\quad = \text{arctan}(y_2, x_2)$   (Maple)

It is easier to use this result to define $\cos^{-1}x$ directly:

**The inverse cosine function $\cos^{-1} x$ or Arccos $x$**

$$\cos^{-1} x = \frac{\pi}{2} - \sin^{-1} x \qquad \text{for} \quad -1 \le x \le 1.$$

The cancellation identities for $\cos^{-1}x$ are

$$\cos^{-1}(\cos x) = \arccos(\cos x) = x \qquad \text{for } 0 \le x \le \pi$$
$$\cos(\cos^{-1} x) = \cos(\arccos x) = x \qquad \text{for } -1 \le x \le 1$$

The derivative of $\cos^{-1} x$ is the negative of that of $\sin^{-1} x$ (why?):

$$\frac{d}{dx} \cos^{-1} x = -\frac{1}{\sqrt{1-x^2}}.$$

The graph of $\cos^{-1}$ is shown in Figure 6.25(a).

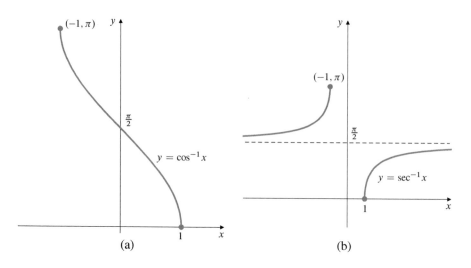

Figure 6.25 The graphs of $\cos^{-1}$ and $\sec^{-1}$

(a)      (b)

Scientific calculators usually implement only the primary trigonometric functions—sine, cosine, and tangent—and the inverses of these three. The secondary functions—secant, cosecant, and cotangent—are calculated using the reciprocal key; to calculate $\sec x$ you calculate $\cos x$ and take the reciprocal of the answer. The inverses of the secondary trigonometric functions are also easily expressed in terms of those of their reciprocal functions. For example, we define:

**The inverse secant function $\sec^{-1} x$ (or Arcsec $x$)**

$$\sec^{-1} x = \cos^{-1}\left(\frac{1}{x}\right) \qquad \text{for} \quad |x| \ge 1.$$

The domain of $\sec^{-1}$ is the union of intervals $(-\infty, -1] \cup [1, \infty)$, and its range is $\left[0, \frac{\pi}{2}\right) \cup \left(\frac{\pi}{2}, \pi\right]$. The graph of $y = \sec^{-1}x$ is shown in Figure 6.25(b). It is the reflection in the line $y = x$ of that part of the graph of $\sec x$ for $x$ between $0$ and $\pi$.

Observe that

$$\sec(\sec^{-1} x) = \sec\left(\cos^{-1}\left(\frac{1}{x}\right)\right)$$

$$= \frac{1}{\cos\left(\cos^{-1}\left(\frac{1}{x}\right)\right)} = \frac{1}{\frac{1}{x}} = x \qquad \text{for } |x| \geq 1,$$

$$\sec^{-1}(\sec x) = \cos^{-1}\left(\frac{1}{\sec x}\right)$$

$$= \cos^{-1}(\cos x) = x \qquad \text{for } x \text{ in } [0, \pi], \ x \neq \frac{\pi}{2}.$$

We calculate the derivative of $\sec^{-1}$ from that of $\cos^{-1}$:

Some authors prefer to define $\sec^{-1}$ as the inverse of the restriction of $\sec x$ to the separated intervals $[0, \pi/2)$ and $[\pi, 3\pi/2)$ because this prevents the absolute value from appearing in the formula for the derivative. However, it is much harder to calculate values with that definition. Our definition makes it easy to obtain a value such as $\sec^{-1}(-3)$ from a calculator. Scientific calculators usually have just the inverses of sine, cosine, and tangent built in.

$$\frac{d}{dx}\sec^{-1} x = \frac{d}{dx}\cos^{-1}\left(\frac{1}{x}\right) = \frac{-1}{\sqrt{1 - \frac{1}{x^2}}}\left(-\frac{1}{x^2}\right)$$

$$= \frac{1}{x^2}\sqrt{\frac{x^2}{x^2 - 1}} = \frac{1}{x^2}\frac{|x|}{\sqrt{x^2 - 1}} = \frac{1}{|x|\sqrt{x^2 - 1}}.$$

Note that we had to use $\sqrt{x^2} = |x|$ in the last line. There are negative values of $x$ in the domain of $\sec^{-1}$. Observe in Figure 6.25(b) that the slope of $y = \sec^{-1}(x)$ is always positive.

$$\frac{d}{dx}\sec^{-1} x = \frac{1}{|x|\sqrt{x^2 - 1}}.$$

The corresponding integration formula takes different forms on intervals where $x \geq 1$ or $x \leq -1$:

$$\int \frac{1}{x\sqrt{x^2 - 1}}\, dx = \begin{cases} \sec^{-1}x + C & \text{on intervals where } x \geq 1 \\ -\sec^{-1}x + C & \text{on intervals where } x \leq -1 \end{cases}$$

Finally, note that $\csc^{-1}$ and $\cot^{-1}$ are defined similarly to $\sec^{-1}$. They are seldom encountered.

**DEFINITION**

**14**

**The inverse cosecant and inverse cotangent functions**

$$\csc^{-1} x = \sin^{-1}\left(\frac{1}{x}\right), \quad (|x| \geq 1); \qquad \cot^{-1} x = \tan^{-1}\left(\frac{1}{x}\right), \quad (x \neq 0)$$

## EXERCISES 6.5

In Exercises 1–12, evaluate the given expression.

**1.** $\sin^{-1}\frac{\sqrt{3}}{2}$

**2.** $\cos^{-1}\left(\frac{-1}{2}\right)$

**3.** $\tan^{-1}(-1)$

**4.** $\sec^{-1}\sqrt{2}$

**5.** $\sin(\sin^{-1} 0.7)$

**6.** $\cos(\sin^{-1} 0.7)$

**7.** $\tan^{-1}\left(\tan\frac{2\pi}{3}\right)$

**8.** $\sin^{-1}(\cos 40°)$

**9.** $\cos^{-1}(\sin(-0.2))$

**10.** $\sin\left(\cos^{-1}\left(\frac{-1}{3}\right)\right)$

**11.** $\cos\left(\tan^{-1}\frac{1}{2}\right)$

**12.** $\tan(\tan^{-1} 200)$

In Exercises 13–18, simplify the given expression.

**13.** $\sin(\cos^{-1} x)$

**14.** $\cos(\sin^{-1} x)$

**15.** $\cos(\tan^{-1} x)$

**16.** $\sin(\tan^{-1} x)$

**17.** $\tan(\cos^{-1} x)$

**18.** $\tan(\sec^{-1} x)$

In Exercises 19–32, differentiate the given function and simplify the answer whenever possible.

**19.** $y = \sin^{-1}\left(\dfrac{2x-1}{3}\right)$

**20.** $y = \tan^{-1}(ax+b)$

**21.** $y = \cos^{-1}\left(\dfrac{x-b}{a}\right)$

**22.** $f(x) = x\sin^{-1} x$

**23.** $f(t) = t\tan^{-1} t$

**24.** $u = z^2 \sec^{-1}(1+z^2)$

**25.** $F(x) = (1+x^2)\tan^{-1} x$

**26.** $y = \sin^{-1}\dfrac{a}{x}$

**27.** $G(x) = \dfrac{\sin^{-1} x}{\sin^{-1} 2x}$

**28.** $H(t) = \dfrac{\sin^{-1} t}{\sin t}$

**29.** $f(x) = (\sin^{-1} x^2)^{1/2}$

**30.** $y = \cos^{-1}\dfrac{a}{\sqrt{a^2+x^2}}$

**31.** $y = \sqrt{a^2-x^2} + a\sin^{-1}\dfrac{x}{a}$   $(a > 0)$

**32.** $y = a\cos^{-1}\left(1-\dfrac{x}{a}\right) - \sqrt{2ax-x^2}$   $(a > 0)$

**33.** Find the slope of the curve $\tan^{-1}\left(\dfrac{2x}{y}\right) = \dfrac{\pi x}{y^2}$ at the point $(1, 2)$.

**34.** Find equations of two straight lines tangent to the graph of $y = \sin^{-1} x$ and having slope 2.

**❷ 35.** Show that, on their respective domains, $\sin^{-1}$ and $\tan^{-1}$ are increasing functions and $\cos^{-1}$ is a decreasing function.

**❷ 36.** The derivative of $\sec^{-1} x$ is positive for every $x$ in the domain of $\sec^{-1}$. Does this imply that $\sec^{-1}$ is increasing on its domain? Why?

**37.** Sketch the graph of $\csc^{-1} x$ and find its derivative.

**38.** Sketch the graph of $\cot^{-1} x$ and find its derivative.

**39.** Show that $\tan^{-1} x + \cot^{-1} x = \dfrac{\pi}{2}$ for $x > 0$. What is the sum if $x < 0$?

**40.** Find the derivative of $g(x) = \tan(\tan^{-1} x)$ and sketch the graph of $g$.

In Exercises 41–44, plot the graphs of the given functions by first calculating and simplifying the derivative of the function. Where is each function continuous? Where is it differentiable?

**⚠ 41.** $\cos^{-1}(\cos x)$

**⚠ 42.** $\sin^{-1}(\cos x)$

**⚠ 43.** $\tan^{-1}(\tan x)$

**⚠ 44.** $\tan^{-1}(\cot x)$

**45.** Show that $\sin^{-1} x = \tan^{-1}\left(\dfrac{x}{\sqrt{1-x^2}}\right)$ if $|x| < 1$.

**46.** Show that $\sec^{-1} x = \begin{cases} \tan^{-1}\sqrt{x^2-1} & \text{if } x \geq 1 \\ \pi - \tan^{-1}\sqrt{x^2-1} & \text{if } x \leq -1 \end{cases}$

**47.** Show that $\tan^{-1} x = \sin^{-1}\left(\dfrac{x}{\sqrt{1+x^2}}\right)$ for all $x$.

**48.** Show that $\sec^{-1} x = \begin{cases} \sin^{-1}\dfrac{\sqrt{x^2-1}}{x} & \text{if } x \geq 1 \\ \pi + \sin^{-1}\dfrac{\sqrt{x^2-1}}{x} & \text{if } x \leq -1 \end{cases}$

**❷ 49.** Show that the function $f(x)$ of Example 9 is also constant on the interval $(-\infty, -1)$. Find the value of the constant. *Hint:* Find $\lim_{x \to -\infty} f(x)$.

**❷ 50.** Find the derivative of $f(x) = x - \tan^{-1}(\tan x)$. What does your answer imply about $f(x)$? Calculate $f(0)$ and $f(\pi)$. Is there a contradiction here?

**⚠ 51.** Find the derivative of $f(x) = x - \sin^{-1}(\sin x)$ for $-\pi \leq x \leq \pi$ and sketch the graph of $f$ on that interval.

In Exercises 52–55, solve the initial-value problems.

**✳ 52.** $\begin{cases} y' = \dfrac{1}{1+x^2} \\ y(0) = 1 \end{cases}$

**✳ 53.** $\begin{cases} y' = \dfrac{1}{9+x^2} \\ y(3) = 2 \end{cases}$

**✳ 54.** $\begin{cases} y' = \dfrac{1}{\sqrt{1-x^2}} \\ y(1/2) = 1 \end{cases}$

**✳ 55.** $\begin{cases} y' = \dfrac{4}{\sqrt{25-x^2}} \\ y(0) = 0 \end{cases}$

---

**6.6** Hyperbolic Functions

Any function defined on the real line can be expressed (in a unique way) as the sum of an even function and an odd function. The **hyperbolic functions** $\cosh x$ and $\sinh x$ are, respectively, the even and odd functions whose sum is the exponential function $e^x$.

**DEFINITION**

**15**

**The hyperbolic cosine and hyperbolic sine functions**

For any real $x$ the **hyperbolic cosine**, $\cosh x$, and the **hyperbolic sine**, $\sinh x$, are defined by

$$\cosh x = \frac{e^x + e^{-x}}{2}, \qquad \sinh x = \frac{e^x - e^{-x}}{2}.$$

(The symbol "sinh" is somewhat hard to pronounce as written. Some people say "shine," and others say "sinch.") Recall that cosine and sine are called *circular functions* because, for any $t$, the point $(\cos t, \sin t)$ lies on the circle with equation $x^2 + y^2 = 1$. Similarly, cosh and sinh are called *hyperbolic functions* because the point $(\cosh t, \sinh t)$ lies on the rectangular hyperbola with equation $x^2 - y^2 = 1$,

$$\cosh^2 t - \sinh^2 t = 1 \quad \text{for any real } t.$$

To see this, observe that

$$\cosh^2 t - \sinh^2 t = \left(\frac{e^t + e^{-t}}{2}\right)^2 - \left(\frac{e^t - e^{-t}}{2}\right)^2$$

$$= \frac{1}{4}\left(e^{2t} + 2 + e^{-2t} - (e^{2t} - 2 + e^{-2t})\right)$$

$$= \frac{1}{4}(2 + 2) = 1.$$

There is no interpretation of $t$ as an arc length or angle as there was in the circular case; however, the *area* of the *hyperbolic sector* bounded by $y = 0$, the hyperbola $x^2 - y^2 = 1$, and the ray from the origin to $(\cosh t, \sinh t)$ is $t/2$ square units, just as is the area of the circular sector bounded by $y = 0$, the circle $x^2 + y^2 = 1$, and the ray from the origin to $(\cos t, \sin t)$. (See Figure 6.26.)

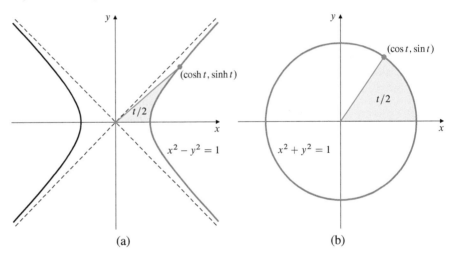

Figure 6.26    Both shaded areas are $t/2$ square units

(a)                    (b)

Observe that, similar to the corresponding values of $\cos x$ and $\sin x$, we have

$$\cosh 0 = 1 \quad \text{and} \quad \sinh 0 = 0,$$

and $\cosh x$, like $\cos x$, is an even function, and $\sinh x$, like $\sin x$, is an odd function:

$$\cosh(-x) = \cosh x, \qquad \sinh(-x) = -\sinh x.$$

The graphs of cosh and sinh are shown in Figure 6.27. The graph $y = \cosh x$ is called a **catenary**. A chain hanging by its ends will assume the shape of a catenary.

Many other properties of the hyperbolic functions resemble those of the corresponding circular functions, sometimes with signs changed.

---

**EXAMPLE 1**    Show that

$$\frac{d}{dx}\cosh x = \sinh x \quad \text{and} \quad \frac{d}{dx}\sinh x = \cosh x.$$

*Solution* We have

$$\frac{d}{dx}\cosh x = \frac{d}{dx}\frac{e^x + e^{-x}}{2} = \frac{e^x + e^{-x}(-1)}{2} = \sinh x$$

$$\frac{d}{dx}\sinh x = \frac{d}{dx}\frac{e^x - e^{-x}}{2} = \frac{e^x - e^{-x}(-1)}{2} = \cosh x.$$

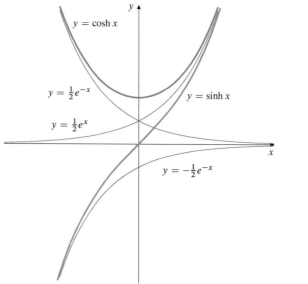

**Figure 6.27** The graphs of cosh (red) and sinh (blue), and some exponential graphs (green) to which they are asymptotic

The following addition formulas and double-angle formulas can be checked algebraically by using the definition of cosh and sinh and the laws of exponents:

$$\cosh(x + y) = \cosh x \cosh y + \sinh x \sinh y,$$
$$\sinh(x + y) = \sinh x \cosh y + \cosh x \sinh y,$$

$$\cosh(2x) = \cosh^2 x + \sinh^2 x = 1 + 2\sinh^2 x = 2\cosh^2 x - 1,$$
$$\sinh(2x) = 2\sinh x \cosh x.$$

By analogy with the trigonometric functions, four other hyperbolic functions can be defined in terms of cosh and sinh.

**DEFINITION**

**16**

**Other hyperbolic functions**

$$\tanh x = \frac{\sinh x}{\cosh x} = \frac{e^x - e^{-x}}{e^x + e^{-x}} \qquad \operatorname{sech} x = \frac{1}{\cosh x} = \frac{2}{e^x + e^{-x}}$$

$$\coth x = \frac{\cosh x}{\sinh x} = \frac{e^x + e^{-x}}{e^x - e^{-x}} \qquad \operatorname{csch} x = \frac{1}{\sinh x} = \frac{2}{e^x - e^{-x}}$$

Multiplying the numerator and denominator of the fraction defining $\tanh x$ by $e^{-x}$ and $e^x$, respectively, we obtain

$$\lim_{x \to \infty} \tanh x = \lim_{x \to \infty} \frac{1 - e^{-2x}}{1 + e^{-2x}} = 1 \qquad \text{and}$$

$$\lim_{x \to -\infty} \tanh x = \lim_{x \to -\infty} \frac{e^{2x} - 1}{e^{2x} + 1} = -1,$$

so that the graph of $y = \tanh x$ has two horizontal asymptotes. The graph of $\tanh x$ (Figure 6.28) resembles those of $x/\sqrt{1 + x^2}$ and $(2/\pi)\tan^{-1} x$ in shape, but, of course, they are not identical.

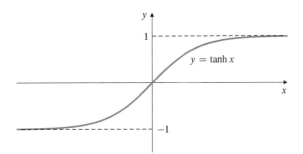

$y = \tanh x$

**Figure 6.28**    The graph of tanh $x$

The derivatives of the remaining hyperbolic functions

$$\frac{d}{dx} \tanh x = \operatorname{sech}^2 x \qquad \frac{d}{dx} \operatorname{sech} x = -\operatorname{sech} x \tanh x$$

$$\frac{d}{dx} \coth x = -\operatorname{csch}^2 x \qquad \frac{d}{dx} \operatorname{csch} x = -\operatorname{csch} x \coth x$$

are easily calculated from those of cosh $x$ and sinh $x$ using the Reciprocal and Quotient Rules. For example,

$$\frac{d}{dx} \tanh x = \frac{d}{dx} \frac{\sinh x}{\cosh x} = \frac{(\cosh x)(\cosh x) - (\sinh x)(\sinh x)}{\cosh^2 x}$$

$$= \frac{1}{\cosh^2 x} = \operatorname{sech}^2 x.$$

***Remark***    The distinction between trigonometric and hyperbolic functions largely disappears if we allow complex numbers instead of just real numbers as variables. If $i$ is the imaginary unit (so that $i^2 = -1$), then

$$e^{ix} = \cos x + i \sin x \qquad \text{and} \qquad e^{-ix} = \cos x - i \sin x.$$

(See Appendix I.) Therefore,

$$\cosh(ix) = \frac{e^{ix} + e^{-ix}}{2} = \cos x, \qquad \cos(ix) = \cosh(-x) = \cosh x,$$

$$\sinh(ix) = \frac{e^{ix} - e^{-ix}}{2} = i \sin x, \qquad \sin(ix) = \frac{1}{i} \sinh(-x) = i \sinh x.$$

## Inverse Hyperbolic Functions

The functions sinh and tanh are increasing and therefore one-to-one and invertible on the whole real line. Their inverses are denoted $\sinh^{-1}$ and $\tanh^{-1}$, respectively:

$$y = \sinh^{-1} x \quad \Longleftrightarrow \quad x = \sinh y,$$

$$y = \tanh^{-1} x \quad \Longleftrightarrow \quad x = \tanh y.$$

Since the hyperbolic functions are defined in terms of exponentials, it is not surprising that their inverses can be expressed in terms of logarithms.

**EXAMPLE 2**    Express the functions $\sinh^{-1} x$ and $\tanh^{-1} x$ in terms of natural logarithms.

***Solution***    Let $y = \sinh^{-1} x$. Then

$$x = \sinh y = \frac{e^y - e^{-y}}{2} = \frac{(e^y)^2 - 1}{2e^y}.$$

(We multiplied the numerator and denominator of the first fraction by $e^y$ to get the second fraction.) Therefore,

$$(e^y)^2 - 2xe^y - 1 = 0.$$

This is a quadratic equation in $e^y$, and it can be solved by the quadratic formula:

$$e^y = \frac{2x \pm \sqrt{4x^2 + 4}}{2} = x \pm \sqrt{x^2 + 1}.$$

Note that $\sqrt{x^2 + 1} > x$. Since $e^y$ cannot be negative, we need to use the positive sign:

$$e^y = x + \sqrt{x^2 + 1}.$$

Hence, $y = \ln\left(x + \sqrt{x^2 + 1}\right)$, and we have

$$\sinh^{-1} x = \ln\left(x + \sqrt{x^2 + 1}\right).$$

Now let $y = \tanh^{-1} x$. Then

$$x = \tanh y = \frac{e^y - e^{-y}}{e^y + e^{-y}} = \frac{e^{2y} - 1}{e^{2y} + 1} \qquad (-1 < x < 1),$$

$$xe^{2y} + x = e^{2y} - 1,$$

$$e^{2y} = \frac{1 + x}{1 - x}, \qquad y = \frac{1}{2}\ln\left(\frac{1 + x}{1 - x}\right).$$

Thus,

$$\tanh^{-1} x = \frac{1}{2}\ln\left(\frac{1 + x}{1 - x}\right), \qquad (-1 < x < 1).$$

Since cosh is not one-to-one, its domain must be restricted before an inverse can be defined. Let us define the principal value of cosh to be

$$\text{Cosh } x = \cosh x \qquad (x \geq 0).$$

The inverse, $\cosh^{-1}$, is then defined by

$$y = \cosh^{-1} x \quad \Longleftrightarrow \quad x = \text{Cosh } y$$
$$\Longleftrightarrow \quad x = \cosh y \qquad (y \geq 0).$$

As we did for $\sinh^{-1}$, we can obtain the formula

$$\cosh^{-1} x = \ln\left(x + \sqrt{x^2 - 1}\right), \qquad (x \geq 1).$$

As was the case for the inverses of the reciprocal trigonometric functions, the inverses of the remaining three hyperbolic functions, coth, sech, and csch, are best defined using the inverses of their reciprocals.

$$\coth^{-1} x = \tanh^{-1}\left(\frac{1}{x}\right) = \frac{1}{2}\ln\left(\frac{1+\frac{1}{x}}{1-\frac{1}{x}}\right) \qquad \text{for } \left|\frac{1}{x}\right| < 1$$

$$= \frac{1}{2}\ln\left(\frac{x+1}{x-1}\right) \qquad \text{for } x > 1 \text{ or } x < 1$$

$$\operatorname{sech}^{-1} x = \cosh^{-1}\left(\frac{1}{x}\right) = \ln\left(\frac{1}{x} + \sqrt{\frac{1}{x^2} - 1}\right) \qquad \text{for } \frac{1}{x} \geq 1$$

$$= \ln\left(\frac{1+\sqrt{1-x^2}}{x}\right) \qquad \text{for } 0 < x \leq 1$$

$$\operatorname{csch}^{-1} x = \sinh^{-1}\left(\frac{1}{x}\right) = \ln\left(\frac{1}{x} + \sqrt{\frac{1}{x^2} + 1}\right)$$

$$= \begin{cases} \ln\left(\dfrac{1+\sqrt{1+x^2}}{x}\right) & \text{if } x > 0 \\[4mm] \ln\left(\dfrac{1-\sqrt{1+x^2}}{x}\right) & \text{if } x < 0. \end{cases}$$

The derivatives of all six inverse hyperbolic functions are left as exercises for the reader. See Exercise 5 and Exercises 8–10 below.

## EXERCISES 6.6

1. Verify the formulas for the derivatives of $\operatorname{sech} x$, $\operatorname{csch} x$, and $\coth x$ given in this section.

2. Verify the addition formulas

$$\cosh(x + y) = \cosh x \cosh y + \sinh x \sinh y,$$
$$\sinh(x + y) = \sinh x \cosh y + \cosh x \sinh y.$$

Proceed by expanding the right-hand side of each identity in terms of exponentials. Find similar formulas for $\cosh(x - y)$ and $\sinh(x - y)$.

3. Obtain addition formulas for $\tanh(x + y)$ and $\tanh(x - y)$ from those for sinh and cosh.

4. Sketch the graphs of $y = \coth x$, $y = \operatorname{sech} x$, and $y = \operatorname{csch} x$, showing any asymptotes.

5. Calculate the derivatives of $\sinh^{-1} x$, $\cosh^{-1} x$, and $\tanh^{-1} x$. Hence, express each of the indefinite integrals

$$\int \frac{dx}{\sqrt{x^2 + 1}}, \qquad \int \frac{dx}{\sqrt{x^2 - 1}}, \qquad \int \frac{dx}{1 - x^2}$$

in terms of inverse hyperbolic functions.

6. Calculate the derivatives of the functions $\sinh^{-1}(x/a)$, $\cosh^{-1}(x/a)$, and $\tanh^{-1}(x/a)$ (where $a > 0$), and use your answers to provide formulas for certain indefinite integrals.

7. Simplify the following expressions:  (a)  $\sinh \ln x$,
(b) $\cosh \ln x$,   (c) $\tanh \ln x$,   (d) $\dfrac{\cosh \ln x + \sinh \ln x}{\cosh \ln x - \sinh \ln x}$.

8. Find the domain, range, and derivative of $\coth^{-1} x$ and sketch the graph of $y = \coth^{-1} x$.

9. Find the domain, range, and derivative of $\operatorname{sech}^{-1} x$ and sketch the graph of $y = \operatorname{sech}^{-1} x$.

10. Find the domain, range, and derivative of $\operatorname{csch}^{-1} x$, and sketch the graph of $y = \operatorname{csch}^{-1} x$.

11. Show that the functions $f_{A,B}(x) = Ae^{kx} + Be^{-kx}$ and $g_{C,D}(x) = C \cosh kx + D \sinh kx$ are both solutions of the differential equation $y'' - k^2 y = 0$. (They are both general solutions.) Express $f_{A,B}$ in terms of $g_{C,D}$, and express $g_{C,D}$ in terms of $f_{A,B}$.

12. Show that $h_{L,M}(x) = L \cosh k(x - a) + M \sinh k(x - a)$ is also a solution of the differential equation in the previous exercise. Express $h_{L,M}$ in terms of the function $f_{A,B}$ above.

13. Solve the initial-value problem $y'' - k^2 y = 0$,   $y(a) = y_0$, $y'(a) = v_0$. Express the solution in terms of the function $h_{L,M}$ of Exercise 12.

# Second-Order Linear DEs with Constant Coefficients

A differential equation of the form

$$a\,y'' + b\,y' + cy = 0, \qquad (*)$$

where $a$, $b$, and $c$ are constants and $a \neq 0$, is called a **second-order, linear, homogeneous** differential equation with constant coefficients. The *second-order* refers to the highest order derivative present; the terms *linear* and *homogeneous* refer to the fact that if $y_1(t)$ and $y_2(t)$ are two solutions of the equation, then so is $y(t) = Ay_1(t) + By_2(t)$ for any constants $A$ and $B$:

> If $ay_1''(t) + by_1'(t) + cy_1(t) = 0$ and $ay_2''(t) + by_2'(t) + cy_2(t) = 0$,
> and if $y(t) = Ay_1(t) + By_2(t)$, then $ay''(t) + by'(t) + cy(t) = 0$.

(See Section 11.1 for more details on this terminology.) Throughout this section we will assume that the independent variable in our functions is $t$ rather than $x$, so the prime ($'$) refers to the derivative $d/dt$. This is because in most applications of such equations the independent variable is time.

Equations of type $(*)$ arise in many applications of mathematics. In particular, they can model mechanical vibrations such as the motion of a mass suspended from an elastic spring or the current in certain electrical circuits. In most such applications the three constants $a$, $b$, and $c$ are positive, although sometimes we may have $b = 0$.

## Recipe for Solving $ay'' + by' + cy = 0$

In Section 6.4 we observed that the first-order, constant-coefficient equation $y' = ky$ has solution $y = Ce^{kt}$. Let us try to find a solution of equation $(*)$ having the form $y = e^{rt}$. Substituting this expression into equation $(*)$, we obtain

$$ar^2 e^{rt} + bre^{rt} + ce^{rt} = 0.$$

Since $e^{rt}$ is never zero, $y = e^{rt}$ will be a solution of the differential equation $(*)$ if and only if $r$ satisfies the quadratic **auxiliary equation**

$$ar^2 + br + c = 0, \qquad (**)$$

which has roots given by the quadratic formula,

$$r = \frac{-b \pm \sqrt{b^2 - 4ac}}{2a} = -\frac{b}{2a} \pm \frac{\sqrt{D}}{2a},$$

where $D = b^2 - 4ac$ is called the **discriminant** of the auxiliary equation $(**)$.

There are three cases to consider, depending on whether the discriminant $D$ is positive, zero, or negative.

**CASE I**   Suppose $D = b^2 - 4ac > 0$. Then the auxiliary equation has two different real roots, $r_1$ and $r_2$, given by

$$r_1 = \frac{-b - \sqrt{D}}{2a}, \qquad r_2 = \frac{-b + \sqrt{D}}{2a}.$$

(Sometimes these roots can be found easily by factoring the left side of the auxiliary equation.) In this case both $y = y_1(t) = e^{r_1 t}$ and $y = y_2(t) = e^{r_2 t}$ are solutions of the differential equation $(*)$, and neither is a multiple of the other. As noted above, the function

$$y = A e^{r_1 t} + B e^{r_2 t}$$

is also a solution for any choice of the constants $A$ and $B$. Since the differential equation is of second order and this solution involves two arbitrary constants, we suspect it is the **general solution**, that is, that every solution of the differential equation can be written in this form. Exercise 18 at the end of this section outlines a way to prove this.

**CASE II** Suppose $D = b^2 - 4ac = 0$. Then the auxiliary equation has two equal roots, $r_1 = r_2 = -b/(2a) = r$, say. Certainly, $y = e^{rt}$ is a solution of ($*$). We can find the general solution by letting $y = e^{rt}u(t)$ and calculating:

$$y' = e^{rt}\big(u'(t) + ru(t)\big),$$
$$y'' = e^{rt}\big(u''(t) + 2ru'(t) + r^2 u(t)\big).$$

Substituting these expressions into ($*$), we obtain

$$e^{rt}\big(au''(t) + (2ar + b)u'(t) + (ar^2 + br + c)u(t)\big) = 0.$$

Since $e^{rt} \neq 0$, $2ar + b = 0$ and $r$ satisfies ($**$), this equation reduces to $u''(t) = 0$, which has general solution $u(t) = A + Bt$ for arbitrary constants $A$ and $B$. Thus, the general solution of ($*$) in this case is

$$y = A e^{rt} + Bt\, e^{rt}.$$

**CASE III** Suppose $D = b^2 - 4ac < 0$. Then the auxiliary equation ($**$) has complex conjugate roots given by

$$r = \frac{-b \pm \sqrt{b^2 - 4ac}}{2a} = k \pm i\omega,$$

where $k = -b/(2a)$, $\omega = \sqrt{4ac - b^2}/(2a)$, and $i$ is the imaginary unit ($i^2 = -1$; see Appendix I). As in Case I, the functions $y_1^*(t) = e^{(k+i\omega)t}$ and $y_2^*(t) = e^{(k-i\omega)t}$ are two independent solutions of ($*$), but they are not real-valued. However, since

$$e^{ix} = \cos x + i \sin x \qquad \text{and} \qquad e^{-ix} = \cos x - i \sin x$$

We can find two real-valued functions that are solutions of ($*$) by suitably combining $y_1^*$ and $y_2^*$:

$$y_1(t) = \frac{1}{2} y_1^*(t) + \frac{1}{2} y_2^*(t) = e^{kt} \cos(\omega t),$$
$$y_2(t) = \frac{1}{2i} y_1^*(t) - \frac{1}{2i} y_2^*(t) = e^{kt} \sin(\omega t).$$

Therefore, the general solution of ($*$) in this case is

$$y = A e^{kt} \cos(\omega t) + B e^{kt} \sin(\omega t).$$

The following examples illustrate the recipe for solving ($*$) in each of the three cases.

---

**EXAMPLE 1** Find the general solution of
$$y'' + y' - 2y = 0.$$

**Solution** The auxiliary equation is $r^2 + r - 2 = 0$, or $(r + 2)(r - 1) = 0$. The auxiliary roots are $r_1 = -2$ and $r_2 = 1$, which are real and unequal. According to Case I, the general solution of the differential equation is

$$y = A e^{-2t} + B e^t.$$

---

**EXAMPLE 2**    Find the general solution of $y'' + 6y' + 9y = 0$.

*Solution*    The auxiliary equation is $r^2 + 6r + 9 = 0$, or $(r+3)^2 = 0$, which has equal roots $r = -3$. According to Case II, the general solution of the differential equation is

$$y = A e^{-3t} + Bt\, e^{-3t}.$$

---

**EXAMPLE 3**    Find the general solution of $y'' + 4y' + 13y = 0$.

*Solution*    The auxiliary equation is $r^2 + 4r + 13 = 0$, which has solutions

$$r = \frac{-4 \pm \sqrt{16 - 52}}{2} = \frac{-4 \pm \sqrt{-36}}{2} = -2 \pm 3i.$$

Thus, $k = -2$ and $\omega = 3$. According to Case III, the general solution of the given differential equation is

$$y = A e^{-2t} \cos(3t) + B e^{-2t} \sin(3t).$$

---

Initial-value problems for $ay'' + by' + cy = 0$ specify values for $y$ and $y'$ at an initial point. These values can be used to determine the values of the constants $A$ and $B$ in the general solution, so the initial-value problem has a unique solution.

---

**EXAMPLE 4**    Solve the initial-value problem

$$\begin{cases} y'' + 2y' + 2y = 0 \\ y(0) = 2 \\ y'(0) = -3. \end{cases}$$

*Solution*    The auxiliary equation is $r^2 + 2r + 2 = 0$, which has roots

$$r = \frac{-2 \pm \sqrt{4 - 8}}{2} = -1 \pm i.$$

Thus, Case III applies, with $k = -1$ and $\omega = 1$. Therefore, the differential equation has the general solution

$$y = A e^{-t} \cos t + B e^{-t} \sin t.$$

Also,

$$\begin{aligned} y' &= e^{-t}\left(-A \cos t - B \sin t - A \sin t + B \cos t\right) \\ &= (B - A) e^{-t} \cos t - (A + B) e^{-t} \sin t. \end{aligned}$$

Applying the initial conditions $y(0) = 2$ and $y'(0) = -3$, we obtain $A = 2$ and $B - A = -3$. Hence, $B = -1$ and the initial-value problem has the solution

$$y = 2 e^{-t} \cos t - e^{-t} \sin t.$$

---

## Simple Harmonic Motion

Many natural phenomena exhibit periodic behaviour. The swinging of a clock pendulum, the vibrating of a guitar string or drum membrane, the altitude of a rider on a rotating ferris wheel, the motion of an object floating in wavy seas, and the voltage produced by an alternating current generator are but a few examples where quantities depend on time in a periodic way. Being periodic, the circular functions sine and cosine provide a useful model for such behaviour.

It often happens that a quantity displaced from an equilibrium value experiences a restoring force that tends to move it back in the direction of its equilibrium. Besides the obvious examples of elastic motions in physics, one can imagine such a model applying, say, to a biological population in equilibrium with its food supply or the price of a commodity in an elastic economy where increasing price causes decreasing demand and hence decreasing price. In the simplest models, the restoring force is proportional to the amount of displacement from equilibrium. Such a force causes the quantity to oscillate sinusoidally; we say that it executes *simple harmonic motion.*

As a specific example, suppose a mass $m$ is suspended by an elastic spring so that it hangs unmoving in its equilibrium position with the upward spring tension force balancing the downward gravitational force on the mass. If the mass is displaced vertically by an amount $y$ from this position, the spring tension changes; the extra force exerted by the spring is directed to restore the mass to its equilibrium position. (See Figure 6.29.) This extra force is proportional to the displacement (Hooke's Law); its magnitude is $-ky$, where $k$ is a positive constant called the **spring constant**. Assuming the spring is weightless, this force imparts to the mass $m$ an acceleration $d^2y/dt^2$ that satisfies, by Newton's Second Law, $m(d^2y/dt^2) = -ky$ (mass × acceleration = force). Dividing this equation by $m$, we obtain the equation

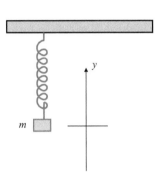

**Figure 6.29**

$$\frac{d^2y}{dt^2} + \omega^2 y = 0, \qquad \text{where} \quad \omega^2 = \frac{k}{m}.$$

The second-order differential equation

$$\frac{d^2y}{dt^2} + \omega^2 y = 0$$

is called the **equation of simple harmonic motion**. Its auxiliary equation, $r^2 + \omega^2 = 0$, has complex roots $r = \pm i\omega$, so it has general solution

$$y = A \cos \omega t + B \sin \omega t,$$

where $A$ and $B$ are arbitrary constants.

For any values of the constants $R$ and $t_0$, the function

$$y = R \cos\big(\omega(t - t_0)\big)$$

is also a general solution of the differential equation of simple harmonic motion. If we expand this formula using the addition formula for cosine, we get

$$y = R \cos \omega t_0 \cos \omega t + R \sin \omega t_0 \sin \omega t$$
$$= A \cos \omega t + B \sin \omega t,$$

where

$$A = R \cos(\omega t_0), \qquad\qquad B = R \sin(\omega t_0),$$
$$R^2 = A^2 + B^2, \qquad\qquad \tan(\omega t_0) = B/A.$$

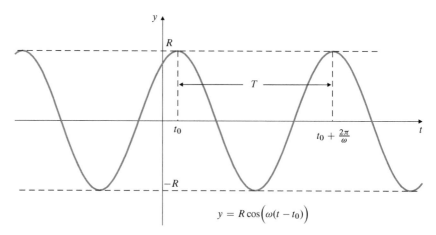

$$y = R\cos\big(\omega(t - t_0)\big)$$

Figure 6.30   Simple harmonic motion

The constants $A$ and $B$ are related to the position $y_0$ and the velocity $v_0$ of the mass $m$ at time $t = 0$:

$$y_0 = y(0) = A\cos 0 + B\sin 0 = A,$$
$$v_0 = y'(0) = -A\omega\sin 0 + B\omega\cos 0 = B\omega.$$

The constant $R = \sqrt{A^2 + B^2}$ is called the **amplitude** of the motion. Because $\cos x$ oscillates between $-1$ and $1$, the displacement $y$ varies between $-R$ and $R$. Note in Figure 6.30 that the graph of the displacement as a function of time is the curve $y = R\cos\omega t$ shifted $t_0$ units to the right. The number $t_0$ is called the **time-shift**. (The related quantity $\omega t_0$ is called a **phase-shift**.) The **period** of this curve is $T = 2\pi/\omega$; it is the time interval between consecutive instants when the mass is at the same height moving in the same direction. The reciprocal $1/T$ of the period is called the **frequency** of the motion. It is usually measured in Hertz (Hz), that is, cycles per second. The quantity $\omega = 2\pi/T$ is called the **circular frequency**. It is measured in radians per second since 1 cycle = 1 revolution = $2\pi$ radians.

**EXAMPLE 5**   Solve the initial-value problem

$$\begin{cases} y'' + 16y = 0 \\ y(0) = -6 \\ y'(0) = 32. \end{cases}$$

Find the amplitude, frequency, and period of the solution.

*Solution*   Here, $\omega^2 = 16$, so $\omega = 4$. The solution is of the form

$$y = A\cos(4t) + B\sin(4t).$$

Since $y(0) = -6$, we have $A = -6$. Also, $y'(t) = -4A\sin(4t) + 4B\cos(4t)$. Since $y'(0) = 32$, we have $4B = 32$, or $B = 8$. Thus, the solution is

$$y = -6\cos(4t) + 8\sin(4t).$$

The amplitude is $\sqrt{(-6)^2 + 8^2} = 10$, the frequency is $\omega/(2\pi) \approx 0.637\,\text{Hz}$, and the period is $2\pi/\omega \approx 1.57$ s.

**EXAMPLE 6**   **(Spring-mass problem)**  Suppose that a 100 g mass is suspended from a spring and that a force of $3 \times 10^4$ dynes ($3 \times 10^4$ g-cm/s$^2$) is required to produce a displacement from equilibrium of 1/3 cm. At time $t = 0$ the mass is pulled down 2 cm below equilibrium and flicked upward with a velocity of 60 cm/s. Find its subsequent displacement at any time $t > 0$. Find the frequency, period, amplitude, and time-shift of the motion. Express the position of the mass at time $t$ in terms of the amplitude and the time-shift.

***Solution***   The spring constant $k$ is determined from Hooke's Law, $F = -ky$. Here $F = -3 \times 10^4$ g-cm/s$^2$ is the force of the spring on the mass displaced 1/3 cm:

$$-3 \times 10^4 = -\frac{1}{3}k,$$

so $k = 9 \times 10^4$ g/s$^2$. Hence, the circular frequency is $\omega = \sqrt{k/m} = 30$ rad/s, the frequency is $\omega/2\pi = 15/\pi \approx 4.77$ Hz, and the period is $2\pi/\omega \approx 0.209$ s.

Since the displacement at time $t = 0$ is $y_0 = -2$ and the velocity at that time is $v_0 = 60$, the subsequent displacement is $y = A\cos(30t) + B\sin(30t)$, where $A = y_0 = -2$ and $B = v_0/\omega = 60/30 = 2$. Thus,

$$y = -2\cos(30t) + 2\sin(30t), \qquad (y \text{ in cm}, t \text{ in seconds}).$$

The amplitude of the motion is $R = \sqrt{(-2)^2 + 2^2} = 2\sqrt{2} \approx 2.83$ cm. The time-shift $t_0$ must satisfy

$$-2 = A = R\cos(\omega t_0) = 2\sqrt{2}\cos(30t_0),$$
$$2 = B = R\sin(\omega t_0) = 2\sqrt{2}\sin(30t_0),$$

so $\sin(30t_0) = 1/\sqrt{2} = -\cos(30t_0)$. Hence the phase-shift is $30t_0 = 3\pi/4$ radians, and the time-shift is $t_0 = \pi/40 \approx 0.0785$ s. The position of the mass at time $t > 0$ is also given by

$$y = 2\sqrt{2}\cos\left[30\left(t - \frac{\pi}{40}\right)\right].$$

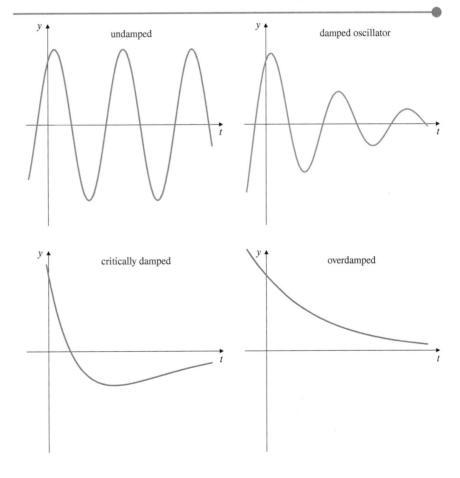

Figure 6.31
Undamped oscillator ($b = 0$)
Damped oscillator ($b > 0, b^2 < 4ac$)
Critically damped case ($b > 0, b^2 = 4ac$)
Overdamped case ($b > 0, b^2 > 4ac$)

## Damped Harmonic Motion

If $a$ and $c$ are positive and $b = 0$, then equation

$$ay'' + by' + cy = 0$$

is the differential equation of simple harmonic motion and has oscillatory solutions of fixed amplitude as shown above. If $a > 0$, $b > 0$, and $c > 0$, then the roots of the auxiliary equation are either negative real numbers or, if $b^2 < 4ac$, complex numbers $k \pm i\omega$ with negative real parts $k = -b/(2a)$ (Case III). In this latter case the solutions still oscillate, but the amplitude diminishes exponentially as $t \to \infty$ because of the factor $e^{kt} = e^{-(b/2a)t}$. (See Exercise 17 below.) A system whose behaviour is modelled by such an equation is said to exhibit **damped harmonic motion**. If $b^2 = 4ac$ (Case II), the system is said to be **critically damped**, and if $b^2 > 4ac$ (Case I), it is **overdamped**. In these cases the behaviour is no longer oscillatory. (See Figure 6.31. Imagine a mass suspended by a spring in a jar of oil.)

## EXERCISES 6.7

In Exercises 1–12, find the general solutions for the given second-order equations.

**1.** $y'' + 7y' + 10y = 0$

**2.** $y'' - 2y' - 3y = 0$

**3.** $y'' + 2y' = 0$

**4.** $4y'' - 4y' - 3y = 0$

**5.** $y'' + 8y' + 16y = 0$

**6.** $y'' - 2y' + y = 0$

**7.** $y'' - 6y' + 10y = 0$

**8.** $9y'' + 6y' + y = 0$

**9.** $y'' + 2y' + 5y = 0$

**10.** $y'' - 4y' + 5y = 0$

**11.** $y'' + 2y' + 3y = 0$

**12.** $y'' + y' + y = 0$

In Exercises 13–15, solve the given initial-value problems.

**13.** $\begin{cases} 2y'' + 5y' - 3y = 0 \\ y(0) = 1 \\ y'(0) = 0. \end{cases}$

**14.** $\begin{cases} y'' + 10y' + 25y = 0 \\ y(1) = 0 \\ y'(1) = 2. \end{cases}$

**15.** $\begin{cases} y'' + 4y' + 5y = 0 \\ y(0) = 2 \\ y'(0) = 2. \end{cases}$

**16.** Show that if $\epsilon \neq 0$, the function $y_\epsilon(t) = \dfrac{e^{(1+\epsilon)t} - e^t}{\epsilon}$ satisfies the equation $y'' - (2 + \epsilon)y' + (1 + \epsilon)y = 0$. Calculate $y(t) = \lim_{\epsilon \to 0} y_\epsilon(t)$ and verify that, as expected, it is a solution of $y'' - 2y' + y = 0$.

**17.** If $a > 0$, $b > 0$, and $c > 0$, prove that all solutions of the differential equation $ay'' + by' + cy = 0$ satisfy $\lim_{t \to \infty} y(t) = 0$.

**18.** Prove that the solution given in the discussion of Case I, namely, $y = A e^{r_1 t} + B e^{r_2 t}$, is the general solution for that case as follows: First, let $y = e^{r_1 t}u$ and show that $u$ satisfies the equation

$$u'' - (r_2 - r_1)u' = 0.$$

Then let $v = u'$, so that $v$ must satisfy $v' = (r_2 - r_1)v$. The general solution of this equation is $v = C e^{(r_2 - r_1)t}$, as shown in the discussion of the equation $y' = ky$ in Section 6.4. Hence, find $u$ and $y$.

**Simple harmonic motion**

Exercises 19–22 all refer to the differential equation of simple harmonic motion:

$$\frac{d^2 y}{dt^2} + \omega^2 y = 0, \qquad (\omega \neq 0). \qquad (\dagger)$$

Together they show that $y = A \cos \omega t + B \sin \omega t$ is a *general solution* of this equation, that is, every solution is of this form for some choice of the constants $A$ and $B$.

**19.** Show that $y = A \cos \omega t + B \sin \omega t$ is a solution of $(\dagger)$.

**20.** If $f(t)$ is any solution of $(\dagger)$, show that $\omega^2 (f(t))^2 + (f'(t))^2$ is constant.

**21.** If $g(t)$ is a solution of $(\dagger)$ satisfying $g(0) = g'(0) = 0$, show that $g(t) = 0$ for all $t$.

**22.** Suppose that $f(t)$ is any solution of the differential equation $(\dagger)$. Show that $f(t) = A \cos \omega t + B \sin \omega t$, where $A = f(0)$ and $B\omega = f'(0)$.
(*Hint:* Let $g(t) = f(t) - A \cos \omega t - B \sin \omega t$.)

**23.** If $b^2 - 4ac < 0$, show that the substitution $y = e^{kt}u(t)$, where $k = -b/(2a)$, transforms $ay'' + by' + cy = 0$ into the equation $u'' + \omega^2 u = 0$, where $\omega^2 = (4ac - b^2)/(4a^2)$. Together with the result of Exercise 22, this confirms the recipe for Case III, in case you didn't feel comfortable with the complex number argument given in the text.

In Exercises 24–25, solve the given initial-value problems. For each problem determine the circular frequency, the frequency, the period, and the amplitude of the solution.

**24.** $\begin{cases} y'' + 4y = 0 \\ y(0) = 2 \\ y'(0) = -5. \end{cases}$

**25.** $\begin{cases} y'' + 100y = 0 \\ y(0) = 0 \\ y'(0) = 3. \end{cases}$

**26.** Show that $y = \alpha \cos(\omega(t - c)) + \beta \sin(\omega(t - c))$ is a solution of the differential equation $y'' + \omega^2 y = 0$, and that it satisfies $y(c) = \alpha$ and $y'(c) = \beta\omega$. Express the solution in the form $y = A \cos(\omega t) + B \sin(\omega t)$ for certain values of the constants $A$ and $B$ depending on $\alpha$, $\beta$, $c$, and $\omega$.

**27.** Solve $\begin{cases} y'' + y = 0 \\ y(2) = 3 \\ y'(2) = -4. \end{cases}$

**28.** Solve $\begin{cases} y'' + \omega^2 y = 0 \\ y(a) = A \\ y'(a) = B. \end{cases}$

**29.** What mass should be suspended from the spring in Example 6 to provide a system whose natural frequency of oscillation is 10 Hz? Find the displacement of such a mass from its equilibrium position $t$ s after it is pulled down 1 cm from equilibrium and flicked upward with a speed of 2 cm/s. What is the amplitude of this motion?

**30.** A mass of 400 g suspended from a certain elastic spring will oscillate with a frequency of 24 Hz. What would be the frequency if the 400 g mass were replaced with a 900 g mass? a 100 g mass?

**31.** Show that if $t_0$, $A$, and $B$ are constants and $k = -b/(2a)$ and $\omega = \sqrt{4ac - b^2}/(2a)$, then

$$y = e^{kt}\left[A\cos\left(\omega(t - t_0)\right) + B\sin\left(\omega(t - t_0)\right)\right]$$

is an alternative to the general solution of the equation $ay'' + by' + cy = 0$ for Case III ($b^2 - 4ac < 0$). This form of the general solution is useful for solving initial-value problems where $y(t_0)$ and $y'(t_0)$ are specified.

**32.** Show that if $t_0$, $A$, and $B$ are constants and $k = -b/(2a)$ and $\omega = \sqrt{b^2 - 4ac}/(2a)$, then

$$y = e^{kt}\left[A\cosh\left(\omega(t - t_0)\right) + B\sinh\left(\omega(t - t_0)\right)\right]$$

is an alternative to the general solution of the equation $ay'' + by' + cy = 0$ for Case I ($b^2 - 4ac > 0$). This form of the general solution is useful for solving initial-value problems where $y(t_0)$ and $y'(t_0)$ are specified.

Use the forms of solution provided by the previous two exercises to solve the initial-value problems in Exercises 33–34.

**33.** $\begin{cases} y'' + 2y' + 5y = 0 \\ y(3) = 2 \\ y'(3) = 0. \end{cases}$

**34.** $\begin{cases} y'' + 4y' + 3y = 0 \\ y(3) = 1 \\ y'(3) = 0. \end{cases}$

**35.** By using the change of dependent variable $u(x) = c - k^2 y(x)$, solve the initial-value problem

$$\begin{cases} y''(x) = c - k^2 y(x) \\ y(0) = a \\ y'(0) = b. \end{cases}$$

**36.** A mass is attached to a spring mounted horizontally so the mass can slide along the top of a table. With a suitable choice of units, the position $x(t)$ of the mass at time $t$ is governed by the differential equation

$$x'' = -x + F,$$

where the $-x$ term is due to the elasticity of the spring, and the $F$ is due to the friction of the mass with the table. The frictional force should be constant in magnitude and directed opposite to the velocity of the mass when the mass is moving. When the mass is stopped, the friction should be constant and opposed to the spring force unless the spring force has the smaller magnitude, in which case the friction force should just cancel the spring force and the mass should remain at rest thereafter. For this problem, let the magnitude of the friction force be 1/5. Accordingly,

$$F = \begin{cases} -\dfrac{1}{5} & \text{if } x' > 0 \text{ or if } x' = 0 \text{ and } x < -\dfrac{1}{5} \\ \dfrac{1}{5} & \text{if } x' < 0 \text{ or if } x' = 0 \text{ and } x > \dfrac{1}{5} \\ x & \text{if } x' = 0 \text{ and } |x| \le \dfrac{1}{5}. \end{cases}$$

Find the position $x(t)$ of the mass at all times $t > 0$ if $x(0) = 1$ and $x'(0) = 0$.

# CHAPTER REVIEW

## Key Ideas

- State the laws of exponents.
- State the laws of logarithms.
- What is the significance of the number $e$?
- What do the following statements and phrases mean?
  - $f$ is one-to-one.
  - $f$ is invertible.
  - Function $f^{-1}$ is the inverse of function $f$.
  - $a^b = c$
  - $\log_a b = c$
  - the natural logarithm of $x$
  - logarithmic differentiation
  - the half-life of a varying quantity
  - The quantity $y$ exhibits exponential growth.
  - The quantity $y$ exhibits logistic growth.
  - $y = \sin^{-1} x$
  - $y = \tan^{-1} x$
  - The quantity $y$ exhibits simple harmonic motion.
  - The quantity $y$ exhibits damped harmonic motion.
- Define the functions $\sinh x$, $\cosh x$, and $\tanh x$.
- What kinds of functions satisfy second-order differential equations with constant coefficients?

## Review Exercises

**1.** If $f(x) = 3x + x^3$, show that $f$ has an inverse and find the slope of $y = f^{-1}(x)$ at $x = 0$.

**2.** Let $f(x) = \sec^2 x \tan x$. Show that $f$ is increasing on the interval $(-\pi/2, \pi/2)$ and, hence, one-to-one and invertible there. What is the domain of $f^{-1}$? Find $(f^{-1})'(2)$. *Hint:* $f(\pi/4) = 2$.

Exercises 3–5 refer to the function $f(x) = x e^{-x^2}$.

**3.** Find $\lim_{x \to \infty} f(x)$ and $\lim_{x \to -\infty} f(x)$.

**4.** On what intervals is $f$ increasing? decreasing?

**5.** What are the maximum and minimum values of $f(x)$?

**6.** Find the points on the graph of $y = e^{-x} \sin x$, $(0 \le x \le 2\pi)$, where the graph has a horizontal tangent line.

**7.** Suppose that a function $f(x)$ satisfies $f'(x) = x f(x)$ for all real $x$, and $f(2) = 3$. Calculate the derivative of $f(x)/e^{x^2/2}$, and use the result to help you find $f(x)$ explicitly.

**8.** A lump of modelling clay is being rolled out so that it maintains the shape of a circular cylinder. If the length is increasing at a rate proportional to itself, show that the radius is decreasing at a rate proportional to itself.

**9.** (a) What nominal interest rate, compounded continuously, will cause an investment to double in 5 years?

    (b) By about how many days will the doubling time in part (a) increase if the nominal interest rate drops by 0.5%?

**10.** (A poor man's natural logarithm)

    (a) Show that if $a > 0$, then

$$\lim_{h \to 0} \frac{a^h - 1}{h} = \ln a.$$

    Hence, show that

$$\lim_{n \to \infty} n(a^{1/n} - 1) = \ln a.$$

    (b) Most calculators, even nonscientific ones, have a square root key. If $n$ is a power of 2, say $n = 2^k$, then $a^{1/n}$ can be calculated by entering $a$ and hitting the square root key $k$ times:

$$a^{1/2^k} = \sqrt{\sqrt{\cdots \sqrt{a}}} \quad (k \text{ square roots}).$$

    Then you can subtract 1 and multiply by $n$ to get an approximation for $\ln a$. Use $n = 2^{10} = 1024$ and $n = 2^{11} = 2048$ to find approximations for $\ln 2$. Based on the agreement of these two approximations, quote a value of $\ln 2$ to as many decimal places as you feel justified.

**11.** A nonconstant function $f$ satisfies

$$\frac{d}{dx}\left(f(x)\right)^2 = \left(f'(x)\right)^2$$

for all $x$. If $f(0) = 1$, find $f(x)$.

**12.** If $f(x) = (\ln x)/x$, show that $f'(x) > 0$ for $0 < x < e$ and $f'(x) < 0$ for $x > e$, so that $f(x)$ has a maximum value at $x = e$. Use this to show that $e^{\pi} > \pi^e$.

**13.** Find an equation of a straight line that passes through the origin and is tangent to the curve $y = x^x$.

**14.** (a) Find $x \ne 2$ such that $\dfrac{\ln x}{x} = \dfrac{\ln 2}{2}$.

    (b) Find $b > 1$ such that there is *no* $x \ne b$ with $\dfrac{\ln x}{x} = \dfrac{\ln b}{b}$.

**15.** Investment account A bears simple interest at a certain rate. Investment account B bears interest at the same nominal rate but compounded instantaneously. If $1,000 is invested in each account, B produces $10 more in interest after one year than does A. Find the nominal rate both accounts use.

**16.** Express each of the functions $\cos^{-1} x$, $\cot^{-1} x$, and $\csc^{-1} x$ in terms of $\tan^{-1}$.

**17.** Express each of the functions $\cos^{-1} x$, $\cot^{-1} x$, and $\csc^{-1} x$ in terms of $\sin^{-1}$.

**18.** (A warming problem) A bottle of milk at $5\,°C$ is removed from a refrigerator into a room maintained at $20\,°C$. After 12 min the temperature of the milk is $12\,°C$. How much longer will it take for the milk to warm up to $18\,°C$?

**19.** (A cooling problem) A kettle of hot water at $96\,°C$ is allowed to sit in an air-conditioned room. The water cools to $60\,°C$ in 10 min and then to $40\,°C$ in another 10 min. What is the temperature of the room?

**20.** Show that $e^x > 1 + x$ if $x \ne 0$.

**21.** Use mathematical induction to show that

$$e^x > 1 + x + \frac{x^2}{2!} + \cdots + \frac{x^n}{n!}$$

if $x > 0$ and $n$ is any positive integer.

### Challenging Problems

**1.** (a) Show that the function $f(x) = x^x$ is strictly increasing on $[e^{-1}, \infty)$.

    (b) If $g$ is the inverse function to $f$ of part (a), show that

$$\lim_{y \to \infty} \frac{g(y) \ln(\ln y)}{\ln y} = 1$$

    *Hint:* Start with the equation $y = x^x$ and take the ln of both sides twice.

**Two models for incorporating air resistance into the analysis of the motion of a falling body**

**2.** (Air resistance proportional to speed) An object falls under gravity near the surface of the earth, and its motion is impeded by air resistance proportional to its speed. Its velocity $v$ therefore satisfies the equation

$$\frac{dv}{dt} = -g - kv, \tag{*}$$

where $k$ is a positive constant depending on such factors as the shape and density of the object and the density of the air.

    (a) Find the velocity of the object as a function of time $t$, given that it was $v_0$ at $t = 0$.

    (b) Find the limiting velocity $\lim_{t \to \infty} v(t)$. Observe that this can be done either directly from (*) or from the solution found in (a).

    (c) If the object was at height $y_0$ at time $t = 0$, find its height $y(t)$ at any time during its fall.

**3.** (Air resistance proportional to the square of speed) Under certain conditions a better model for the effect of air resistance on a moving object is one where the resistance is proportional to the square of the speed. For an object falling under constant gravitational acceleration $g$, the equation of motion is

$$\frac{dv}{dt} = -g - kv|v|,$$

where $k > 0$. Note that $v|v|$ is used instead of $v^2$ to ensure that the resistance is always in the opposite direction to the velocity. For an object falling from rest at time $t = 0$, we have $v(0) = 0$ and $v(t) < 0$ for $t > 0$, so the equation of motion becomes

$$\frac{dv}{dt} = -g + kv^2.$$

We are not (yet) in a position to solve this equation. However, we can verify its solution.

(a) Verify that the velocity is given for $t \geq 0$ by

$$v(t) = \sqrt{\frac{g}{k}}\, \frac{1 - e^{2t\sqrt{gk}}}{1 + e^{2t\sqrt{gk}}}.$$

(b) What is the limiting velocity $\lim_{t \to \infty} v(t)$?

(c) Also verify that if the falling object was at height $y_0$ at time $t = 0$, then its height at subsequent times during its fall is given by

$$y(t) = y_0 + \sqrt{\frac{g}{k}}\, t - \frac{1}{k} \ln\left(\frac{1 + e^{2t\sqrt{gk}}}{2}\right).$$

✳ 4. (**A model for the spread of a new technology**) When a new and superior technology is introduced, the percentage $p$ of potential clients that adopt it might be expected to increase logistically with time. However, even newer technologies are continually being introduced, so adoption of a particular one will fall off exponentially over time. The following model exhibits this behaviour:

$$\frac{dp}{dt} = kp\left(1 - \frac{p}{e^{-bt}M}\right).$$

This DE suggests that the growth in $p$ is logistic but that the asymptotic limit is not a constant but rather $e^{-bt}M$, which decreases exponentially with time.

(a) Show that the change of variable $p = e^{-bt}y(t)$ transforms the equation above into a standard logistic equation, and hence find an explicit formula for $p(t)$ given that $p(0) = p_0$. It will be necessary to assume that $M < 100k/(b+k)$ to ensure that $p(t) < 100$.

(b) If $k = 10$, $b = 1$, $M = 90$, and $p_0 = 1$, how large will $p(t)$ become before it starts to decrease?

# CHAPTER 7

# More Applications of Differentiation

## 7.1 Related Rates

When two or more quantities that change with time are linked by an equation, that equation can be differentiated with respect to time to produce an equation linking the rates of change of the quantities. Any one of these rates may then be determined when the others, and the values of the quantities themselves, are known. We will consider a couple of examples before formulating a list of procedures for dealing with such problems.

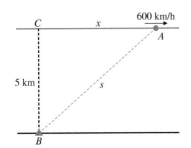

**Figure 7.1**

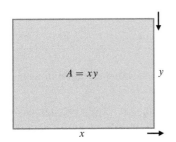

**Figure 7.2**    Rectangle with sides changing

<hr>

**EXAMPLE 1**    An aircraft is flying horizontally at a speed of 600 km/h. How fast is the distance between the aircraft and a radio beacon increasing 1 min after the aircraft passes 5 km directly above the beacon?

***Solution***    A diagram is useful here; see Figure 7.1. Let $C$ be the point on the aircraft's path directly above the beacon $B$.    Let $A$ be the position of the aircraft $t$ min after it is at $C$, and let $x$ and $s$ be the distances $CA$ and $BA$, respectively. From the right triangle $BCA$ we have

$$s^2 = x^2 + 5^2.$$

We differentiate this equation implicitly with respect to $t$ to obtain

$$2s\frac{ds}{dt} = 2x\frac{dx}{dt}.$$

We are given that $dx/dt = 600$ km/h $= 10$ km/min.  Therefore, $x = 10$ km at time $t = 1$ min. At that time $s = \sqrt{10^2 + 5^2} = 5\sqrt{5}$ km and is increasing at the rate

$$\frac{ds}{dt} = \frac{x}{s}\frac{dx}{dt} = \frac{10}{5\sqrt{5}}(600) = \frac{1,200}{\sqrt{5}} \approx 536.7 \text{ km/h}.$$

One minute after the aircraft passes over the beacon, its distance from the beacon is increasing at about 537 km/h.

<hr>

**EXAMPLE 2**    How fast is the area of a rectangle changing if one side is 10 cm long and is increasing at a rate of 2 cm/s and the other side is 8 cm long and is decreasing at a rate of 3 cm/s?

***Solution***    Let the lengths of the sides of the rectangle at time $t$ be $x$ cm and $y$ cm, respectively.  Thus, the area at time $t$ is $A = xy$ cm$^2$.  (See Figure 7.2.)  We want to know the value of $dA/dt$ when $x = 10$ and $y = 8$, given that $dx/dt = 2$ and $dy/dt = -3$.  (Note the negative sign to indicate that $y$ is decreasing.)  Since all the quantities in the equation $A = xy$ are functions of time, we can differentiate that equation implicitly with respect to time and obtain

$$\left.\frac{dA}{dt}\right|_{\substack{x=10\\y=8}} = \left.\left(\frac{dx}{dt}y + x\frac{dy}{dt}\right)\right|_{\substack{x=10\\y=8}} = 2(8) + 10(-3) = -14.$$

At the time in question, the area of the rectangle is decreasing at a rate of 14 cm$^2$/s.

<hr>

## Procedures for Related-Rates Problems

In view of these examples we can formulate a few general procedures for dealing with related-rates problems.

**How to solve related-rates problems**

1. Read the problem very carefully. Try to understand the relationships between the variable quantities. What is given? What is to be found?

2. Make a sketch if appropriate.

3. Define any symbols you want to use that are not defined in the statement of the problem. Express given and required quantities and rates in terms of these symbols.

4. From a careful reading of the problem or consideration of the sketch, identify one or more equations linking the variable quantities. (You will need as many equations as quantities or rates to be found in the problem.)

5. Differentiate the equation(s) implicitly with respect to time, regarding all variable quantities as functions of time. You can manipulate the equation(s) algebraically before the differentiation is performed (for instance, you could solve for the quantities whose rates are to be found), but it is usually easier to differentiate the equations as they are originally obtained and solve for the desired items later.

6. Substitute any given values for the quantities and their rates, then solve the resulting equation(s) for the unknown quantities and rates.

7. Make a concluding statement answering the question asked. Is your answer reasonable? If not, check back through your solution to see what went wrong.

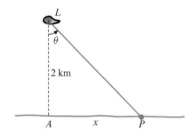

Figure 7.3

**EXAMPLE 3**   A lighthouse $L$ is located on a small island 2 km from the nearest point $A$ on a long, straight shoreline. If the lighthouse lamp rotates at 3 revolutions per minute, how fast is the illuminated spot $P$ on the shoreline moving along the shoreline when it is 4 km from $A$?

**Solution**   Referring to Figure 7.3, let $x$ be the distance $AP$, and let $\theta$ be the angle $PLA$. Then $x = 2\tan\theta$ and

$$\frac{dx}{dt} = 2\sec^2\theta\,\frac{d\theta}{dt}.$$

Now

$$\frac{d\theta}{dt} = (3\text{ rev/min})(2\pi\text{ radians/rev}) = 6\pi\text{ radians/min}.$$

When $x = 4$, we have $\tan\theta = 2$ and $\sec^2\theta = 1 + \tan^2\theta = 5$. Thus,

$$\frac{dx}{dt} = (2)(5)(6\pi) = 60\pi \approx 188.5.$$

The spot of light is moving along the shoreline at a rate of about 189 km/min when it is 4 km from $A$.

(Note that it was essential to convert the rate of change of $\theta$ from revolutions per minute to radians per minute. If $\theta$ were not measured in radians we could not assert that $(d/d\theta)\tan\theta = \sec^2\theta$.)

**EXAMPLE 4**   A leaky water tank is in the shape of an inverted right circular cone with depth 5 m and top radius 2 m. When the water in the tank is 4 m deep, it is leaking out at a rate of 1/12 m³/min. How fast is the water level in the tank dropping at that time?

*Solution*   Let $r$ and $h$ denote the surface radius and depth of water in the tank at time $t$ (both measured in metres). Thus, the volume $V$ (in cubic metres) of water in the tank at time $t$ is

$$V = \frac{1}{3} \pi r^2 h.$$

Using similar triangles (see Figure 7.4), we can find a relationship between $r$ and $h$:

$$\frac{r}{h} = \frac{2}{5}, \quad \text{so} \quad r = \frac{2h}{5} \quad \text{and} \quad V = \frac{1}{3}\pi \left(\frac{2h}{5}\right)^2 h = \frac{4\pi}{75}h^3.$$

Differentiating this equation with respect to $t$, we obtain

$$\frac{dV}{dt} = \frac{4\pi}{25} h^2 \frac{dh}{dt}.$$

Since $dV/dt = -1/12$ when $h = 4$, we have

$$\frac{-1}{12} = \frac{4\pi}{25}(4^2)\frac{dh}{dt}, \quad \text{so} \quad \frac{dh}{dt} = -\frac{25}{768\pi}.$$

When the water in the tank is 4 m deep, its level is dropping at a rate of $25/(768\pi)$ m/min, or about 1.036 cm/min.

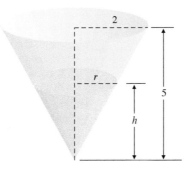

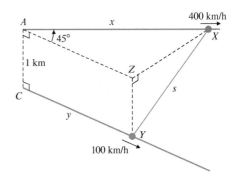

**Figure 7.4**   The conical tank of Example 4          **Figure 7.5**   Aircraft and car paths in Example 5

---

**EXAMPLE 5**   At a certain instant an aircraft flying due east at 400 km/h passes directly over a car travelling due southeast at 100 km/h on a straight, level road. If the aircraft is flying at an altitude of 1 km, how fast is the distance between the aircraft and the car increasing 36 s after the aircraft passes directly over the car?

*Solution*   A good diagram is essential here. See Figure 7.5. Let time $t$ be measured in hours from the time the aircraft was at position $A$ directly above the car at position $C$. Let $X$ and $Y$ be the positions of the aircraft and the car, respectively, at time $t$. Let $x$ be the distance $AX$, $y$ the distance $CY$, and $s$ the distance $XY$, all measured in kilometres. Let $Z$ be the point 1 km above $Y$. Since angle $XAZ = 45°$, the Pythagorean Theorem and Cosine Law yield

$$s^2 = 1 + (ZX)^2 = 1 + x^2 + y^2 - 2xy\cos 45°$$
$$= 1 + x^2 + y^2 - \sqrt{2}\,xy.$$

Thus,

$$2s\frac{ds}{dt} = 2x\frac{dx}{dt} + 2y\frac{dy}{dt} - \sqrt{2}\frac{dx}{dt}y - \sqrt{2}x\frac{dy}{dt}$$
$$= 400(2x - \sqrt{2}y) + 100(2y - \sqrt{2}x),$$

since $dx/dt = 400$ and $dy/dt = 100$. When $t = 1/100$ (i.e., 36 s after $t = 0$), we have $x = 4$ and $y = 1$. Hence,

$$s^2 = 1 + 16 + 1 - 4\sqrt{2} = 18 - 4\sqrt{2}$$
$$s \approx 3.5133.$$
$$\frac{ds}{dt} = \frac{1}{2s}\left(400(8 - \sqrt{2}) + 100(2 - 4\sqrt{2})\right) \approx 322.86.$$

The aircraft and the car are separating at a rate of about 323 km/h after 36 s. (Note that it was necessary to convert 36 s to hours in the solution. In general, all measurements should be in compatible units.)

# EXERCISES 7.1

1. Find the rate of change of the area of a square whose side is 8 cm long, if the side length is increasing at 2 cm/min.

2. The area of a square is decreasing at 2 ft$^2$/s. How fast is the side length changing when it is 8 ft?

3. A pebble dropped into a pond causes a circular ripple to expand outward from the point of impact. How fast is the area enclosed by the ripple increasing when the radius is 20 cm and is increasing at a rate of 4 cm/s?

4. The area of a circle is decreasing at a rate of 2 cm$^2$/min. How fast is the radius of the circle changing when the area is 100 cm$^2$?

5. The area of a circle is increasing at $1/3$ km$^2$/h. Express the rate of change of the radius of the circle as a function of (a) the radius $r$ and (b) the area $A$ of the circle.

6. At a certain instant the length of a rectangle is 16 m and the width is 12 m. The width is increasing at 3 m/s. How fast is the length changing if the area of the rectangle is not changing?

7. Air is being pumped into a spherical balloon. The volume of the balloon is increasing at a rate of 20 cm$^3$/s when the radius is 30 cm. How fast is the radius increasing at that time? (The volume of a ball of radius $r$ units is $V = \frac{4}{3}\pi r^3$ cubic units.)

8. When the diameter of a ball of ice is 6 cm, it is decreasing at a rate of 0.5 cm/h due to melting of the ice. How fast is the volume of the ice ball decreasing at that time?

9. How fast is the surface area of a cube changing when the volume of the cube is 64 cm$^3$ and is increasing at 2 cm$^3$/s?

10. The volume of a right circular cylinder is 60 cm$^3$ and is increasing at 2 cm$^3$/min at a time when the radius is 5 cm and is increasing at 1 cm/min. How fast is the height of the cylinder changing at that time?

11. How fast is the volume of a rectangular box changing when the length is 6 cm, the width is 5 cm, and the depth is 4 cm, if the length and depth are both increasing at a rate of 1 cm/s and the width is decreasing at a rate of 2 cm/s?

12. The area of a rectangle is increasing at a rate of 5 m$^2$/s while the length is increasing at a rate of 10 m/s. If the length is 20 m and the width is 16 m, how fast is the width changing?

13. A point moves on the curve $y = x^2$. How fast is $y$ changing when $x = -2$ and $x$ is decreasing at a rate of 3?

14. A point is moving to the right along the first-quadrant portion of the curve $x^2 y^3 = 72$. When the point has coordinates $(3, 2)$, its horizontal velocity is 2 units/s. What is its vertical velocity?

15. The point $P$ moves so that at time $t$ it is at the intersection of the curves $xy = t$ and $y = tx^2$. How fast is the distance of $P$ from the origin changing at time $t = 2$?

16. **(Radar guns)** A police officer is standing near a highway using a radar gun to catch speeders. (See Figure 7.6.) He aims the gun at a car that has just passed his position and, when the gun is pointing at an angle of $45°$ to the direction of the highway, notes that the distance between the car and the gun is increasing at a rate of 100 km/h. How fast is the car travelling?

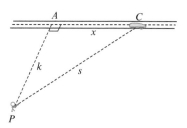

Figure 7.6

17. If the radar gun of Exercise 16 is aimed at a car travelling at 90 km/h along a straight road, what will its reading be when it is aimed making an angle of $30°$ with the road?

18. The top of a ladder 5 m long rests against a vertical wall. If the base of the ladder is being pulled away from the base of the wall at a rate of 1/3 m/s, how fast is the top of the ladder slipping down the wall when it is 3 m above the base of the wall?

19. A man 2 m tall walks toward a lamppost on level ground at a rate of 0.5 m/s. If the lamp is 5 m high on the post, how fast is the length of the man's shadow decreasing when he is 3 m from the post? How fast is the shadow of his head moving at that time?

20. A woman 6 ft tall is walking at 2 ft/s along a straight path on level ground. There is a lamppost 5 ft to the side of the path. A light 15 ft high on the lamppost casts the woman's shadow on the ground. How fast is the length of her shadow changing when the woman is 12 feet from the point on the path closest to the lamppost?

21. **(Cost of production)** It costs a coal mine owner $C each day to maintain a production of x tonnes of coal, where $C = 10,000 + 3x + x^2/8,000$. At what rate is the production increasing when it is 12,000 tonnes and the daily cost is increasing at $600 per day?

22. **(Distance between ships)** At 1:00 p.m. ship A is 25 km due north of ship B. If ship A is sailing west at a rate of 16 km/h and ship B is sailing south at 20 km/h, at what rate is the distance between the two ships changing at 1:30 p.m?

23. What is the first time after 3:00 p.m. that the hands of a clock are together?

24. **(Tracking a balloon)** A balloon released at point A rises vertically with a constant speed of 5 m/s. Point B is level with and 100 m distant from point A. How fast is the angle of elevation of the balloon at B changing when the balloon is 200 m above A?

25. Sawdust is falling onto a pile at a rate of 1/2 m³/min. If the pile maintains the shape of a right circular cone with height equal to half the diameter of its base, how fast is the height of the pile increasing when the pile is 3 m high?

26. **(Conical tank)** A water tank is in the shape of an inverted right circular cone with top radius 10 m and depth 8 m. Water is flowing in at a rate of 1/10 m³/min. How fast is the depth of water in the tank increasing when the water is 4 m deep?

27. **(Leaky tank)** Repeat Exercise 26 with the added assumption that water is leaking out of the bottom of the tank at a rate of $h^3/1,000$ m³/min when the depth of water in the tank is $h$ m. How full can the tank get in this case?

28. **(Another leaky tank)** Water is pouring into a leaky tank at a rate of 10 m³/h. The tank is a cone with vertex down, 9 m in depth and 6 m in diameter at the top. The surface of water in the tank is rising at a rate of 20 cm/h when the depth is 6 m. How fast is the water leaking out at that time?

29. **(Kite flying)** How fast must you let out line if the kite you are flying is 30 m high, 40 m horizontally away from you, and moving horizontally away from you at a rate of 10 m/min?

30. **(Ferris wheel)** You are on a Ferris wheel of diameter 20 m. It is rotating at 1 revolution per minute. How fast are you rising or falling when you are 6 m horizontally away from the vertical line passing through the centre of the wheel?

31. **(Distance between aircraft)** An aircraft is 144 km east of an airport and is travelling west at 200 km/h. At the same time, a second aircraft at the same altitude is 60 km north of the airport and travelling north at 150 km/h. How fast is the distance between the two aircraft changing?

32. **(Production rate)** If a truck factory employs $x$ workers and has daily operating expenses of $y, it can produce $P = (1/3)x^{0.6}y^{0.4}$ trucks per year. How fast are the daily expenses decreasing when they are $10,000 and the number of workers is 40, if the number of workers is increasing at 1 per day and production is remaining constant?

33. A lamp is located at point $(3, 0)$ in the $xy$-plane. An ant is crawling in the first quadrant of the plane and the lamp casts its shadow onto the $y$-axis. How fast is the ant's shadow moving along the $y$-axis when the ant is at position $(1, 2)$ and moving so that its $x$-coordinate is increasing at rate 1/3 units/s and its $y$-coordinate is decreasing at 1/4 units/s?

34. A straight highway and a straight canal intersect at right angles, the highway crossing over the canal on a bridge 20 m above the water. A boat travelling at 20 km/h passes under the bridge just as a car travelling at 80 km/h passes over it. How fast are the boat and car separating after one minute?

35. **(Filling a trough)** The cross section of a water trough is an equilateral triangle with top edge horizontal. If the trough is 10 m long and 30 cm deep, and if water is flowing in at a rate of 1/4 m³/min, how fast is the water level rising when the water is 20 cm deep at the deepest?

36. **(Draining a pool)** A rectangular swimming pool is 8 m wide and 20 m long. (See Figure 7.7.) Its bottom is a sloping plane, the depth increasing from 1 m at the shallow end to 3 m at the deep end. Water is draining out of the pool at a rate of 1 m³/min. How fast is the surface of the water falling when the depth of water at the deep end is (a) 2.5 m? (b) 1 m?

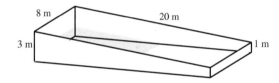

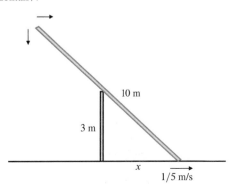

Figure 7.7

**!** 37. One end of a 10 m long ladder is on the ground. The ladder is supported partway along its length by resting on top of a 3 m high fence. (See Figure 7.8.) If the bottom of the ladder is 4 m from the base of the fence and is being dragged along the ground away from the fence at a rate of 1/5 m/s, how fast is the free top end of the ladder moving (a) vertically and (b) horizontally?

10 m

3 m

$x$

1/5 m/s

Figure 7.8

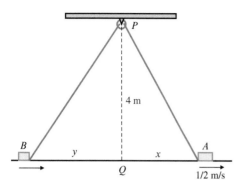

Figure 7.9

above a point $Q$ on the floor directly between the two crates. (See Figure 7.9.) If crate $A$ is 3 m from $Q$ and is being pulled directly away from $Q$ at a rate of 1/2 m/s, how fast is crate $B$ moving toward $Q$?

39. **(Tracking a rocket)** Shortly after launch, a rocket is 100 km high and 50 km downrange. If it is travelling at 4 km/s at an angle of $30°$ above the horizontal, how fast is its angle of elevation, as measured at the launch site, changing?

40. **(Shadow of a falling ball)** A lamp is 20 m high on a pole. At time $t = 0$ a ball is dropped from a point level with the lamp and 10 m away from it. The ball falls under gravity (its acceleration is 9.8 m/s$^2$) until it hits the ground. How fast is the shadow of the ball moving along the ground (a) 1 s after the ball is dropped? (b) just as the ball hits the ground?

41. **(Tracking a rocket)** A rocket blasts off at time $t = 0$ and climbs vertically with acceleration 10 m/s$^2$. The progress of the rocket is monitored by a tracking station located 2 km horizontally away from the launch pad. How fast is the tracking station antenna rotating upward 10 s after launch?

■ 38. Two crates, $A$ and $B$, are on the floor of a warehouse. The crates are joined by a rope 15 m long, each crate being hooked at floor level to an end of the rope. The rope is stretched tight and pulled over a pulley $P$ that is attached to a rafter 4 m

## 7.2  Finding Roots of Equations

Finding solutions (roots) of equations is an important mathematical problem to which calculus can make significant contributions. There are only a few general classes of equations of the form $f(x) = 0$ that we can solve exactly. These include **linear equations**:

$$ax + b = 0, \quad (a \neq 0) \qquad \Rightarrow \qquad x = -\frac{b}{a}$$

and **quadratic equations**:

$$ax^2 + bx + c = 0, \quad (a \neq 0) \qquad \Rightarrow \qquad x = \frac{-b \pm \sqrt{b^2 - 4ac}}{2a}.$$

Cubic and quartic (3rd- and 4th-degree polynomial) equations can also be solved, but the formulas are very complicated. We usually solve these and most other equations approximately by using numerical methods, often with the aid of a calculator or computer.

We discussed the Bisection Method for approximating a root of an equation $f(x) = 0$. That method uses the Intermediate-Value Theorem and depends only on the continuity of $f$ and our ability to find an interval $[x_1, x_2]$ that must contain the root because $f(x_1)$ and $f(x_2)$ have opposite signs. The method is rather slow; it requires between three and four iterations to gain one significant figure of precision in the root being approximated.

If we know that $f$ is more than just continuous, we can devise better (i.e., faster) methods for finding roots of $f(x) = 0$. We study two such methods in this section:

(a) **Fixed-Point Iteration**, which looks for solutions of an equation of the form $x = f(x)$. Such solutions are called **fixed points** of the function $f$.

(b) **Newton's Method**, which looks for solutions of the equation $f(x) = 0$ as fixed points of the function $g(x) = x - \dfrac{f(x)}{f'(x)}$, that is, points $x$ such that $x = g(x)$. This method is usually very efficient, but it requires that $f$ be differentiable.

Like the Bisection Method, both of these methods require that we have at the outset a rough idea of where a root can be found, and they generate sequences of approximations that get closer and closer to the root.

## Discrete Maps and Fixed-Point Iteration

A **discrete map** is an equation of the form

$$x_{n+1} = f(x_n), \qquad \text{for } n = 0, 1, 2, \ldots,$$

which generates a sequence of values $x_1, x_2, x_3, \ldots$, from a given starting value $x_0$. In certain circumstances this sequence of numbers will converge to a limit, $r = \lim_{n \to \infty} x_n$, in which case this limit will be a fixed point of $f$: $r = f(r)$. (For our purposes here, an intuitive understanding will suffice: $\lim_{n \to \infty} x_n = r$ if $|x_n - r|$ approaches 0 as $n \to \infty$.)

For certain kinds of functions $f$, we can solve the equation $f(r) = r$ by starting with an initial guess $x_0$ and calculating subsequent values of the discrete map until sufficient accuracy is achieved. This is the **Method of Fixed-Point Iteration**. Let us begin by investigating a simple example:

**EXAMPLE 1**  Find a root of the equation $\cos x = 5x$.

**Solution**  This equation is of the form $f(x) = x$, where $f(x) = \frac{1}{5} \cos x$. Since $\cos x$ is close to 1 for $x$ near 0, we see that $\frac{1}{5} \cos x$ will be close to $\frac{1}{5}$ when $x = \frac{1}{5}$. This suggests that a reasonable first guess at the fixed point is $x_0 = \frac{1}{5} = 0.2$. The values of subsequent approximations

$$x_1 = \frac{1}{5} \cos x_0, \quad x_2 = \frac{1}{5} \cos x_1, \quad x_3 = \frac{1}{5} \cos x_2, \ldots$$

are presented in Table 1. The root is $0.196\,164\,28$ to 8 decimal places.

Table 1.

| $n$ | $x_n$ |
|---|---|
| 0 | 0.2 |
| 1 | 0.196 013 32 |
| 2 | 0.196 170 16 |
| 3 | 0.196 164 05 |
| 4 | 0.196 164 29 |
| 5 | 0.196 164 28 |
| 6 | 0.196 164 28 |

Why did the method used in Example 1 work? Will it work for any function $f$? In order to answer these questions, examine the polygonal line in Figure 7.10. Starting at $x_0$ it goes vertically to the curve $y = f(x)$, the height there being $x_1$. Then it goes horizontally to the line $y = x$, meeting that line at a point whose $x$-coordinate must therefore also be $x_1$. Then the process repeats; the line goes vertically to the curve $y = f(x)$ and horizontally to $y = x$, arriving at $x = x_2$. The line continues in this way, "spiralling" closer and closer to the intersection of $y = f(x)$ and $y = x$. Each value of $x_n$ is closer to the fixed point $r$ than the previous value.

Now consider the function $f$ whose graph appears in Figure 7.11(a). If we try the same method there, starting with $x_0$, the polygonal line spirals outward, away from the root, and the resulting values $x_n$ will not "converge" to the root as they did in Example 1. To see why the method works for the function in Figure 7.10 but not for the function in Figure 7.11(a), observe the slopes of the two graphs $y = f(x)$ near the fixed point $r$. Both slopes are negative, but in Figure 7.10 the absolute value of the slope is less than 1 while the absolute value of the slope of $f$ in Figure 7.11(a) is greater than 1. Close consideration of the graphs should convince you that it is this fact that caused the points $x_n$ to get closer to $r$ in Figure 7.10 and farther from $r$ in Figure 7.11(a).

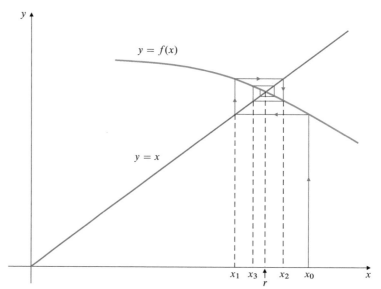

**Figure 7.10**    Iterations of $x_{n+1} = f(x_n)$ "spiral" toward the fixed point

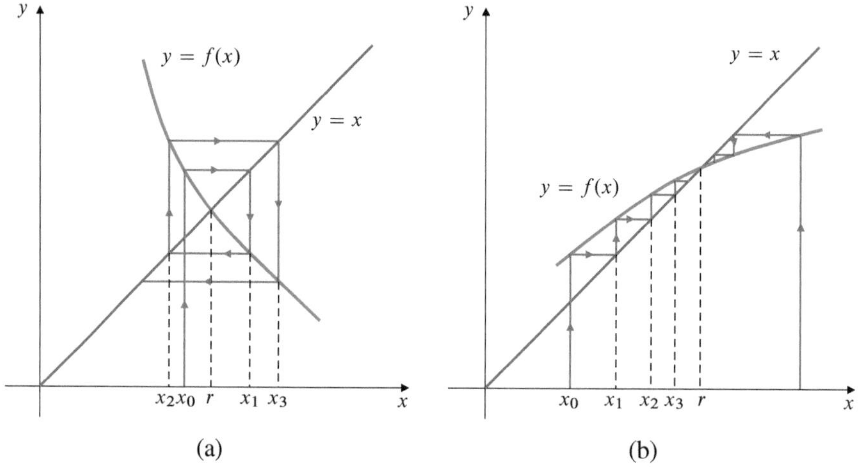

**Figure 7.11**

(a) A function $f$ for which the iterations $x_{n+1} = f(x_n)$ do not converge

(b) "Staircase" convergence to the fixed point

(a)

(b)

A third example, Figure 7.11(b), shows that the method can be expected to work for functions whose graphs have positive slope near the fixed point $r$, provided that the slope is less than 1. In this case the polygonal line forms a "staircase" rather than a "spiral," and the successive approximations $x_n$ increase toward the root if $x_0 < r$ and decrease toward it if $x_0 > r$.

**Remark**    Note that if $|f'(x)| > 1$ near a fixed point $r$ of $f$, you may still be able to find that fixed point by applying fixed-point iteration to $f^{-1}(x)$. Evidently $f^{-1}(r) = r$ if and only if $r = f(r)$.

The following theorem guarantees that the method of fixed-point iteration will work for a particular class of functions.

**THEOREM**

**1**

**A fixed-point theorem**

Suppose that $f$ is defined on an interval $I = [a, b]$ and satisfies the following two conditions:

(i) $f(x)$ belongs to $I$ whenever $x$ belongs to $I$ and

(ii) there exists a constant $K$ with $0 < K < 1$ such that for every $u$ and $v$ in $I$,

$$|f(u) - f(v)| \le K|u - v|.$$

Then $f$ has a unique fixed point $r$ in $I$, that is, $f(r) = r$, and starting with any number $x_0$ in $I$, the iterates

$$x_1 = f(x_0), \quad x_2 = f(x_1), \quad \ldots \quad \text{converge to } r.$$

You are invited to prove this theorem by a method outlined in Exercises 26 and 27 at the end of this section.

---

**EXAMPLE 2**  Show that if $0 < k < 1$, then $f(x) = k \cos x$ satisfies the conditions of Theorem 1 on the interval $I = [0, 1]$. Observe that if $k = 1/5$, the fixed point is that calculated in Example 1 above.

**Solution**  Since $0 < k < 1$, $f$ maps $I$ into $I$. If $u$ and $v$ are in $I$, then the Mean-Value Theorem says there exists $c$ between $u$ and $v$ such that

$$|f(u) - f(v)| = |(u - v) f'(c)| = k|u - v| \sin c \le k|u - v|.$$

Thus, the conditions of Theorem 1 are satisfied and $f$ has a fixed point $r$ in $[0, 1]$. Of course, even if $k \ge 1$, $f$ may still have a fixed point in $I$ locatable by iteration, provided the slope of $f$ near that point is less than 1.

---

## Newton's Method

We want to find a **root** of the equation $f(x) = 0$, that is, a number $r$ such that $f(r) = 0$. Such a number is also called a **zero** of the function $f$. If $f$ is differentiable near the root, then tangent lines can be used to produce a sequence of approximations to the root that approaches the root quite quickly. The idea is as follows (see Figure 7.12). Make an initial guess at the root, say $x = x_0$. Draw the tangent line to $y = f(x)$ at $(x_0, f(x_0))$, and find $x_1$, the $x$-intercept of this tangent line. Under certain circumstances $x_1$ will be closer to the root than $x_0$ was. The process can be repeated over and over to get numbers $x_2, x_3, \ldots$, getting closer and closer to the root $r$. The number $x_{n+1}$ is the $x$-intercept of the tangent line to $y = f(x)$ at $(x_n, f(x_n))$.

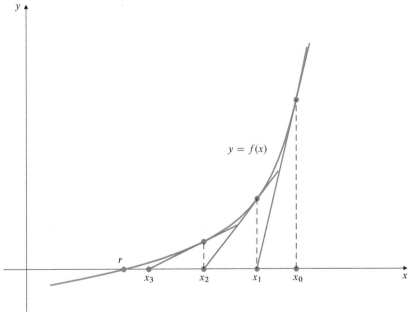

Figure 7.12

The tangent line to $y = f(x)$ at $x = x_0$ has equation

$$y = f(x_0) + f'(x_0)(x - x_0).$$

Since the point $(x_1, 0)$ lies on this line, we have $0 = f(x_0) + f'(x_0)(x_1 - x_0)$. Hence,

$$x_1 = x_0 - \frac{f(x_0)}{f'(x_0)}.$$

Similar formulas produce $x_2$ from $x_1$, then $x_3$ from $x_2$, and so on. The formula producing $x_{n+1}$ from $x_n$ is the discrete map $x_{n+1} = g(x_n)$, where $g(x) = x - \frac{f(x)}{f'(x)}$. That is,

$$x_{n+1} = x_n - \frac{f(x_n)}{f'(x_n)},$$

which is known as the **Newton's Method formula**. If $r$ is a fixed point of $g$ then $f(r) = 0$ and $r$ is a zero of $f$. We usually use a calculator or computer to calculate the successive approximations $x_1$, $x_2$, $x_3$, ..., and observe whether these numbers appear to converge to a limit. Convergence will not occur if the graph of $f$ has a horizontal or vertical tangent at any of the numbers in the sequence. However, if $\lim_{n \to \infty} x_n = r$ exists, and if $f/f'$ is continuous near $r$, then $r$ must be a zero of $f$. This method is known as **Newton's Method** or **The Newton-Raphson Method**. Since Newton's Method is just a special case of fixed-point iteration applied to the function $g(x)$ defined above, the general properties of fixed-point iteration apply to Newton's Method as well.

**EXAMPLE 3**    Use Newton's Method to find the only real root of the equation $x^3 - x - 1 = 0$ correct to 10 decimal places.

**Solution**    We have $f(x) = x^3 - x - 1$ and $f'(x) = 3x^2 - 1$. Since $f$ is continuous and since $f(1) = -1$ and $f(2) = 5$, the equation has a root in the interval $[1, 2]$. Figure 7.13 shows that the equation has only one root to the right of $x = 0$. Let us make the initial guess $x_0 = 1.5$. The Newton's Method formula here is

$$x_{n+1} = x_n - \frac{x_n^3 - x_n - 1}{3x_n^2 - 1} = \frac{2x_n^3 + 1}{3x_n^2 - 1},$$

so that, for example, the approximation $x_1$ is given by

$$x_1 = \frac{2(1.5)^3 + 1}{3(1.5)^2 - 1} \approx 1.347\,826\ldots.$$

The values of $x_1$, $x_2$, $x_3$, ... are given in Table 2.

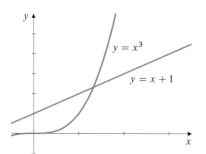

**Figure 7.13**    The graphs of $x^3$ and $x + 1$ meet only once to the right of $x = 0$, and that meeting is between 1 and 2

Table 2.

| $n$ | $x_n$ | $f(x_n)$ |
|---|---|---|
| 0 | 1.5 | 0.875 000 000 000 $\cdots$ |
| 1 | 1.347 826 086 96 $\cdots$ | 0.100 682 173 091 $\cdots$ |
| 2 | 1.325 200 398 95 $\cdots$ | 0.002 058 361 917 $\cdots$ |
| 3 | 1.324 718 174 00 $\cdots$ | 0.000 000 924 378 $\cdots$ |
| 4 | 1.324 717 957 24 $\cdots$ | 0.000 000 000 000 $\cdots$ |
| 5 | 1.324 717 957 24 $\cdots$ | |

The values in Table 2 were obtained with a scientific calculator. Evidently $r = 1.324\,717\,957\,2$ correctly rounded to 10 decimal places.

Observe the behaviour of the numbers $x_n$. By the third iteration, $x_3$, we have apparently achieved a precision of 6 decimal places, and by $x_4$ over 10 decimal places. It is characteristic of Newton's Method that when you begin to get close to the root the convergence can be very rapid. Compare these results with those obtained for the same equation by the Bisection Method; there we achieved only 3 decimal place precision after 11 iterations.

**EXAMPLE 4**    Solve the equation $x^3 = \cos x$ to 11 decimal places.

**Solution**    We are looking for the $x$-coordinate $r$ of the intersection of the curves $y = x^3$ and $y = \cos x$. From Figure 7.14 it appears that the curves intersect slightly to the left of $x = 1$. Let us start with the guess $x_0 = 0.8$. If $f(x) = x^3 - \cos x$, then $f'(x) = 3x^2 + \sin x$. The Newton's Method formula for this function is

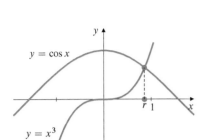

$y = \cos x$

$y = x^3$

**Figure 7.14**    Solving $x^3 = \cos x$

$$x_{n+1} = x_n - \frac{x_n^3 - \cos x_n}{3x_n^2 + \sin x_n} = \frac{2x_n^3 + x_n \sin x_n + \cos x_n}{3x_n^2 + \sin x_n}.$$

The approximations $x_1, x_2, \ldots$ are given in Table 3.

Table 3.

| $n$ | $x_n$ | $f(x_n)$ |
|---|---|---|
| 0 | 0.8 | $-0.184\,706\,709\,347\cdots$ |
| 1 | $0.870\,034\,801\,135\cdots$ | $0.013\,782\,078\,762\cdots$ |
| 2 | $0.865\,494\,102\,425\cdots$ | $0.000\,006\,038\,051\cdots$ |
| 3 | $0.865\,474\,033\,493\cdots$ | $0.000\,000\,001\,176\cdots$ |
| 4 | $0.865\,474\,033\,102\cdots$ | $0.000\,000\,000\,000\cdots$ |
| 5 | $0.865\,474\,033\,102\cdots$ | |

The two curves intersect at $x = 0.865\,474\,033\,10$, rounded to 11 decimal places.

**Remark**    Example 4 shows how useful a sketch can be for determining an initial guess $x_0$. Even a rough sketch of the graph of $y = f(x)$ can show you how many roots the equation $f(x) = 0$ has and approximately where they are. Usually, the closer the initial approximation is to the actual root, the smaller the number of iterations needed to achieve the desired precision. Similarly, for an equation of the form $g(x) = h(x)$, making a sketch of the graphs of $g$ and $h$ (on the same set of axes) can suggest starting approximations for any intersection points. In either case, you can then apply Newton's Method to improve the approximations.

**Remark**    When using Newton's Method to solve an equation that is of the form $g(x) = h(x)$ (such as the one in Example 4), we must rewrite the equation in the form $f(x) = 0$ and apply Newton's Method to $f$. Usually we just use $f(x) = g(x) - h(x)$, although $f(x) = \big(g(x)/h(x)\big) - 1$ is also a possibility.

**Remark**    If your calculator is programmable, you should learn how to program the Newton's Method formula for a given equation so that generating new iterations requires pressing only a few buttons. If your calculator has graphing capabilities, you can use them to locate a good initial guess.

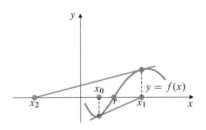

**Figure 7.15**    Here the Newton's Method iterations do not converge to the root

Newton's Method does not always work as well as it does in the preceding examples. If the first derivative $f'$ is very small near the root, or if the second derivative $f''$ is very large near the root, a single iteration of the formula can take us from quite close to the root to quite far away. Figure 7.15 illustrates this possibility. (Also see Exercises 21 and 22 at the end of this section.)

Before you try to use Newton's Method to find a real root of a funcion $f$, you should make sure that a real root actually exists. If you use the method starting with a real initial guess, but the function has no real root nearby, the successive "approximations" can exhibit strange behaviour. The following example illustrates this for a very simple function.

**EXAMPLE 5**    Consider the function $f(x) = 1 + x^2$. Clearly $f$ has no real roots though it does have complex roots $x = \pm i$. The Newton's Method formula for $f$ is

$$x_{n+1} = x_n - \frac{1 + x_n^2}{2x_n} = \frac{x_n^2 - 1}{2x_n}.$$

If we start with a real guess $x_0 = 2$, iterate this formula 20,000 times, and plot the resulting points $(n, x_n)$, we obtain Figure 7.16, which was done using a Maple procedure. It is clear from this plot that not only do the iterations not converge (as one might otherwise expect), but they do not diverge to $\infty$ or $-\infty$, and they are not periodic either. This phenomenon is known as **chaos**.

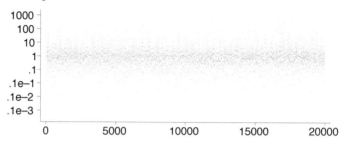

**Figure 7.16**  Plot of 20,000 points $(n, x_n)$ for Example 5

A definitive characteristic of this phenomenon is sensitivity to initial conditions. To demonstrate this sensitivity in the case at hand we make a change of variables. Let

$$y_n = \frac{1}{1 + x_n^2},$$

then the Newton's Method formula for $f$ becomes

$$y_{n+1} = 4y_n(1 - y_n),$$

(see Exercise 24), which is a special case of a discrete map called the **logistic map**. It represents one of the best-known and simplest examples of chaos. If, for example, $y_n = \sin^2(u_n)$, for $n = 0, 1, 2, \ldots$, then it follows (see Exercise 25 below) that $u_n = 2^n u_0$. Unless $u_0$ is a rational multiple of $\pi$, it follows that two different choices of $u_0$ will lead to differences in the resulting values of $u_n$ that grow exponentially with $n$. In Exercise 25 it is shown that this sensitivity is carried through to the first order in $x_n$.

---

***Remark***   The above example does not imply that Newton's Method cannot be used to find complex roots; the formula simply cannot escape from the real line if a real initial guess is used. To accomodate a complex initial guess, $z_0 = a_0 + i b_0$, we can substitute, $z_n = a_n + i b_n$ into the complex version of Newton's Method formula $z_{n+1} = \dfrac{z_n^2 - 1}{2z_n}$ to get the following coupled equations:

$$a_{n+1} = \frac{a_n^3 + a_n(b_n^2 - 1)}{2(a_n^2 + b_n^2)}$$

$$b_{n+1} = \frac{b_n^3 + b_n(a_n^2 + 1)}{2(a_n^2 + b_n^2)}.$$

With initial guess $z_0 = 1 + i$, the next six members of the sequence of complex numbers (in 14-figure precision) become

$$z_1 = \quad 0.250\,000\,000\,000\,00 + i\,0.750\,000\,000\,000\,00$$
$$z_2 = -0.075\,000\,000\,000\,00 + i\,0.975\,000\,000\,000\,00$$
$$z_3 = \quad 0.001\,715\,686\,274\,51 + i\,0.997\,303\,921\,568\,63$$
$$z_4 = -0.000\,004\,641\,846\,27 + i\,1.000\,002\,160\,490\,67$$
$$z_5 = -0.000\,000\,000\,010\,03 + i\,0.999\,999\,999\,991\,56$$
$$z_6 = \quad 0.000\,000\,000\,000\,00 + i\,1.000\,000\,000\,000\,00$$

converging to the root $+i$. For an initial guess, $1 - i$, the resulting sequence converges as rapidly to the root $-i$. Note that for the real initial guess $z_0 = 0 + i0$, neither $a_1$ nor $b_1$ is defined, so the process fails. This corresponds to the fact that $1 + x^2$ has a horizontal tangent $y = 1$ at $(0, 1)$, and this tangent has no finite $x$-intercept.

The following theorem gives sufficient conditions for the Newton approximations to converge to a root $r$ of the equation $f(x) = 0$ if the initial guess $x_0$ is sufficiently close to that root.

**THEOREM**

**2**

**Error bounds for Newton's Method**

Suppose that $f$, $f'$, and $f''$ are continuous on an interval $I$ containing $x_n$, $x_{n+1}$, and a root $x = r$ of $f(x) = 0$. Suppose also that there exist constants $K > 0$ and $L > 0$ such that for all $x$ in $I$ we have

(i) $|f''(x)| \le K$ and

(ii) $|f'(x)| \ge L$.

Then

(a) $|x_{n+1} - r| \le \dfrac{K}{2L}|x_{n+1} - x_n|^2$ and

(b) $|x_{n+1} - r| \le \dfrac{K}{2L}|x_n - r|^2$.

Conditions (i) and (ii) assert that near $r$ the slope of $y = f(x)$ is not too small in size and does not change too rapidly. If $K/(2L) < 1$, the theorem shows that $x_n$ converges quickly to $r$ once $n$ becomes large enough that $|x_n - r| < 1$.

The proof of Theorem 2 depends on the Mean-Value Theorem. We will not give it since the theorem is of little practical use. In practice, we calculate successive approximations using Newton's formula and observe whether they seem to converge to a limit. If they do, and if the values of $f$ at these approximations approach 0, we can be confident that we have located a root.

## "Solve" Routines

Many of the more advanced models of scientific calculators and most computer-based mathematics software have built-in routines for solving general equations numerically or, in a few cases, symbolically. These "Solve" routines assume continuity of the left and right sides of the given equations and often require the user to specify an interval in which to search for the root or an initial guess at the value of the root, or both. Typically the calculator or computer software also has graphing capabilities, and you are expected to use them to get an idea of how many roots the equation has and roughly where they are located before invoking the solving routines. It may also be possible to specify a *tolerance* on the difference of the two sides of the equation. For instance, if we want a solution to the equation $f(x) = 0$, it may be more important to us to be sure that an approximate solution $\hat{x}$ satisfies $|f(\hat{x})| < 0.0001$ than it is to be sure that $\hat{x}$ is within any particular distance of the actual root.

The methods used by the solve routines vary from one calculator or software package to another and are frequently very sophisticated, making use of numerical differentiation and other techniques to find roots very quickly, even when the search interval is large. If you have an advanced scientific calculator and/or computer software with similar capabilities, it is well worth your while to read the manuals that describe how to make effective use of your hardware/software for solving equations. Applications of mathematics to solving "real-world" problems frequently require finding approximate solutions of equations that are intractable by exact methods.

## EXERCISES 7.2

Use fixed-point iteration to solve the equations in Exercises 1–6. Obtain 5 decimal place precision.

**1.** $2x = e^{-x}$, start with $x_0 = 0.3$

**2.** $1 + \frac{1}{4}\sin x = x$     **3.** $\cos\frac{x}{3} = x$

**4.** $(x+9)^{1/3} = x$     **5.** $\dfrac{1}{2+x^2} = x$

**6.** Solve $x^3 + 10x - 10 = 0$ by rewriting it in the form $1 - \frac{1}{10}x^3 = x$.

In Exercises 7–16, use Newton's Method to solve the given equations to the precision permitted by your calculator.

**7.** Find $\sqrt{2}$ by solving $x^2 - 2 = 0$.

**8.** Find $\sqrt{3}$ by solving $x^2 - 3 = 0$.

**9.** Find the root of $x^3 + 2x - 1 = 0$ between 0 and 1.

**10.** Find the root of $x^3 + 2x^2 - 2 = 0$ between 0 and 1.

**11.** Find the two roots of $x^4 - 8x^2 - x + 16 = 0$ in $[1, 3]$.

**12.** Find the three roots of $x^3 + 3x^2 - 1 = 0$ in $[-3, 1]$.

**13.** Solve $\sin x = 1 - x$. A sketch can help you make a guess $x_0$.

**14.** Solve $\cos x = x^2$. How many roots are there?

**15.** How many roots does the equation $\tan x = x$ have? Find the one between $\pi/2$ and $3\pi/2$.

**16.** Solve $\dfrac{1}{1+x^2} = \sqrt{x}$ by rewriting it $(1+x^2)\sqrt{x} - 1 = 0$.

**17.** If your calculator has a built-in Solve routine, or if you use computer software with such a routine, use it to solve the equations in Exercises 7–16.

Find the maximum and minimum values of the functions in Exercises 18–19.

**18.** $\dfrac{\sin x}{1 + x^2}$     **19.** $\dfrac{\cos x}{1 + x^2}$

**20.** Let $f(x) = x^2$. The equation $f(x) = 0$ clearly has solution $x = 0$. Find the Newton's Method iterations $x_1, x_2$, and $x_3$, starting with $x_0 = 1$.

(a) What is $x_n$?

(b) How many iterations are needed to find the root with error less than 0.0001 in absolute value?

(c) How many iterations are needed to get an approximation $x_n$ for which $|f(x_n)| < 0.0001$?

(d) Why do the Newton's Method iterations converge more slowly here than in the examples done in this section?

**21. (Oscillation)** Apply Newton's Method to

$$f(x) = \begin{cases} \sqrt{x} & \text{if } x \geq 0, \\ \sqrt{-x} & \text{if } x < 0, \end{cases}$$

starting with the initial guess $x_0 = a > 0$. Calculate $x_1$ and $x_2$. What happens? (Make a sketch.) If you ever observed this behaviour when you were using Newton's Method to find a root of an equation, what would you do next?

**22. (Divergent oscillations)** Apply Newton's Method to $f(x) = x^{1/3}$ with $x_0 = 1$. Calculate $x_1, x_2, x_3$, and $x_4$. What is happening? Find a formula for $x_n$.

**23. (Convergent oscillations)** Apply Newton's Method to find $f(x) = x^{2/3}$ with $x_0 = 1$. Calculate $x_1, x_2, x_3$, and $x_4$. What is happening? Find a formula for $x_n$.

**24.** Verify that the Newton's Method map for $1 + x^2$, namely

$$x_{n+1} = x_n - \frac{1 + x_n^2}{2x_n}, \text{ transforms into the logistic map}$$

$y_{n+1} = 4y_n(1 - y_n)$ under the transformation $y_n = \dfrac{1}{1 + x_n^2}$.

**❷ 25.** Sensitivity to initial conditions is regarded as a definitive property of chaos. If the initial values of two sequences differ, and the differences between the two sequences tends to grow exponentially, the map is said to be sensitive to initial values. Growing exponentially in this sense does not require that each sequence grow exponentially on its own. In fact, for chaos the growth should only be exponential in the differential. Moreover, the growth only needs to be exponential for large $n$.

a) Show that the logistic map is sensitive to initial conditions by making the substitution $y_j = \sin^2 u_j$ and taking the differential, given that $u_0$ is not an integral multiple of $\pi$.

b) Use part (a) to show that the Newton's Method map for $1 + x^2$ is also sensitive to initial conditions. Make the reasonable assumption, based on Figure 7.16, that the iterates neither converge nor diverge.

Exercises 26–27 constitute a proof of Theorem 1.

**❷ 26.** Condition (ii) of Theorem 1 implies that $f$ is continuous on $I = [a, b]$. Use condition (i) to show that $f$ has a unique fixed point $r$ on $I$. *Hint:* Apply the Intermediate-Value Theorem to $g(x) = f(x) - x$ on $[a, b]$.

**❷ 27.** Use condition (ii) of Theorem 1 and mathematical induction to show that $|x_n - r| \leq K^n|x_0 - r|$. Since $0 < K < 1$, we know that $K^n \to 0$ as $n \to \infty$. This shows that $\lim_{n\to\infty} x_n = r$.

---

**7.3     Indeterminate Forms**

In Section 5.5 we showed that

$$\lim_{x \to 0} \frac{\sin x}{x} = 1.$$

We could not readily see this by substituting $x = 0$ into the function $(\sin x)/x$ because both $\sin x$ and $x$ are zero at $x = 0$. We call $(\sin x)/x$ an **indeterminate form** of type $[0/0]$ at $x = 0$. The limit of such an indeterminate form can be any number. For instance, each of the quotients $kx/x$, $x/x^3$, and $x^3/x^2$ is an indeterminate form of type $[0/0]$ at $x = 0$, but

$$\lim_{x \to 0} \frac{kx}{x} = k, \qquad \lim_{x \to 0} \frac{x}{x^3} = \infty, \qquad \lim_{x \to 0} \frac{x^3}{x^2} = 0.$$

There are other types of indeterminate forms. Table 4 lists them together with an example of each type.

Table 4.  Types of indeterminate forms

| Type | Example |
|------|---------|
| $[0/0]$ | $\displaystyle\lim_{x \to 0} \frac{\sin x}{x}$ |
| $[\infty/\infty]$ | $\displaystyle\lim_{x \to 0} \frac{\ln(1/x^2)}{\cot(x^2)}$ |
| $[0 \cdot \infty]$ | $\displaystyle\lim_{x \to 0+} x \ln \frac{1}{x}$ |
| $[\infty - \infty]$ | $\displaystyle\lim_{x \to (\pi/2)-} \left( \tan x - \frac{1}{\pi - 2x} \right)$ |
| $[0^0]$ | $\displaystyle\lim_{x \to 0+} x^x$ |
| $[\infty^0]$ | $\displaystyle\lim_{x \to (\pi/2)-} (\tan x)^{\cos x}$ |
| $[1^\infty]$ | $\displaystyle\lim_{x \to \infty} \left( 1 + \frac{1}{x} \right)^x$ |

Indeterminate forms of type $[0/0]$ are the most common. You can evaluate many indeterminate forms of type $[0/0]$ with simple algebra, typically by cancelling common factors. We will now develop another method called **l'Hôpital's Rules**[1] for evaluating limits of indeterminate forms of the types $[0/0]$ and $[\infty/\infty]$. The other types of indeterminate forms can usually be reduced to one of these two by algebraic manipulation and the taking of logarithms. We will discover yet another method for evaluating limits of type $[0/0]$.

## l'Hôpital's Rules

**THEOREM 3**

**The first l'Hôpital Rule**

Suppose the functions $f$ and $g$ are differentiable on the interval $(a, b)$, and $g'(x) \neq 0$ there. Suppose also that

(i) $\displaystyle\lim_{x \to a+} f(x) = \lim_{x \to a+} g(x) = 0$ and

(ii) $\displaystyle\lim_{x \to a+} \frac{f'(x)}{g'(x)} = L$ (where $L$ is finite or $\infty$ or $-\infty$).

Then

$$\lim_{x \to a+} \frac{f(x)}{g(x)} = L.$$

Similar results hold if every occurrence of $\lim_{x \to a+}$ is replaced by $\lim_{x \to b-}$ or even $\lim_{x \to c}$ where $a < c < b$. The cases $a = -\infty$ and $b = \infty$ are also allowed.

---

[1]  The Marquis de l'Hôpital (1661–1704), for whom these rules are named, published the first textbook on calculus. The circumflex ( ˆ ) did not come into use in the French language until after the French Revolution. The Marquis would have written his name "l'Hospital."

***PROOF***   We prove the case involving $\lim_{x \to a+}$ for finite $a$. Define

$$F(x) = \begin{cases} f(x) & \text{if } a < x < b \\ 0 & \text{if } x = a \end{cases} \qquad \text{and} \qquad G(x) = \begin{cases} g(x) & \text{if } a < x < b \\ 0 & \text{if } x = a \end{cases}$$

Then $F$ and $G$ are continuous on the interval $[a, x]$ and differentiable on the interval $(a, x)$ for every $x$ in $(a, b)$. By the Generalized Mean-Value Theorem (Theorem 16 of Section 5.8) there exists a number $c$ in $(a, x)$ such that

$$\frac{f(x)}{g(x)} = \frac{F(x)}{G(x)} = \frac{F(x) - F(a)}{G(x) - G(a)} = \frac{F'(c)}{G'(c)} = \frac{f'(c)}{g'(c)}.$$

Since $a < c < x$, if $x \to a+$, then necessarily $c \to a+$, so we have

$$\lim_{x \to a+} \frac{f(x)}{g(x)} = \lim_{c \to a+} \frac{f'(c)}{g'(c)} = L.$$

The case involving $\lim_{x \to b-}$ for finite $b$ is proved similarly. The cases where $a = -\infty$ or $b = \infty$ follow from the cases already considered via the change of variable $x = 1/t$:

$$\lim_{x \to \infty} \frac{f(x)}{g(x)} = \lim_{t \to 0+} \frac{f\left(\dfrac{1}{t}\right)}{g\left(\dfrac{1}{t}\right)} = \lim_{t \to 0+} \frac{f'\left(\dfrac{1}{t}\right)\left(\dfrac{-1}{t^2}\right)}{g'\left(\dfrac{1}{t}\right)\left(\dfrac{-1}{t^2}\right)} = \lim_{x \to \infty} \frac{f'(x)}{g'(x)} = L.$$

---

**EXAMPLE 1**   Evaluate $\lim_{x \to 1} \dfrac{\ln x}{x^2 - 1}$.

***Solution***   We have $\quad \lim_{x \to 1} \dfrac{\ln x}{x^2 - 1} \qquad \left[ \dfrac{0}{0} \right]$

$$= \lim_{x \to 1} \frac{1/x}{2x} = \lim_{x \to 1} \frac{1}{2x^2} = \frac{1}{2}.$$

---

**BEWARE!**   Note that in applying l'Hôpital's Rule we calculate the quotient of the derivatives, *not* the derivative of the quotient.

This example illustrates how calculations based on l'Hôpital's Rule are carried out. Having identified the limit as that of a $[0/0]$ indeterminate form, we replace it by the limit of the quotient of derivatives; the existence of this latter limit will justify the equality. It is possible that the limit of the quotient of derivatives may still be indeterminate, in which case a second application of l'Hôpital's Rule can be made. Such applications may be strung out until a limit can finally be extracted, which then justifies all the previous applications of the rule.

---

**EXAMPLE 2**   Evaluate $\lim_{x \to 0} \dfrac{2 \sin x - \sin(2x)}{2e^x - 2 - 2x - x^2}$.

***Solution***   We have (using l'Hôpital's Rule three times)

$$\lim_{x \to 0} \frac{2 \sin x - \sin(2x)}{2e^x - 2 - 2x - x^2} \qquad \left[ \frac{0}{0} \right]$$

$$= \lim_{x \to 0} \frac{2 \cos x - 2 \cos(2x)}{2e^x - 2 - 2x} \qquad \text{cancel the 2s}$$

$$= \lim_{x \to 0} \frac{\cos x - \cos(2x)}{e^x - 1 - x} \qquad \text{still} \quad \left[ \frac{0}{0} \right]$$

$$= \lim_{x \to 0} \frac{-\sin x + 2 \sin(2x)}{e^x - 1} \qquad \text{still} \quad \left[ \frac{0}{0} \right]$$

$$= \lim_{x \to 0} \frac{-\cos x + 4 \cos(2x)}{e^x} = \frac{-1 + 4}{1} = 3.$$

---

**EXAMPLE 3** Evaluate (a) $\displaystyle\lim_{x\to(\pi/2)-} \frac{2x-\pi}{\cos^2 x}$ and (b) $\displaystyle\lim_{x\to1+} \frac{x}{\ln x}$.

**Solution**

(a) $\displaystyle\lim_{x\to(\pi/2)-} \frac{2x-\pi}{\cos^2 x}$ $\qquad \left[\dfrac{0}{0}\right]$

$\qquad = \displaystyle\lim_{x\to(\pi/2)-} \frac{2}{-2\sin x \cos x} = -\infty$

(b) l'Hôpital's Rule cannot be used to evaluate $\lim_{x\to1+} x/(\ln x)$ because this is not an indeterminate form. The denominator approaches 0 as $x \to 1+$, but the numerator does not approach 0. Since $\ln x > 0$ for $x > 1$, we have, directly,

$$\lim_{x\to1+} \frac{x}{\ln x} = \infty.$$

(Had we tried to apply l'Hôpital's Rule, we would have been led to the erroneous answer $\lim_{x\to1+}(1/(1/x)) = 1$.)

> **BEWARE!** Do not use l'Hôpital's Rule to evaluate a limit that is not indeterminate.

---

**EXAMPLE 4** Evaluate $\displaystyle\lim_{x\to0+} \left( \frac{1}{x} - \frac{1}{\sin x} \right)$.

**Solution** The indeterminate form here is of type $[\infty - \infty]$, to which l'Hôpital's Rule cannot be applied. However, it becomes $[0/0]$ after we combine the fractions into one fraction:

$$\lim_{x\to0+} \left( \frac{1}{x} - \frac{1}{\sin x} \right) \qquad [\infty - \infty]$$

$$= \lim_{x\to0+} \frac{\sin x - x}{x \sin x} \qquad \left[\frac{0}{0}\right]$$

$$= \lim_{x\to0+} \frac{\cos x - 1}{\sin x + x \cos x} \qquad \left[\frac{0}{0}\right]$$

$$= \lim_{x\to0+} \frac{-\sin x}{2\cos x - x \sin x} = \frac{-0}{2} = 0.$$

---

A version of l'Hôpital's Rule also holds for indeterminate forms of the type $[\infty/\infty]$.

**THEOREM**

**4**

**The second l'Hôpital Rule**

Suppose that $f$ and $g$ are differentiable on the interval $(a, b)$ and that $g'(x) \neq 0$ there. Suppose also that

(i) $\displaystyle\lim_{x\to a+} g(x) = \pm\infty$ and

(ii) $\displaystyle\lim_{x\to a+} \frac{f'(x)}{g'(x)} = L$ (where $L$ is finite, or $\infty$ or $-\infty$).

Then

$$\lim_{x\to a+} \frac{f(x)}{g(x)} = L.$$

Again, similar results hold for $\lim_{x\to b-}$ and for $\lim_{x\to c}$, and the cases $a = -\infty$ and $b = \infty$ are allowed.

The proof of the second l'Hôpital Rule is technically rather more difficult than that of the first Rule and we will not give it here. A sketch of the proof is outlined in Exercise 35 at the end of this section.

*Remark*  Do *not* try to use l'Hôpital's Rules to evaluate limits that are not indeterminate of type $[0/0]$ or $[\infty/\infty]$; such attempts will almost always lead to false conclusions, as observed in Example 3(b) above. (Strictly speaking, the second l'Hôpital Rule can be applied to the form $[a/\infty]$, but there is no point to doing so if $a$ is not infinite, since the limit is obviously 0 in that case.)

*Remark*  No conclusion about $\lim f(x)/g(x)$ can be made using either l'Hôpital Rule if $\lim f'(x)/g'(x)$ does not exist. Other techniques might still be used. For example, $\lim_{x\to 0} (x^2 \sin(1/x))/\sin(x) = 0$ by the Squeeze Theorem even though $\lim_{x\to 0} (2x \sin(1/x) - \cos(1/x))/\cos(x)$ does not exist.

---

**EXAMPLE 5**   Evaluate   (a) $\displaystyle\lim_{x\to\infty} \frac{x^2}{e^x}$   and   (b) $\displaystyle\lim_{x\to 0+} x^a \ln x$, where $a > 0$.

*Solution*  Both of these limits are covered by Theorem 5 in Section 6.4. We do them here by l'Hôpital's Rule.

(a)   $\displaystyle\lim_{x\to\infty} \frac{x^2}{e^x}$   $\left[\dfrac{\infty}{\infty}\right]$

$= \displaystyle\lim_{x\to\infty} \frac{2x}{e^x}$   still $\left[\dfrac{\infty}{\infty}\right]$

$= \displaystyle\lim_{x\to\infty} \frac{2}{e^x} = 0.$

Similarly, one can show that $\lim_{x\to\infty} x^n/e^x = 0$ for any positive integer $n$ by repeated applications of l'Hôpital's Rule.

(b)   $\displaystyle\lim_{x\to 0+} x^a \ln x$   $(a > 0)$   $[0 \cdot (-\infty)]$

$= \displaystyle\lim_{x\to 0+} \frac{\ln x}{x^{-a}}$   $\left[\dfrac{-\infty}{\infty}\right]$

$= \displaystyle\lim_{x\to 0+} \frac{1/x}{-ax^{-a-1}} = \lim_{x\to 0+} \frac{x^a}{-a} = 0.$

---

The easiest way to deal with indeterminate forms of types $[0^0]$, $[\infty^0]$, and $[1^\infty]$ is to take logarithms of the expressions involved. Here are two examples.

---

**EXAMPLE 6**   Evaluate $\displaystyle\lim_{x\to 0+} x^x$.

*Solution*  This indeterminate form is of type $[0^0]$. Let $y = x^x$. Then

$$\lim_{x\to 0+} \ln y = \lim_{x\to 0+} x \ln x = 0,$$

by Example 5(b). Hence, $\displaystyle\lim_{x\to 0} x^x = \lim_{x\to 0+} y = e^0 = 1.$

---

**EXAMPLE 7**   Evaluate $\displaystyle\lim_{x\to\infty} \left(1 + \sin\frac{3}{x}\right)^x$.

*Solution*  This indeterminate form is of type $1^\infty$. Let $y = \left(1 + \sin\dfrac{3}{x}\right)^x$. Then, taking ln of both sides,

$$\lim_{x\to\infty} \ln y = \lim_{x\to\infty} x \ln\left(1 + \sin\frac{3}{x}\right) \qquad [\infty \cdot 0]$$

$$= \lim_{x\to\infty} \frac{\ln\left(1 + \sin\frac{3}{x}\right)}{\frac{1}{x}} \qquad \left[\frac{0}{0}\right]$$

$$= \lim_{x\to\infty} \frac{\frac{1}{1+\sin\frac{3}{x}}\left(\cos\frac{3}{x}\right)\left(-\frac{3}{x^2}\right)}{-\frac{1}{x^2}} = \lim_{x\to\infty} \frac{3\cos\frac{3}{x}}{1+\sin\frac{3}{x}} = 3.$$

Hence, $\displaystyle\lim_{x\to\infty}\left(1 + \sin\frac{3}{x}\right)^x = e^3.$

## EXERCISES 7.3

Evaluate the limits in Exercises 1–32.

**1.** $\displaystyle\lim_{x\to0} \frac{3x}{\tan 4x}$

**2.** $\displaystyle\lim_{x\to2} \frac{\ln(2x-3)}{x^2-4}$

**3.** $\displaystyle\lim_{x\to0} \frac{\sin ax}{\sin bx}$

**4.** $\displaystyle\lim_{x\to0} \frac{1-\cos ax}{1-\cos bx}$

**5.** $\displaystyle\lim_{x\to0} \frac{\sin^{-1} x}{\tan^{-1} x}$

**6.** $\displaystyle\lim_{x\to1} \frac{x^{1/3}-1}{x^{2/3}-1}$

**7.** $\displaystyle\lim_{x\to0} x \cot x$

**8.** $\displaystyle\lim_{x\to0} \frac{1-\cos x}{\ln(1+x^2)}$

**9.** $\displaystyle\lim_{t\to\pi} \frac{\sin^2 t}{t-\pi}$

**10.** $\displaystyle\lim_{x\to0} \frac{10^x - e^x}{x}$

**11.** $\displaystyle\lim_{x\to\pi/2} \frac{\cos 3x}{\pi - 2x}$

**12.** $\displaystyle\lim_{x\to1} \frac{\ln(ex)-1}{\sin\pi x}$

**13.** $\displaystyle\lim_{x\to\infty} x \sin\frac{1}{x}$

**14.** $\displaystyle\lim_{x\to0} \frac{x-\sin x}{x^3}$

**15.** $\displaystyle\lim_{x\to0} \frac{x-\sin x}{x-\tan x}$

**16.** $\displaystyle\lim_{x\to0} \frac{2-x^2-2\cos x}{x^4}$

**17.** $\displaystyle\lim_{x\to0+} \frac{\sin^2 x}{\tan x - x}$

**18.** $\displaystyle\lim_{r\to\pi/2} \frac{\ln\sin r}{\cos r}$

**19.** $\displaystyle\lim_{t\to\pi/2} \frac{\sin t}{t}$

**20.** $\displaystyle\lim_{x\to1-} \frac{\arccos x}{x-1}$

**21.** $\displaystyle\lim_{x\to\infty} x(2\tan^{-1} x - \pi)$

**22.** $\displaystyle\lim_{t\to(\pi/2)-} (\sec t - \tan t)$

**23.** $\displaystyle\lim_{t\to0} \left(\frac{1}{t} - \frac{1}{te^{at}}\right)$

**24.** $\displaystyle\lim_{x\to0+} x^{\sqrt{x}}$

**‼ 25.** $\displaystyle\lim_{x\to0+} (\csc x)^{\sin^2 x}$

**‼ 26.** $\displaystyle\lim_{x\to1+} \left(\frac{x}{x-1} - \frac{1}{\ln x}\right)$

**‼ 27.** $\displaystyle\lim_{t\to0} \frac{3\sin t - \sin 3t}{3\tan t - \tan 3t}$

**‼ 28.** $\displaystyle\lim_{x\to0} \left(\frac{\sin x}{x}\right)^{1/x^2}$

**‼ 29.** $\displaystyle\lim_{t\to0} (\cos 2t)^{1/t^2}$

**‼ 30.** $\displaystyle\lim_{x\to0+} \frac{\csc x}{\ln x}$

**‼ 31.** $\displaystyle\lim_{x\to1-} \frac{\ln\sin\pi x}{\csc\pi x}$

**‼ 32.** $\displaystyle\lim_{x\to0} (1 + \tan x)^{1/x}$

**33. (A Newton quotient for the second derivative)** Evaluate $\displaystyle\lim_{h\to0} \frac{f(x+h)-2f(x)+f(x-h)}{h^2}$ if $f$ is a twice differentiable function.

**34.** If $f$ has a continuous third derivative, evaluate

$$\lim_{h\to0} \frac{f(x+3h)-3f(x+h)+3f(x-h)-f(x-3h)}{h^3}.$$

**‼ 35. (Proof of the second l'Hôpital Rule)** Fill in the details of the following outline of a proof of the second l'Hôpital Rule (Theorem 4) for the case where $a$ and $L$ are both finite. Let $a < x < t < b$ and show that there exists $c$ in $(x, t)$ such that

$$\frac{f(x)-f(t)}{g(x)-g(t)} = \frac{f'(c)}{g'(c)}.$$

Now juggle the above equation algebraically into the form

$$\frac{f(x)}{g(x)} - L = \frac{f'(c)}{g'(c)} - L + \frac{1}{g(x)}\left(f(t) - g(t)\frac{f'(c)}{g'(c)}\right).$$

It follows that

$$\left|\frac{f(x)}{g(x)} - L\right|$$

$$\leq \left|\frac{f'(c)}{g'(c)} - L\right| + \frac{1}{|g(x)|}\left(|f(t)| + |g(t)|\left|\frac{f'(c)}{g'(c)}\right|\right).$$

Now show that the right side of the above inequality can be made as small as you wish (say, less than a positive number $\epsilon$) by choosing first $t$ and then $x$ close enough to $a$. Remember, you are given that $\lim_{c\to a+}\left(f'(c)/g'(c)\right) = L$ and $\lim_{x\to a+} |g(x)| = \infty$.

## 7.4    Extreme Values

The first derivative of a function is a source of much useful information about the behaviour of the function. As we have already seen, the sign of $f'$ tells us whether $f$ is increasing or decreasing. In this section we use this information to find maximum and minimum values of functions. In Section 7.6 we will put the techniques developed here to use solving problems that require finding maximum and minimum values.

### Maximum and Minimum Values

Recall that a function has a maximum value at $x_0$ if $f(x) \leq f(x_0)$ for all $x$ in the domain of $f$. The maximum value is $f(x_0)$. To be more precise, we should call such a maximum value an *absolute* or *global* maximum because it is the largest value that $f$ attains anywhere on its entire domain.

**DEFINITION**

**1**

> **Absolute extreme values**
>
> Function $f$ has an **absolute maximum value** $f(x_0)$ at the point $x_0$ in its domain if $f(x) \leq f(x_0)$ holds for every $x$ in the domain of $f$.
> Similarly, $f$ has an **absolute minimum value** $f(x_1)$ at the point $x_1$ in its domain if $f(x) \geq f(x_1)$ holds for every $x$ in the domain of $f$.

A function can have at most one absolute maximum or minimum value, although this value can be assumed at many points. For example, $f(x) = \sin x$ has absolute maximum value 1 occurring at every point of the form $x = (\pi/2)+2n\pi$, where $n$ is an integer, and an absolute minimum value $-1$ at every point of the form $x = -(\pi/2)+2n\pi$. A function need not have any absolute extreme values. The function $f(x) = 1/x$ becomes arbitrarily large as $x$ approaches 0 from the right, so has no finite absolute maximum. (Remember, $\infty$ is not a number and is not a value of $f$.) It doesn't have an absolute minimum either. Even a bounded function may not have an absolute maximum or minimum value. The function $g(x) = x$ with domain specified to be the *open* interval $(0, 1)$ has neither; the range of $g$ is also the interval $(0, 1)$, and there is no largest or smallest number in this interval. Of course, if the domain of $g$ (and therefore also its range) were extended to be the *closed* interval $[0, 1]$, then $g$ would have both a maximum value, 1, and a minimum value, 0.

Maximum and minimum values of a function are collectively referred to as **extreme values**. The following theorem is a restatement (and slight generalization). It will prove very useful in some circumstances when we want to find extreme values.

**THEOREM**

**5**

**Existence of extreme values**

If the domain of the function $f$ is a *closed, finite interval* or a union of finitely many such intervals, and if $f$ is *continuous* on that domain, then $f$ must have an absolute maximum value and an absolute minimum value.

Consider the graph $y = f(x)$ shown in Figure 7.17. Evidently the absolute maximum value of $f$ is $f(x_2)$, and the absolute minimum value is $f(x_3)$. In addition to these extreme values, $f$ has several other "local" maximum and minimum values corresponding to points on the graph that are higher or lower than neighbouring points. Observe that $f$ has *local maximum values* at $a$, $x_2$, $x_4$, and $x_6$ and local minimum values at $x_1$, $x_3$, $x_5$, and $b$. The absolute maximum is the highest of the local maxima; the absolute minimum is the lowest of the local minima.

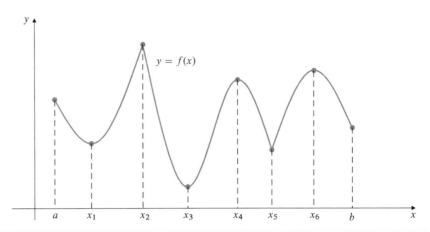

Figure 7.17    Local extreme values

## DEFINITION

**2**

**Local extreme values**

Function $f$ has a **local maximum value (loc max)** $f(x_0)$ at the point $x_0$ in its domain provided there exists a number $h > 0$ such that $f(x) \leq f(x_0)$ whenever $x$ is in the domain of $f$ and $|x - x_0| < h$.

Similarly, $f$ has a **local minimum value (loc min)** $f(x_1)$ at the point $x_1$ in its domain provided there exists a number $h > 0$ such that $f(x) \geq f(x_1)$ whenever $x$ is in the domain of $f$ and $|x - x_1| < h$.

Thus, $f$ has a local maximum (or minimum) value at $x$ if it has an absolute maximum (or minimum) value at $x$ when its domain is restricted to points sufficiently near $x$. Geometrically, the graph of $f$ is at least as high (or low) at $x$ as it is at nearby points.

## Critical Points, Singular Points, and Endpoints

Figure 7.17 suggests that a function $f(x)$ can have local extreme values only at points $x$ of three special types:

(i) **critical points** of $f$ (points $x$ in $\mathcal{D}(f)$ where $f'(x) = 0$),

(ii) **singular points** of $f$ (points $x$ in $\mathcal{D}(f)$ where $f'(x)$ is not defined), and

(iii) **endpoints** of the domain of $f$ (points in $\mathcal{D}(f)$ that do not belong to any open interval contained in $\mathcal{D}(f)$).

In Figure 7.17, $x_1$, $x_3$, $x_4$, and $x_6$ are critical points, $x_2$ and $x_5$ are singular points, and $a$ and $b$ are endpoints.

## THEOREM

**6**

**Locating extreme values**

If the function $f$ is defined on an interval $I$ and has a local maximum (or local minimum) value at point $x = x_0$ in $I$, then $x_0$ must be either a critical point of $f$, a singular point of $f$, or an endpoint of $I$.

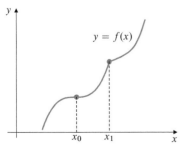

Figure 7.18    A function need not have extreme values at a critical point or a singular point

***PROOF***   Suppose that $f$ has a local maximum value at $x_0$ and that $x_0$ is neither an endpoint of the domain of $f$ nor a singular point of $f$. Then for some $h > 0$, $f(x)$ is defined on the open interval $(x_0 - h, x_0 + h)$ and has an absolute maximum (for that interval) at $x_0$. Also, $f'(x_0)$ exists. By Theorem 14 of Section 5.8, $f'(x_0) = 0$. The proof for the case where $f$ has a local minimum value at $x_0$ is similar.

Although a function cannot have extreme values anywhere other than at endpoints, critical points, and singular points, it need not have extreme values at such points. Figure 7.18 shows the graph of a function with a critical point $x_0$ and a singular point $x_1$ at neither of which it has an extreme value. It is more difficult to draw the graph of a function whose domain has an endpoint at which the function fails to have an extreme value. See Exercise 49 at the end of this section for an example of such a function.

## Finding Absolute Extreme Values

If a function $f$ is defined on a closed interval or a union of finitely many closed intervals, Theorem 5 assures us that $f$ must have an absolute maximum value and an absolute minimum value. Theorem 6 tells us how to find them. We need only check the values of $f$ at any critical points, singular points, and endpoints.

---

**EXAMPLE 1**  Find the maximum and minimum values of the function $g(x) = x^3 - 3x^2 - 9x + 2$ on the interval $-2 \leq x \leq 2$.

*Solution*  Since $g$ is a polynomial, it can have no singular points. For critical points, we calculate

$$g'(x) = 3x^2 - 6x - 9 = 3(x^2 - 2x - 3)$$
$$= 3(x + 1)(x - 3)$$
$$= 0 \quad \text{if} \quad x = -1 \text{ or } x = 3.$$

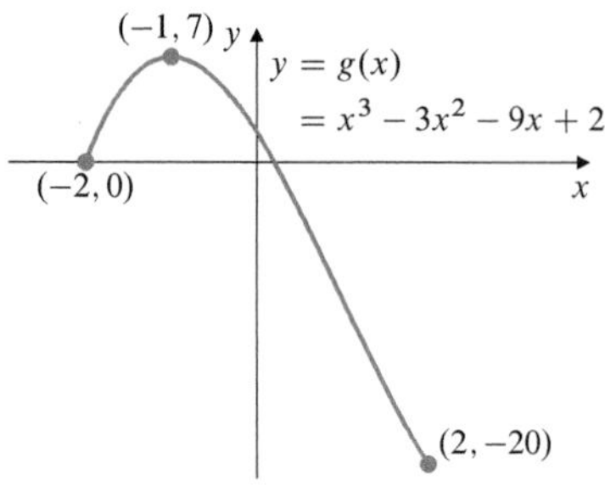

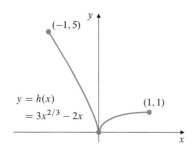

**Figure 7.19**  $g$ has maximum and minimum values 7 and −20, respectively

However, $x = 3$ is not in the domain of $g$, so we can ignore it. We need to consider only the values of $g$ at the critical point $x = -1$ and at the endpoints $x = -2$ and $x = 2$:

$$g(-2) = 0, \qquad g(-1) = 7, \qquad g(2) = -20.$$

The maximum value of $g(x)$ on $-2 \leq x \leq 2$ is 7, at the critical point $x = -1$, and the minimum value is −20, at the endpoint $x = 2$. See Figure 7.19.

---

**EXAMPLE 2**  Find the maximum and minimum values of $h(x) = 3x^{2/3} - 2x$ on the interval $[-1, 1]$.

*Solution*  The derivative of $h$ is

$$h'(x) = 3\left(\frac{2}{3}\right)x^{-1/3} - 2 = 2(x^{-1/3} - 1).$$

Note that $x^{-1/3}$ is not defined at the point $x = 0$ in $\mathcal{D}(h)$, so $x = 0$ is a singular point of $h$. Also, $h$ has a critical point where $x^{-1/3} = 1$, that is, at $x = 1$, which also happens to be an endpoint of the domain of $h$. We must therefore examine the values of $h$ at the points $x = 0$ and $x = 1$, as well as at the other endpoint $x = -1$. We have

$$h(-1) = 5, \qquad h(0) = 0, \qquad h(1) = 1.$$

**Figure 7.20**  $h$ has absolute minimum value 0 at a singular point

The function $h$ has maximum value 5 at the endpoint −1 and minimum value 0 at the singular point $x = 0$. See Figure 7.20.

---

## The First Derivative Test

Most functions you will encounter in elementary calculus have nonzero derivatives everywhere on their domains except possibly at a finite number of critical points, singular points, and endpoints of their domains. On intervals between these points the derivative exists and is not zero, so the function is either increasing or decreasing there. If $f$ is continuous and increases to the left of $x_0$ and decreases to the right, then it must have a local maximum value at $x_0$. The following theorem collects several results of this type together.

**THEOREM**

**7**

**The First Derivative Test**

**PART I.** Testing interior critical points and singular points.

Suppose that $f$ is continuous at $x_0$, and $x_0$ is not an endpoint of the domain of $f$.

(a) If there exists an open interval $(a, b)$ containing $x_0$ such that $f'(x) > 0$ on $(a, x_0)$ and $f'(x) < 0$ on $(x_0, b)$, then $f$ has a local maximum value at $x_0$.

(b) If there exists an open interval $(a, b)$ containing $x_0$ such that $f'(x) < 0$ on $(a, x_0)$ and $f'(x) > 0$ on $(x_0, b)$, then $f$ has a local minimum value at $x_0$.

**PART II.** Testing endpoints of the domain.

Suppose $a$ is a left endpoint of the domain of $f$ and $f$ is right continuous at $a$.

(c) If $f'(x) > 0$ on some interval $(a, b)$, then $f$ has a local minimum value at $a$.

(d) If $f'(x) < 0$ on some interval $(a, b)$, then $f$ has a local maximum value at $a$.

Suppose $b$ is a right endpoint of the domain of $f$ and $f$ is left continuous at $b$.

(e) If $f'(x) > 0$ on some interval $(a, b)$, then $f$ has a local maximum value at $b$.

(f) If $f'(x) < 0$ on some interval $(a, b)$, then $f$ has a local minimum value at $b$.

*Remark*  If $f'$ is positive (or negative) on *both* sides of a critical or singular point, then $f$ has neither a maximum nor a minimum value at that point.

---

**EXAMPLE 3**  Find the local and absolute extreme values of $f(x) = x^4 - 2x^2 - 3$ on the interval $[-2, 2]$. Sketch the graph of $f$.

*Solution*  We begin by calculating and factoring the derivative $f'(x)$:

$$f'(x) = 4x^3 - 4x = 4x(x^2 - 1) = 4x(x - 1)(x + 1).$$

The critical points are 0, $-1$, and 1. The corresponding values are $f(0) = -3$, $f(-1) = f(1) = -4$. There are no singular points. The values of $f$ at the endpoints $-2$ and 2 are $f(-2) = f(2) = 5$. The factored form of $f'(x)$ is also convenient for determining the sign of $f'(x)$ on intervals between these endpoints and critical points. Where an odd number of the factors of $f'(x)$ are negative, $f'(x)$ will itself be negative; where an even number of factors are negative, $f'(x)$ will be positive. We summarize the positive/negative properties of $f'(x)$ and the implied increasing/decreasing behaviour of $f(x)$ in chart form:

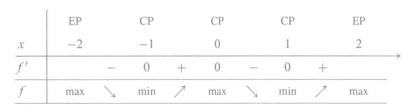

|       | EP    |       | CP    |       | CP    |       | CP    |       | EP    |
|-------|-------|-------|-------|-------|-------|-------|-------|-------|-------|
| $x$   | $-2$  |       | $-1$  |       | 0     |       | 1     |       | 2     |
| $f'$  |       | $-$   | 0     | $+$   | 0     | $-$   | 0     | $+$   |       |
| $f$   | max   | ↘     | min   | ↗     | max   | ↘     | min   | ↗     | max   |

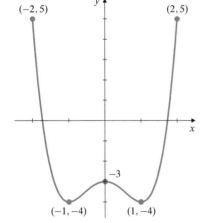

Figure 7.21   The graph $y = x^4 - 2x^2 - 3$

Note how the sloping arrows indicate visually the appropriate classification of the endpoints (EP) and critical points (CP) as determined by the First Derivative Test. We will make extensive use of such charts in future sections. The graph of $f$ is shown in Figure 7.21. Since the domain is a closed, finite interval, $f$ must have absolute maximum and minimum values. These are 5 (at $\pm 2$) and $-4$ (at $\pm 1$).

---

**EXAMPLE 4**  Find and classify the local and absolute extreme values of the function $f(x) = x - x^{2/3}$ with domain $[-1, 2]$. Sketch the graph of $f$.

**Solution**  $f'(x) = 1 - \frac{2}{3}x^{-1/3} = \left(x^{1/3} - \frac{2}{3}\right)/x^{1/3}$. There is a singular point, $x = 0$, and a critical point, $x = 8/27$. The endpoints are $x = -1$ and $x = 2$. The values of $f$ at these points are $f(-1) = -2$, $f(0) = 0$, $f(8/27) = -4/27$, and $f(2) = 2 - 2^{2/3} \approx 0.4126$ (see Figure 7.22). Another interesting point on the graph is the $x$-intercept at $x = 1$. Information from $f'$ is summarized in the chart:

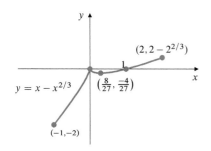

|  | EP | SP | CP | EP |
|---|---|---|---|---|
| $x$ | $-1$ | $0$ | $8/27$ | $2$ |
| $f'$ |  | $+$  undef  $-$ | $0$  $+$ | |
| $f$ | min ↗ | max ↘ | min ↗ | max |

$y = x - x^{2/3}$

$(2, 2 - 2^{2/3})$

$\left(\frac{8}{27}, \frac{-4}{27}\right)$

$(-1, -2)$

**Figure 7.22**    The graph for Example 4

There are two local minima and two local maxima. The absolute maximum of $f$ is $2 - 2^{2/3}$ at $x = 2$; the absolute minimum is $-2$ at $x = -1$.

## Functions Not Defined on Closed, Finite Intervals

If the function $f$ is not defined on a closed, finite interval, then Theorem 5 cannot be used to guarantee the existence of maximum and minimum values for $f$. Of course, $f$ may still have such extreme values. In many applied situations we will want to find extreme values of functions defined on infinite and/or open intervals. The following theorem adapts Theorem 5 to cover some such situations.

**THEOREM**

**8**

**Existence of extreme values on open intervals**

If $f$ is continuous on the open interval $(a, b)$, and if

$$\lim_{x \to a+} f(x) = L \quad \text{and} \quad \lim_{x \to b-} f(x) = M,$$

then the following conclusions hold:

(i) If $f(u) > L$ and $f(u) > M$ for some $u$ in $(a, b)$, then $f$ has an absolute maximum value on $(a, b)$.

(ii) If $f(v) < L$ and $f(v) < M$ for some $v$ in $(a, b)$, then $f$ has an absolute minimum value on $(a, b)$.

In this theorem $a$ may be $-\infty$, in which case $\lim_{x \to a+}$ should be replaced with $\lim_{x \to -\infty}$, and $b$ may be $\infty$, in which case $\lim_{x \to b-}$ should be replaced with $\lim_{x \to \infty}$. Also, either or both of $L$ and $M$ may be either $\infty$ or $-\infty$.

**PROOF**  We prove part (i); the proof of (ii) is similar. We are given that there is a number $u$ in $(a, b)$ such that $f(u) > L$ and $f(u) > M$. Here, $L$ and $M$ may be finite numbers or $-\infty$. Since $\lim_{x \to a+} f(x) = L$, there must exist a number $x_1$ in $(a, u)$ such that

$$f(x) < f(u) \quad \text{whenever} \quad a < x < x_1.$$

Similarly, there must exist a number $x_2$ in $(u, b)$ such that

$$f(x) < f(u) \quad \text{whenever} \quad x_2 < x < b.$$

(See Figure 7.23.) Thus, $f(x) < f(u)$ at all points of $(a, b)$ that are not in the closed, finite subinterval $[x_1, x_2]$. By Theorem 5, the function $f$, being continuous on $[x_1, x_2]$, must have an absolute maximum value on that interval, say at the point $w$. Since $u$ belongs to $[x_1, x_2]$, we must have $f(w) \geq f(u)$, so $f(w)$ is the maximum value of $f(x)$ for all of $(a, b)$.

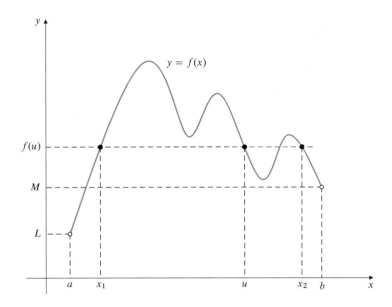

**Figure 7.23**

Theorem 6 still tells us where to look for extreme values. There are no endpoints to consider in an open interval, but we must still look at the values of the function at any critical points or singular points in the interval.

---

**EXAMPLE 5** Show that $f(x) = x + (4/x)$ has an absolute minimum value on the interval $(0, \infty)$, and find that minimum value.

**Solution** We have

$$\lim_{x \to 0+} f(x) = \infty \qquad \text{and} \qquad \lim_{x \to \infty} f(x) = \infty.$$

Since $f(1) = 5 < \infty$, Theorem 8 guarantees that $f$ must have an absolute minimum value at some point in $(0, \infty)$. To find the minimum value we must check the values of $f$ at any critical points or singular points in the interval. We have

$$f'(x) = 1 - \frac{4}{x^2} = \frac{x^2 - 4}{x^2} = \frac{(x-2)(x+2)}{x^2},$$

which equals 0 only at $x = 2$ and $x = -2$. Since $f$ has domain $(0, \infty)$, it has no singular points and only one critical point, namely, $x = 2$, where $f$ has the value $f(2) = 4$. This must be the minimum value of $f$ on $(0, \infty)$. (See Figure 7.24.)

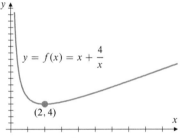

**Figure 7.24** $f$ has minimum value 4 at $x = 2$

---

**EXAMPLE 6** Let $f(x) = x e^{-x^2}$. Find and classify the critical points of $f$, evaluate $\lim_{x \to \pm\infty} f(x)$, and use these results to help you sketch the graph of $f$.

**Solution** $f'(x) = e^{-x^2}(1 - 2x^2) = 0$ only if $1 - 2x^2 = 0$ since the exponential is always positive. Thus, the critical points are $\pm\frac{1}{\sqrt{2}}$. We have $f\left(\pm\frac{1}{\sqrt{2}}\right) = \pm\frac{1}{\sqrt{2e}}$. $f'$ is positive (or negative) when $1 - 2x^2$ is positive (or negative). We summarize the intervals where $f$ is increasing and decreasing in chart form:

| $x$ | | CP $-1/\sqrt{2}$ | | CP $1/\sqrt{2}$ | |
|---|---|---|---|---|---|
| $f'$ | $-$ | 0 | $+$ | 0 | $-$ |
| $f$ | $\searrow$ | min | $\nearrow$ | max | $\searrow$ |

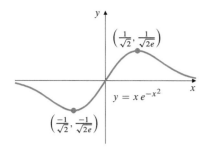

Figure 7.25    The graph for Example 6

Note that $f(0) = 0$ and that $f$ is an odd function ($f(-x) = -f(x)$), so the graph is symmetric about the origin. Also,

$$\lim_{x \to \pm\infty} x\, e^{-x^2} = \left( \lim_{x \to \pm\infty} \frac{1}{x} \right) \left( \lim_{x \to \pm\infty} \frac{x^2}{e^{x^2}} \right) = 0 \times 0 = 0$$

because $\lim_{x \to \pm\infty} x^2\, e^{-x^2} = \lim_{u \to \infty} u\, e^{-u} = 0$ by Theorem 5 of Section 6.4. Since $f(x)$ is positive at $x = 1/\sqrt{2}$ and is negative at $x = -1/\sqrt{2}$, $f$ must have absolute maximum and minimum values by Theorem 8. These values can only be the values $\pm 1/\sqrt{2e}$ at the two critical points. The graph is shown in Figure 7.25. The $x$-axis is an asymptote as $x \to \pm\infty$.

## EXERCISES 7.4

In Exercises 1–17, determine whether the given function has any local or absolute extreme values, and find those values if possible.

**1.** $f(x) = x + 2$ on $[-1, 1]$    **2.** $f(x) = x + 2$ on $(-\infty, 0]$

**3.** $f(x) = x + 2$ on $[-1, 1)$    **4.** $f(x) = x^2 - 1$

**5.** $f(x) = x^2 - 1$ on $[-2, 3]$    **6.** $f(x) = x^2 - 1$ on $(2, 3)$

**7.** $f(x) = x^3 + x - 4$ on $[a, b]$

**8.** $f(x) = x^3 + x - 4$ on $(a, b)$

**9.** $f(x) = x^5 + x^3 + 2x$ on $(a, b]$

**10.** $f(x) = \dfrac{1}{x - 1}$    **11.** $f(x) = \dfrac{1}{x - 1}$ on $(0, 1)$

**12.** $f(x) = \dfrac{1}{x - 1}$ on $[2, 3]$    **13.** $f(x) = |x - 1|$ on $[-2, 2]$

**14.** $|x^2 - x - 2|$ on $[-3, 3]$    **15.** $f(x) = \dfrac{1}{x^2 + 1}$

**16.** $f(x) = (x + 2)^{2/3}$    **17.** $f(x) = (x - 2)^{1/3}$

In Exercises 18–40, locate and classify all local extreme values of the given function. Determine whether any of these extreme values are absolute. Sketch the graph of the function.

**18.** $f(x) = x^2 + 2x$    **19.** $f(x) = x^3 - 3x - 2$

**20.** $f(x) = (x^2 - 4)^2$    **21.** $f(x) = x^3(x - 1)^2$

**22.** $f(x) = x^2(x - 1)^2$    **23.** $f(x) = x(x^2 - 1)^2$

**24.** $f(x) = \dfrac{x}{x^2 + 1}$    **25.** $f(x) = \dfrac{x^2}{x^2 + 1}$

**26.** $f(x) = \dfrac{x}{\sqrt{x^4 + 1}}$    **27.** $f(x) = x\sqrt{2 - x^2}$

**28.** $f(x) = x + \sin x$    **29.** $f(x) = x - 2\sin x$

**30.** $f(x) = x - 2\tan^{-1} x$    **31.** $f(x) = 2x - \sin^{-1} x$

**32.** $f(x) = e^{-x^2/2}$    **33.** $f(x) = x\, 2^{-x}$

**34.** $f(x) = x^2\, e^{-x^2}$    **35.** $f(x) = \dfrac{\ln x}{x}$

**36.** $f(x) = |x + 1|$    **37.** $f(x) = |x^2 - 1|$

**38.** $f(x) = \sin |x|$    **39.** $f(x) = |\sin x|$

**!** **40.** $f(x) = (x - 1)^{2/3} - (x + 1)^{2/3}$

In Exercises 41–46, determine whether the given function has absolute maximum or absolute minimum values. Justify your answers. Find the extreme values if you can.

**41.** $\dfrac{x}{\sqrt{x^2 + 1}}$    **42.** $\dfrac{x}{\sqrt{x^4 + 1}}$

**43.** $x\sqrt{4 - x^2}$    **44.** $\dfrac{x^2}{\sqrt{4 - x^2}}$

**!** **45.** $\dfrac{1}{x \sin x}$ on $(0, \pi)$    **!** **46.** $\dfrac{\sin x}{x}$

**?** **47.** If a function has an absolute maximum value, must it have any local maximum values? If a function has a local maximum value, must it have an absolute maximum value? Give reasons for your answers.

**?** **48.** If the function $f$ has an absolute maximum value and $g(x) = |f(x)|$, must $g$ have an absolute maximum value? Justify your answer.

**?** **49.** **(A function with no max or min at an endpoint)** Let

$$f(x) = \begin{cases} x \sin \dfrac{1}{x} & \text{if } x > 0 \\ 0 & \text{if } x = 0. \end{cases}$$

Show that $f$ is continuous on $[0, \infty)$ and differentiable on $(0, \infty)$ but that it has neither a local maximum nor a local minimum value at the endpoint $x = 0$.

## 7.5    Concavity and Inflections

Like the first derivative, the second derivative of a function also provides useful information about the behaviour of the function and the shape of its graph: it determines whether the graph is *bending upward* (i.e., has increasing slope) or *bending downward* (i.e., has decreasing slope) as we move along the graph toward the right.

**DEFINITION**

**3**

We say that the function $f$ is **concave up** on an open interval $I$ if it is differentiable there and the derivative $f'$ is an increasing function on $I$. Similarly, $f$ is **concave down** on $I$ if $f'$ exists and is decreasing on $I$.

The terms "concave up" and "concave down" are used to describe the graph of the function as well as the function itself.

Note that concavity is defined only for differentiable functions, and even for those, only on intervals on which their derivatives are not constant. According to the above definition, a function is neither concave up nor concave down on an interval where its graph is a straight line segment. We say the function has no concavity on such an interval. We also say a function has opposite concavity on two intervals if it is concave up on one interval and concave down on the other.

The function $f$ whose graph is shown in Figure 7.26 is concave up on the interval $(a, b)$ and concave down on the interval $(b, c)$.

Some geometric observations can be made about concavity:

(i) If $f$ is concave up on an interval, then, on that interval, the graph of $f$ lies above its tangents, and chords joining points on the graph lie above the graph.

(ii) If $f$ is concave down on an interval, then, on that interval, the graph of $f$ lies below its tangents, and chords to the graph lie below the graph.

(iii) If the graph of $f$ has a tangent at a point, and if the concavity of $f$ is opposite on opposite sides of that point, then the graph crosses its tangent at that point. (This occurs at the point $(b, f(b))$ in Figure 7.26. Such a point is called an *inflection point* of the graph of $f$.)

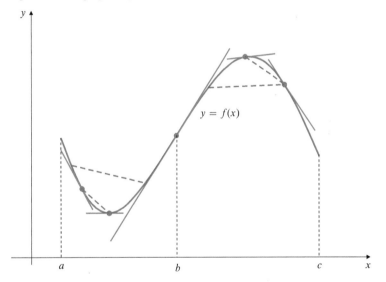

**Figure 7.26** $f$ is concave up on $(a, b)$ and concave down on $(b, c)$

**DEFINITION**

**4**

**Inflection points**

We say that the point $(x_0, f(x_0))$ *is* an **inflection point** of the curve $y = f(x)$ (or that the function $f$ *has* an **inflection point** at $x_0$) if the following two conditions are satisfied:

(a) the graph of $y = f(x)$ has a tangent line at $x = x_0$, and

(b) the concavity of $f$ is opposite on opposite sides of $x_0$.

Note that (a) implies that either $f$ is differentiable at $x_0$ or its graph has a vertical tangent line there, and (b) implies that the graph crosses its tangent line at $x_0$. An inflection point of a function $f$ is a point on the graph of a function, rather than a point in its domain like a critical point or a singular point. A function may or may not have an inflection point at a critical point or singular point. In general, a point $P$

is an inflection point (or simply *an inflection*) of a curve $C$ (which is not necessarily the graph of a function) if $C$ has a tangent at $P$ and arcs of $C$ extending in opposite directions from $P$ are on opposite sides of that tangent line.

Figures 7.27–7.29 illustrate some situations involving critical and singular points and inflections.

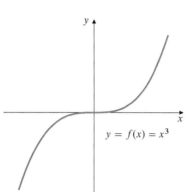

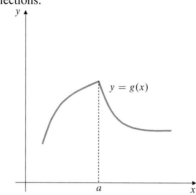

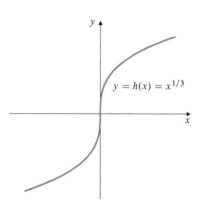

**Figure 7.27**    $x = 0$ is a critical point of $f(x) = x^3$, and $f$ has an inflection point there

**Figure 7.28**    The concavity of $g$ is opposite on opposite sides of the singular point $a$, but its graph has no tangent and therefore no inflection point there

**Figure 7.29**    This graph of $h$ has an inflection point at the origin even though $x = 0$ is a singular point of $h$

If a function $f$ has a second derivative $f''$, the sign of that second derivative tells us whether the first derivative $f'$ is increasing or decreasing and hence determines the concavity of $f$.

**THEOREM**

**9**

**Concavity and the second derivative**

(a) If $f''(x) > 0$ on interval $I$, then $f$ is concave up on $I$.

(b) If $f''(x) < 0$ on interval $I$, then $f$ is concave down on $I$.

(c) If $f$ has an inflection point at $x_0$ and $f''(x_0)$ exists, then $f''(x_0) = 0$.

**PROOF**    Parts (a) and (b) follow from applying Theorem 12 of Section 5.8 to the derivative $f'$ of $f$. If $f$ has an inflection point at $x_0$ and $f''(x_0)$ exists, then $f$ must be differentiable in an open interval containing $x_0$. Since $f'$ is increasing on one side of $x_0$ and decreasing on the other side, it must have a local maximum or minimum value at $x_0$. By Theorem 6, $f''(x_0) = 0$.

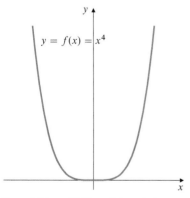

**Figure 7.30**    $f''(0) = 0$, but $f$ does not have an inflection point at 0

Theorem 9 tells us that to find (the $x$-coordinates of) inflection points of a twice differentiable function $f$, we need only look at points where $f''(x) = 0$. However, not every such point has to be an inflection point. For example, $f(x) = x^4$, whose graph is shown in Figure 7.30, does not have an inflection point at $x = 0$ even though $f''(0) = 12x^2|_{x=0} = 0$. In fact, $x^4$ is concave up on every interval.

**EXAMPLE 1**    Determine the intervals of concavity of $f(x) = x^6 - 10x^4$ and the inflection points of its graph.

*Solution*    We have
$$f'(x) = 6x^5 - 40x^3,$$
$$f''(x) = 30x^4 - 120x^2 = 30x^2(x - 2)(x + 2).$$

Having factored $f''(x)$ in this manner, we can see that it vanishes only at $x = -2$, $x = 0$, and $x = 2$. On the intervals $(-\infty, -2)$ and $(2, \infty)$, $f''(x) > 0$, so $f$ is

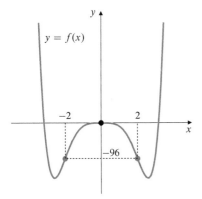

**Figure 7.31**    The graph of
$f(x) = x^6 - 10x^4$

concave up. On $(-2, 0)$ and $(0, 2)$, $f''(x) < 0$, so $f$ is concave down. $f''(x)$ changes sign as we pass through $-2$ and $2$. Since $f(\pm 2) = -96$, the graph of $f$ has inflection points at $(\pm 2, -96)$. However, $f''(x)$ does not change sign at $x = 0$, since $x^2 > 0$ for both positive and negative $x$. Thus, there is no inflection point at $0$. As was the case for the first derivative, information about the sign of $f''(x)$ and the consequent concavity of $f$ can be conveniently conveyed in a chart:

| $x$ | | $-2$ | | $0$ | | $2$ | |
|---|---|---|---|---|---|---|---|
| $f''$ | $+$ | $0$ | $-$ | $0$ | $-$ | $0$ | $+$ |
| $f$ | ⌣ | infl | ⌢ | | ⌢ | infl | ⌣ |

The graph of $f$ is sketched in Figure 7.31.

---

**EXAMPLE 2**    Determine the intervals of increase and decrease, the local extreme values, and the concavity of $f(x) = x^4 - 2x^3 + 1$. Use the information to sketch the graph of $f$.

*Solution*

$$f'(x) = 4x^3 - 6x^2 = 2x^2(2x - 3) = 0 \quad \text{at } x = 0 \text{ and } x = 3/2,$$
$$f''(x) = 12x^2 - 12x = 12x(x - 1) = 0 \quad \text{at } x = 0 \text{ and } x = 1.$$

The behaviour of $f$ is summarized in the following chart:

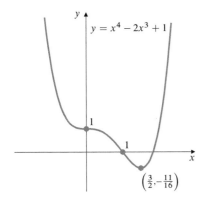

**Figure 7.32**    The function of Example 2

| | | CP | | | | CP | |
|---|---|---|---|---|---|---|---|
| $x$ | | $0$ | | $1$ | | $3/2$ | |
| $f'$ | $-$ | $0$ | $-$ | | $-$ | $0$ | $+$ |
| $f''$ | $+$ | $0$ | $-$ | $0$ | $+$ | | $+$ |
| $f$ | ↘ | | ↘ | | ↘ | min | ↗ |
| | ⌣ | infl | ⌢ | infl | ⌣ | | ⌣ |

Note that $f$ has an inflection at the critical point $x = 0$. We calculate the values of $f$ at the "interesting values of $x$" in the charts:

$$f(0) = 1, \qquad f(1) = 0, \qquad f\left(\tfrac{3}{2}\right) = -\tfrac{11}{16}.$$

The graph of $f$ is sketched in Figure 7.32.

---

## The Second Derivative Test

A function $f$ will have a local maximum (or minimum) value at a critical point if its graph is concave down (or up) in an interval containing that point. In fact, we can often use the value of the second derivative at the critical point to determine whether the function has a local maximum or a local minimum value there.

**THEOREM**

**10**

**The Second Derivative Test**

(a) If $f'(x_0) = 0$ and $f''(x_0) < 0$, then $f$ has a local maximum value at $x_0$.

(b) If $f'(x_0) = 0$ and $f''(x_0) > 0$, then $f$ has a local minimum value at $x_0$.

(c) If $f'(x_0) = 0$ and $f''(x_0) = 0$, no conclusion can be drawn; $f$ may have a local maximum at $x_0$ or a local minimum, or it may have an inflection point instead.

*PROOF* Suppose that $f'(x_0) = 0$ and $f''(x_0) < 0$. Since

$$\lim_{h \to 0} \frac{f'(x_0 + h)}{h} = \lim_{h \to 0} \frac{f'(x_0 + h) - f'(x_0)}{h} = f''(x_0) < 0,$$

it follows that $f'(x_0 + h) < 0$ for all sufficiently small positive $h$, and $f'(x_0 + h) > 0$ for all sufficiently small negative $h$. By the first derivative test (Theorem 7), $f$ must have a local maximum value at $x_0$. The proof of the local minimum case is similar.

The functions $f(x) = x^4$ (Figure 7.30), $f(x) = -x^4$, and $f(x) = x^3$ (Figure 7.27) all satisfy $f'(0) = 0$ and $f''(0) = 0$. But $x^4$ has a minimum value at $x = 0$, $-x^4$ has a maximum value at $x = 0$, and $x^3$ has neither a maximum nor a minimum value at $x = 0$ but has an inflection there. Therefore, we cannot make any conclusion about the nature of a critical point based on knowing that $f''(x) = 0$ there.

---

**EXAMPLE 3**    Find and classify the critical points of $f(x) = x^2 e^{-x}$.

*Solution*    We begin by calculating the first two derivatives of $f$:

$$f'(x) = (2x - x^2)e^{-x} = x(2 - x)e^{-x} = 0 \quad \text{at } x = 0 \text{ and } x = 2,$$
$$f''(x) = (2 - 4x + x^2)e^{-x}$$
$$f''(0) = 2 > 0, \qquad f''(2) = -2e^{-2} < 0.$$

Thus, $f$ has a local minimum value at $x = 0$ and a local maximum value at $x = 2$. See Figure 7.33.

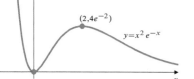

**Figure 7.33**    The critical points of $f(x) = x^2 e^{-x}$

---

For many functions the second derivative is more complicated to calculate than the first derivative, so the First Derivative Test is likely to be of more use in classifying critical points than is the Second Derivative Test. Also note that the First Derivative Test can classify local extreme values that occur at endpoints and singular points as well as at critical points.

It is possible to generalize the Second Derivative Test to obtain a higher derivative test to deal with some situations where the second derivative is zero at a critical point. (See Exercise 40 at the end of this section.)

## EXERCISES 7.5

In Exercises 1–22, determine the intervals of constant concavity of the given function, and locate any inflection points.

**1.** $f(x) = \sqrt{x}$

**2.** $f(x) = 2x - x^2$

**3.** $f(x) = x^2 + 2x + 3$

**4.** $f(x) = x - x^3$

**5.** $f(x) = 10x^3 - 3x^5$

**6.** $f(x) = 10x^3 + 3x^5$

**7.** $f(x) = (3 - x^2)^2$

**8.** $f(x) = (2 + 2x - x^2)^2$

**9.** $f(x) = (x^2 - 4)^3$

**10.** $f(x) = \dfrac{x}{x^2 + 3}$

**11.** $f(x) = \sin x$

**12.** $f(x) = \cos 3x$

**13.** $f(x) = x + \sin 2x$

**14.** $f(x) = x - 2\sin x$

**15.** $f(x) = \tan^{-1} x$

**16.** $f(x) = x e^x$

**17.** $f(x) = e^{-x^2}$

**18.** $f(x) = \dfrac{\ln(x^2)}{x}$

**19.** $f(x) = \ln(1 + x^2)$

**20.** $f(x) = (\ln x)^2$

**21.** $f(x) = \dfrac{x^3}{3} - 4x^2 + 12x - \dfrac{25}{3}$

**22.** $f(x) = (x - 1)^{1/3} + (x + 1)^{1/3}$

**23.** Discuss the concavity of the linear function $f(x) = ax + b$. Does it have any inflections?

Classify the critical points of the functions in Exercises 24–35 using the Second Derivative Test whenever possible.

**24.** $f(x) = 3x^3 - 36x - 3$

**25.** $f(x) = x(x - 2)^2 + 1$

**26.** $f(x) = x + \dfrac{4}{x}$

**27.** $f(x) = x^3 + \dfrac{1}{x}$

**28.** $f(x) = \dfrac{x}{2^x}$

**29.** $f(x) = \dfrac{x}{1 + x^2}$

**30.** $f(x) = xe^x$

**31.** $f(x) = x \ln x$

**32.** $f(x) = (x^2 - 4)^2$

**33.** $f(x) = (x^2 - 4)^3$

**34.** $f(x) = (x^2 - 3)e^x$       **35.** $f(x) = x^2 e^{-2x^2}$

**36.** Let $f(x) = x^2$ if $x \geq 0$ and $f(x) = -x^2$ if $x < 0$. Is 0 a
critical point of $f$? Does $f$ have an inflection point there? Is
$f''(0) = 0$? If a function has a nonvertical tangent line at an
inflection point, does the second derivative of the function
necessarily vanish at that point?

**⚠ 37.** Verify that if $f$ is concave up on an interval, then its graph
lies above its tangent lines on that interval. *Hint:* Suppose $f$ is
concave up on an open interval containing $x_0$. Let $h(x) =
f(x) - f(x_0) - f'(x_0)(x - x_0)$. Show that $h$ has a local
minimum value at $x_0$ and hence that $h(x) \geq 0$ on the interval.
Show that $h(x) > 0$ if $x \neq x_0$.

**⚠ 38.** Verify that the graph $y = f(x)$ crosses its tangent line at an
inflection point. *Hint:* Consider separately the cases where the
tangent line is vertical and nonvertical.

**39.** Let $f_n(x) = x^n$ and $g_n(x) = -x^n$, $(n = 2, 3, 4, \ldots)$.
Determine whether each function has a local maximum, a
local minimum, or an inflection point at $x = 0$.

**⚠ 40. (Higher Derivative Test)** Use your conclusions from Exercise
39 to suggest a generalization of the Second Derivative Test
that applies when

$$f'(x_0) = f''(x_0) = \ldots = f^{(k-1)}(x_0) = 0, \ f^{(k)}(x_0) \neq 0,$$

for some $k \geq 2$.

**⚠ 41.** This problem shows that no test based solely on the signs of
derivatives at $x_0$ can determine whether every function with a
critical point at $x_0$ has a local maximum or minimum or an

inflection point there. Let

$$f(x) = \begin{cases} e^{-1/x^2} & \text{if } x \neq 0 \\ 0 & \text{if } x = 0. \end{cases}$$

Prove the following:

(a) $\lim_{x \to 0} x^{-n} f(x) = 0$ for $n = 0, 1, 2, 3, \ldots$.

(b) $\lim_{x \to 0} P(1/x) f(x) = 0$ for every polynomial $P$.

(c) For $x \neq 0$, $f^{(k)}(x) = P_k(1/x) f(x)(k = 1, 2, 3, \ldots)$,
where $P_k$ is a polynomial.

(d) $f^{(k)}(0)$ exists and equals 0 for $k = 1, 2, 3, \ldots$.

(e) $f$ has a local minimum at $x = 0$; $-f$ has a local
maximum at $x = 0$.

(f) If $g(x) = xf(x)$, then $g^{(k)}(0) = 0$ for every positive
integer $k$ and $g$ has an inflection point at $x = 0$.

**⚠ 42.** A function may have neither a local maximum nor a local
minimum nor an inflection at a critical point. Show this by
considering the following function:

$$f(x) = \begin{cases} x^2 \sin \dfrac{1}{x} & \text{if } x \neq 0 \\ 0 & \text{if } x = 0. \end{cases}$$

Show that $f'(0) = f(0) = 0$, so the $x$-axis is tangent to the
graph of $f$ at $x = 0$; but $f'(x)$ is not continuous at $x = 0$, so
$f''(0)$ does not exist. Show that the concavity of $f$ is not
constant on any interval with endpoint 0.

## 7.6  Extreme-Value Problems

In this section we solve various word problems that, when translated into mathematical terms, require the finding of a maximum or minimum value of a function of one variable. Such problems can range from simple to very complex and difficult; they can be phrased in terminology appropriate to some other discipline, or they can be already partially translated into a more mathematical context. We have already encountered a few such problems in earlier chapters.

Let us consider a couple of examples before attempting to formulate any general principles for dealing with such problems.

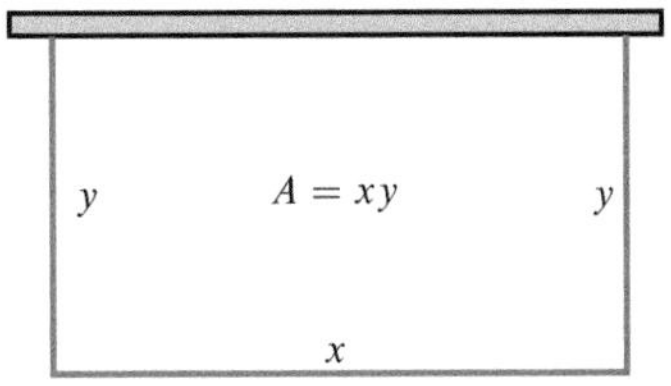

Figure 7.34

**EXAMPLE 1**  A rectangular animal enclosure is to be constructed having one side along an existing long wall and the other three sides fenced. If 100 m of fence are available, what is the largest possible area for the enclosure?

*Solution*  This problem, like many others, is essentially a geometric one. A sketch should be made at the outset, as we have done in Figure 7.34. Let the length and width of the enclosure be $x$ and $y$ m, respectively, and let its area be $A$ m$^2$. Thus $A = xy$. Since the total length of the fence is 100 m, we must have $x + 2y = 100$. $A$ appears to be a function of two variables, $x$ and $y$, but these variables are not independent; they are related by the *constraint* $x + 2y = 100$. This constraint equation can be solved for one variable in terms of the other, and $A$ can therefore be written as a function of only one variable:

$$x = 100 - 2y,$$
$$A = A(y) = (100 - 2y)y = 100y - 2y^2.$$

Evidently, we require $y \geq 0$ and $y \leq 50$ (i.e., $x \geq 0$) in order that the area make sense. (It would otherwise be negative.) Thus, we must maximize the function $A(y)$ on the interval $[0, 50]$. Being continuous on this closed, finite interval, $A$ must have a maximum value, by Theorem 5. Clearly, $A(0) = A(50) = 0$ and $A(y) > 0$ for $0 < y < 50$. Hence, the maximum cannot occur at an endpoint. Since $A$ has no singular points, the maximum must occur at a critical point. To find any critical points, we set

$$0 = A'(y) = 100 - 4y.$$

Therefore, $y = 25$. Since $A$ must have a maximum value and there is only one possible point where it can be, the maximum must occur at $y = 25$. The greatest possible area for the enclosure is therefore $A(25) = 1,250$ m$^2$.

---

**EXAMPLE 2**    A lighthouse $L$ is located on a small island 5 km north of a point $A$ on a straight east-west shoreline. A cable is to be laid from $L$ to point $B$ on the shoreline 10 km east of $A$. The cable will be laid through the water in a straight line from $L$ to a point $C$ on the shoreline between $A$ and $B$, and from there to $B$ along the shoreline. (See Figure 7.35.) The part of the cable lying in the water costs \$5,000/km, and the part along the shoreline costs \$3,000/km.

(a) Where should $C$ be chosen to minimize the total cost of the cable?

(b) Where should $C$ be chosen if $B$ is only 3 km from $A$?

*Solution*

(a) Let $C$ be $x$ km from $A$ toward $B$. Thus $0 \leq x \leq 10$. The length of $LC$ is $\sqrt{25 + x^2}$ km, and the length of $CB$ is $10 - x$ km, as illustrated in Figure 7.35. Hence, the total cost of the cable is \$$T$, where

$$T = T(x) = 5,000\sqrt{25 + x^2} + 3,000(10 - x), \qquad (0 \leq x \leq 10).$$

$T$ is continuous on the closed, finite interval $[0, 10]$, so it has a minimum value that may occur at one of the endpoints $x = 0$ or $x = 10$ or at a critical point in the interval $(0, 10)$. ($T$ has no singular points.) To find any critical points, we set

$$0 = \frac{dT}{dx} = \frac{5,000x}{\sqrt{25 + x^2}} - 3,000.$$

Thus,    $$5,000x = 3,000\sqrt{25 + x^2}$$
$$25x^2 = 9(25 + x^2)$$
$$16x^2 = 225$$
$$x^2 = \frac{225}{16} = \frac{15^2}{4^2}.$$

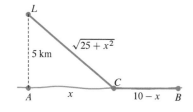

$L$
$\sqrt{25 + x^2}$
5 km
$C$
$A$    $x$    $10 - x$    $B$

**Figure 7.35**

This equation has two solutions, but only one, $x = 15/4 = 3.75$, lies in the interval $(0, 10)$. Since $T(0) = 55,000$, $T(15/4) = 50,000$, and $T(10) \approx 55,902$, the critical point 3.75 evidently provides the minimum value for $T(x)$. For minimal cost, $C$ should be 3.75 km from $A$.

(b) If $B$ is 3 km from $A$, the corresponding total cost function is

$$T(x) = 5{,}000\sqrt{25 + x^2} + 3{,}000(3 - x), \qquad (0 \le x \le 3),$$

which differs from the total cost function $T(x)$ of part (a) only in the added constant (9,000 rather than 30,000). It therefore has the same critical point, $x = 15/4 = 3.75$, which does not lie in the interval $(0, 3)$. Since $T(0) = 34{,}000$ and $T(3) \approx 29{,}155$, in this case we should choose $x = 3$. To minimize the total cost, the cable should go straight from $L$ to $B$.

## Procedure for Solving Extreme-Value Problems

Based on our experience with the examples above, we can formulate a checklist of steps involved in solving optimization problems.

**Solving extreme-value problems**

1. Read the problem very carefully, perhaps more than once. You must understand clearly what is given and what must be found.

2. Make a diagram if appropriate. Many problems have a geometric component, and a good diagram can often be an essential part of the solution process.

3. Define any symbols you wish to use that are not already specified in the statement of the problem.

4. Express the quantity $Q$ to be maximized or minimized as a function of one or more variables.

5. If $Q$ depends on $n$ variables, where $n > 1$, find $n - 1$ equations (constraints) linking these variables. (If this cannot be done, the problem cannot be solved by single-variable techniques.)

6. Use the constraints to eliminate variables and hence express $Q$ as a function of only one variable. Determine the interval(s) in which this variable must lie for the problem to make sense. Alternatively, regard the constraints as implicitly defining $n - 1$ of the variables, and hence $Q$, as functions of the remaining variable.

7. Find the required extreme value of the function $Q$ using the techniques of Section 7.4. Remember to consider any critical points, singular points, and endpoints. Make sure to give a convincing argument that your extreme value is the one being sought; for example, if you are looking for a maximum, the value you have found should not be a minimum.

8. Make a concluding statement answering the question asked. Is your answer for the question *reasonable*? If not, check back through the solution to see what went wrong.

**EXAMPLE 3**  Find the length of the shortest ladder that can extend from a vertical wall, over a fence 2 m high located 1 m away from the wall, to a point on the ground outside the fence.

*Solution*  Let $\theta$ be the angle of inclination of the ladder, as shown in Figure 7.36. Using the two right-angled triangles in the figure, we obtain the length $L$ of the ladder as a function of $\theta$:

$$L = L(\theta) = \frac{1}{\cos\theta} + \frac{2}{\sin\theta},$$

where $0 < \theta < \pi/2$. Since

$$\lim_{\theta \to (\pi/2)-} L(\theta) = \infty \quad \text{and} \quad \lim_{\theta \to 0+} L(\theta) = \infty,$$

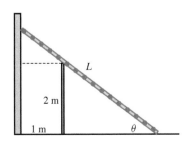

**Figure 7.36**

$L(\theta)$ must have a minimum value on $(0, \pi/2)$, occurring at a critical point. ($L$ has no singular points in $(0, \pi/2)$.) To find any critical points, we set

$$0 = L'(\theta) = \frac{\sin\theta}{\cos^2\theta} - \frac{2\cos\theta}{\sin^2\theta} = \frac{\sin^3\theta - 2\cos^3\theta}{\cos^2\theta\sin^2\theta}.$$

Any critical point satisfies $\sin^3\theta = 2\cos^3\theta$, or, equivalently, $\tan^3\theta = 2$. We don't need to solve this equation for $\theta = \tan^{-1}(2^{1/3})$ since it is really the corresponding value of $L(\theta)$ that we want. Observe that

$$\sec^2\theta = 1 + \tan^2\theta = 1 + 2^{2/3}.$$

It follows that

$$\cos\theta = \frac{1}{(1 + 2^{2/3})^{1/2}} \quad \text{and} \quad \sin\theta = \tan\theta\cos\theta = \frac{2^{1/3}}{(1 + 2^{2/3})^{1/2}}.$$

Therefore, the minimal value of $L(\theta)$ is

$$\frac{1}{\cos\theta} + \frac{2}{\sin\theta} = (1 + 2^{2/3})^{1/2} + 2\frac{(1 + 2^{2/3})^{1/2}}{2^{1/3}} = \left(1 + 2^{2/3}\right)^{3/2} \approx 4.16.$$

The shortest ladder that can extend from the wall over the fence to the ground outside is about 4.16 m long.

---

**EXAMPLE 4**   Find the most economical shape of a cylindrical tin can.

*Solution*   This problem is stated in a rather vague way. We must consider what is meant by "most economical" and even "shape." Without further information, we can take one of two points of view:

(i)  the volume of the tin can is to be regarded as given, and we must choose the dimensions to minimize the total surface area, or

(ii) the total surface area is given (we can use just so much metal), and we must choose the dimensions to maximize the volume.

We will discuss other possible interpretations later. Since a cylinder is determined by its radius and height (Figure 7.37), its shape is determined by the ratio radius/height. Let $r$, $h$, $S$, and $V$ denote, respectively, the radius, height, total surface area, and volume of the can. The volume of a cylinder is the base area times the height:

$$V = \pi r^2 h.$$

The surface of the can is made up of the cylindrical wall and circular disks for the top and bottom. The disks each have area $\pi r^2$, and the cylindrical wall is really just a rolled-up rectangle with base $2\pi r$ (the circumference of the can) and height $h$. Therefore, the total surface area of the can is

$$S = 2\pi rh + 2\pi r^2.$$

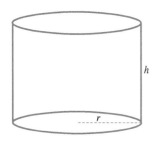

Figure 7.37

Let us use interpretation (i): $V$ is a given constant, and $S$ is to be minimized. We can use the equation for $V$ to eliminate one of the two variables $r$ and $h$ on which $S$ depends. Say we solve for $h = V/(\pi r^2)$ and substitute into the equation for $S$ to obtain $S$ as a function of $r$ alone:

$$S = S(r) = 2\pi r\frac{V}{\pi r^2} + 2\pi r^2 = \frac{2V}{r} + 2\pi r^2 \qquad (0 < r < \infty).$$

Evidently, $\lim_{r\to 0+} S(r) = \infty$ and $\lim_{r\to\infty} S(r) = \infty$. Being differentiable and therefore continuous on $(0,\infty)$, $S(r)$ must have a minimum value, and it must occur at a critical point. To find any critical points,

$$0 = S'(r) = -\frac{2V}{r^2} + 4\pi r,$$

$$r^3 = \frac{2V}{4\pi} = \frac{1}{2\pi}\pi r^2 h = \frac{1}{2}r^2 h.$$

Thus, $h = 2r$ at the critical point of $S$. Under interpretation (i), the most economical can is shaped so that its height equals the diameter of its base. You are encouraged to show that interpretation (ii) leads to the same conclusion.

**Remark**  A different approach to the problem in Example 4 shows directly that interpretations (i) and (ii) must give the same solution. Again, we start from the two equations

$$V = \pi r^2 h \qquad \text{and} \qquad S = 2\pi rh + 2\pi r^2.$$

If we regard $h$ as a function of $r$ and differentiate implicitly, we obtain

$$\frac{dV}{dr} = 2\pi rh + \pi r^2 \frac{dh}{dr},$$

$$\frac{dS}{dr} = 2\pi h + 2\pi r \frac{dh}{dr} + 4\pi r.$$

Under interpretation (i), $V$ is constant and we want a critical point of $S$; under interpretation (ii), $S$ is constant and we want a critical point of $V$. In *either* case, $dV/dr = 0$ and $dS/dr = 0$. Hence, both interpretations yield

$$2\pi rh + \pi r^2 \frac{dh}{dr} = 0 \qquad \text{and} \qquad 2\pi h + 4\pi r + 2\pi r \frac{dh}{dr} = 0.$$

If we divide the first equation by $\pi r^2$ and the second equation by $2\pi r$ and subtract to eliminate $dh/dr$, we again get $h = 2r$.

**Remark**  **Modifying Example 4** Given the sparse information provided in the statement of the problem in Example 4, interpretations (i) and (ii) are the best we can do. The problem could be made more meaningful economically (from the point of view, say, of a tin can manufacturer) if more elements were brought into it. For example:

(a) Most cans use thicker material for the cylindrical wall than for the top and bottom disks. If the cylindrical wall material costs $\$A$ per unit area and the material for the top and bottom costs $\$B$ per unit area, we might prefer to minimize the total cost of materials for a can of given volume. What is the optimal shape if $A = 2B$?

(b) Large numbers of cans are to be manufactured. The material is probably being cut out of sheets of metal. The cylindrical walls are made by bending up rectangles, and rectangles can be cut from the sheet with little or no waste. There will, however, always be a proportion of material wasted when the disks are cut out. The exact proportion will depend on how the disks are arranged; two possible arrangements are shown in Figure 7.38. What is the optimal shape of the can if a square packing of disks is used? A hexagonal packing? Any such modification of the original problem will alter the optimal shape to some extent. In "real-world" problems, many factors may have to be taken into account to come up with a "best" strategy.

(c) The problem makes no provision for costs of manufacturing the can other than the cost of sheet metal. There may also be costs for joining the opposite edges of the rectangle to make the cylinder and for joining the top and bottom disks to the cylinder. These costs may be proportional to the lengths of the joins.

In most of the examples above, the maximum or minimum value being sought occurred at a critical point. Our final example is one where this is not the case.

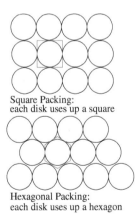

Square Packing:
each disk uses up a square

Hexagonal Packing:
each disk uses up a hexagon

**Figure 7.38**    Square and hexagonal packing of disks in a plane

EXAMPLE 5 A man can run twice as fast as he can swim. He is standing at point $A$ on the edge of a circular swimming pool 40 m in diameter, and he wishes to get to the diametrically opposite point $B$ as quickly as possible. He can run around the edge to point $C$, then swim directly from $C$ to $B$. Where should $C$ be chosen to minimize the total time taken to get from $A$ to $B$?

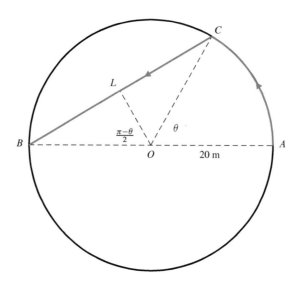

**Figure 7.39** Running and swimming to get from $A$ to $B$

**Solution** It is convenient to describe the position of $C$ in terms of the angle $AOC$, where $O$ is the centre of the pool. (See Figure 7.39.) Let $\theta$ denote this angle. Clearly, $0 \le \theta \le \pi$. (If $\theta = 0$, the man swims the whole way; if $\theta = \pi$, he runs the whole way.) The radius of the pool is 20 m, so arc $AC = 20\theta$. Since angle $BOC = \pi - \theta$, we have angle $BOL = (\pi - \theta)/2$ and chord $BC = 2BL = 40 \sin\big((\pi - \theta)/2\big)$.

Suppose the man swims at a rate $k$ m/s and therefore runs at a rate $2k$ m/s. If $t$ is the total time he takes to get from $A$ to $B$, then

$$t = t(\theta) = \text{time running} + \text{time swimming}$$
$$= \frac{20\theta}{2k} + \frac{40}{k} \sin \frac{\pi - \theta}{2}.$$

(We are assuming that no time is wasted in jumping into the water at $C$.) The domain of $t$ is $[0, \pi]$ and $t$ has no singular points. Since $t$ is continuous on a closed, finite interval, it must have a minimum value, and that value must occur at a critical point or an endpoint. For critical points,

$$0 = t'(\theta) = \frac{10}{k} - \frac{20}{k} \cos \frac{\pi - \theta}{2}.$$

Thus,

$$\cos \frac{\pi - \theta}{2} = \frac{1}{2}, \qquad \frac{\pi - \theta}{2} = \frac{\pi}{3}, \qquad \theta = \frac{\pi}{3}.$$

This is the only critical value of $\theta$ lying in the interval $[0, \pi]$. We have

$$t\left(\frac{\pi}{3}\right) = \frac{10\pi}{3k} + \frac{40}{k} \sin \frac{\pi}{3} = \frac{10}{k}\left(\frac{\pi}{3} + \frac{4\sqrt{3}}{2}\right) \approx \frac{45.11}{k}.$$

We must also look at the endpoints $\theta = 0$ and $\theta = \pi$:

$$t(0) = \frac{40}{k}, \qquad t(\pi) = \frac{10\pi}{k} \approx \frac{31.4}{k}.$$

Evidently, $t(\pi)$ is the least of these three times. To get from $A$ to $B$ as quickly as possible, the man should run the entire distance.

*Remark*   This problem shows how important it is to check every candidate point to see whether it gives a maximum or minimum. Here, the critical point $\theta = \pi/3$ yielded the *worst* possible strategy: running one-third of the way around and then swimming the remainder would take the greatest time, not the least.

## EXERCISES 7.6

1. Two positive numbers have sum 7. What is the largest possible value for their product?

2. Two positive numbers have product 8. What is the smallest possible value for their sum?

3. Two nonnegative numbers have sum 60. What are the numbers if the product of one of them and the square of the other is maximal?

4. Two numbers have sum 16. What are the numbers if the product of the cube of one and the fifth power of the other is as large as possible?

5. The sum of two nonnegative numbers is 10. What is the smallest value of the sum of the cube of one number and the square of the other?

6. Two nonnegative numbers have sum $n$. What is the smallest possible value for the sum of their squares?

7. Among all rectangles of given area, show that the square has the least perimeter.

8. Among all rectangles of given perimeter, show that the square has the greatest area.

9. Among all isosceles triangles of given perimeter, show that the equilateral triangle has the greatest area.

10. Find the largest possible area for an isosceles triangle if the length of each of its two equal sides is 10 m.

11. Find the area of the largest rectangle that can be inscribed in a semicircle of radius $R$ if one side of the rectangle lies along the diameter of the semicircle.

12. Find the largest possible perimeter of a rectangle inscribed in a semicircle of radius $R$ if one side of the rectangle lies along the diameter of the semicircle. (It is interesting that the rectangle with the largest perimeter has a different shape than the one with the largest area, obtained in Exercise 11.)

13. A rectangle with sides parallel to the coordinate axes is inscribed in the ellipse

$$\frac{x^2}{a^2} + \frac{y^2}{b^2} = 1.$$

Find the largest possible area for this rectangle.

14. Let $ABC$ be a triangle right-angled at $C$ and having area $S$. Find the maximum area of a rectangle inscribed in the triangle if (a) one corner of the rectangle lies at $C$, or (b) one side of the rectangle lies along the hypotenuse, $AB$.

15. Find the maximum area of an isosceles triangle whose equal sides are 10 cm in length. Use half the length of the third side of the triangle as the variable in terms of which to express the area of the triangle.

16. Repeat Exercise 15, but use instead the angle between the equal sides of the triangle as the variable in terms of which to express the area of the triangle. Which solution is easier?

17. (**Designing a billboard**) A billboard is to be made with 100 m² of printed area and with margins of 2 m at the top and bottom and 4 m on each side. Find the outside dimensions of the billboard if its total area is to be a minimum.

18. (**Designing a box**) A box is to be made from a rectangular sheet of cardboard 70 cm by 150 cm by cutting equal squares out of the four corners and bending up the resulting four flaps to make the sides of the box. (The box has no top.) What is the largest possible volume of the box?

19. (**Using rebates to maximize profit**) An automobile manufacturer sells 2,000 cars per month, at an average profit of $1,000 per car. Market research indicates that for each $50 of factory rebate the manufacturer offers to buyers it can expect to sell 200 more cars each month. How much of a rebate should it offer to maximize its monthly profit?

20. (**Maximizing rental profit**) All 80 rooms in a motel will be rented each night if the manager charges $40 or less per room. If he charges $(40 + x)$ per room, then $2x$ rooms will remain vacant. If each rented room costs the manager $10 per day and each unrented room $2 per day in overhead, how much should the manager charge per room to maximize his daily profit?

21. (**Minimizing travel time**) You are in a dune buggy in the desert 12 km due south of the nearest point $A$ on a straight east-west road. You wish to get to point $B$ on the road 10 km east of $A$. If your dune buggy can average 15 km/h travelling over the desert and 39 km/h travelling on the road, toward what point on the road should you head in order to minimize your travel time to $B$?

22. Repeat Exercise 21, but assume that $B$ is only 4 km from $A$.

23. (**Flying with least energy**) At the altitude of airliners, winds can typically blow at a speed of about 100 knots (nautical miles per hour) from the west toward the east. A westward-flying passenger jet from London, England, on its way to Toronto, flies directly against this wind for 3,000 nautical miles. The energy per unit time expended by the airliner is proportional to $v^3$, where $v$ is the speed of the airliner relative to the air. This reflects the power required to push aside the air exerting ram pressure proportional to $v^2$. What speed uses the least energy on this trip? Estimate the time it would take to fly this route at the resulting optimal speed. Is this a typical speed at which airliners travel? Explain.

24. (**Energy for a round trip**) In the preceding problem we found that an airliner flying against the wind at speed $v$ with respect to the air consumes the least energy over a flight if it travels at $v = 3u/2$, where $u$ is the speed of the headwind with respect to the ground. Assume the power (energy per unit time) required to push aside the air is $kv^3$.

   (a) Write the general expression for energy consumed over a trip of distance $\ell$ flying with an airspeed $v$ into a headwind of speed $u$. Also write the general expression for energy used on the return journey along the same path with airspeed $w$ aided by a tailwind of speed $u$.

(b) Show that the energy consumed in the return journey is a strictly increasing function of $w$. What is the least energy consumed in the return journey if the airliner must have a minimum airspeed of $s$ (known as "stall speed") to stay aloft?

(c) What is the least energy consumed in the round trip if $u > 2s/3$? What is the energy consumed when $u < 2s/3$?

**25.** A one-metre length of stiff wire is cut into two pieces. One piece is bent into a circle, the other piece into a square. Find the length of the part used for the square if the sum of the areas of the circle and the square is (a) maximum and (b) minimum.

**26.** Find the area of the largest rectangle that can be drawn so that each of its sides passes through a different vertex of a rectangle having sides $a$ and $b$.

**27.** What is the length of the shortest line segment having one end on the $x$-axis, the other end on the $y$-axis, and passing through the point $(9, \sqrt{3})$?

**28.** **(Getting around a corner)** Find the length of the longest beam that can be carried horizontally around the corner from a hallway of width $a$ m to a hallway of width $b$ m. (See Figure 7.40; assume the beam has no width.)

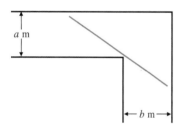

Figure 7.40

**29.** If the height of both hallways in Exercise 28 is $c$ m, and if the beam need not be carried horizontally, how long can it be and still get around the corner? *Hint:* You can use the result of the previous exercise to do this one easily.

**30.** The fence in Example 3 is demolished and a new fence is built 2 m away from the wall. How high can the fence be if a 6 m ladder must be able to extend from the wall, over the fence, to the ground outside?

**31.** Find the shortest distance from the origin to the curve $x^2 y^4 = 1$.

**32.** Find the shortest distance from the point $(8, 1)$ to the curve $y = 1 + x^{3/2}$.

**33.** Find the dimensions of the largest right-circular cylinder that can be inscribed in a sphere of radius $R$.

**34.** Find the dimensions of the circular cylinder of greatest volume that can be inscribed in a cone of base radius $R$ and height $H$ if the base of the cylinder lies in the base of the cone.

**35.** A box with square base and no top has a volume of 4 m$^3$. Find the dimensions of the most economical box.

**36.** **(Folding a pyramid)** A pyramid with a square base and four faces, each in the shape of an isosceles triangle, is made by

cutting away four triangles from a 2 ft square piece of cardboard (as shown in Figure 7.41) and bending up the resulting triangles to form the walls of the pyramid. What is the largest volume the pyramid can have? *Hint:* The volume of a pyramid having base area $A$ and height $h$ measured perpendicular to the base is $V = \frac{1}{3} A h$.

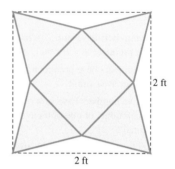

Figure 7.41

**37.** **(Getting the most light)** A window has perimeter 10 m and is in the shape of a rectangle with the top edge replaced by a semicircle. Find the dimensions of the rectangle if the window admits the greatest amount of light.

**38.** **(Fuel tank design)** A fuel tank is made of a cylindrical part capped by hemispheres at each end. If the hemispheres are twice as expensive per unit area as the cylindrical wall, and if the volume of the tank is $V$, find the radius and height of the cylindrical part to minimize the total cost. The surface area of a sphere of radius $r$ is $4\pi r^2$; its volume is $\frac{4}{3} \pi r^3$.

**39.** **(Reflection of light)** Light travels in such a way that it requires the minimum possible time to get from one point to another. A ray of light from $C$ reflects off a plane mirror $AB$ at $X$ and then passes through $D$. (See Figure 7.42.) Show that the rays $CX$ and $XD$ make equal angles with the normal to $AB$ at $X$. (*Remark:* You may wish to give a proof based on elementary geometry without using any calculus, or you can minimize the travel time on $CXD$.)

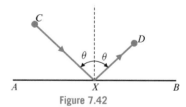

Figure 7.42

**40.** **(Snell's Law)** If light travels with speed $v_1$ in one medium and speed $v_2$ in a second medium, and if the two media are separated by a plane interface, show that a ray of light passing from point $A$ in one medium to point $B$ in the other is bent at the interface in such a way that

$$\frac{\sin i}{\sin r} = \frac{v_1}{v_2},$$

where $i$ and $r$ are the angles of incidence and refraction, as is shown in Figure 7.43. This is known as Snell's Law. Deduce it from the least-time principle stated in Exercise 39.

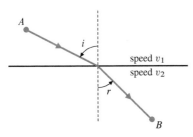

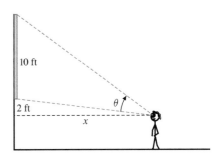

Figure 7.43

**41. (Cutting the stiffest beam)** The stiffness of a wooden beam of rectangular cross section is proportional to the product of the width and the cube of the depth of the cross section. Find the width and depth of the stiffest beam that can be cut out of a circular log of radius $R$.

**42.** Find the equation of the straight line of maximum slope tangent to the curve $y = 1 + 2x - x^3$.

**43.** A quantity $Q$ grows according to the differential equation

$$\frac{dQ}{dt} = kQ^3(L - Q)^5,$$

where $k$ and $L$ are positive constants. How large is $Q$ when it is growing most rapidly?

**⚠ 44.** Find the smallest possible volume of a right-circular cone that can contain a sphere of radius $R$. (The volume of a cone of base radius $r$ and height $h$ is $\frac{1}{3}\pi r^2 h$.)

**⚠ 45. (Ferry loading)** A ferry runs between the mainland and the island of Dedlos. The ferry has a maximum capacity of 1,000 cars, but loading near capacity is very time consuming. It is found that the number of cars that can be loaded in $t$ hours is

$$f(t) = 1,000\,\frac{t}{e^{-t} + t}.$$

(Note that $\lim_{t\to\infty} f(t) = 1,000$, as expected.) Further, it is found that it takes $x/1,000$ hours to unload $x$ cars. The sailing time to or from the island is 1 hour. Assume there are always more cars waiting for each sailing than can be loaded. How many cars should be loaded on the ferry for each sailing to maximize the average movement of cars back and forth to the island? (You will need to use a graphing calculator or computer software like Maple's `fsolve` routine to find the appropriate critical point.)

**⚠ 46. (The best view of a mural)** How far back from a mural should one stand to view it best if the mural is 10 ft high and the bottom of it is 2 ft above eye level? (See Figure 7.44.)

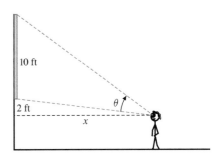

Figure 7.44

**⚠ 47. (Improving the enclosure of Example 1)** An enclosure is to be constructed having part of its boundary along an existing straight wall. The other part of the boundary is to be fenced in the shape of an arc of a circle. If 100 m of fencing is available, what is the area of the largest possible enclosure? Into what fraction of a circle is the fence bent?

**⚠ 48. (Designing a Dixie cup)** A sector is cut out of a circular disk of radius $R$, and the remaining part of the disk is bent up so that the two edges join and a cone is formed (see Figure 7.45). What is the largest possible volume for the cone?

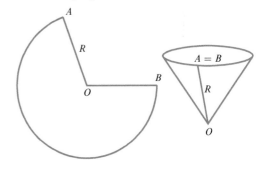

Figure 7.45

**⚠ 49. (Minimize the fold)** One corner of a strip of paper $a$ cm wide is folded up so that it lies along the opposite edge. (See Figure 7.46.) Find the least possible length for the fold line.

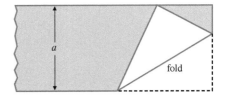

Figure 7.46

---

## 7.7 Linear Approximations

Many problems in applied mathematics are too difficult to be solved exactly—that is why we resort to using computers, even though in many cases they may only give approximate answers. However, not all approximation is done with machines. Linear approximation can be a very effective way to estimate values or test the plausibility of

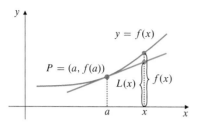

**Figure 7.47**    The linearization of function $f$ about $a$

numbers given by a computer. In Section 5.7 we observed how differentials could be used to approximate (changes in) the values of functions between nearby points. In this section we reconsider such approximations in a more formal way and obtain estimates for the size of the errors encountered when such "linear" approximations are made.

The tangent to the graph $y = f(x)$ at $x = a$ describes the behaviour of that graph near the point $P = (a, f(a))$ better than any other straight line through $P$, because it goes through $P$ in the same direction as the curve $y = f(x)$. (See Figure 7.47.) We exploit this fact by using the height to the tangent line to calculate approximate values of $f(x)$ for values of $x$ near $a$. The tangent line has equation $y = f(a) + f'(a)(x - a)$. We call the right side of this equation the linearization of $f$ about $a$ (or the linearization of $f(x)$ about $x = a$).

**DEFINITION**

**8**

The **linearization** of the function $f$ about $a$ is the function $L$ defined by

$$L(x) = f(a) + f'(a)(x - a).$$

We say that $f(x) \approx L(x) = f(a) + f'(a)(x - a)$ provides **linear approximations** for values of $f$ near $a$.

---

**EXAMPLE 1**    Find linearizations of (a) $f(x) = \sqrt{1 + x}$ about $x = 0$ and (b) $g(t) = 1/t$ about $t = 1/2$.

*Solution*

(a) We have $f(0) = 1$ and, since $f'(x) = 1/(2\sqrt{1 + x})$, $f'(0) = 1/2$. The linearization of $f$ about $0$ is

$$L(x) = 1 + \frac{1}{2}(x - 0) = 1 + \frac{x}{2}.$$

(b) We have $g(1/2) = 2$ and, since $g'(t) = -1/t^2$, $g'(1/2) = -4$. The linearization of $g(t)$ about $t = 1/2$ is

$$L(t) = 2 - 4\left(t - \frac{1}{2}\right) = 4 - 4t.$$

---

## Approximating Values of Functions

We have already made use of linearization in Section 5.7, where it was disguised as the formula

$$\Delta y \approx \frac{dy}{dx}\,\Delta x$$

and used to approximate a small change $\Delta y = f(a + \Delta x) - f(a)$ in the values of function $f$ corresponding to the small change in the argument of the function from $a$ to $a + \Delta x$. This is just the linear approximation

$$f(a + \Delta x) \approx L(a + \Delta x) = f(a) + f'(a)\Delta x.$$

---

**EXAMPLE 2**    A ball of ice melts so that its radius decreases from 5 cm to 4.92 cm. By approximately how much does the volume of the ball decrease?

*Solution*    The volume $V$ of a ball of radius $r$ is $V = \frac{4}{3}\pi r^3$, so that $dV/dr = 4\pi r^2$ and $L(r + \Delta r) = V(r) + 4\pi r^2\,\Delta r$. Thus,

$$\Delta V \approx L(r + \Delta r) = 4\pi r^2\,\Delta r.$$

For $r = 5$ and $\Delta r = -0.08$, we have

$$\Delta V \approx 4\pi(5^2)(-0.08) = -8\pi \approx -25.13.$$

The volume of the ball decreases by about $25 \text{ cm}^3$.

The following example illustrates the use of linearization to find an approximate value of a function near a point where the values of the function and its derivative are known.

**EXAMPLE 3**    Use the linearization for $\sqrt{x}$ about $x = 25$ to find an approximate value for $\sqrt{26}$.

**Solution**    If $f(x) = \sqrt{x}$, then $f'(x) = 1/(2\sqrt{x})$. Since we know that $f(25) = 5$ and $f'(25) = 1/10$, the linearization of $f(x)$ about $x = 25$ is

$$L(x) = 5 + \frac{1}{10}(x - 25).$$

Putting $x = 26$, we get

$$\sqrt{26} = f(26) \approx L(26) = 5 + \frac{1}{10}(26 - 25) = 5.1.$$

If we use the square root function on a calculator we can obtain the "true value" of $\sqrt{26}$ (actually, just another approximation, although presumably a better one): $\sqrt{26} = 5.0990195\ldots$, but if we have such a calculator we don't need the approximation in the first place. Approximations are useful when there is no easy way to obtain the true value. However, if we don't know the true value, we would at least like to have some way of determining how good the approximation must be; that is, we want an *estimate for the error*. After all, *any number* is an approximation to $\sqrt{26}$, but the error may be unacceptably large; for instance, the size of the error in the approximation $\sqrt{26} \approx 1{,}000{,}000$ is greater than 999,994.

## Error Analysis

In any approximation, the **error** is defined by

error = true value − approximate value.

If the linearization of $f$ about $a$ is used to approximate $f(x)$ near $x = a$, that is,

$$f(x) \approx L(x) = f(a) + f'(a)(x - a),$$

then the error $E(x)$ in this approximation is

$$E(x) = f(x) - L(x) = f(x) - f(a) - f'(a)(x - a).$$

It is the vertical distance at $x$ between the graph of $f$ and the tangent line to that graph at $x = a$, as shown in Figure 7.48. Observe that if $x$ is "near" $a$, then $E(x)$ is small compared to the horizontal distance between $x$ and $a$.

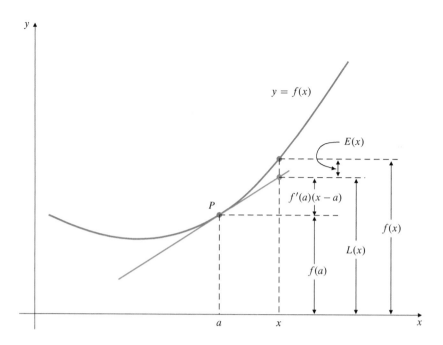

**Figure 7.48** $f(x)$ and its linearization $L(x)$ about $x = a$. $E(x)$ is the error in the approximation $f(x) \approx L(x)$

The following theorem and its corollaries give us a way to estimate this error if we know bounds for the *second derivative* of $f$.

**THEOREM**

**11**

**An error formula for linearization**

If $f''(t)$ exists for all $t$ in an interval containing $a$ and $x$, then there exists some point $s$ between $a$ and $x$ such that the error $E(x) = f(x) - L(x)$ in the linear approximation $f(x) \approx L(x) = f(a) + f'(a)(x - a)$ satisfies

$$E(x) = \frac{f''(s)}{2} (x - a)^2.$$

**PROOF** Let us assume that $x > a$. (The proof for $x < a$ is similar.) Since

$$E(t) = f(t) - f(a) - f'(a)(t - a),$$

we have $E'(t) = f'(t) - f'(a)$. We apply the Generalized Mean-Value Theorem (Theorem 16 of Section 5.8) to the two functions $E(t)$ and $(t - a)^2$ on $[a, x]$. Noting that $E(a) = 0$, we obtain a number $u$ in $(a, x)$ such that

$$\frac{E(x)}{(x - a)^2} = \frac{E(x) - E(a)}{(x - a)^2 - (a - a)^2} = \frac{E'(u)}{2(u - a)} = \frac{f'(u) - f'(a)}{2(u - a)} = \frac{1}{2} f''(s)$$

for some $s$ in $(a, u)$; the latter expression is a consequence of applying the Mean-Value Theorem again, this time to $f'$ on $[a, u]$. Thus,

$$E(x) = \frac{f''(s)}{2} (x - a)^2$$

as claimed.

The following three corollaries are immediate consequences of Theorem 11.

**Corollary A.** If $f''(t)$ has constant sign (i.e., is always positive or always negative) between $a$ and $x$, then the error $E(x)$ in the linear approximation $f(x) \approx L(x)$ in the Theorem has that same sign; if $f''(t) > 0$ between $a$ and $x$, then $f(x) > L(x)$; if $f''(t) < 0$ between $a$ and $x$, then $f(x) < L(x)$.

**Corollary B.** If $|f''(t)| < K$ for all $t$ between $a$ and $x$ (where $K$ is a constant), then $|E(x)| < (K/2)(x-a)^2$.

**Corollary C.** If $f''(t)$ satisfies $M < f''(t) < N$ for all $t$ between $a$ and $x$ (where $M$ and $N$ are constants), then

$$L(x) + \frac{M}{2}(x-a)^2 < f(x) < L(x) + \frac{N}{2}(x-a)^2.$$

If $M$ and $N$ have the same sign, a better approximation to $f(x)$ is given by the midpoint of this interval containing $f(x)$:

$$f(x) \approx L(x) + \frac{M+N}{4}(x-a)^2.$$

For this approximation the error is less than half the length of the interval:

$$|\text{Error}| < \frac{N-M}{4}(x-a)^2.$$

**EXAMPLE 4** Determine the sign and estimate the size of the error in the approximation $\sqrt{26} \approx 5.1$ obtained in Example 3. Use these to give a small interval that you can be sure contains $\sqrt{26}$.

**Solution** For $f(t) = t^{1/2}$, we have

$$f'(t) = \frac{1}{2}t^{-1/2} \quad \text{and} \quad f''(t) = -\frac{1}{4}t^{-3/2}.$$

For $25 < t < 26$, we have $f''(t) < 0$, so $\sqrt{26} = f(26) < L(26) = 5.1$. Also, $t^{3/2} > 25^{3/2} = 125$, so $|f''(t)| < (1/4)(1/125) = 1/500$ and

$$|E(26)| < \frac{1}{2} \times \frac{1}{500} \times (26-25)^2 = \frac{1}{1,000} = 0.001.$$

Therefore, $f(26) > L(26) - 0.001 = 5.099$, and $\sqrt{26}$ is in the interval $(5.099, 5.1)$.

**Remark** We can use Corollary C of Theorem 11 and the fact that $\sqrt{26} < 5.1$ to find a better (i.e., smaller) interval containing $\sqrt{26}$ as follows. If $25 < t < 26$, then $125 = 25^{3/2} < t^{3/2} < 26^{3/2} < 5.1^3$. Thus,

$$M = -\frac{1}{4 \times 125} < f''(t) < -\frac{1}{4 \times 5.1^3} = N$$

$$\sqrt{26} \approx L(26) + \frac{M+N}{4} = 5.1 - \frac{1}{4}\left(\frac{1}{4 \times 125} + \frac{1}{4 \times 5.1^3}\right) \approx 5.099\,028\,8$$

$$|\text{Error}| < \frac{N-M}{4} = \frac{1}{16}\left(-\frac{1}{5.1^3} + \frac{1}{125}\right) \approx 0.000\,028\,8.$$

Thus, $\sqrt{26}$ lies in the interval $(5.099\,00, 5.099\,06)$.

**EXAMPLE 5** Use a suitable linearization to find an approximate value for $\cos 36° = \cos(\pi/5)$. Is the true value greater than or less than your approximation? Estimate the size of the error, and give an interval that you can be sure contains $\cos 36°$.

*Solution*   Let $f(t) = \cos t$, so that $f'(t) = -\sin t$ and $f''(t) = -\cos t$. The value of $a$ nearest to $36°$ for which we know $\cos a$ is $a = 30° = \pi/6$, so we use the linearization about that point:

$$L(x) = \cos\frac{\pi}{6} - \sin\frac{\pi}{6}\left(x - \frac{\pi}{6}\right) = \frac{\sqrt{3}}{2} - \frac{1}{2}\left(x - \frac{\pi}{6}\right).$$

Since $(\pi/5) - (\pi/6) = \pi/30$, our approximation is

$$\cos 36° = \cos\frac{\pi}{5} \approx L\left(\frac{\pi}{5}\right) = \frac{\sqrt{3}}{2} - \frac{1}{2}\left(\frac{\pi}{30}\right) \approx 0.813\,67.$$

If $(\pi/6) < t < (\pi/5)$, then $f''(t) < 0$ and $|f''(t)| < \cos(\pi/6) = \sqrt{3}/2$. Therefore, $\cos 36° < 0.813\,67$ and

$$|E(36°)| < \frac{\sqrt{3}}{4}\left(\frac{\pi}{30}\right)^2 < 0.004\,75.$$

Thus, $0.813\,67 - 0.004\,75 < \cos 36° < 0.813\,67$, so $\cos 36°$ lies in the interval $(0.808\,92, 0.813\,67)$.

---

*Remark*   The error in the linearization of $f(x)$ about $x = a$ can be interpreted in terms of differentials (see Section 5.7 and the beginning of this section) as follows: if $\Delta x = dx = x - a$, then the change in $f(x)$ as we pass from $x = a$ to $x = a + \Delta x$ is $f(a + \Delta x) - f(a) = \Delta y$, and the corresponding change in the linearization $L(x)$ is $f'(a)(x - a) = f'(a)\,dx$, which is just the value at $x = a$ of the differential $dy = f'(x)\,dx$. Thus,

$$E(x) = \Delta y - dy.$$

The error $E(x)$ is small compared with $\Delta x$ as $\Delta x$ approaches $0$, as seen in Figure 7.48. In fact,

$$\lim_{\Delta x \to 0}\frac{\Delta y - dy}{\Delta x} = \lim_{\Delta x \to 0}\left(\frac{\Delta y}{\Delta x} - \frac{dy}{dx}\right) = \frac{dy}{dx} - \frac{dy}{dx} = 0.$$

If $|f''(t)| \le K$ (constant) near $t = a$, a stronger assertion can be made:

$$\left|\frac{\Delta y - dy}{(\Delta x)^2}\right| = \left|\frac{E(x)}{(\Delta x)^2}\right| \le \frac{K}{2}, \qquad \text{so} \qquad |\Delta y - dy| \le \frac{K}{2}(\Delta x)^2.$$

## EXERCISES 7.7

In Exercises 1–10, find the linearization of the given function about the given point.

1. $x^2$ about $x = 3$

2. $x^{-3}$ about $x = 2$

3. $\sqrt{4 - x}$ about $x = 0$

4. $\sqrt{3 + x^2}$ about $x = 1$

5. $1/(1 + x)^2$ about $x = 2$

6. $1/\sqrt{x}$ about $x = 4$

7. $\sin x$ about $x = \pi$

8. $\cos(2x)$ about $x = \pi/3$

9. $\sin^2 x$ about $x = \pi/6$

10. $\tan x$ about $x = \pi/4$

11. By approximately how much does the area of a square increase if its side length increases from 10 cm to 10.4 cm?

12. By about how much must the edge length of a cube decrease from 20 cm to reduce the volume of the cube by 12 cm$^3$?

13. A spacecraft orbits the earth at a distance of 4,100 miles from the centre of the earth. By about how much will the circumference of its orbit decrease if the radius decreases by 10 miles?

14. (**Acceleration of gravity**) The acceleration $a$ of gravity at an altitude of $h$ miles above the surface of the earth is given by

$$a = g\left(\frac{R}{R + h}\right)^2,$$

where $g \approx 32$ ft/s$^2$ is the acceleration at the surface of the earth, and $R \approx 3,960$ miles is the radius of the earth. By about what percentage will $a$ decrease if $h$ increases from 0 to 10 miles?

In Exercises 15–22, use a suitable linearization to approximate the indicated value. Determine the sign of the error and estimate its size. Use this information to specify an interval you can be sure contains the value.

**15.** $\sqrt{50}$

**16.** $\sqrt{47}$

**17.** $\sqrt[4]{85}$

**18.** $\dfrac{1}{2.003}$

**19.** $\cos 46°$

**20.** $\sin \dfrac{\pi}{5}$

**21.** $\sin(3.14)$

**22.** $\sin 33°$

Use Corollary C of Theorem 11 in the manner suggested in the remark following Example 4 to find better intervals and better approximations to the values in Exercises 23–26.

**23.** $\sqrt{50}$ as first approximated in Exercise 15.

**24.** $\sqrt{47}$ as first approximated in Exercise 16.

**25.** $\cos 36°$ as first approximated in Example 5.

**26.** $\sin 33°$ as first approximated in Exercise 22.

**27.** If $f(2) = 4$, $f'(2) = -1$, and $0 \le f''(x) \le 1/x$ for $x > 0$, find the smallest interval you can be sure contains $f(3)$.

**28.** If $f(2) = 4$, $f'(2) = -1$, and $\dfrac{1}{2x} \le f''(x) \le \dfrac{1}{x}$ for $2 \le x \le 3$, find the best approximation you can for $f(3)$.

**29.** If $g(2) = 1$, $g'(2) = 2$, and $|g''(x)| < 1 + (x-2)^2$ for all $x > 0$, find the best approximation you can for $g(1.8)$. How large can the error be?

**30.** Show that the linearization of $\sin \theta$ at $\theta = 0$ is $L(\theta) = \theta$. How large can the percentage error in the approximation $\sin \theta \approx \theta$ be if $|\theta|$ is less than $17°$?

**31.** A spherical balloon is inflated so that its radius increases from 20.00 cm to 20.20 cm in 1 min. By approximately how much has its volume increased in that minute?

# CHAPTER 8

# Integration

> **❝** There are in this world optimists who feel that any symbol that starts off with an integral sign must necessarily denote something that will have every property that they should like an integral to possess. This of course is quite annoying to us rigorous mathematicians; what is even more annoying is that by doing so they often come up with the right answer. **❞**

**E. J. McShane**
*Bulletin of the American Mathematical Society, v. 69, p. 611, 1963*

## Introduction

The second fundamental problem addressed by calculus is the problem of areas, that is, the problem of determining the area of a region of the plane bounded by various curves. Like the problem of tangents considered in Chapter 5, many practical problems in various disciplines require the evaluation of areas for their solution, and the solution of the problem of areas necessarily involves the notion of limits. On the surface the problem of areas appears unrelated to the problem of tangents. However, we will see that the two problems are very closely related; one is the inverse of the other. Finding an area is equivalent to finding an antiderivative or, as we prefer to say, finding an integral. The relationship between areas and antiderivatives is called the Fundamental Theorem of Calculus. When we have proved it, we will be able to find areas at will, provided only that we can integrate (i.e., antidifferentiate) the various functions we encounter.

We would like to have at our disposal a set of integration rules similar to the differentiation rules developed in Chapter 5. We can find the derivative of any differentiable function using those differentiation rules. Unfortunately, integration is generally more difficult; indeed, some fairly simple functions are not themselves derivatives of simple functions. For example, $e^{x^2}$ is not the derivative of any finite combination of elementary functions. Later, in Chapter 9, we will examine how to approximate areas bounded by graphs of functions that we cannot antidifferentiate.

## 8.1 Sums and Sigma Notation

When we begin calculating areas in the next section, we will often encounter sums of values of functions. We need to have a convenient notation for representing sums of arbitrary (possibly large) numbers of terms, and we need to develop techniques for evaluating some such sums.

We use the symbol $\sum$ to represent a sum; it is an enlarged Greek capital letter $S$ called *sigma*.

DEFINITION

**Sigma notation**

If $m$ and $n$ are integers with $m \leq n$, and if $f$ is a function defined at the integers $m, m+1, m+2, \ldots, n$, the symbol $\sum_{i=m}^{n} f(i)$ represents the sum of the values of $f$ at those integers:

$$\sum_{i=m}^{n} f(i) = f(m) + f(m+1) + f(m+2) + \cdots + f(n).$$

The explicit sum appearing on the right side of this equation is the **expansion** of the sum represented in sigma notation on the left side.

---

**EXAMPLE 1**   $\displaystyle\sum_{i=1}^{5} i^2 = 1^2 + 2^2 + 3^2 + 4^2 + 5^2 = 55.$

---

The $i$ that appears in the symbol $\sum_{i=m}^{n} f(i)$ is called an **index of summation**. To evaluate $\sum_{i=m}^{n} f(i)$, replace the index $i$ with the integers $m, m+1, \ldots, n$, successively, and sum the results. Observe that the value of the sum does not depend on what we call the index; the index does not appear on the right side of the definition. If we use another letter in place of $i$ in the sum in Example 1, we still get the same value for the sum:

$$\sum_{k=1}^{5} k^2 = 1^2 + 2^2 + 3^2 + 4^2 + 5^2 = 55.$$

The index of summation is a *dummy variable* used to represent an arbitrary point where the function is evaluated to produce a term to be included in the sum. On the other hand, the sum $\sum_{i=m}^{n} f(i)$ does depend on the two numbers $m$ and $n$, called the **limits of summation**; $m$ is the **lower limit**, and $n$ is the **upper limit**.

---

**EXAMPLE 2**   **(Examples of sums using sigma notation)**

$$\sum_{j=1}^{20} j = 1 + 2 + 3 + \cdots + 18 + 19 + 20$$

$$\sum_{i=0}^{n} x^i = x^0 + x^1 + x^2 + \cdots + x^{n-1} + x^n$$

$$\sum_{m=1}^{n} 1 = \underbrace{1 + 1 + 1 + \cdots + 1}_{n \text{ terms}}$$

$$\sum_{k=-2}^{3} \frac{1}{k+7} = \frac{1}{5} + \frac{1}{6} + \frac{1}{7} + \frac{1}{8} + \frac{1}{9} + \frac{1}{10}$$

---

Sometimes we use a subscripted variable $a_i$ to denote the $i$th term of a general sum instead of using the functional notation $f(i)$:

$$\sum_{i=m}^{n} a_i = a_m + a_{m+1} + a_{m+2} + \cdots + a_n.$$

In particular, an **infinite series** is such a sum with infinitely many terms:

$$\sum_{n=1}^{\infty} a_n = a_1 + a_2 + a_3 + \cdots.$$

When no final term follows the $\cdots$, it is understood that the terms go on forever.

When adding finitely many numbers, the order in which they are added is unimportant; any order will give the same sum. If all the numbers have a common factor, then that factor can be removed from each term and multiplied after the sum is evaluated: $ca + cb = c(a + b)$. These laws of arithmetic translate into the following *linearity* rule for finite sums; if $A$ and $B$ are constants, then

$$\sum_{i=m}^{n}\left(Af(i) + Bg(i)\right) = A\sum_{i=m}^{n} f(i) + B\sum_{i=m}^{n} g(i).$$

Both of the sums $\sum_{j=m}^{m+n} f(j)$ and $\sum_{i=0}^{n} f(i + m)$ have the same expansion, namely, $f(m) + f(m + 1) + \cdots + f(m + n)$. Therefore, the two sums are equal.

$$\sum_{j=m}^{m+n} f(j) = \sum_{i=0}^{n} f(i + m).$$

This equality can also be derived by substituting $i + m$ for $j$ everywhere $j$ appears on the left side, noting that $i + m = m$ reduces to $i = 0$, and $i + m = m + n$ reduces to $i = n$. It is often convenient to make such a **change of index** in a summation.

**EXAMPLE 3**    Express $\sum_{j=3}^{17} \sqrt{1 + j^2}$ in the form $\sum_{i=1}^{n} f(i)$.

*Solution*   Let $j = i + 2$. Then $j = 3$ corresponds to $i = 1$ and $j = 17$ corresponds to $i = 15$. Thus,

$$\sum_{j=3}^{17} \sqrt{1 + j^2} = \sum_{i=1}^{15} \sqrt{1 + (i + 2)^2}.$$

## Evaluating Sums

There is a **closed form** expression for the sum $S$ of the first $n$ positive integers, namely,

$$S = \sum_{i=1}^{n} i = 1 + 2 + 3 + \cdots + n = \frac{n(n + 1)}{2}.$$

To see this, write the sum forwards and backwards and add the two to get

$$\begin{aligned} S &= \quad 1 \quad + \quad 2 \quad + \quad 3 \quad + \cdots + (n-1) + \quad n \\ S &= \quad n \quad + (n-1) + (n-2) + \cdots + \quad 2 \quad + \quad 1 \\ \hline 2S &= (n+1) + (n+1) + (n+1) + \cdots + (n+1) + (n+1) = n(n+1) \end{aligned}$$

The formula for $S$ follows when we divide by 2.

It is not usually this easy to evaluate a general sum in closed form. We can only simplify $\sum_{i=m}^{n} f(i)$ for a small class of functions $f$. The only such formulas we will need in the next sections are collected in Theorem 1.

THEOREM

1

**Summation formulas**

(a) $\displaystyle\sum_{i=1}^{n} 1 = \underbrace{1 + 1 + 1 + \cdots + 1}_{n \text{ terms}} = n.$

(b) $\displaystyle\sum_{i=1}^{n} i = 1 + 2 + 3 + \cdots + n = \frac{n(n+1)}{2}.$

(c) $\displaystyle\sum_{i=1}^{n} i^2 = 1^2 + 2^2 + 3^2 + \cdots + n^2 = \frac{n(n+1)(2n+1)}{6}.$

(d) $\displaystyle\sum_{i=1}^{n} r^{i-1} = 1 + r + r^2 + r^3 + \cdots + r^{n-1} = \frac{r^n - 1}{r - 1}$   if $r \neq 1.$

*PROOF*  Formula (a) is trivial; the sum of $n$ ones is $n$. One proof of formula (b) was given above.

To prove (c) we write $n$ copies of the identity

$$(k+1)^3 - k^3 = 3k^2 + 3k + 1,$$

one for each value of $k$ from 1 to $n$, and add them up:

| | | | | | | | |
|---|---|---|---|---|---|---|---|
| $2^3$ | $- \ 1^3$ | $=$ | $3 \times 1^2$ | $+$ | $3 \times 1$ | $+$ | $1$ |
| $3^3$ | $- \ 2^3$ | $=$ | $3 \times 2^2$ | $+$ | $3 \times 2$ | $+$ | $1$ |
| $4^3$ | $- \ 3^3$ | $=$ | $3 \times 3^2$ | $+$ | $3 \times 3$ | $+$ | $1$ |
| $\vdots$ | $\vdots$ | | $\vdots$ | | $\vdots$ | | $\vdots$ |
| $n^3$ | $- \ (n-1)^3$ | $=$ | $3(n-1)^2$ | $+$ | $3(n-1)$ | $+$ | $1$ |
| $(n+1)^3$ | $- \ n^3$ | $=$ | $3 n^2$ | $+$ | $3n$ | $+$ | $1$ |
| $(n+1)^3$ | $- \ 1^3$ | $=$ | $3\left(\sum_{i=1}^{n} i^2\right)$ | $+$ | $3\left(\sum_{i=1}^{n} i\right)$ | $+$ | $n$ |
| | | $=$ | $3\left(\sum_{i=1}^{n} i^2\right)$ | $+$ | $\dfrac{3n(n+1)}{2}$ | $+$ | $n.$ |

We used formula (b) in the last line. The final equation can be solved for the desired sum to give formula (c). Note the cancellations that occurred when we added up the left sides of the $n$ equations. The term $2^3$ in the first line cancelled the $-2^3$ in the second line, and so on, leaving us with only two terms, the $(n+1)^3$ from the $n$th line and the $-1^3$ from the first line:

$$\sum_{k=1}^{n} \left( (k+1)^3 - k^3 \right) = (n+1)^3 - 1^3.$$

This is an example of what we call a **telescoping sum**. In general, a sum of the form $\sum_{i=m}^{n} \left( f(i+1) - f(i) \right)$ telescopes to the closed form $f(n+1) - f(m)$ because all but the first and last terms cancel out.

To prove formula (d), let $s = \sum_{i=1}^{n} r^{i-1}$ and subtract $s$ from $rs$:

$$(r-1)s = rs - s = (r + r^2 + r^3 + \cdots + r^n) - (1 + r + r^2 + \cdots + r^{n-1})$$
$$= r^n - 1.$$

The result follows on division by $r - 1$.

Other proofs of (b) – (d) are suggested in Exercises 36–38.

────────────────────────────────────

EXAMPLE 4  Evaluate $\displaystyle\sum_{k=m+1}^{n} (6k^2 - 4k + 3)$, where $1 \leq m < n.$

*Solution*  Using the rules of summation and various summation formulas from Theorem 1, we calculate

$$\sum_{k=1}^{n}(6k^2 - 4k + 3) = 6\sum_{k=1}^{n}k^2 - 4\sum_{k=1}^{n}k + 3\sum_{k=1}^{n}1$$

$$= 6\frac{n(n+1)(2n+1)}{6} - 4\frac{n(n+1)}{2} + 3n$$

$$= 2n^3 + n^2 + 2n$$

Thus,

$$\sum_{k=m+1}^{n}(6k^2 - 4k + 3) = \sum_{k=1}^{n}(6k^2 - 4k + 3) - \sum_{k=1}^{m}(6k^2 - 4k + 3)$$

$$= 2n^3 + n^2 + 2n - 2m^3 - m^2 - 2m.$$

**Remark**  Maple can find closed form expressions for some sums. For example,

```
>  sum(i^4, i=1..n); factor(%);
```

$$\frac{1}{5}(n+1)^5 - \frac{1}{2}(n+1)^4 + \frac{1}{3}(n+1)^3 - \frac{1}{30}n - \frac{1}{30}$$

$$\frac{1}{30}n(2n+1)(n+1)(3n^2 + 3n - 1)$$

## EXERCISES 8.1

Expand the sums in Exercises 1–6.

**1.** $\displaystyle\sum_{i=1}^{4} i^3$

**2.** $\displaystyle\sum_{j=1}^{100} \frac{j}{j+1}$

**3.** $\displaystyle\sum_{i=1}^{n} 3^i$

**4.** $\displaystyle\sum_{i=0}^{n-1} \frac{(-1)^i}{i+1}$

**5.** $\displaystyle\sum_{j=3}^{n} \frac{(-2)^j}{(j-2)^2}$

**6.** $\displaystyle\sum_{j=1}^{n} \frac{j^2}{n^3}$

Write the sums in Exercises 7–14 using sigma notation. (Note that the answers are not unique.)

**7.** $5 + 6 + 7 + 8 + 9$

**8.** $2 + 2 + 2 + \cdots + 2$    (200 terms)

**9.** $2^2 - 3^2 + 4^2 - 5^2 + \cdots - 99^2$

**10.** $1 + 2x + 3x^2 + 4x^3 + \cdots + 100x^{99}$

**11.** $1 + x + x^2 + x^3 + \cdots + x^n$

**12.** $1 - x + x^2 - x^3 + \cdots + x^{2n}$

**13.** $1 - \dfrac{1}{4} + \dfrac{1}{9} - \dfrac{1}{16} + \cdots + \dfrac{(-1)^{n-1}}{n^2}$

**14.** $\dfrac{1}{2} + \dfrac{2}{4} + \dfrac{3}{8} + \dfrac{4}{16} + \cdots + \dfrac{n}{2^n}$

Express the sums in Exercises 15–16 in the form $\sum_{i=1}^{n} f(i)$.

**15.** $\displaystyle\sum_{j=0}^{99} \sin(j)$

**16.** $\displaystyle\sum_{k=-5}^{m} \frac{1}{k^2+1}$

Find closed form values for the sums in Exercises 17–28.

**17.** $\displaystyle\sum_{i=1}^{n} (i^2 + 2i)$

**18.** $\displaystyle\sum_{j=1}^{1,000} (2j + 3)$

**19.** $\displaystyle\sum_{k=1}^{n} (\pi^k - 3)$

**20.** $\displaystyle\sum_{i=1}^{n} (2^i - i^2)$

**21.** $\displaystyle\sum_{m=1}^{n} \ln m$

**22.** $\displaystyle\sum_{i=0}^{n} e^{i/n}$

**23.** The sum in Exercise 8.    **24.** The sum in Exercise 11.

**25.** The sum in Exercise 12.

**26.** The sum in Exercise 10. *Hint:* Differentiate the sum $\sum_{i=0}^{100} x^i$.

**27.** The sum in Exercise 9. *Hint:* The sum is

$$\sum_{k=1}^{49}\left((2k)^2 - (2k+1)^2\right) = \sum_{k=1}^{49}(-4k - 1).$$

**28.** The sum in Exercise 14. *Hint:* apply the method of proof of Theorem 1(d) to this sum.

**29.** Verify the formula for the value of a telescoping sum:

$$\sum_{i=m}^{n}\left(f(i+1) - f(i)\right) = f(n+1) - f(m).$$

Why is the word "telescoping" used to describe this sum?

In Exercises 30–32, evaluate the given telescoping sums.

**30.** $\displaystyle\sum_{n=1}^{10}\left(n^4-(n-1)^4\right)$    **31.** $\displaystyle\sum_{j=1}^{m}(2^j-2^{j-1})$

**32.** $\displaystyle\sum_{i=m}^{2m}\left(\frac{1}{i}-\frac{1}{i+1}\right)$

**33.** Show that $\dfrac{1}{j(j+1)}=\dfrac{1}{j}-\dfrac{1}{j+1}$, and hence evaluate

$$\sum_{j=1}^{n}\frac{1}{j(j+1)}.$$

**34.** Figure 8.1 shows a square of side $n$ subdivided into $n^2$ smaller squares of side 1. How many small squares are shaded? Obtain the closed form expression for $\sum_{i=1}^{n} i$ by considering the sum of the areas of the shaded squares.

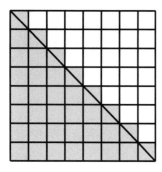

Figure 8.1

**35.** Write $n$ copies of the identity $(k+1)^2-k^2=2k+1$, one for each integer $k$ from 1 to $n$, and add them up to obtain the formula

$$\sum_{i=1}^{n} i=\frac{n(n+1)}{2}$$

in a manner similar to the proof of Theorem 1(c).

**36.** Use mathematical induction to prove Theorem 1(b).

**37.** Use mathematical induction to prove Theorem 1(c).

**38.** Use mathematical induction to prove Theorem 1(d).

**39.** Figure 8.2 shows a square of side $\sum_{i=1}^{n} i=n(n+1)/2$ subdivided into a small square of side 1 and $n-1$

L-shaped regions whose short edges are 2, 3, ..., $n$. Show that the area of the L-shaped region with short side $i$ is $i^3$, and hence verify that

$$\sum_{i=1}^{n} i^3=\frac{n^2(n+1)^2}{4}.$$

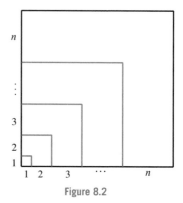

Figure 8.2

**40.** Write $n$ copies of the identity

$$(k+1)^4-k^4=4k^3+6k^2+4k+1,$$

one for each integer $k$ from 1 to $n$, and add them up to obtain the formula

$$\sum_{i=1}^{n} i^3=\frac{n^2(n+1)^2}{4}$$

in a manner similar to the proof of Theorem 1(c).

**41.** Use mathematical induction to verify the formula for the sum of cubes given in Exercise 40.

**42.** Extend the method of Exercise 40 to find a closed form expression for $\sum_{i=1}^{n} i^4$. You will probably want to use Maple or other computer algebra software to do all the algebra.

**43.** Use Maple or another computer algebra system to find $\sum_{i=1}^{n} i^k$ for $k=5,6,7,8$. Observe the term involving the highest power of $n$ in each case. Predict the highest-power term in $\sum_{i=1}^{n} i^{10}$ and verify your prediction.

## 8.2 Areas as Limits of Sums

We began the study of derivatives in Chapter 5 by defining what is meant by a tangent line to a curve at a particular point. We would like to begin the study of integrals by defining what is meant by the **area** of a plane region, but a definition of area is much more difficult to give than a definition of tangency. Let us assume (as we did, for example, in Section 6.3) that we know intuitively what area means and list some of its properties. (See Figure 8.3.)

(i) The area of a plane region is a nonnegative real number of *square units*.

(ii) The area of a rectangle with width $w$ and height $h$ is $A=wh$.

(iii) The areas of congruent plane regions are equal.

(iv) If region $S$ is contained in region $R$, then the area of $S$ is less than or equal to that of $R$.

(v) If region $R$ is a union of (finitely many) nonoverlapping regions, then the area of $R$ is the sum of the areas of those regions.

Using these five properties we can calculate the area of any **polygon** (a region bounded by straight line segments). First, we note that properties (iii) and (v) show that the area of a parallelogram is the same as that of a rectangle having the same base width and height. Any triangle can be butted against a congruent copy of itself to form a parallelogram, so a triangle has area half the base width times the height. Finally, any polygon can be subdivided into finitely many nonoverlapping triangles so its area is the sum of the areas of those triangles.

We can't go beyond polygons without taking limits. If a region has a curved boundary, its area can only be approximated by using rectangles or triangles; calculating the exact area requires the evaluation of a limit. We showed how this could be done for a circle.

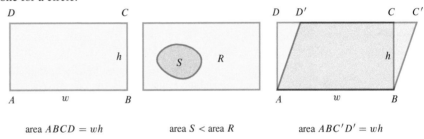

area $ABCD = wh$       area $S <$ area $R$       area $ABC'D' = wh$

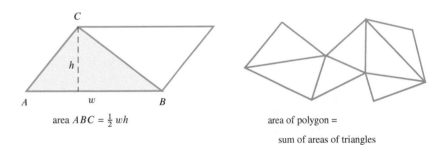

area $ABC = \frac{1}{2}wh$              area of polygon =

                                        sum of areas of triangles

**Figure 8.3**    Properties of area

## The Basic Area Problem

In this section we are going to consider how to find the area of a region $R$ lying under the graph $y = f(x)$ of a nonnegative-valued, continuous function $f$, above the $x$-axis and between the vertical lines $x = a$ and $x = b$, where $a < b$. (See Figure 8.4.) To accomplish this, we proceed as follows. Divide the interval $[a, b]$ into $n$ subintervals by using division points:

$$a = x_0 < x_1 < x_2 < x_3 < \cdots < x_{n-1} < x_n = b.$$

Denote by $\Delta x_i$ the length of the $i$th subinterval $[x_{i-1}, x_i]$:

$$\Delta x_i = x_i - x_{i-1}, \qquad (i = 1, 2, 3, \ldots, n).$$

Vertically above each subinterval $[x_{i-1}, x_i]$ build a rectangle whose base has length $\Delta x_i$ and whose height is $f(x_i)$. The area of this rectangle is $f(x_i)\,\Delta x_i$. Form the sum of these areas:

$$S_n = f(x_1)\,\Delta x_1 + f(x_2)\,\Delta x_2 + f(x_3)\,\Delta x_3 + \cdots + f(x_n)\,\Delta x_n = \sum_{i=1}^{n} f(x_i)\,\Delta x_i.$$

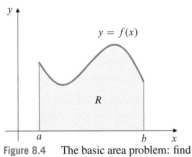

**Figure 8.4**    The basic area problem: find the area of region $R$

The rectangles are shown shaded in Figure 8.5 for a decreasing function $f$. For an increasing function, the tops of the rectangles would lie above the graph of $f$ rather than below it. Evidently, $S_n$ is an approximation to the area of the region $R$, and the approximation gets better as $n$ increases, provided we choose the points $a = x_0 < x_1 < \cdots < x_n = b$ in such a way that the width $\Delta x_i$ of the widest rectangle approaches zero.

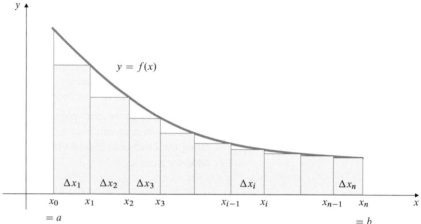

**Figure 8.5**     Approximating the area under the graph of a decreasing function using rectangles

Observe in Figure 8.6, for example, that subdividing a subinterval into two smaller subintervals reduces the error in the approximation by reducing that part of the area under the curve that is not contained in the rectangles. It is reasonable, therefore, to calculate the area of $R$ by finding the limit of $S_n$ as $n \to \infty$ with the restriction that the largest of the subinterval widths $\Delta x_i$ must approach zero:

$$\text{Area of } R = \lim_{\substack{n \to \infty \\ \max \Delta x_i \to 0}} S_n.$$

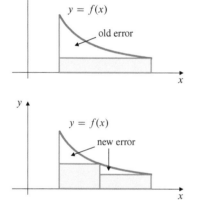

**Figure 8.6**     Using more rectangles makes the error smaller

Sometimes, but not always, it is useful to choose the points $x_i$ $(0 \le i \le n)$ in $[a, b]$ in such a way that the subinterval lengths $\Delta x_i$ are all equal. In this case we have

$$\Delta x_i = \Delta x = \frac{b - a}{n}, \qquad x_i = a + i\,\Delta x = a + \frac{i}{n}(b - a).$$

## Some Area Calculations

We devote the rest of this section to some examples in which we apply the technique described above for finding areas under graphs of functions by approximating with rectangles. Let us begin with a region for which we already know the area so we can satisfy ourselves that the method does give the correct value.

**EXAMPLE 1**     Find the area $A$ of the region lying under the straight line $y = x + 1$, above the $x$-axis, and between the lines $x = 0$ and $x = 2$.

**Solution**     The region is shaded in Figure 8.7(a). It is a *trapezoid* (a four-sided polygon with one pair of parallel sides) and has area 4 square units. (It can be divided into a rectangle and a triangle, each of area 2 square units.) We will calculate the area as a limit of sums of areas of rectangles constructed as described above. Divide the interval $[0, 2]$ into $n$ subintervals *of equal length* by points

$$x_0 = 0, \; x_1 = \frac{2}{n}, \; x_2 = \frac{4}{n}, \; x_3 = \frac{6}{n}, \; \ldots \; x_n = \frac{2n}{n} = 2.$$

The value of $y = x + 1$ at $x = x_i$ is $x_i + 1 = \dfrac{2i}{n} + 1$ and the $i$th subinterval, $\left[\dfrac{2(i-1)}{n}, \dfrac{2i}{n}\right]$, has length $\Delta x_i = \dfrac{2}{n}$. Observe that $\Delta x_i \to 0$ as $n \to \infty$.

The sum of the areas of the approximating rectangles shown in Figure 8 .7(a) is

$$S_n = \sum_{i=1}^{n} \left( \frac{2i}{n} + 1 \right) \frac{2}{n}$$

$$= \left( \frac{2}{n} \right) \left[ \frac{2}{n} \sum_{i=1}^{n} i + \sum_{i=1}^{n} 1 \right] \qquad \text{(Use parts (b) and (a) of Theorem 1.)}$$

$$= \left( \frac{2}{n} \right) \left[ \frac{2}{n} \frac{n(n+1)}{2} + n \right]$$

$$= 2 \frac{n+1}{n} + 2.$$

Therefore, the required area $A$ is given by

$$A = \lim_{n \to \infty} S_n = \lim_{n \to \infty} \left( 2 \frac{n+1}{n} + 2 \right) = 2 + 2 = 4 \text{ square units.}$$

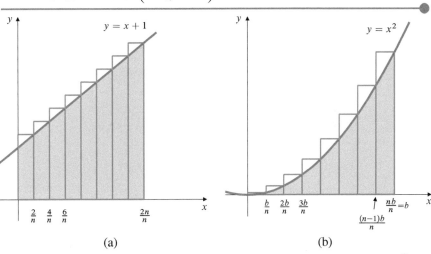

**Figure 8.7**

(a) The region of Example 1

(b) The region of Example 2

(a)                    (b)

---
**EXAMPLE 2**   Find the area of the region bounded by the parabola $y = x^2$ and the straight lines $y = 0$, $x = 0$, and $x = b$, where $b > 0$.

*Solution*   The area $A$ of the region is the limit of the sum $S_n$ of areas of the rectangles shown in Figure 8.7(b). Again we have used equal subintervals, each of length $b/n$. The height of the $i$th rectangle is $(ib/n)^2$. Thus,

$$S_n = \sum_{i=1}^{n} \left( \frac{ib}{n} \right)^2 \frac{b}{n} = \frac{b^3}{n^3} \sum_{i=1}^{n} i^2 = \frac{b^3}{n^3} \frac{n(n+1)(2n+1)}{6},$$

by formula (c) of Theorem 1. Hence, the required area is

$$A = \lim_{n \to \infty} S_n = \lim_{n \to \infty} b^3 \frac{(n+1)(2n+1)}{6n^2} = \frac{b^3}{3} \text{ square units.}$$

---
Finding an area under the graph of $y = x^k$ over an interval $I$ becomes more and more difficult as $k$ increases if we continue to try to subdivide $I$ into subintervals of equal length. (See Exercise 14 at the end of this section for the case $k = 3$.) It is, however, possible to find the area for arbitrary $k$ if we subdivide the interval $I$ into subintervals whose lengths increase in geometric progression. Example 3 illustrates this.

---
**EXAMPLE 3**   Let $b > a > 0$, and let $k$ be any real number except $-1$. Show that the area $A$ of the region bounded by $y = x^k$, $y = 0$, $x = a$, and $x = b$ is

$$A = \frac{b^{k+1} - a^{k+1}}{k+1} \text{ square units.}$$

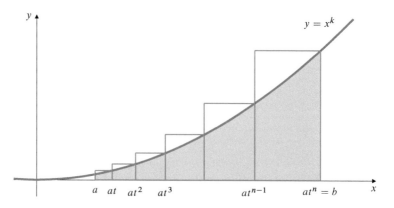

Figure 8.8    For this partition the subinterval lengths increase exponentially

BEWARE!    This is a long and rather difficult example. Either skip over it or take your time and check each step carefully.

*Solution*   Let $t = (b/a)^{1/n}$ and let

$$x_0 = a, \ x_1 = at, \ x_2 = at^2, \ x_3 = at^3, \ \ldots \ x_n = at^n = b.$$

These points subdivide the interval $[a, b]$ into $n$ subintervals of which the $i$th, $[x_{i-1}, x_i]$, has length $\Delta x_i = at^{i-1}(t - 1)$. If $f(x) = x^k$, then $f(x_i) = a^k t^{ki}$. The sum of the areas of the rectangles shown in Figure 8.8 is:

$$S_n = \sum_{i=1}^{n} f(x_i)\, \Delta x_i$$

$$= \sum_{i=1}^{n} a^k\, t^{ki}\, at^{i-1}(t - 1)$$

$$= a^{k+1}\,(t - 1)\, t^k \sum_{i=1}^{n} t^{(k+1)(i-1)}$$

$$= a^{k+1}\,(t - 1)\, t^k \sum_{i=1}^{n} r^{(i-1)} \qquad \text{where } r = t^{k+1}$$

$$= a^{k+1}\,(t - 1)\, t^k\, \frac{r^n - 1}{r - 1} \qquad \text{(by Theorem 1(d))}$$

$$= a^{k+1}\,(t - 1)\, t^k\, \frac{t^{(k+1)n} - 1}{t^{k+1} - 1}.$$

Now replace $t$ with its value $(b/a)^{1/n}$ and rearrange factors to obtain

$$S_n = a^{k+1}\left(\left(\frac{b}{a}\right)^{1/n} - 1\right)\left(\frac{b}{a}\right)^{k/n} \frac{\left(\dfrac{b}{a}\right)^{k+1} - 1}{\left(\dfrac{b}{a}\right)^{(k+1)/n} - 1}$$

$$= \left(b^{k+1} - a^{k+1}\right) c^{k/n}\, \frac{c^{1/n} - 1}{c^{(k+1)/n} - 1}, \qquad \text{where } c = \frac{b}{a}.$$

Of the three factors in the final line above, the first does not depend on $n$, and the second, $c^{k/n}$, approaches $c^0 = 1$ as $n \to \infty$. The third factor is an indeterminate form of type $[0/0]$, which we evaluate using l'Hôpital's Rule. First let $u = 1/n$. Then

$$\lim_{n \to \infty} \frac{c^{1/n} - 1}{c^{(k+1)/n} - 1} = \lim_{u \to 0+} \frac{c^u - 1}{c^{(k+1)u} - 1} \qquad \left[\frac{0}{0}\right]$$

$$= \lim_{u \to 0+} \frac{c^u \ln c}{(k + 1)\, c^{(k+1)u} \ln c} = \frac{1}{k + 1}.$$

Therefore, the required area is

$$A = \lim_{n \to \infty} S_n = \left(b^{k+1} - a^{k+1}\right) \times 1 \times \frac{1}{k+1} = \frac{b^{k+1} - a^{k+1}}{k+1} \text{ square units.}$$

As you can see, it can be rather difficult to calculate areas bounded by curves by the methods developed above. Fortunately, there is an easier way, as we will discover in Section 8.5.

**Remark**  For technical reasons it was necessary to assume $a > 0$ in Example 3. The result is also valid for $a = 0$ provided $k > -1$. In this case we have $\lim_{a \to 0+} a^{k+1} = 0$, so the area under $y = x^k$, above $y = 0$, between $x = 0$ and $x = b > 0$ is $A = b^{k+1}/(k+1)$ square units. For $k = 2$ this agrees with the result of Example 2.

---

**EXAMPLE 4**  Identify the limit $L = \lim_{n \to \infty} \sum_{i=1}^{n} \frac{n-i}{n^2}$ as an area, and evaluate it.

**Solution**  We can rewrite the $i$th term of the sum so that it depends on $i/n$:

$$L = \lim_{n \to \infty} \sum_{i=1}^{n} \left(1 - \frac{i}{n}\right) \frac{1}{n}.$$

The terms now appear to be the areas of rectangles of base $1/n$ and heights $1 - x_i$, $(1 \le i \le n)$, where

$$x_1 = \frac{1}{n}, \quad x_2 = \frac{2}{n}, \quad x_3 = \frac{3}{n}, \quad \dots, \quad x_n = \frac{n}{n}.$$

Thus, the limit $L$ is the area under the curve $y = 1 - x$ from $x = 0$ to $x = 1$. (See Figure 8.9.) This region is a triangle having area $1/2$ square unit, so $L = 1/2$.

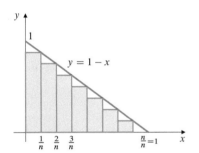

**Figure 8.9**    Recognizing a sum of areas

---

# EXERCISES 8.2

Use the techniques of Examples 1 and 2 (with subintervals of equal length) to find the areas of the regions specified in Exercises 1–13.

1. Below $y = 3x$, above $y = 0$, from $x = 0$ to $x = 1$.

2. Below $y = 2x + 1$, above $y = 0$, from $x = 0$ to $x = 3$.

3. Below $y = 2x - 1$, above $y = 0$, from $x = 1$ to $x = 3$.

4. Below $y = 3x + 4$, above $y = 0$, from $x = -1$ to $x = 2$.

5. Below $y = x^2$, above $y = 0$, from $x = 1$ to $x = 3$.

6. Below $y = x^2 + 1$, above $y = 0$, from $x = 0$ to $x = a > 0$.

7. Below $y = x^2 + 2x + 3$, above $y = 0$, from $x = -1$ to $x = 2$.

8. Above $y = x^2 - 1$, below $y = 0$.

9. Above $y = 1 - x$, below $y = 0$, from $x = 2$ to $x = 4$.

10. Above $y = x^2 - 2x$, below $y = 0$.

11. Below $y = 4x - x^2 + 1$, above $y = 1$.

‼ 12. Below $y = e^x$, above $y = 0$, from $x = 0$ to $x = b > 0$.

‼ 13. Below $y = 2^x$, above $y = 0$, from $x = -1$ to $x = 1$.

14. Use the formula $\sum_{i=1}^{n} i^3 = n^2(n+1)^2/4$, from Exercises 39–41 of Section 8.1, to find the area of the region lying under $y = x^3$, above the $x$-axis, and between the vertical lines at $x = 0$ and $x = b > 0$.

15. Use the subdivision of $[a, b]$ given in Example 3 to find the area under $y = 1/x$, above $y = 0$, from $x = a > 0$ to $x = b > a$. Why should your answer not be surprising?

In Exercises 16–19, interpret the given sum $S_n$ as a sum of areas of rectangles approximating the area of a certain region in the plane and hence evaluate $\lim_{n \to \infty} S_n$.

16. $S_n = \sum_{i=1}^{n} \frac{2}{n}\left(1 - \frac{i}{n}\right)$

17. $S_n = \sum_{i=1}^{n} \frac{2}{n}\left(1 - \frac{2i}{n}\right)$

18. $S_n = \sum_{i=1}^{n} \frac{2n + 3i}{n^2}$

‼ 19. $S_n = \sum_{j=1}^{n} \frac{1}{n}\sqrt{1 - (j/n)^2}$

## 8.3    The Definite Integral

In this section we generalize and make more precise the procedure used for finding areas developed in Section 8.2, and we use it to define the *definite integral* of a function $f$ on an interval $I$. Let us assume, for the time being, that $f(x)$ is defined and continuous on the closed, finite interval $[a, b]$. We no longer assume that the values of $f$ are nonnegative.

### Partitions and Riemann Sums

Let $P$ be a finite set of points arranged in order between $a$ and $b$ on the real line, say

$$P = \{x_0, x_1, x_2, x_3, \ldots, x_{n-1}, x_n\},$$

where $a = x_0 < x_1 < x_2 < x_3 < \cdots < x_{n-1} < x_n = b$. Such a set $P$ is called a **partition** of $[a, b]$; it divides $[a, b]$ into $n$ subintervals of which the $i$th is $[x_{i-1}, x_i]$. We call these the subintervals of the partition $P$. The number $n$ depends on the particular partition, so we write $n = n(P)$. The length of the $i$th subinterval of $P$ is

$$\Delta x_i = x_i - x_{i-1}, \qquad \text{(for } 1 \leq i \leq n),$$

and we call the greatest of these numbers $\Delta x_i$ the **norm** of the partition $P$ and denote it $\|P\|$:

$$\|P\| = \max_{1 \leq i \leq n} \Delta x_i.$$

Since $f$ is continuous on each subinterval $[x_{i-1}, x_i]$ of $P$, it takes on maximum and minimum values at points of that interval. Thus, there are numbers $l_i$ and $u_i$ in $[x_{i-1}, x_i]$ such that

$$f(l_i) \leq f(x) \leq f(u_i) \qquad \text{whenever } x_{i-1} \leq x \leq x_i.$$

If $f(x) \geq 0$ on $[a, b]$, then $f(l_i)\, \Delta x_i$ and $f(u_i)\, \Delta x_i$ represent the areas of rectangles having the interval $[x_{i-1}, x_i]$ on the $x$-axis as base, and having tops passing through the lowest and highest points, respectively, on the graph of $f$ on that interval. (See Figure 8.10.) If $A_i$ is that part of the area under $y = f(x)$ and above the $x$-axis that lies in the vertical strip between $x = x_{i-1}$ and $x = x_i$, then

$$f(l_i)\, \Delta x_i \leq A_i \leq f(u_i)\, \Delta x_i.$$

If $f$ can have negative values, then one or both of $f(l_i)\, \Delta x_i$ and $f(u_i)\, \Delta x_i$ can be negative and will then represent the negative of the area of a rectangle lying below the $x$-axis. In any event, we always have $f(l_i)\, \Delta x_i \leq f(u_i)\, \Delta x_i$.

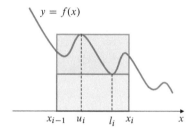

$y = f(x)$

$x_{i-1}\quad u_i \qquad l_i\ \ x_i \qquad\qquad x$

**Figure 8.10**

**DEFINITION**

**2**

**Upper and lower Riemann sums**

The **lower (Riemann) sum**, $L(f, P)$, and the **upper (Riemann) sum**, $U(f, P)$, for the function $f$ and the partition $P$ are defined by:

$$L(f, P) = f(l_1)\, \Delta x_1 + f(l_2)\, \Delta x_2 + \cdots + f(l_n)\, \Delta x_n$$

$$= \sum_{i=1}^{n} f(l_i)\, \Delta x_i,$$

$$U(f, P) = f(u_1)\, \Delta x_1 + f(u_2)\, \Delta x_2 + \cdots + f(u_n)\, \Delta x_n$$

$$= \sum_{i=1}^{n} f(u_i)\Delta x_i.$$

Figure 8.11 illustrates these Riemann sums as sums of *signed* areas of rectangles; any such areas that lie below the $x$-axis are counted as negative.

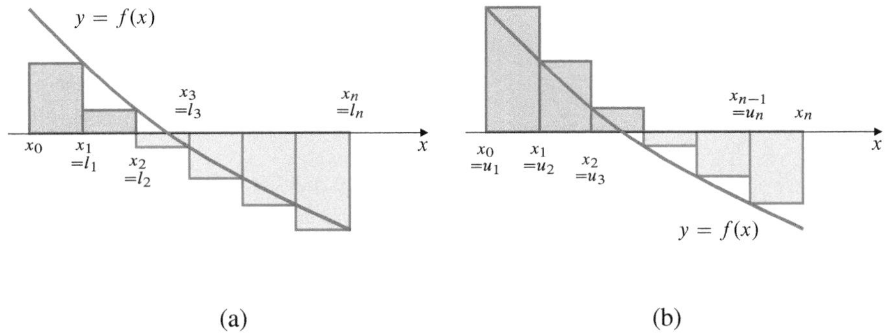

Figure 8.11    (a) A lower Riemann sum and (b) an upper Riemann sum for a decreasing function $f$. The areas of rectangles shaded in green are counted as positive; those shaded in blue are counted as negative

**EXAMPLE 1**    Calculate lower and upper Riemann sums for the function $f(x) = 1/x$ on the interval $[1, 2]$, corresponding to the partition $P$ of $[1, 2]$ into four subintervals of equal length.

**Solution**    The partition $P$ consists of the points $x_0 = 1$, $x_1 = 5/4$, $x_2 = 3/2$, $x_3 = 7/4$, and $x_4 = 2$. Since $1/x$ is decreasing on $[1, 2]$, its minimum and maximum values on the $i$th subinterval $[x_{i-1}, x_i]$ are $1/x_i$ and $1/x_{i-1}$, respectively. Thus, the lower and upper Riemann sums are

$$L(f, P) = \frac{1}{4}\left(\frac{4}{5} + \frac{2}{3} + \frac{4}{7} + \frac{1}{2}\right) = \frac{533}{840} \approx 0.6345,$$

$$U(f, P) = \frac{1}{4}\left(1 + \frac{4}{5} + \frac{2}{3} + \frac{4}{7}\right) = \frac{319}{420} \approx 0.7595.$$

**EXAMPLE 2**    Calculate the lower and upper Riemann sums for the function $f(x) = x^2$ on the interval $[0, a]$ (where $a > 0$), corresponding to the partition $P_n$ of $[0, a]$ into $n$ subintervals of equal length.

**Solution**    Each subinterval of $P_n$ has length $\Delta x = a/n$, and the division points are given by $x_i = ia/n$ for $i = 0, 1, 2, \ldots, n$. Since $x^2$ is increasing on $[0, a]$, its minimum and maximum values over the $i$th subinterval $[x_{i-1}, x_i]$ occur at $l_i = x_{i-1}$ and $u_i = x_i$, respectively. Thus, the lower Riemann sum of $f$ for $P_n$ is

$$L(f, P_n) = \sum_{i=1}^{n} (x_{i-1})^2 \Delta x = \frac{a^3}{n^3} \sum_{i=1}^{n} (i-1)^2$$

$$= \frac{a^3}{n^3} \sum_{j=0}^{n-1} j^2 = \frac{a^3}{n^3} \frac{(n-1)n(2(n-1)+1)}{6} = \frac{(n-1)(2n-1)a^3}{6n^2},$$

where we have used Theorem 1(c) of Section 8.1 to evaluate the sum of squares. Similarly, the upper Riemann sum is

$$U(f, P_n) = \sum_{i=1}^{n} (x_i)^2 \Delta x$$

$$= \frac{a^3}{n^3} \sum_{i=1}^{n} i^2 = \frac{a^3}{n^3} \frac{n(n+1)(2n+1)}{6} = \frac{(n+1)(2n+1)a^3}{6n^2}.$$

## The Definite Integral

If we calculate $L(f, P)$ and $U(f, P)$ for partitions $P$ having more and more points spaced closer and closer together, we expect that, in the limit, these Riemann sums will converge to a common value that will be the area bounded by $y = f(x)$, $y = 0$, $x = a$, and $x = b$ if $f(x) \geq 0$ on $[a, b]$. This is indeed the case, but we cannot fully prove it yet.

If $P_1$ and $P_2$ are two partitions of $[a, b]$ such that every point of $P_1$ also belongs to $P_2$, then we say that $P_2$ is a **refinement** of $P_1$. It is not difficult to show that in this case

$$L(f, P_1) \leq L(f, P_2) \leq U(f, P_2) \leq U(f, P_1);$$

adding more points to a partition increases the lower sum and decreases the upper sum. (See Exercise 18 at the end of this section.) Given any two partitions, $P_1$ and $P_2$, we can form their **common refinement** $P$, which consists of all of the points of $P_1$ and $P_2$. Thus,

$$L(f, P_1) \leq L(f, P) \leq U(f, P) \leq U(f, P_2).$$

Hence, every lower sum is less than or equal to every upper sum. Since the real numbers are complete, there must exist *at least one* real number $I$ such that

$$L(f, P) \leq I \leq U(f, P) \qquad \text{for every partition } P.$$

If there is *only one* such number, we will call it the definite integral of $f$ on $[a, b]$.

**DEFINITION**

**3**

**The definite integral**

Suppose there is exactly one number $I$ such that for every partition $P$ of $[a, b]$ we have

$$L(f, P) \leq I \leq U(f, P).$$

Then we say that the function $f$ is **integrable** on $[a, b]$, and we call $I$ the **definite integral** of $f$ on $[a, b]$. The definite integral is denoted by the symbol

$$I = \int_a^b f(x)\, dx.$$

The definite integral of $f(x)$ over $[a, b]$ is a *number*; it is not a function of $x$. It depends on the numbers $a$ and $b$ and on the particular function $f$, but not on the variable $x$ (which is a **dummy variable** like the variable $i$ in the sum $\sum_{i=1}^n f(i)$). Replacing $x$ with another variable does not change the value of the integral:

$$\int_a^b f(x)\, dx = \int_a^b f(t)\, dt.$$

While we normally write the definite integral of $f(x)$ as

$$\int_a^b f(x)\, dx,$$

it is equally correct to write it as

$$\int_a^b dx\, f(x).$$

This latter form will become quite useful when we deal with multiple integrals.

The various parts of the symbol $\int_a^b f(x)\, dx$ have their own names:

(i) $\int$ is called the **integral sign**; it resembles the letter S since it represents the limit of a sum.

(ii) $a$ and $b$ are called the **limits of integration**; $a$ is the **lower limit**, $b$ is the **upper limit**.

(iii) The function $f$ is the **integrand**; $x$ is the **variable of integration**.

(iv) $dx$ is the **differential** of $x$. It replaces $\Delta x$ in the Riemann sums. If an integrand depends on more than one variable, the differential tells you which one is the variable of integration.

**EXAMPLE 3**    Show that $f(x) = x^2$ is integrable over the interval $[0, a]$, where $a > 0$, and evaluate $\int_0^a x^2\, dx$.

*Solution*  We evaluate the limits as $n \to \infty$ of the lower and upper sums of $f$ over $[0, a]$ obtained in Example 2 above.

$$\lim_{n\to\infty} L(f, P_n) = \lim_{n\to\infty} \frac{(n-1)(2n-1)a^3}{6n^2} = \frac{a^3}{3},$$

$$\lim_{n\to\infty} U(f, P_n) = \lim_{n\to\infty} \frac{(n+1)(2n+1)a^3}{6n^2} = \frac{a^3}{3}.$$

If $L(f, P_n) \le I \le U(f, P_n)$, we must have $I = a^3/3$. Thus, $f(x) = x^2$ is integrable over $[0, a]$, and

$$\int_0^a f(x)\, dx = \int_0^a x^2\, dx = \frac{a^3}{3}.$$

For all partitions $P$ of $[a, b]$, we have

$$L(f, P) \le \int_a^b f(x)\, dx \le U(f, P).$$

If $f(x) \ge 0$ on $[a, b]$, then the area of the region $R$ bounded by the graph of $y = f(x)$, the $x$-axis, and the lines $x = a$ and $x = b$ is $A$ square units, where $A = \int_a^b f(x)\, dx$. If $f(x) \le 0$ on $[a, b]$, the area of $R$ is $-\int_a^b f(x)\, dx$ square units. For general $f$, $\int_a^b f(x)\, dx$ is the area of that part of $R$ lying above the $x$-axis minus the area of that part lying below the $x$-axis. (See Figure 8.12.) You can think of $\int_a^b f(x)\, dx$ as a "sum" of "areas" of infinitely many rectangles with heights $f(x)$ and "infinitesimally small widths" $dx$; it is a limit of the upper and lower Riemann sums.

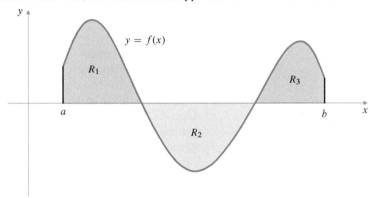

**Figure 8.12** $\displaystyle\int_a^b f(x)\, dx$ equals area $R_1 -$ area $R_2 +$ area $R_3$

## General Riemann Sums

Let $P = \{x_0, x_1, x_2, \ldots, x_n\}$, where $a = x_0 < x_1 < x_2 < \cdots < x_n = b$, be a partition of $[a, b]$ having norm $\|P\| = \max_{1 \le i \le n} \Delta x_i$. In each subinterval $[x_{i-1}, x_i]$ of $P$, pick a point $c_i$ (called a *tag*). Let $c = (c_1, c_2, \ldots, c_n)$ denote the set of these tags. The sum

$$R(f, P, c) = \sum_{i=1}^n f(c_i)\, \Delta x_i$$
$$= f(c_1)\, \Delta x_1 + f(c_2)\, \Delta x_2 + f(c_3)\, \Delta x_3 + \cdots + f(c_n)\, \Delta x_n$$

is called the **Riemann sum** of $f$ on $[a, b]$ corresponding to partition $P$ and tags $c$.

Note in Figure 8.13 that $R(f, P, c)$ is a sum of *signed* areas of rectangles between the $x$-axis and the curve $y = f(x)$. For any choice of the tags $c$, the Riemann sum $R(f, P, c)$ satisfies

$$L(f, P) \le R(f, P, c) \le U(f, P).$$

Therefore, if $f$ is integrable on $[a, b]$, then its integral is the limit of such Riemann sums, where the limit is taken as the number $n(P)$ of subintervals of $P$ increases to infinity in such a way that the lengths of all the subintervals approach zero. That is,

$$\lim_{\substack{n(P) \to \infty \\ \|P\| \to 0}} R(f, P, c) = \int_a^b f(x)\, dx.$$

As we will see in Chapter 10, many applications of integration depend on recognizing that a limit of Riemann sums is a definite integral.

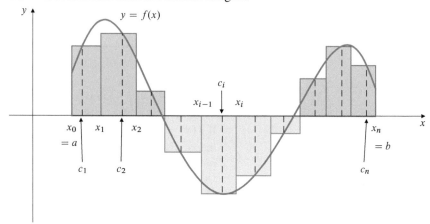

**Figure 8.13**    The Riemann sum $R(f, P, c)$ is the sum of areas of the rectangles shaded in green minus the sum of the areas of the rectangles shaded in blue

**THEOREM**

**2**

If $f$ is continuous on $[a, b]$, then $f$ is integrable on $[a, b]$.

**Remark**    The assumption that $f$ is continuous in Theorem 2 may seem a bit superfluous since continuity was required throughout the above discussion leading to the definition of the definite integral. We cannot, however, prove this theorem yet. Its proof makes subtle use of the completeness property of the real numbers and is given in Appendix IV in the context of an extended definition of definite integral that is meaningful for a larger class of functions that are not necessarily continuous. (The integral studied in Appendix IV is called the **Riemann integral**.)

We can, however, make the following observation. In order to prove that $f$ is integrable on $[a, b]$, it is sufficient that, for any given positive number $\epsilon$, we should be able to find a partition $P$ of $[a, b]$ for which $U(f, P) - L(f, P) < \epsilon$. This condition prevents there being more than one number $I$ that is both greater than every lower sum and less than every upper sum. It is not difficult to find such a partition if the function $f$ is nondecreasing (or if it is nonincreasing) on $[a, b]$. (See Exercise 17 at the end of this section.) Therefore, nondecreasing and nonincreasing continuous functions are integrable; so, therefore, is any continuous function that is the sum of a nondecreasing and a nonincreasing function. This class of functions includes any continuous functions we are likely to encounter in concrete applications of calculus but, unfortunately, does not include all continuous functions.

Meanwhile, in Sections 8.4 and 9.5 we will extend the definition of the definite integral to certain kinds of functions that are not continuous, or where the interval of integration is not closed or not bounded.

**EXAMPLE 4**    Express the limit $\displaystyle\lim_{n \to \infty} \sum_{i=1}^{n} \frac{2}{n} \left(1 + \frac{2i - 1}{n}\right)^{1/3}$ as a definite integral.

**Solution**    We want to interpret the sum as a Riemann sum for $f(x) = (1 + x)^{1/3}$. The factor $2/n$ suggests that the interval of integration has length 2 and is partitioned into $n$ equal subintervals, each of length $2/n$. Let $c_i = (2i-1)/n$ for $i = 1, 2, 3, \ldots, n$. As $n \to \infty$, $c_1 = 1/n \to 0$ and $c_n = (2n-1)/n \to 2$. Thus, the interval is $[0, 2]$, and the points of the partition are $x_i = 2i/n$. Observe that $x_{i-1} = (2i-2)/n < c_i < 2i/n = x_i$ for each $i$, so that the sum is indeed a Riemann sum for $f(x)$ over $[0, 2]$. Since $f$ is continuous on that interval, it is integrable there, and

$$\lim_{n \to \infty} \sum_{i=1}^{n} \frac{2}{n} \left( 1 + \frac{2i-1}{n} \right)^{1/3} = \int_0^2 (1+x)^{1/3} \, dx.$$

## EXERCISES 8.3

In Exercises 1–6, let $P_n$ denote the partition of the given interval $[a, b]$ into $n$ subintervals of equal length $\Delta x_i = (b-a)/n$. Evaluate $L(f, P_n)$ and $U(f, P_n)$ for the given functions $f$ and the given values of $n$.

**1.** $f(x) = x$ on $[0, 2]$, with $n = 8$

**2.** $f(x) = x^2$ on $[0, 4]$, with $n = 4$

**3.** $f(x) = e^x$ on $[-2, 2]$, with $n = 4$

**4.** $f(x) = \ln x$ on $[1, 2]$, with $n = 5$

**5.** $f(x) = \sin x$ on $[0, \pi]$, with $n = 6$

**6.** $f(x) = \cos x$ on $[0, 2\pi]$, with $n = 4$

In Exercises 7–10, calculate $L(f, P_n)$ and $U(f, P_n)$ for the given function $f$ over the given interval $[a, b]$, where $P_n$ is the partition of the interval into $n$ subintervals of equal length $\Delta x = (b-a)/n$. Show that

$$\lim_{n \to \infty} L(f, P_n) = \lim_{n \to \infty} U(f, P_n).$$

Hence, $f$ is integrable on $[a, b]$. (Why?) What is $\int_a^b f(x) \, dx$?

**7.** $f(x) = x$, $[a, b] = [0, 1]$

**8.** $f(x) = 1 - x$, $[a, b] = [0, 2]$

**9.** $f(x) = x^3$, $[a, b] = [0, 1]$

**10.** $f(x) = e^x$, $[a, b] = [0, 3]$

In Exercises 11–16, express the given limit as a definite integral.

**11.** $\displaystyle \lim_{n \to \infty} \sum_{i=1}^{n} \frac{1}{n} \sqrt{\frac{i}{n}}$

**12.** $\displaystyle \lim_{n \to \infty} \sum_{i=1}^{n} \frac{1}{n} \sqrt{\frac{i-1}{n}}$

**13.** $\displaystyle \lim_{n \to \infty} \sum_{i=1}^{n} \frac{\pi}{n} \sin\left( \frac{\pi i}{n} \right)$

**14.** $\displaystyle \lim_{n \to \infty} \sum_{i=1}^{n} \frac{2}{n} \ln\left( 1 + \frac{2i}{n} \right)$

**15.** $\displaystyle \lim_{n \to \infty} \sum_{i=1}^{n} \frac{1}{n} \tan^{-1}\left( \frac{2i-1}{2n} \right)$

**16.** $\displaystyle \lim_{n \to \infty} \sum_{i=1}^{n} \frac{n}{n^2 + i^2}$

**! 17.** If $f$ is continuous and nondecreasing on $[a, b]$, and $P_n$ is the partition of $[a, b]$ into $n$ subintervals of equal length $(\Delta x_i = (b-a)/n$ for $1 \le i \le n)$, show that

$$U(f, P_n) - L(f, P_n) = \frac{(b-a)\left( f(b) - f(a) \right)}{n}.$$

Since we can make the right side as small as we please by choosing $n$ large enough, $f$ must be integrable on $[a, b]$.

**! 18.** Let $P = \{a = x_0 < x_1 < x_2 < \cdots < x_n = b\}$ be a partition of $[a, b]$, and let $P'$ be a refinement of $P$ having one more point, $x'$, satisfying, say, $x_{i-1} < x' < x_i$ for some $i$ between 1 and $n$. Show that

$$L(f, P) \le L(f, P') \le U(f, P') \le U(f, P)$$

for any continuous function $f$. (*Hint:* Consider the maximum and minimum values of $f$ on the intervals $[x_{i-1}, x_i]$, $[x_{i-1}, x']$, and $[x', x_i]$.) Hence, deduce that

$$L(f, P) \le L(f, P'') \le U(f, P'') \le U(f, P) \text{ if } P''$$

is *any* refinement of $P$.

## 8.4  Properties of the Definite Integral

It is convenient to extend the definition of the definite integral $\int_a^b f(x) \, dx$ to allow $a = b$ and $a > b$ as well as $a < b$. The extension still involves partitions $P$ having $x_0 = a$ and $x_n = b$ with intermediate points occurring in order between these end points, so that if $a = b$, then we must have $\Delta x_i = 0$ for every $i$, and hence the integral is zero. If $a > b$, we have $\Delta x_i < 0$ for each $i$, so the integral will be negative for positive functions $f$ and vice versa.

Some of the most important properties of the definite integral are summarized in the following theorem.

**THEOREM**

**3**

Let $f$ and $g$ be integrable on an interval containing the points $a$, $b$, and $c$. Then

(a) An integral over an interval of zero length is zero.

$$\int_a^a f(x)\,dx = 0.$$

(b) Reversing the limits of integration changes the sign of the integral.

$$\int_b^a f(x)\,dx = -\int_a^b f(x)\,dx.$$

(c) An integral depends linearly on the integrand. If $A$ and $B$ are constants, then

$$\int_a^b \left(Af(x) + Bg(x)\right) dx = A \int_a^b f(x)\,dx + B \int_a^b g(x)\,dx.$$

(d) An integral depends additively on the interval of integration.

$$\int_a^b f(x)\,dx + \int_b^c f(x)\,dx = \int_a^c f(x)\,dx.$$

(e) If $a \le b$ and $f(x) \le g(x)$ for $a \le x \le b$, then

$$\int_a^b f(x)\,dx \le \int_a^b g(x)\,dx.$$

(f) The **triangle inequality** for sums extends to definite integrals. If $a \le b$, then

$$\left| \int_a^b f(x)\,dx \right| \le \int_a^b |f(x)|\,dx.$$

(g) The integral of an odd function over an interval symmetric about zero is zero. If $f$ is an odd function (i.e., $f(-x) = -f(x)$), then

$$\int_{-a}^a f(x)\,dx = 0.$$

(h) The integral of an even function over an interval symmetric about zero is twice the integral over the positive half of the interval. If $f$ is an even function (i.e., $f(-x) = f(x)$), then

$$\int_{-a}^a f(x)\,dx = 2 \int_0^a f(x)\,dx.$$

The proofs of parts (a) and (b) are suggested in the first paragraph of this section. We postpone giving formal proofs of parts (c)–(h) until Appendix IV (see Exercises 5–8 in that Appendix). Nevertheless, all of these results should appear intuitively reasonable if you regard the integrals as representing (signed) areas. For instance, properties (d) and (e) are, respectively, properties (v) and (iv) of areas mentioned in the first paragraph of Section 8.2. (See Figure 8.14.)

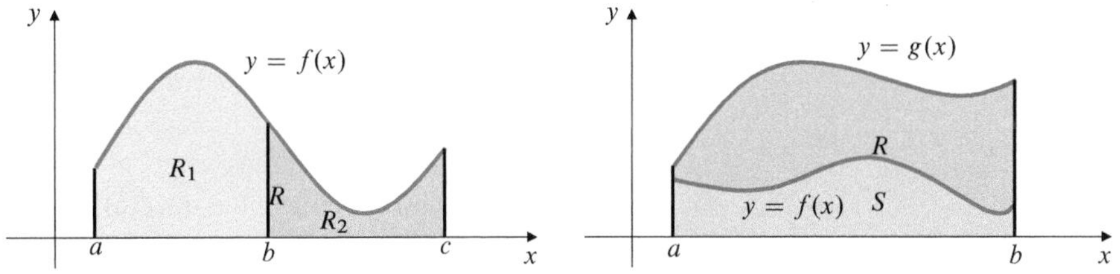

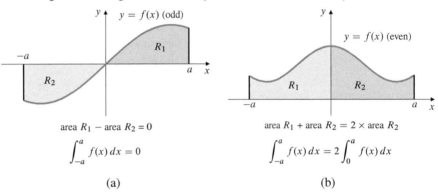

**Figure 8.14**

(a) Property (d) of Theorem 3

(b) Property (e) of Theorem 3

area $R_1$ + area $R_2$ = area $R$

$$\int_a^b f(x)\,dx + \int_b^c f(x)\,dx = \int_a^c f(x)\,dx$$

(a)

area $S \le$ area $R$

$$\int_a^b f(x)\,dx \le \int_a^b g(x)\,dx$$

(b)

Property (f) is a generalization of the triangle inequality for numbers:

$$|x + y| \le |x| + |y|, \quad \text{or more generally,} \quad \left|\sum_{i=1}^n x_i\right| \le \sum_{i=1}^n |x_i|.$$

It follows from property (e) (assuming that $|f|$ is integrable on $[a, b]$), since $-|f(x)| \le f(x) \le |f(x)|$. The symmetry properties (g) and (h), which are illustrated in Figure 8.15, are particularly useful and should always be kept in mind when evaluating definite integrals because they can save much unnecessary work.

**Figure 8.15**

(a) Property (g) of Theorem 3

(b) Property (h) of Theorem 3

area $R_1$ − area $R_2$ = 0

$$\int_{-a}^a f(x)\,dx = 0$$

(a)

area $R_1$ + area $R_2$ = 2 × area $R_2$

$$\int_{-a}^a f(x)\,dx = 2\int_0^a f(x)\,dx$$

(b)

As yet we have no easy method for evaluating definite integrals. However, some such integrals can be simplified by using various properties in Theorem 3, and others can be interpreted as known areas.

**EXAMPLE 1**    Evaluate

(a) $\int_{-2}^2 (2 + 5x)\,dx$,    (b) $\int_0^3 (2 + x)\,dx$,    and    (c) $\int_{-3}^3 \sqrt{9 - x^2}\,dx$.

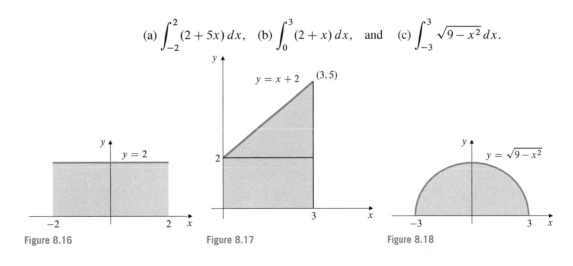

Figure 8.16

Figure 8.17

Figure 8.18

*Solution*   See Figures 8.16–8.18.

(a) By the linearity property (c), $\int_{-2}^{2}(2+5x)\,dx = \int_{-2}^{2} 2\,dx + 5\int_{-2}^{2} x\,dx$. The first integral on the right represents the area of a rectangle of width 4 and height 2 (Figure 8.16), so it has value 8. The second integral on the right is 0 because its integrand is odd and the interval is symmetric about 0. Thus,

$$\int_{-2}^{2}(2+5x)\,dx = 8 + 0 = 8.$$

(b) $\int_{0}^{3}(2+x)\,dx$ represents the area of the trapezoid in Figure 8.17. Adding the areas of the rectangle and triangle comprising this trapezoid, we get

$$\int_{0}^{3}(2+x)\,dx = (3 \times 2) + \frac{1}{2}(3 \times 3) = \frac{21}{2}.$$

While areas are measured in squared units of length, definite integrals are numbers and have no units. Even when you use an area to find an integral, do not quote units for the integral.

(c) $\int_{-3}^{3}\sqrt{9-x^2}\,dx$ represents the area of a semicircle of radius 3 (Figure 8.18), so

$$\int_{-3}^{3}\sqrt{9-x^2}\,dx = \frac{1}{2}\pi(3^2) = \frac{9\pi}{2}.$$

## A Mean-Value Theorem for Integrals

Let $f$ be a function continuous on the interval $[a, b]$. Then $f$ assumes a minimum value $m$ and a maximum value $M$ on the interval, say at points $x = l$ and $x = u$, respectively:

$$m = f(l) \le f(x) \le f(u) = M \qquad \text{for all } x \text{ in } [a, b].$$

For the 2-point partition $P$ of $[a, b]$ having $x_0 = a$ and $x_1 = b$, we have

$$m(b-a) = L(f, P) \le \int_{a}^{b} f(x)\,dx \le U(f, P) = M(b-a).$$

Therefore,

$$f(l) = m \le \frac{1}{b-a}\int_{a}^{b} f(x)\,dx \le M = f(u).$$

By the Intermediate-Value Theorem, $f(x)$ must take on every value between the two values $f(l)$ and $f(u)$ at some point between $l$ and $u$ (Figure 8.19). Hence, there is a number $c$ between $l$ and $u$ such that

$$f(c) = \frac{1}{b-a}\int_{a}^{b} f(x)\,dx.$$

That is, $\int_{a}^{b} f(x)\,dx$ is equal to the area $(b-a)f(c)$ of a rectangle with base width $b-a$ and height $f(c)$ for some $c$ between $a$ and $b$. This is the Mean-Value Theorem for integrals.

**THEOREM**

**4**

**The Mean-Value Theorem for integrals**

If $f$ is continuous on $[a, b]$, then there exists a point $c$ in $[a, b]$ such that

$$\int_{a}^{b} f(x)\,dx = (b-a)f(c).$$

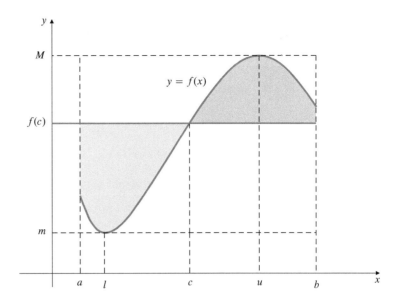

**Figure 8.19**   Half of the area between $y = f(x)$ and the horizontal line $y = f(c)$ lies above the line, and the other half lies below the line

Observe in Figure 8.19 that the area below the curve $y = f(x)$ and above the line $y = f(c)$ is equal to the area above $y = f(x)$ and below $y = f(c)$. In this sense, $f(c)$ is the average value of the function $f(x)$ on the interval $[a, b]$.

**DEFINITION**

**4**

**Average value of a function**

If $f$ is integrable on $[a, b]$, then the **average value** or **mean value** of $f$ on $[a, b]$, denoted by $\bar{f}$, is

$$\bar{f} = \frac{1}{b - a} \int_a^b f(x)\, dx.$$

**EXAMPLE 2**   Find the average value of $f(x) = 2x$ on the interval $[1, 5]$.

*Solution*   The average value (see Figure 8.20) is

$$\bar{f} = \frac{1}{5 - 1} \int_1^5 2x\, dx = \frac{1}{4}\left(4 \times 2 + \frac{1}{2}(4 \times 8)\right) = 6.$$

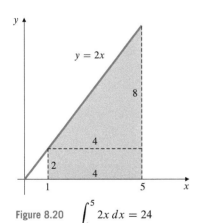

**Figure 8.20**   $\int_1^5 2x\, dx = 24$

## Definite Integrals of Piecewise Continuous Functions

The definition of integrability and the definite integral given above can be extended to a wider class than just continuous functions. One simple but very important extension is to the class of *piecewise continuous functions*.

Consider the graph $y = f(x)$ shown in Figure 8.21(a). Although $f$ is not continuous at all points in $[a, b]$ (it is discontinuous at $c_1$ and $c_2$), clearly the region lying under the graph and above the $x$-axis between $x = a$ and $x = b$ does have an area. We would like to represent this area as

$$\int_a^{c_1} f(x)\, dx + \int_{c_1}^{c_2} f(x)\, dx + \int_{c_2}^b f(x)\, dx.$$

This is reasonable because there are continuous functions on $[a, c_1]$, $[c_1, c_2]$, and $[c_2, b]$ equal to $f(x)$ on the corresponding open intervals, $(a, c_1)$, $(c_1, c_2)$, and $(c_2, b)$.

DEFINITION

5

**Piecewise continuous functions**

Let $c_0 < c_1 < c_2 < \cdots < c_n$ be a finite set of points on the real line. A function $f$ defined on $[c_0, c_n]$ except possibly at some of the points $c_i$, $(0 \le i \le n)$, is called **piecewise continuous** on that interval if for each $i$ $(1 \le i \le n)$ there exists a function $F_i$ continuous on the *closed* interval $[c_{i-1}, c_i]$ such that

$$f(x) = F_i(x) \qquad \text{on the } \textit{open} \text{ interval} \quad (c_{i-1}, c_i).$$

In this case, we define the definite integral of $f$ from $c_0$ to $c_n$ to be

$$\int_{c_0}^{c_n} f(x)\, dx = \sum_{i=1}^{n} \int_{c_{i-1}}^{c_i} F_i(x)\, dx.$$

**EXAMPLE 3**    Find $\displaystyle\int_0^3 f(x)\, dx$, where $f(x) = \begin{cases} \sqrt{1 - x^2} & \text{if } 0 \le x \le 1 \\ 2 & \text{if } 1 < x \le 2 \\ x - 2 & \text{if } 2 < x \le 3. \end{cases}$

*Solution*    The value of the integral is the sum of the shaded areas in Figure 8.21(b):

$$\int_0^3 f(x)\, dx = \int_0^1 \sqrt{1 - x^2}\, dx + \int_1^2 2\, dx + \int_2^3 (x - 2)\, dx$$
$$= \left( \frac{1}{4} \times \pi \times 1^2 \right) + (2 \times 1) + \left( \frac{1}{2} \times 1 \times 1 \right) = \frac{\pi + 10}{4}.$$

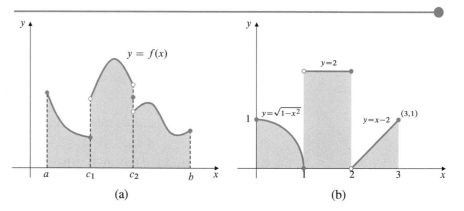

**Figure 8.21**    Two piecewise continuous functions

(a)                                        (b)

---

# EXERCISES 8.4

**1.** Simplify $\displaystyle\int_a^b f(x)\, dx + \int_b^c f(x)\, dx + \int_c^a f(x)\, dx$.

**2.** Simplify $\displaystyle\int_0^2 3f(x)\, dx + \int_1^3 3f(x)\, dx - \int_0^3 2f(x)\, dx$
$- \displaystyle\int_1^2 3f(x)\, dx$.

Evaluate the integrals in Exercises 3–16 by using the properties of the definite integral and interpreting integrals as areas.

**3.** $\displaystyle\int_{-2}^2 (x + 2)\, dx$

**4.** $\displaystyle\int_0^2 (3x + 1)\, dx$

**5.** $\displaystyle\int_a^b x\, dx$

**6.** $\displaystyle\int_{-1}^2 (1 - 2x)\, dx$

**7.** $\displaystyle\int_{-\sqrt{2}}^{\sqrt{2}} \sqrt{2 - t^2}\, dt$

**8.** $\displaystyle\int_{-\sqrt{2}}^0 \sqrt{2 - x^2}\, dx$

**9.** $\displaystyle\int_{-\pi}^{\pi} \sin(x^3)\, dx$

**10.** $\displaystyle\int_{-a}^a (a - |s|)\, ds$

**11.** $\displaystyle\int_{-1}^1 (u^5 - 3u^3 + \pi)\, du$

**12.** $\displaystyle\int_0^2 \sqrt{2x - x^2}\, dx$

**13.** $\displaystyle\int_{-4}^4 (e^x - e^{-x})\, dx$

**14.** $\displaystyle\int_{-3}^3 (2 + t)\sqrt{9 - t^2}\, dt$

**!** **15.** $\displaystyle\int_0^1 \sqrt{4 - x^2}\, dx$

**!** **16.** $\displaystyle\int_1^2 \sqrt{4 - x^2}\, dx$

Given that $\int_0^a x^2\,dx = \dfrac{a^3}{3}$, evaluate the integrals in Exercises 17–22.

**17.** $\displaystyle\int_0^2 6x^2\,dx$

**18.** $\displaystyle\int_2^3 (x^2 - 4)\,dx$

**19.** $\displaystyle\int_{-2}^2 (4 - t^2)\,dt$

**20.** $\displaystyle\int_0^2 (v^2 - v)\,dv$

**21.** $\displaystyle\int_0^1 (x^2 + \sqrt{1 - x^2})\,dx$

**22.** $\displaystyle\int_{-6}^6 x^2(2 + \sin x)\,dx$

The definition of $\ln x$ as an area in Section 6.3 implies that

$$\int_1^x \frac{1}{t}\,dt = \ln x$$

for $x > 0$. Use this to evaluate the integrals in Exercises 23–26.

**23.** $\displaystyle\int_1^2 \frac{1}{x}\,dx$

**24.** $\displaystyle\int_2^4 \frac{1}{t}\,dt$

**25.** $\displaystyle\int_{1/3}^1 \frac{1}{t}\,dt$

**26.** $\displaystyle\int_{1/4}^3 \frac{1}{s}\,ds$

Find the average values of the functions in Exercises 27–32 over the given intervals.

**27.** $f(x) = x + 2$ over $[0, 4]$

**28.** $g(x) = x + 2$ over $[a, b]$

**29.** $f(t) = 1 + \sin t$ over $[-\pi, \pi]$

**30.** $k(x) = x^2$ over $[0, 3]$

**31.** $f(x) = \sqrt{4 - x^2}$ over $[0, 2]$

**32.** $g(s) = 1/s$ over $[1/2, 2]$

**Piecewise continuous functions**

**33.** Evaluate $\displaystyle\int_{-1}^2 \operatorname{sgn} x\,dx$. Recall that $\operatorname{sgn} x$ is 1 if $x > 0$ and $-1$ if $x < 0$.

**34.** Find $\displaystyle\int_{-3}^2 f(x)\,dx$, where $f(x) = \begin{cases} 1 + x & \text{if } x < 0 \\ 2 & \text{if } x \geq 0. \end{cases}$

**35.** Find $\displaystyle\int_0^2 g(x)\,dx$, where $g(x) = \begin{cases} x^2 & \text{if } 0 \leq x \leq 1 \\ x & \text{if } 1 < x \leq 2. \end{cases}$

**36.** Evaluate $\displaystyle\int_0^3 |2 - x|\,dx$.

**37.** Evaluate $\displaystyle\int_0^2 \sqrt{4 - x^2}\,\operatorname{sgn}(x - 1)\,dx$.

**38.** Evaluate $\displaystyle\int_0^{3.5} \lfloor x \rfloor\,dx$, where $\lfloor x \rfloor$ is the greatest integer less than or equal to $x$. (See Example 10.)

Evaluate the integrals in Exercises 39–40 by inspecting the graphs of the integrands.

**39.** $\displaystyle\int_{-3}^4 \left( |x + 1| - |x - 1| + |x + 2| \right) dx$

**40.** $\displaystyle\int_0^3 \frac{x^2 - x}{|x - 1|}\,dx$

**41.** Find the average value of the function $f(x) = |x + 1|\operatorname{sgn} x$ on the interval $[-2, 2]$.

**42.** If $a < b$ and $f$ is continuous on $[a, b]$, show that $\displaystyle\int_a^b \left( f(x) - \bar{f} \right) dx = 0$.

**43.** Suppose that $a < b$ and $f$ is continuous on $[a, b]$. Find the constant $k$ that minimizes the integral $\displaystyle\int_a^b \left( f(x) - k \right)^2 dx$.

---

## 8.5    The Fundamental Theorem of Calculus

In this section we demonstrate the relationship between the definite integral defined in Section 8.3 and the indefinite integral (or general antiderivative). A consequence of this relationship is that we will be able to calculate definite integrals of functions whose antiderivatives we can find.

In Section 6.3 we wanted to find a function whose derivative was $1/x$. We solved this problem by defining the desired function ($\ln x$) in terms of the area under the graph of $y = 1/x$. This idea motivates, and is a special case of, the following theorem.

**THEOREM**

**5**

**The Fundamental Theorem of Calculus**

Suppose that the function $f$ is continuous on an interval $I$ containing the point $a$.

**PART I.** Let the function $F$ be defined on $I$ by

$$F(x) = \int_a^x f(t)\,dt.$$

Then $F$ is differentiable on $I$, and $F'(x) = f(x)$ there. Thus, $F$ is an antiderivative of $f$ on $I$:

$$\frac{d}{dx} \int_a^x f(t)\, dt = f(x).$$

**PART II.** If $G(x)$ is *any* antiderivative of $f(x)$ on $I$, so that $G'(x) = f(x)$ on $I$, then for any $b$ in $I$, we have

$$\int_a^b f(x)\, dx = G(b) - G(a).$$

***PROOF***    Using the definition of the derivative, we calculate

$$
\begin{aligned}
F'(x) &= \lim_{h \to 0} \frac{F(x+h) - F(x)}{h} \\[2mm]
&= \lim_{h \to 0} \frac{1}{h} \left( \int_a^{x+h} f(t)\, dt - \int_a^x f(t)\, dt \right) \\[2mm]
&= \lim_{h \to 0} \frac{1}{h} \int_x^{x+h} f(t)\, dt \quad \text{by Theorem 3(d)}
\end{aligned}
$$

$$
\begin{aligned}
&= \lim_{h \to 0} \frac{1}{h} h f(c) \qquad && \text{for some } c = c(h) \text{ (depending on } h) \\
& && \text{between } x \text{ and } x + h \text{ (Theorem 4)} \\
&= \lim_{c \to x} f(c) && \text{since } c \to x \text{ as } h \to 0 \\
&= f(x) && \text{since } f \text{ is continuous.}
\end{aligned}
$$

Also, if $G'(x) = f(x)$, then $F(x) = G(x) + C$ on $I$ for some constant $C$ (by Theorem 13 of Section 5.8). Hence,

$$\int_a^x f(t)\, dt = F(x) = G(x) + C.$$

Let $x = a$ and obtain $0 = G(a) + C$ via Theorem 3(a), so $C = -G(a)$. Now let $x = b$ to get

$$\int_a^b f(t)\, dt = G(b) + C = G(b) - G(a).$$

Of course, we can replace $t$ with $x$ (or any other variable) as the variable of integration on the left-hand side.

***Remark***    You should remember *both* conclusions of the Fundamental Theorem; they are both useful. Part I concerns the derivative of an integral; it tells you how to differentiate a definite integral with respect to its upper limit. Part II concerns the integral of a derivative; it tells you how to evaluate a definite integral if you can find an antiderivative of the integrand.

**DEFINITION**

**6**

To facilitate the evaluation of definite integrals using the Fundamental Theorem of Calculus, we define the **evaluation symbol**:

$$F(x) \Big|_a^b = F(b) - F(a).$$

Thus,

$$\int_a^b f(x)\,dx = \left(\int f(x)\,dx\right)\Bigg|_a^b,$$

where $\int f(x)\,dx$ denotes the indefinite integral or general antiderivative of $f$. (See Section 5.10.) When evaluating a definite integral this way, we will omit the constant of integration $(+C)$ from the indefinite integral because it cancels out in the subtraction:

$$(F(x)+C)\Bigg|_a^b = F(b) + C - (F(a) + C) = F(b) - F(a) = F(x)\Bigg|_a^b.$$

*Any* antiderivative of $f$ can be used to calculate the definite integral.

**EXAMPLE 1**    Evaluate    (a) $\displaystyle\int_0^a x^2\,dx$    and    (b) $\displaystyle\int_{-1}^2 (x^2 - 3x + 2)\,dx$.

*Solution*

(a) $\displaystyle\int_0^a x^2\,dx = \frac{1}{3}x^3\Bigg|_0^a = \frac{1}{3}a^3 - \frac{1}{3}0^3 = \frac{a^3}{3}$    (because $\dfrac{d}{dx}\dfrac{x^3}{3} = x^2$).

(b) $\displaystyle\int_{-1}^2 (x^2 - 3x + 2)\,dx = \left(\frac{1}{3}x^3 - \frac{3}{2}x^2 + 2x\right)\Bigg|_{-1}^2$

$$= \frac{1}{3}(8) - \frac{3}{2}(4) + 4 - \left(\frac{1}{3}(-1) - \frac{3}{2}(1) + (-2)\right) = \frac{9}{2}.$$

> **BEWARE!**   Be careful to keep track of all the minus signs when substituting a negative lower limit.

**EXAMPLE 2**    Find the area $A$ of the plane region lying above the $x$-axis and under the curve $y = 3x - x^2$.

*Solution*   We need to find the points where the curve $y = 3x - x^2$ meets the $x$-axis. These are solutions of the equation

$$0 = 3x - x^2 = x(3 - x).$$

The only roots are $x = 0$ and $x = 3$. (See Figure 8.22.) Hence, the area of the region is given by

$$A = \int_0^3 (3x - x^2)\,dx = \left(\frac{3}{2}x^2 - \frac{1}{3}x^3\right)\Bigg|_0^3$$

$$= \frac{27}{2} - \frac{27}{3} - (0 - 0) = \frac{27}{6} = \frac{9}{2}\ \text{square units.}$$

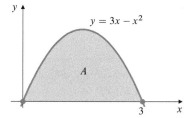

$y = 3x - x^2$

$A$

**Figure 8.22**

**EXAMPLE 3**    Find the area under the curve $y = \sin x$, above $y = 0$, from $x = 0$ to $x = \pi$.

*Solution*   The required area, illustrated in Figure 8.23, is

$$A = \int_0^\pi \sin x\,dx = -\cos x\Bigg|_0^\pi = -(-1 - (1)) = 2\ \text{square units.}$$

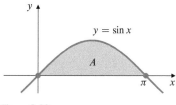

$y = \sin x$

$A$

**Figure 8.23**

Note that while the definite integral is a pure number, an area is a geometric quantity that implicitly involves units. If the units along the $x$- and $y$-axes are, for example, metres, the area should be quoted in square metres ($m^2$). If units of length along the $x$-axis and $y$-axis are not specified, areas should be quoted in square units.

**EXAMPLE 4**    Find the area of the region $R$ lying above the line $y = 1$ and below the curve $y = 5/(x^2 + 1)$.

*Solution*    The region $R$ is shaded in Figure 8.24. To find the intersections of $y = 1$ and $y = 5/(x^2 + 1)$, we must solve these equations simultaneously:

$$1 = \frac{5}{x^2 + 1},$$

so $x^2 + 1 = 5$, $x^2 = 4$, and $x = \pm 2$.

The area $A$ of the region $R$ is the area under the curve $y = 5/(x^2 + 1)$ and above the $x$-axis between $x = -2$ and $x = 2$, minus the area of a rectangle of width 4 and height 1. Since $\tan^{-1} x$ is an antiderivative of $1/(x^2 + 1)$,

$$A = \int_{-2}^{2} \frac{5}{x^2 + 1}\, dx - 4 = 2 \int_{0}^{2} \frac{5}{x^2 + 1}\, dx - 4$$

$$= 10 \tan^{-1} x \Big|_{0}^{2} - 4 = 10 \tan^{-1} 2 - 4 \text{ square units.}$$

Observe the use of even symmetry (Theorem 3(h) of Section 8.4) to replace the lower limit of integration by 0. It is easier to substitute 0 into the antiderivative than $-2$.

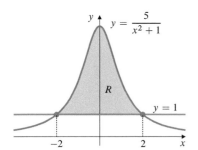

**Figure 8.24**

**EXAMPLE 5**    Find the average value of $f(x) = e^{-x} + \cos x$ on the interval $[-\pi/2, 0]$.

*Solution*    The average value is

$$\bar{f} = \frac{1}{0 - \left(-\dfrac{\pi}{2}\right)} \int_{-(\pi/2)}^{0} (e^{-x} + \cos x)\, dx$$

$$= \frac{2}{\pi} (-e^{-x} + \sin x) \Big|_{-(\pi/2)}^{0}$$

$$= \frac{2}{\pi} \left(-1 + 0 + e^{\pi/2} - (-1)\right) = \frac{2}{\pi} e^{\pi/2}.$$

Beware of integrals of the form $\int_a^b f(x)\, dx$ where $f$ is not continuous at *all* points in the interval $[a, b]$. The Fundamental Theorem does not apply in such cases.

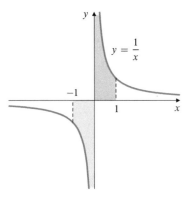

**Figure 8.25**

**EXAMPLE 6**    We know that $\dfrac{d}{dx} \ln|x| = \dfrac{1}{x}$ if $x \neq 0$. It is *incorrect*, however, to state that

$$\int_{-1}^{1} \frac{dx}{x} = \ln|x| \Big|_{-1}^{1} = 0 - 0 = 0,$$

even though $1/x$ is an odd function. In fact, $1/x$ is undefined and has no limit at $x = 0$, and it is not integrable on $[-1, 0]$ or $[0, 1]$ (Figure 8.25). Observe that

$$\lim_{c \to 0+} \int_{c}^{1} \frac{1}{x}\, dx = \lim_{c \to 0+} -\ln c = \infty,$$

so both shaded regions in Figure 8.25 have infinite area. Integrals of this type are called **improper integrals**. We deal with them in Section 9.5.

The following example illustrates, this time using definite integrals, the relationship observed in Example 1 of Section 5.11 between the area under the graph of its velocity and the distance travelled by an object over a time interval.

**EXAMPLE 7**  An object at rest at time $t = 0$ accelerates at a constant $10 \text{ m/s}^2$ during the time interval $[0, T]$. If $0 \le t_0 \le t_1 \le T$, find the distance travelled by the object in the time interval $[t_0, t_1]$.

*Solution*  Let $v(t)$ denote the velocity of the object at time $t$, and let $y(t)$ denote the distance travelled by the object during the time interval $[0, t]$, where $0 \le t \le T$. Then $v(0) = 0$ and $y(0) = 0$. Also $v'(t) = 10$ and $y'(t) = v(t)$. Thus,

$$v(t) = v(t) - v(0) = \int_0^t v'(u)\, du = \int_0^t 10\, du = 10u \Big|_0^t = 10t$$

$$y(t) = y(t) - y(0) = \int_0^t y'(u)\, du = \int_0^t v(u)\, du = \int_0^t 10u\, du = 5u^2 \Big|_0^t = 5t^2.$$

On the time interval $[t_0, t_1]$, the object has travelled distance

$$y(t_1) - y(t_0) = 5t_1^2 - 5t_0^2 = \int_0^{t_1} v(t)\, dt - \int_0^{t_0} v(t)\, dt = \int_{t_0}^{t_1} v(t)\, dt \text{ m.}$$

Observe that this last integral is the area under the graph of $y = v(t)$ above the interval $[t_0, t_1]$ on the $t$ axis.

We now give some examples illustrating the first conclusion of the Fundamental Theorem.

**EXAMPLE 8**  Find the derivatives of the following functions:

(a) $F(x) = \int_x^3 e^{-t^2}\, dt$,  (b) $G(x) = x^2 \int_{-4}^{5x} e^{-t^2}\, dt$,  (c) $H(x) = \int_{x^2}^{x^3} e^{-t^2}\, dt$.

*Solution*  The solutions involve applying the first conclusion of the Fundamental Theorem together with other differentiation rules.

(a) Observe that $F(x) = -\int_3^x e^{-t^2}\, dt$ (by Theorem 3(b)). Therefore, by the Fundamental Theorem, $F'(x) = -e^{-x^2}$.

(b) By the Product Rule and the Chain Rule,

$$G'(x) = 2x \int_{-4}^{5x} e^{-t^2}\, dt + x^2 \frac{d}{dx} \int_{-4}^{5x} e^{-t^2}\, dt$$

$$= 2x \int_{-4}^{5x} e^{-t^2}\, dt + x^2 e^{-(5x)^2}(5)$$

$$= 2x \int_{-4}^{5x} e^{-t^2}\, dt + 5x^2 e^{-25x^2}.$$

(c) Split the integral into a difference of two integrals in each of which the variable $x$ appears only in the upper limit:

$$H(x) = \int_0^{x^3} e^{-t^2}\, dt - \int_0^{x^2} e^{-t^2}\, dt$$

$$H'(x) = e^{-(x^3)^2}(3x^2) - e^{-(x^2)^2}(2x)$$

$$= 3x^2 e^{-x^6} - 2x e^{-x^4}.$$

Parts (b) and (c) of Example 8 are examples of the following formulas that build the Chain Rule into the first conclusion of the Fundamental Theorem:

$$\frac{d}{dx}\int_a^{g(x)} f(t)\,dt = f\big(g(x)\big)\,g'(x)$$

$$\frac{d}{dx}\int_{h(x)}^{g(x)} f(t)\,dt = f\big(g(x)\big)\,g'(x) - f\big(h(x)\big)\,h'(x)$$

**EXAMPLE 9**   Solve the **integral equation** $f(x) = 2 + 3\displaystyle\int_4^x f(t)\,dt$.

*Solution*   Differentiate the integral equation to get $f'(x) = 3f(x)$, the DE for exponential growth, having solution $f(x) = Ce^{3x}$. Now put $x = 4$ into the integral equation to get $f(4) = 2$. Hence $2 = Ce^{12}$, so $C = 2e^{-12}$. Therefore, the integral equation has solution $f(x) = 2e^{3x-12}$.

We conclude with an example showing how the Fundamental Theorem can be used to evaluate limits of Riemann sums.

**EXAMPLE 10**   Evaluate $\displaystyle\lim_{n\to\infty}\frac{1}{n}\sum_{j=1}^{n}\cos\left(\frac{j\pi}{2n}\right)$.

*Solution*   The sum involves values of $\cos x$ at the right endpoints of the $n$ subintervals of the partition

$$0, \quad \frac{\pi}{2n}, \quad \frac{2\pi}{2n}, \quad \frac{3\pi}{2n}, \quad \dots, \quad \frac{n\pi}{2n}$$

of the interval $[0, \pi/2]$. Since each of the subintervals of this partition has length $\pi/(2n)$, and since $\cos x$ is continuous on $[0, \pi/2]$, we have, expressing the limit of a Riemann sum as an integral (see Figure 8.26),

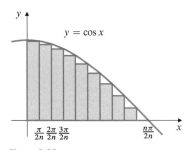

$y = \cos x$

Figure 8.26

$$\lim_{n\to\infty}\frac{\pi}{2n}\sum_{j=1}^{n}\cos\left(\frac{j\pi}{2n}\right) = \int_0^{\pi/2}\cos x\,dx = \sin x\Big|_0^{\pi/2} = 1 - 0 = 1.$$

The given sum differs from the Riemann sum above only in that the factor $\pi/2$ is missing. Thus,

$$\lim_{n\to\infty}\frac{1}{n}\sum_{j=1}^{n}\cos\left(\frac{j\pi}{2n}\right) = \frac{2}{\pi}.$$

## EXERCISES 8.5

Evaluate the definite integrals in Exercises 1–20.

**1.** $\displaystyle\int_0^2 x^3\,dx$

**2.** $\displaystyle\int_0^4 \sqrt{x}\,dx$

**3.** $\displaystyle\int_{1/2}^1 \frac{1}{x^2}\,dx$

**4.** $\displaystyle\int_{-2}^{-1}\left(\frac{1}{x^2} - \frac{1}{x^3}\right)dx$

**5.** $\displaystyle\int_{-1}^2 (3x^2 - 4x + 2)\,dx$

**6.** $\displaystyle\int_1^2\left(\frac{2}{x^3} - \frac{x^3}{2}\right)dx$

**7.** $\displaystyle\int_{-2}^2 (x^2 + 3)^2\,dx$

**8.** $\displaystyle\int_4^9\left(\sqrt{x} - \frac{1}{\sqrt{x}}\right)dx$

**9.** $\displaystyle\int_{-\pi/4}^{-\pi/6}\cos x\,dx$

**10.** $\displaystyle\int_0^{\pi/3}\sec^2\theta\,d\theta$

**11.** $\displaystyle\int_{\pi/4}^{\pi/3}\sin\theta\,d\theta$

**12.** $\displaystyle\int_0^{2\pi}(1 + \sin u)\,du$

**13.** $\displaystyle\int_{-\pi}^{\pi} e^x\,dx$

**14.** $\displaystyle\int_{-2}^2 (e^x - e^{-x})\,dx$

**15.** $\int_0^e a^x \, dx \quad (a > 0)$     **16.** $\int_{-1}^1 2^x \, dx$

**17.** $\int_{-1}^1 \dfrac{dx}{1 + x^2}$     **18.** $\int_0^{1/2} \dfrac{dx}{\sqrt{1 - x^2}}$

**⚠ 19.** $\int_{-1}^1 \dfrac{dx}{\sqrt{4 - x^2}}$     **⚠ 20.** $\int_{-2}^0 \dfrac{dx}{4 + x^2}$

Find the area of the region $R$ specified in Exercises 21–32. It is helpful to make a sketch of the region.

**21.** Bounded by $y = x^4$, $y = 0$, $x = 0$, and $x = 1$

**22.** Bounded by $y = 1/x$, $y = 0$, $x = e$, and $x = e^2$

**23.** Above $y = x^2 - 4x$ and below the $x$-axis

**24.** Bounded by $y = 5 - 2x - 3x^2$, $y = 0$, $x = -1$, and $x = 1$

**25.** Bounded by $y = x^2 - 3x + 3$ and $y = 1$

**26.** Below $y = \sqrt{x}$ and above $y = \dfrac{x}{2}$

**27.** Above $y = x^2$ and to the right of $x = y^2$

**28.** Above $y = |x|$ and below $y = 12 - x^2$

**29.** Bounded by $y = x^{1/3} - x^{1/2}$, $y = 0$, $x = 0$, and $x = 1$

**30.** Under $y = e^{-x}$ and above $y = 0$ from $x = -a$ to $x = 0$

**31.** Below $y = 1 - \cos x$ and above $y = 0$ between two consecutive intersections of these graphs

**32.** Below $y = x^{-1/3}$ and above $y = 0$ from $x = 1$ to $x = 27$

Find the integrals of the piecewise continuous functions in Exercises 33–34.

**33.** $\int_0^{3\pi/2} |\cos x| \, dx$     **34.** $\int_1^3 \dfrac{\text{sgn}\,(x - 2)}{x^2} \, dx$

In Exercises 35–38, find the average values of the given functions over the intervals specified.

**35.** $f(x) = 1 + x + x^2 + x^3$ over $[0, 2]$

**36.** $f(x) = e^{3x}$ over $[-2, 2]$

**37.** $f(x) = 2^x$ over $[0, 1/\ln 2]$

**38.** $g(t) = \begin{cases} 0 & \text{if } 0 \le t \le 1 \\ 1 & \text{if } 1 < t \le 3 \end{cases}$ over $[0, 3]$

Find the indicated derivatives in Exercises 39–46.

**39.** $\dfrac{d}{dx} \int_2^x \dfrac{\sin t}{t} \, dt$     **40.** $\dfrac{d}{dt} \int_t^3 \dfrac{\sin x}{x} \, dx$

**41.** $\dfrac{d}{dx} \int_{x^2}^0 \dfrac{\sin t}{t} \, dt$     **42.** $\dfrac{d}{dx} x^2 \int_0^{x^2} \dfrac{\sin u}{u} \, du$

**43.** $\dfrac{d}{dt} \int_{-\pi}^t \dfrac{\cos y}{1 + y^2} \, dy$     **44.** $\dfrac{d}{d\theta} \int_{\sin \theta}^{\cos \theta} \dfrac{1}{1 - x^2} \, dx$

**45.** $\dfrac{d}{dx} F(\sqrt{x})$, if $F(t) = \int_0^t \cos(x^2) \, dx$

**46.** $H'(2)$, if $H(x) = 3x \int_4^{x^2} e^{-\sqrt{t}} \, dt$

**47.** Solve the integral equation $f(x) = \pi \left( 1 + \int_1^x f(t) \, dt \right)$.

**48.** Solve the integral equation $f(x) = 1 - \int_0^x f(t) \, dt$.

**❷ 49.** Criticize the following erroneous calculation:

$$\int_{-1}^1 \dfrac{dx}{x^2} = -\dfrac{1}{x} \bigg|_{-1}^1 = -1 + \dfrac{1}{-1} = -2.$$

Exactly where did the error occur? Why is $-2$ an unreasonable value for the integral?

**⚠ 50.** Use a definite integral to define a function $F(x)$ having derivative $\dfrac{\sin x}{1 + x^2}$ for all $x$ and satisfying $F(17) = 0$.

**⚠ 51.** Does the function $F(x) = \int_0^{2x - x^2} \cos \left( \dfrac{1}{1 + t^2} \right) dt$ have a maximum or a minimum value? Justify your answer.

Evaluate the limits in Exercises 52–54.

**⚠ 52.** $\lim\limits_{n \to \infty} \dfrac{1}{n} \left( \left(1 + \dfrac{1}{n}\right)^5 + \left(1 + \dfrac{2}{n}\right)^5 + \cdots + \left(1 + \dfrac{n}{n}\right)^5 \right)$

**⚠ 53.** $\lim\limits_{n \to \infty} \dfrac{\pi}{n} \left( \sin \dfrac{\pi}{n} + \sin \dfrac{2\pi}{n} + \sin \dfrac{3\pi}{n} + \cdots + \sin \dfrac{n\pi}{n} \right)$

**⚠ 54.** $\lim\limits_{n \to \infty} \left( \dfrac{n}{n^2 + 1} + \dfrac{n}{n^2 + 4} + \dfrac{n}{n^2 + 9} + \cdots + \dfrac{n}{2n^2} \right)$

## 8.6  The Method of Substitution

As we have seen, the evaluation of definite integrals is most easily carried out if we can antidifferentiate the integrand. In this section and Sections 9 we develop some *techniques of integration*, that is, methods for finding antiderivatives of functions. Although the techniques we develop can be used for a large class of functions, they will not work for all functions we might want to integrate. If a definite integral involves an integrand whose antiderivative is either impossible or very difficult to find, we may wish, instead, to approximate the definite integral by numerical means. Techniques for doing that will be presented in Sections 9.

Let us begin by assembling a table of some known indefinite integrals. These results have all emerged during our development of differentiation formulas for elementary functions. You should *memorize* them.

**Some elementary integrals**

1. $\displaystyle\int 1\,dx = x + C$

2. $\displaystyle\int x\,dx = \frac{1}{2}x^2 + C$

3. $\displaystyle\int x^2\,dx = \frac{1}{3}x^3 + C$

4. $\displaystyle\int \frac{1}{x^2}\,dx = -\frac{1}{x} + C$

5. $\displaystyle\int \sqrt{x}\,dx = \frac{2}{3}x^{3/2} + C$

6. $\displaystyle\int \frac{1}{\sqrt{x}}\,dx = 2\sqrt{x} + C$

7. $\displaystyle\int x^r\,dx = \frac{1}{r+1}x^{r+1} + C \quad (r \neq -1)$

8. $\displaystyle\int \frac{1}{x}\,dx = \ln|x| + C$

9. $\displaystyle\int \sin ax\,dx = -\frac{1}{a}\cos ax + C$

10. $\displaystyle\int \cos ax\,dx = \frac{1}{a}\sin ax + C$

11. $\displaystyle\int \sec^2 ax\,dx = \frac{1}{a}\tan ax + C$

12. $\displaystyle\int \csc^2 ax\,dx = -\frac{1}{a}\cot ax + C$

13. $\displaystyle\int \sec ax \tan ax\,dx = \frac{1}{a}\sec ax + C$

14. $\displaystyle\int \csc ax \cot ax\,dx = -\frac{1}{a}\csc ax + C$

15. $\displaystyle\int \frac{1}{\sqrt{a^2 - x^2}}\,dx = \sin^{-1}\frac{x}{a} + C \quad (a > 0)$

16. $\displaystyle\int \frac{1}{a^2 + x^2}\,dx = \frac{1}{a}\tan^{-1}\frac{x}{a} + C$

17. $\displaystyle\int e^{ax}\,dx = \frac{1}{a}e^{ax} + C$

18. $\displaystyle\int b^{ax}\,dx = \frac{1}{a\ln b}b^{ax} + C$

19. $\displaystyle\int \cosh ax\,dx = \frac{1}{a}\sinh ax + C$

20. $\displaystyle\int \sinh ax\,dx = \frac{1}{a}\cosh ax + C$

Note that formulas 1–6 are special cases of formula 7, which holds on any interval where $x^r$ makes sense. The linearity formula

$$\int (A\,f(x) + B\,g(x))\,dx = A\int f(x)\,dx + B\int g(x)\,dx$$

makes it possible to integrate sums and constant multiples of functions.

---

**EXAMPLE 1**    **(Combining elementary integrals)**

(a) $\displaystyle\int (x^4 - 3x^3 + 8x^2 - 6x - 7)\,dx = \frac{x^5}{5} - \frac{3x^4}{4} + \frac{8x^3}{3} - 3x^2 - 7x + C$

(b) $\displaystyle\int \left(5x^{3/5} - \frac{3}{2+x^2}\right)dx = \frac{25}{8}x^{8/5} - \frac{3}{\sqrt{2}}\tan^{-1}\frac{x}{\sqrt{2}} + C$

(c) $\displaystyle\int (4\cos 5x - 5\sin 3x)\,dx = \frac{4}{5}\sin 5x + \frac{5}{3}\cos 3x + C$

(d) $\displaystyle\int \left(\frac{1}{\pi x} + a^{\pi x}\right)dx = \frac{1}{\pi}\ln|x| + \frac{1}{\pi\ln a}a^{\pi x} + C, \quad (a > 0).$

---

Sometimes it is necessary to manipulate an integrand so that the method can be applied.

---

**EXAMPLE 2**    $\displaystyle\int \frac{(x+1)^3}{x}\,dx = \int \frac{x^3 + 3x^2 + 3x + 1}{x}\,dx$

$$= \int \left(x^2 + 3x + 3 + \frac{1}{x}\right)dx$$

$$= \frac{1}{3}x^3 + \frac{3}{2}x^2 + 3x + \ln|x| + C.$$

---

When an integral cannot be evaluated by inspection, as those in Examples 1–2 can, we require one or more special techniques. The most important of these techniques is the **method of substitution**, the integral version of the Chain Rule. If we rewrite the Chain Rule, $\frac{d}{dx} f(g(x)) = f'(g(x)) g'(x)$, in integral form, we obtain

$$\int f'(g(x)) g'(x)\, dx = f(g(x)) + C.$$

Observe that the following formalism would produce this latter formula even if we did not already know it was true:

Let $u = g(x)$. Then $du/dx = g'(x)$, or in differential form, $du = g'(x)\, dx$. Thus,

$$\int f'(g(x))\, g'(x)\, dx = \int f'(u)\, du = f(u) + C = f(g(x)) + C.$$

---

**EXAMPLE 3**    (**Examples of substitution**) Find the indefinite integrals:

(a) $\displaystyle\int \frac{x}{x^2+1}\, dx$,    (b) $\displaystyle\int \frac{\sin(3\ln x)}{x}\, dx$, and    (c) $\displaystyle\int e^x \sqrt{1+e^x}\, dx$.

*Solution*

(a) $\displaystyle\int \frac{x}{x^2+1}\, dx$    Let $u = x^2 + 1$.
   Then $du = 2x\, dx$    and
   $x\, dx = \frac{1}{2}\, du$

$$= \frac{1}{2} \int \frac{du}{u} = \frac{1}{2} \ln|u| + C = \frac{1}{2} \ln(x^2 + 1) + C = \ln\sqrt{x^2+1} + C.$$

(Both versions of the final answer are equally acceptable.)

(b) $\displaystyle\int \frac{\sin(3\ln x)}{x}\, dx$    Let $u = 3\ln x$.
   Then $du = \dfrac{3}{x}\, dx$

$$= \frac{1}{3} \int \sin u\, du = -\frac{1}{3}\cos u + C = -\frac{1}{3}\cos(3\ln x) + C.$$

(c) $\displaystyle\int e^x \sqrt{1+e^x}\, dx$    Let $v = 1 + e^x$.
   Then $dv = e^x\, dx$

$$= \int v^{1/2}\, dv = \frac{2}{3} v^{3/2} + C = \frac{2}{3}(1 + e^x)^{3/2} + C.$$

---

Sometimes the appropriate substitutions are not as obvious as they were in Example 3, and it may be necessary to manipulate the integrand algebraically to put it into a better form for substitution.

---

**EXAMPLE 4**    Evaluate    (a) $\displaystyle\int \frac{1}{x^2 + 4x + 5}\, dx$    and    (b) $\displaystyle\int \frac{dx}{\sqrt{e^{2x} - 1}}$.

*Solution*

(a) $\displaystyle\int \frac{dx}{x^2 + 4x + 5} = \int \frac{dx}{(x+2)^2 + 1}$    Let $t = x + 2$.
   Then $dt = dx$.

$$= \int \frac{dt}{t^2 + 1}$$

$$= \tan^{-1} t + C = \tan^{-1}(x + 2) + C.$$

(b) $\displaystyle\int \frac{dx}{\sqrt{e^{2x}-1}} = \int \frac{dx}{e^x\sqrt{1-e^{-2x}}}$

$\displaystyle\qquad = \int \frac{e^{-x}\,dx}{\sqrt{1-(e^{-x})^2}}$    Let $u = e^{-x}$.

$\displaystyle\qquad\qquad\qquad\qquad\qquad$ Then $du = -e^{-x}\,dx$.

$\displaystyle\qquad = -\int \frac{du}{\sqrt{1-u^2}}$

$\displaystyle\qquad = -\sin^{-1} u + C = -\sin^{-1}(e^{-x}) + C.$

The method of substitution cannot be *forced* to work. There is no substitution that will do much good with the integral $\int x(2+x^7)^{1/5}\,dx$, for instance. However, the integral $\int x^6(2+x^7)^{1/5}\,dx$ will yield to the substitution $u = 2+x^7$. The substitution $u = g(x)$ is more likely to work if $g'(x)$ is a factor of the integrand.

The following theorem simplifies the use of the method of substitution in definite integrals.

## THEOREM

### 6

**Substitution in a definite integral**

Suppose that $g$ is a differentiable function on $[a, b]$ that satisfies $g(a) = A$ and $g(b) = B$. Also suppose that $f$ is continuous on the range of $g$. Then

$$\int_a^b f\big(g(x)\big)\,g'(x)\,dx = \int_A^B f(u)\,du.$$

**PROOF**   Let $F$ be an antiderivative of $f$; $F'(u) = f(u)$. Then

$$\frac{d}{dx}F\big(g(x)\big) = F'\big(g(x)\big)\,g'(x) = f\big(g(x)\big)\,g'(x).$$

Thus,

$$\int_a^b f\big(g(x)\big)\,g'(x)\,dx = F\big(g(x)\big)\Big|_a^b = F\big(g(b)\big) - F\big(g(a)\big)$$

$$= F(B) - F(A) = F(u)\Big|_A^B = \int_A^B f(u)\,du.$$

---

**EXAMPLE 5**   Evaluate the integral $\displaystyle I = \int_0^8 \frac{\cos\sqrt{x+1}}{\sqrt{x+1}}\,dx$.

**Solution**   **METHOD I.**  Let $u = \sqrt{x+1}$. Then $du = \dfrac{dx}{2\sqrt{x+1}}$. If $x = 0$, then $u = 1$; if $x = 8$, then $u = 3$. Thus,

$$I = 2\int_1^3 \cos u\,du = 2\sin u\Big|_1^3 = 2\sin 3 - 2\sin 1.$$

**METHOD II.**  We use the same substitution as in Method I, but we do not transform the limits of integration from $x$ values to $u$ values. Hence, we must return to the variable $x$ before substituting in the limits:

$$I = 2\int_{x=0}^{x=8} \cos u\,du = 2\sin u\Big|_{x=0}^{x=8} = 2\sin\sqrt{x+1}\,\Big|_0^8 = 2\sin 3 - 2\sin 1.$$

Note that the limits *must* be written $x = 0$ and $x = 8$ at any stage where the variable is not $x$. It would have been *wrong* to write

$$I = 2 \int_0^8 \cos u \, du$$

because this would imply that $u$, rather than $x$, goes from 0 to 8. Method I gives the shorter solution and is therefore preferable. However, in cases where the transformed limits (the $u$-limits) are very complicated, you might prefer to use Method II.

---

**EXAMPLE 6**    Find the area of the region bounded by $y = \left(2 + \sin \dfrac{x}{2}\right)^2 \cos \dfrac{x}{2}$, the $x$-axis, and the lines $x = 0$ and $x = \pi$.

**Solution**    Because $y \geq 0$ when $0 \leq x \leq \pi$, the required area is

$$A = \int_0^\pi \left(2 + \sin \frac{x}{2}\right)^2 \cos \frac{x}{2} \, dx \qquad \text{Let } v = 2 + \sin \frac{x}{2}.$$

$$\text{Then } dv = \frac{1}{2} \cos \frac{x}{2} \, dx$$

$$= 2 \int_2^3 v^2 \, dv = \frac{2}{3} v^3 \Big|_2^3 = \frac{2}{3}(27 - 8) = \frac{38}{3} \text{ square units.}$$

---

**Remark**    The condition that $f$ be continuous on the range of the function $u = g(x)$ (for $a \leq x \leq b$) is essential in Theorem 6. Using the substitution $u = x^2$ in the integral $\int_{-1}^1 x \csc(x^2) \, dx$ leads to the erroneous conclusion

$$\int_{-1}^1 x \csc(x^2) \, dx = \frac{1}{2} \int_1^1 \csc u \, du = 0.$$

Although $x \csc(x^2)$ is an odd function, it is not continuous at 0, and it happens that the given integral represents the difference of *infinite* areas. If we assume that $f$ is continuous on an interval containing $A$ and $B$, then it suffices to know that $u = g(x)$ is one-to-one as well as differentiable. In this case the range of $g$ will lie between $A$ and $B$, so the condition of Theorem 6 will be satisfied.

## Trigonometric Integrals

The method of substitution is often useful for evaluating trigonometric integrals. We begin by listing the integrals of the four trigonometric functions whose integrals we have not yet seen. They arise often in applications and should be memorized.

**Integrals of tangent, cotangent, secant, and cosecant**

$$\int \tan x \, dx = \ln |\sec x| + C,$$

$$\int \cot x \, dx = \ln |\sin x| + C = -\ln |\csc x| + C,$$

$$\int \sec x \, dx = \ln |\sec x + \tan x| + C,$$

$$\int \csc x \, dx = -\ln |\csc x + \cot x| + C = \ln |\csc x - \cot x| + C.$$

All of these can, of course, be checked by differentiating the right-hand sides. The first two can be evaluated directly by rewriting $\tan x$ or $\cot x$ in terms of $\sin x$ and $\cos x$ and using an appropriate substitution. For example,

$$\int \tan x \, dx = \int \frac{\sin x}{\cos x} \, dx \qquad \text{Let } u = \cos x.$$
$$\text{Then } du = -\sin x \, dx.$$
$$= -\int \frac{du}{u} = -\ln |u| + C$$
$$= -\ln |\cos x| + C = \ln \left| \frac{1}{\cos x} \right| + C = \ln |\sec x| + C.$$

The integral of $\sec x$ can be evaluated by rewriting it in the form

$$\int \sec x \, dx = \int \frac{\sec x (\sec x + \tan x)}{\sec x + \tan x} \, dx$$

and using the substitution $u = \sec x + \tan x$. The integral of $\csc x$ can be evaluated similarly. (Show that the two versions given for that integral are equivalent!)

We now consider integrals of the form

$$\int \sin^m x \, \cos^n x \, dx.$$

If either $m$ or $n$ is an odd, positive integer, the integral can be done easily by substitution. If, say, $n = 2k + 1$ where $k$ is an integer, then we can use the identity $\sin^2 x + \cos^2 x = 1$ to rewrite the integral in the form

$$\int \sin^m x \, (1 - \sin^2 x)^k \cos x \, dx,$$

which can be integrated using the substitution $u = \sin x$. Similarly, $u = \cos x$ can be used if $m$ is an odd integer.

---

**EXAMPLE 7**    Evaluate    (a) $\displaystyle\int \sin^3 x \, \cos^8 x \, dx$    and    (b) $\displaystyle\int \cos^5 ax \, dx$.

*Solution*

(a) $\displaystyle\int \sin^3 x \, \cos^8 x \, dx = \int (1 - \cos^2 x) \cos^8 x \sin x \, dx \qquad \text{Let } u = \cos x,$
$$du = -\sin x \, dx.$$
$$= -\int (1 - u^2) u^8 \, du = \int (u^{10} - u^8) \, du$$
$$= \frac{u^{11}}{11} - \frac{u^9}{9} + C = \frac{1}{11} \cos^{11} x - \frac{1}{9} \cos^9 x + C.$$

(b) $\displaystyle\int \cos^5 ax \, dx = \int (1 - \sin^2 ax)^2 \cos ax \, dx \qquad \text{Let } u = \sin ax,$
$$du = a \cos ax \, dx.$$
$$= \frac{1}{a} \int (1 - u^2)^2 \, du = \frac{1}{a} \int (1 - 2u^2 + u^4) \, du$$
$$= \frac{1}{a} \left( u - \frac{2}{3} u^3 + \frac{1}{5} u^5 \right) + C$$
$$= \frac{1}{a} \left( \sin ax - \frac{2}{3} \sin^3 ax + \frac{1}{5} \sin^5 ax \right) + C.$$

---

If the powers of $\sin x$ and $\cos x$ are both even, then we can make use of the *double-angle formulas*:

$$\cos^2 x = \frac{1}{2}(1 + \cos 2x) \qquad \text{and} \qquad \sin^2 x = \frac{1}{2}(1 - \cos 2x).$$

<hr>

EXAMPLE 8     **(Integrating even powers of sine and cosine)** Verify the integration formulas

$$\int \cos^2 x\, dx = \frac{1}{2}(x + \sin x \cos x) + C,$$

$$\int \sin^2 x\, dx = \frac{1}{2}(x - \sin x \cos x) + C.$$

These integrals are encountered frequently and are worth remembering.

*Solution*   Each of the integrals follows from the corresponding double-angle identity. We do the first; the second is similar.

$$\int \cos^2 x\, dx = \frac{1}{2}\int (1 + \cos 2x)\, dx$$

$$= \frac{x}{2} + \frac{1}{4}\sin 2x + C$$

$$= \frac{1}{2}(x + \sin x \cos x) + C \quad (\text{since } \sin 2x = 2\sin x \cos x).$$

<hr>

EXAMPLE 9     Evaluate $\int \sin^4 x\, dx$.

*Solution*   We will have to apply the double-angle formula twice.

$$\int \sin^4 x\, dx = \frac{1}{4}\int (1 - \cos 2x)^2\, dx$$

$$= \frac{1}{4}\int (1 - 2\cos 2x + \cos^2 2x)\, dx$$

$$= \frac{x}{4} - \frac{1}{4}\sin 2x + \frac{1}{8}\int (1 + \cos 4x)\, dx$$

$$= \frac{x}{4} - \frac{1}{4}\sin 2x + \frac{x}{8} + \frac{1}{32}\sin 4x + C$$

$$= \frac{3}{8}x - \frac{1}{4}\sin 2x + \frac{1}{32}\sin 4x + C$$

(Note that there is no point in inserting the constant of integration $C$ until the last integral has been evaluated.)

<hr>

Using the identities $\sec^2 x = 1 + \tan^2 x$ and $\csc^2 x = 1 + \cot^2 x$ and one of the substitutions $u = \sec x$, $u = \tan x$, $u = \csc x$, or $u = \cot x$, we can evaluate integrals of the form

$$\int \sec^m x\, \tan^n x\, dx \qquad \text{or} \qquad \int \csc^m x\, \cot^n x\, dx,$$

unless $m$ is odd and $n$ is even. (If this is the case, these integrals can be handled by integration by parts; see Section 9.1.)

<hr>

EXAMPLE 10     **(Integrals involving secants and tangents)** Evaluate the following integrals:

(a) $\int \tan^2 x\, dx$,     (b) $\int \sec^4 t\, dt$,   and     (c) $\int \sec^3 x\, \tan^3 x\, dx$.

*Solution*

(a) $\int \tan^2 x \, dx = \int (\sec^2 x - 1) \, dx = \tan x - x + C.$

(b) $\int \sec^4 t \, dt = \int (1 + \tan^2 t) \sec^2 t \, dt$      Let $u = \tan t$,

$$du = \sec^2 t \, dt.$$

$$= \int (1 + u^2) \, du = u + \frac{1}{3} u^3 + C = \tan t + \frac{1}{3} \tan^3 t + C.$$

(c) $\int \sec^3 x \tan^3 x \, dx$

$$= \int \sec^2 x \, (\sec^2 x - 1) \sec x \tan x \, dx \qquad \text{Let } u = \sec x,$$

$$du = \sec x \tan x \, dx.$$

$$= \int (u^4 - u^2) \, du = \frac{u^5}{5} - \frac{u^3}{3} + C = \frac{1}{5} \sec^5 x - \frac{1}{3} \sec^3 x + C.$$

## EXERCISES 8.6

Evaluate the integrals in Exercises 1–44. Remember to include a constant of integration with the indefinite integrals. Your answers may appear different from those in the Answers section but may still be correct. For example, evaluating $I = \int \sin x \cos x \, dx$ using the substitution $u = \sin x$ leads to $I = \frac{1}{2} \sin^2 x + C$; using $u = \cos x$ leads to $I = -\frac{1}{2} \cos^2 x + C$; and rewriting $I = \frac{1}{2} \int \sin(2x) \, dx$ leads to $I = -\frac{1}{4} \cos(2x) + C$. These answers are all equal except for different choices for the constant of integration $C$: $\frac{1}{2} \sin^2 x = -\frac{1}{2} \cos^2 x + \frac{1}{2} = -\frac{1}{4} \cos(2x) + \frac{1}{4}$.

You can always check your own answer to an indefinite integral by differentiating it to get back to the integrand. This is often easier than comparing your answer with the answer in the back of the book. You may find integrals that you can't do, but you should not make mistakes in those you can do because the answer is so easily checked. (This is a good thing to remember during tests and exams.)

1. $\int e^{5-2x} \, dx$

2. $\int \cos(ax + b) \, dx$

3. $\int \sqrt{3x + 4} \, dx$

4. $\int e^{2x} \sin(e^{2x}) \, dx$

5. $\int \frac{x \, dx}{(4x^2 + 1)^5}$

6. $\int \frac{\sin \sqrt{x}}{\sqrt{x}} \, dx$

7. $\int x \, e^{x^2} \, dx$

8. $\int x^2 2^{x^3+1} \, dx$

9. $\int \frac{\cos x}{4 + \sin^2 x} \, dx$

10. $\int \frac{\sec^2 x}{\sqrt{1 - \tan^2 x}} \, dx$

! 11. $\int \frac{e^x + 1}{e^x - 1} \, dx$

12. $\int \frac{\ln t}{t} \, dt$

13. $\int \frac{ds}{\sqrt{4 - 5s}}$

14. $\int \frac{x + 1}{\sqrt{x^2 + 2x + 3}} \, dx$

15. $\int \frac{t \, dt}{\sqrt{4 - t^4}}$

16. $\int \frac{x^2 \, dx}{2 + x^6}$

! 17. $\int \frac{dx}{e^x + 1}$

! 18. $\int \frac{dx}{e^x + e^{-x}}$

19. $\int \tan x \ln \cos x \, dx$

20. $\int \frac{x + 1}{\sqrt{1 - x^2}} \, dx$

21. $\int \frac{dx}{x^2 + 6x + 13}$

22. $\int \frac{dx}{\sqrt{4 + 2x - x^2}}$

23. $\int \sin^3 x \cos^5 x \, dx$

24. $\int \sin^4 t \cos^5 t \, dt$

25. $\int \sin ax \cos^2 ax \, dx$

26. $\int \sin^2 x \cos^2 x \, dx$

27. $\int \sin^6 x \, dx$

28. $\int \cos^4 x \, dx$

29. $\int \sec^5 x \tan x \, dx$

30. $\int \sec^6 x \tan^2 x \, dx$

31. $\int \sqrt{\tan x} \sec^4 x \, dx$

32. $\int \sin^{-2/3} x \cos^3 x \, dx$

33. $\int \cos x \sin^4 (\sin x) \, dx$

34. $\int \frac{\sin^3 \ln x \cos^3 \ln x}{x} \, dx$

35. $\int \frac{\sin^2 x}{\cos^4 x} \, dx$

36. $\int \frac{\sin^3 x}{\cos^4 x} \, dx$

37. $\int \csc^5 x \cot^5 x \, dx$

38. $\int \frac{\cos^4 x}{\sin^8 x} \, dx$

39. $\int_0^4 x^3 (x^2 + 1)^{-\frac{1}{2}} \, dx$

40. $\int_1^{\sqrt{e}} \frac{\sin(\pi \ln x)}{x} \, dx$

41. $\int_0^{\pi/2} \sin^4 x \, dx$

42. $\int_{\pi/4}^{\pi} \sin^5 x \, dx$

43. $\int_e^{e^2} \frac{dt}{t \ln t}$

44. $\int_{\frac{\pi^2}{16}}^{\frac{\pi^2}{9}} \frac{2^{\sin \sqrt{x}} \cos \sqrt{x}}{\sqrt{x}} \, dx$

! 45. Use the identities $\cos 2\theta = 2 \cos^2 \theta - 1 = 1 - 2 \sin^2 \theta$ and $\sin \theta = \cos\left(\frac{\pi}{2} - \theta\right)$ to help you evaluate the following:

$$\int_0^{\pi/2} \sqrt{1 + \cos x} \, dx \quad \text{and} \quad \int_0^{\pi/2} \sqrt{1 - \sin x} \, dx$$

**46.** Find the area of the region bounded by
$y = x/(x^2 + 16)$, $y = 0$, $x = 0$, and $x = 2$.

**47.** Find the area of the region bounded by
$y = x/(x^4 + 16)$, $y = 0$, $x = 0$, and $x = 2$.

**48.** Express the area bounded by the ellipse
$(x^2/a^2) + (y^2/b^2) = 1$ as a definite integral. Make a
substitution that converts this integral into one representing
the area of a circle, and hence evaluate it.

**🔒 49.** Use the addition formulas for $\sin(x \pm y)$ and $\cos(x \pm y)$
to establish the following identities:

$$\cos x \, \cos y = \frac{1}{2}\Big(\cos(x - y) + \cos(x + y)\Big),$$

$$\sin x \, \sin y = \frac{1}{2}\Big(\cos(x - y) - \cos(x + y)\Big),$$

$$\sin x \, \cos y = \frac{1}{2}\Big(\sin(x + y) + \sin(x - y)\Big).$$

**🔒 50.** Use the identities established in Exercise 49 to calculate the
following integrals:

$$\int \cos ax \, \cos bx \, dx, \quad \int \sin ax \, \sin bx \, dx,$$

and $\int \sin ax \, \cos bx \, dx.$

**🔒 51.** If $m$ and $n$ are integers, show that:

(i) $\displaystyle\int_{-\pi}^{\pi} \cos mx \, \cos nx \, dx = 0$ if $m \neq n$,

(ii) $\displaystyle\int_{-\pi}^{\pi} \sin mx \, \sin nx \, dx = 0$ if $m \neq n$,

(iii) $\displaystyle\int_{-\pi}^{\pi} \sin mx \, \cos nx \, dx = 0.$

**🔒 52. (Fourier coefficients)** Suppose that for some positive integer
$k$,

$$f(x) = \frac{a_0}{2} + \sum_{n=1}^{k} (a_n \cos nx + b_n \sin nx)$$

holds for all $x$ in $[-\pi, \pi]$. Use the result of Exercise 51 to
show that the coefficients $a_m$ ($0 \leq m \leq k$) and $b_m$
($1 \leq m \leq k$), which are called the Fourier coefficients of $f$
on $[-\pi, \pi]$, are given by

$$a_m = \frac{1}{\pi}\int_{-\pi}^{\pi} f(x) \cos mx \, dx, \quad b_m = \frac{1}{\pi}\int_{-\pi}^{\pi} f(x) \sin mx \, dx.$$

## 8.7   Areas of Plane Regions

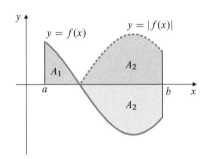

Figure 8.27

In this section we review and extend the use of definite integrals to represent plane
areas. Recall that the integral $\int_a^b f(x)\,dx$ measures the area between the graph of $f$
and the $x$-axis from $x = a$ to $x = b$, but treats as *negative* any part of this area that
lies below the $x$-axis. (We are assuming that $a < b$.) In order to express the total area
bounded by $y = f(x)$, $y = 0$, $x = a$, and $x = b$, counting all of the area positively,
we should integrate the *absolute value* of $f$ (see Figure 8.27):

$$\int_a^b f(x)\,dx = A_1 - A_2 \quad \text{and} \quad \int_a^b |f(x)|\,dx = A_1 + A_2.$$

There is no "rule" for integrating $\int_a^b |f(x)|\,dx$; one must break the integral into a sum
of integrals over intervals where $f(x) > 0$ (so $|f(x)| = f(x)$), and intervals where
$f(x) < 0$ (so $|f(x)| = -f(x)$).

**EXAMPLE 1**   The area bounded by $y = \cos x$, $y = 0$, $x = 0$, and $x = 3\pi/2$
(see Figure 8.28) is

$$A = \int_0^{3\pi/2} |\cos x|\,dx$$

$$= \int_0^{\pi/2} \cos x \, dx + \int_{\pi/2}^{3\pi/2} (-\cos x)\,dx$$

$$= \sin x \Big|_0^{\pi/2} - \sin x \Big|_{\pi/2}^{3\pi/2}$$

$$= (1 - 0) - (-1 - 1) = 3 \text{ square units.}$$

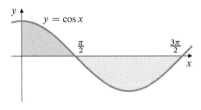

Figure 8.28

## Areas Between Two Curves

Suppose that a plane region $R$ is bounded by the graphs of two continuous functions, $y = f(x)$ and $y = g(x)$, and the vertical straight lines $x = a$ and $x = b$, as shown in Figure 8.29(a). Assume that $a < b$ and that $f(x) \leq g(x)$ on $[a, b]$, so the graph of $f$ lies below that of $g$. If $f(x) \geq 0$ on $[a, b]$, then the area $A$ of $R$ is the area above the $x$-axis and under the graph of $g$ minus the area above the $x$-axis and under the graph of $f$:

$$A = \int_a^b g(x)\,dx - \int_a^b f(x)\,dx = \int_a^b \big(g(x) - f(x)\big)\,dx.$$

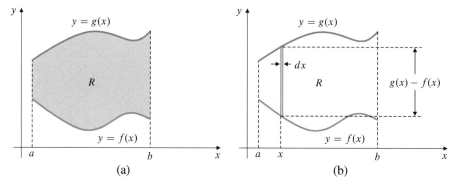

**Figure 8.29**

(a) The region $R$ lying between two graphs

(b) An area element of the region $R$

(a)                                        (b)

It is useful to regard this formula as expressing $A$ as the "sum" (i.e., the integral) of *infinitely many* **area elements**

$$dA = (g(x) - f(x))\,dx,$$

corresponding to values of $x$ between $a$ and $b$. Each such area element is the area of an infinitely thin vertical rectangle of width $dx$ and height $g(x) - f(x)$ located at position $x$ (see Figure 8.29(b)). Even if $f$ and $g$ can take on negative values on $[a, b]$, this interpretation and the resulting area formula

$$A = \int_a^b \big(g(x) - f(x)\big)\,dx$$

remain valid, provided that $f(x) \leq g(x)$ on $[a, b]$ so that all the area elements $dA$ have positive area. Using integrals to represent a quantity as a *sum* of *differential elements* (i.e., a sum of little bits of the quantity) is a very helpful approach. We will do this often in Chapter 10. Of course, what we are really doing is identifying the integral as a *limit* of a suitable Riemann sum.

More generally, if the restriction $f(x) \leq g(x)$ is removed, then the vertical rectangle of width $dx$ at position $x$ extending between the graphs of $f$ and $g$ has height $|f(x) - g(x)|$ and hence area

$$dA = |f(x) - g(x)|\,dx.$$

(See Figure 8.30.) Hence, the total area lying between the graphs $y = f(x)$ and $y = g(x)$ and between the vertical lines $x = a$ and $x = b > a$ is given by

$$A = \int_a^b |f(x) - g(x)|\,dx.$$

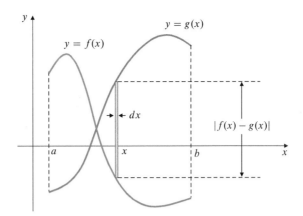

**Figure 8.30**    An area element for the region between $y = f(x)$ and $y = g(x)$

In order to evaluate this integral, we have to determine the intervals on which $f(x) > g(x)$ or $f(x) < g(x)$, and break the integral into a sum of integrals over each of these intervals.

EXAMPLE 2    Find the area of the bounded, plane region $R$ lying between the curves $y = x^2 - 2x$ and $y = 4 - x^2$.

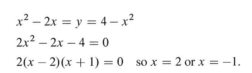

**Figure 8.31**

**Solution**    First, we must find the intersections of the curves, so we solve the equations simultaneously:

$$x^2 - 2x = y = 4 - x^2$$
$$2x^2 - 2x - 4 = 0$$
$$2(x - 2)(x + 1) = 0 \quad \text{so } x = 2 \text{ or } x = -1.$$

The curves are sketched in Figure 8.31, and the bounded (finite) region between them is shaded. (A sketch should always be made in problems of this sort.) Since $4 - x^2 \geq x^2 - 2x$ for $-1 \leq x \leq 2$, the area $A$ of $R$ is given by

$$
\begin{aligned}
A &= \int_{-1}^{2} \left( (4 - x^2) - (x^2 - 2x) \right) dx \\
&= \int_{-1}^{2} (4 - 2x^2 + 2x) \, dx \\
&= \left( 4x - \frac{2}{3}x^3 + x^2 \right) \Big|_{-1}^{2} \\
&= 4(2) - \frac{2}{3}(8) + 4 - \left( -4 + \frac{2}{3} + 1 \right) = 9 \text{ square units.}
\end{aligned}
$$

Note that in representing the area as an integral we *must subtract the height $y$ to the lower curve from the height $y$ to the upper curve* to get a positive area element $dA$. Subtracting the wrong way would have produced a negative value for the area.

EXAMPLE 3    Find the total area $A$ lying between the curves $y = \sin x$ and $y = \cos x$ from $x = 0$ to $x = 2\pi$.

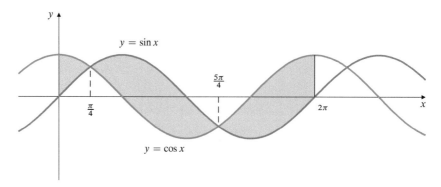

**Figure 8.32**

*Solution*  The region is shaded in Figure 8.32. Between 0 and $2\pi$ the graphs of sine and cosine cross at $x = \pi/4$ and $x = 5\pi/4$. The required area is

$$A = \int_0^{\pi/4} (\cos x - \sin x)\, dx + \int_{\pi/4}^{5\pi/4} (\sin x - \cos x)\, dx$$

$$+ \int_{5\pi/4}^{2\pi} (\cos x - \sin x)\, dx$$

$$= (\sin x + \cos x)\Big|_0^{\pi/4} - (\cos x + \sin x)\Big|_{\pi/4}^{5\pi/4} + (\sin x + \cos x)\Big|_{5\pi/4}^{2\pi}$$

$$= (\sqrt{2} - 1) + (\sqrt{2} + \sqrt{2}) + (1 + \sqrt{2}) = 4\sqrt{2} \text{ square units.}$$

It is sometimes more convenient to use horizontal area elements instead of vertical ones and integrate over an interval of the $y$-axis instead of the $x$-axis. This is usually the case if the region whose area we want to find is bounded by curves whose equations are written in terms of functions of $y$. In Figure 8.33(a), the region $R$ lying to the right of $x = f(y)$ and to the left of $x = g(y)$, and between the horizontal lines $y = c$ and $y = d > c$, has area element $dA = \big(g(y) - f(y)\big)\, dy$. Its area is

$$A = \int_c^d \big(g(y) - f(y)\big)\, dy.$$

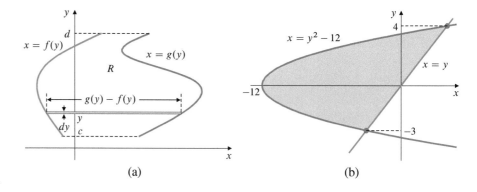

**Figure 8.33**

(a)  A horizontal area element

(b)  The finite region bounded by $x = y^2 - 12$ and $x = y$

(a)                    (b)

**EXAMPLE 4**    Find the area of the plane region lying to the right of the parabola $x = y^2 - 12$ and to the left of the straight line $y = x$, as illustrated in Figure 8.33(b).

*Solution*  For the intersections of the curves:

$$y^2 - 12 = x = y$$
$$y^2 - y - 12 = 0$$
$$(y - 4)(y + 3) = 0 \quad \text{so } y = 4 \text{ or } y = -3.$$

Observe that $y^2 - 12 \le y$ for $-3 \le y \le 4$. Thus, the area is

$$A = \int_{-3}^{4} \left(y - (y^2 - 12)\right) dy = \left(\frac{y^2}{2} - \frac{y^3}{3} + 12y\right)\Bigg|_{-3}^{4} = \frac{343}{6} \text{ square units.}$$

Of course, the same result could have been obtained by integrating in the $x$ direction, but the integral would have been more complicated:

$$A = \int_{-12}^{-3} \left(\sqrt{12+x} - (-\sqrt{12+x})\right) dx + \int_{-3}^{4} \left(\sqrt{12+x} - x\right) dx;$$

different integrals are required over the intervals where the region is bounded below by the parabola and by the straight line.

## EXERCISES 8.7

In Exercises 1–16, sketch and find the area of the plane region bounded by the given curves.

**1.** $y = x$,   $y = x^2$
**2.** $y = \sqrt{x}$,   $y = x^2$
**3.** $y = x^2 - 5$,   $y = 3 - x^2$
**4.** $y = x^2 - 2x$,   $y = 6x - x^2$
**5.** $2y = 4x - x^2$,   $2y + 3x = 6$
**6.** $x - y = 7$,   $x = 2y^2 - y + 3$
**7.** $y = x^3$,   $y = x$
**8.** $y = x^3$,   $y = x^2$
**9.** $y = x^3$,   $x = y^2$
**10.** $x = y^2$,   $x = 2y^2 - y - 2$
**11.** $y = \dfrac{1}{x}$,   $2x + 2y = 5$
**12.** $y = (x^2 - 1)^2$,   $y = 1 - x^2$
**13.** $y = \dfrac{1}{2}x^2$,   $y = \dfrac{1}{x^2+1}$
**14.** $y = \dfrac{4x}{3+x^2}$,   $y = 1$
**15.** $y = \dfrac{4}{x^2}$,   $y = 5 - x^2$
**16.** $x = y^2 - \pi^2$,   $x = \sin y$

Find the areas of the regions described in Exercises 17–28. It is helpful to sketch the regions before writing an integral to represent the area.

**17.** Bounded by $y = \sin x$ and $y = \cos x$, and between two consecutive intersections of these curves

**18.** Bounded by $y = \sin^2 x$ and $y = 1$, and between two consecutive intersections of these curves

**19.** Bounded by $y = \sin x$ and $y = \sin^2 x$, between $x = 0$ and $x = \pi/2$

**20.** Bounded by $y = \sin^2 x$ and $y = \cos^2 x$, and between two consecutive intersections of these curves

**21.** Under $y = 4x/\pi$ and above $y = \tan x$, between $x = 0$ and the first intersection of the curves to the right of $x = 0$

**22.** Bounded by $y = x^{1/3}$ and the component of $y = \tan(\pi x/4)$ that passes through the origin

**23.** Bounded by $y = 2$ and the component of $y = \sec x$ that passes through the point $(0, 1)$

**24.** Bounded by $y = \sqrt{2}\cos(\pi x/4)$ and $y = |x|$

**25.** Bounded by $y = \sin(\pi x/2)$ and $y = x$

**26.** Bounded by $y = e^x$ and $y = x + 2$

**27.** Find the total area enclosed by the curve $y^2 = x^2 - x^4$.

**28.** Find the area of the closed loop of the curve $y^2 = x^4(2 + x)$ that lies to the left of the origin.

**29.** Find the area of the finite plane region that is bounded by the curve $y = e^x$, the line $x = 0$, and the tangent line to $y = e^x$ at $x = 1$.

**30.** Find the area of the finite plane region bounded by the curve $y = x^3$ and the tangent line to that curve at the point $(1, 1)$. *Hint:* Find the other point at which that tangent line meets the curve.

## CHAPTER REVIEW

### Key Ideas

• **What do the following terms and phrases mean?**

⋄ sigma notation
⋄ a partition of an interval
⋄ a Riemann sum
⋄ a definite integral
⋄ an indefinite integral
⋄ an area element
⋄ the triangle inequality for integrals
⋄ a piecewise continuous function
⋄ an integrable function
⋄ an evaluation symbol

⬦ the average value of function $f$ on $[a, b]$

⬦ the method of substitution

- **State the Mean-Value Theorem for integrals.**
- **State the Fundamental Theorem of Calculus.**
- **List as many properties of the definite integral as you can.**
- **What is the relationship between the definite integral and the indefinite integral of a function $f$ on an interval $[a, b]$?**
- **What is the derivative of $\int_{f(x)}^{g(x)} h(t)\, dt$ with respect to $x$?**
- **How can the area between the graphs of two functions be calculated?**

## Review Exercises

**1.** Show that $\dfrac{2j+1}{j^2(j+1)^2} = \dfrac{1}{j^2} - \dfrac{1}{(j+1)^2}$; hence evaluate $\displaystyle\sum_{j=1}^{n} \dfrac{2j+1}{j^2(j+1)^2}$.

**2. (Stacking balls)** A display of golf balls in a sporting goods store is built in the shape of a pyramid with a rectangular base measuring 40 balls long and 30 balls wide. The next layer up is 39 balls by 29 balls, etc. How many balls are in the pyramid?

**3.** Let $P_n = \{x_0 = 1, x_1, x_2, \ldots, x_n = 3\}$ be a partition of $[1, 3]$ into $n$ subintervals of equal length, and let $f(x) = x^2 - 2x + 3$. Evaluate $\displaystyle\int_1^3 f(x)\, dx$ by finding $\lim_{n\to\infty} \sum_{i=1}^{n} f(x_i)\, \Delta x_i$.

**4.** Interpret $R_n = \displaystyle\sum_{i=1}^{n} \frac{1}{n}\sqrt{1 + \frac{i}{n}}$ as a Riemann sum for a certain function $f$ on the interval $[0, 1]$; hence evaluate $\lim_{n\to\infty} R_n$.

Evaluate the integrals in Exercises 5–8 without using the Fundamental Theorem of Calculus.

**5.** $\displaystyle\int_{-\pi}^{\pi} (2 - \sin x)\, dx$

**6.** $\displaystyle\int_0^{\sqrt{5}} \sqrt{5 - x^2}\, dx$

**7.** $\displaystyle\int_1^3 \left(1 - \frac{x}{2}\right) dx$

**8.** $\displaystyle\int_0^{\pi} \cos x\, dx$

Find the average values of the functions in Exercises 9–10 over the indicated intervals.

**9.** $f(x) = 2 - \sin x^3$ on $[-\pi, \pi]$

**10.** $h(x) = |x - 2|$ on $[0, 3]$

Find the derivatives of the functions in Exercises 11–14.

**11.** $f(t) = \displaystyle\int_{13}^{t} \sin(x^2)\, dx$

**12.** $f(x) = \displaystyle\int_{-13}^{\sin x} \sqrt{1 + t^2}\, dt$

**13.** $g(s) = \displaystyle\int_{4s}^{1} e^{\sin u}\, du$

**14.** $g(\theta) = \displaystyle\int_{e^{\sin \theta}}^{e^{\cos \theta}} \ln x\, dx$

**15.** Solve the integral equation $2f(x) + 1 = 3\displaystyle\int_x^1 f(t)\, dt$.

**16.** Use the substitution $x = \pi - u$ to show that

$$\int_0^{\pi} x\, f(\sin x)\, dx = \frac{\pi}{2}\int_0^{\pi} f(\sin x)\, dx$$

for any function $f$ continuous on $[0, 1]$.

Find the areas of the finite plane regions bounded by the indicated graphs in Exercises 17–22.

**17.** $y = 2 + x - x^2$ and $y = 0$

**18.** $y = (x - 1)^2$, $y = 0$, and $x = 0$

**19.** $x = y - y^4$ and $x = 0$

**20.** $y = 4x - x^2$ and $y = 3$

**21.** $y = \sin x$, $y = \cos 2x$, $x = 0$, and $x = \pi/6$

**22.** $y = 5 - x^2$ and $y = 4/x^2$

Evaluate the integrals in Exercises 23–30.

**23.** $\displaystyle\int x^2 \cos(2x^3 + 1)\, dx$

**24.** $\displaystyle\int_1^e \frac{\ln x}{x}\, dx$

**25.** $\displaystyle\int_0^4 \sqrt{9t^2 + t^4}\, dt$

**26.** $\displaystyle\int \sin^3(\pi x)\, dx$

**27.** $\displaystyle\int_0^{\ln 2} \frac{e^u}{4 + e^{2u}}\, du$

**28.** $\displaystyle\int_1^{\sqrt[4]{e}} \frac{\tan^2 \pi \ln x}{x}\, dx$

**29.** $\displaystyle\int \frac{\sin \sqrt{2s + 1}}{\sqrt{2s + 1}}\, ds$

**30.** $\displaystyle\int \cos^2 \frac{t}{5} \sin^2 \frac{t}{5}\, dt$

**31.** Find the minimum value of $F(x) = \displaystyle\int_0^{x^2 - 2x} \frac{1}{1 + t^2}\, dt$. Does $F$ have a maximum value? Why?

**32.** Find the maximum value of $\int_a^b (4x - x^2)\, dx$ for intervals $[a, b]$, where $a < b$. How do you know such a maximum value exists?

**33.** An object moves along the $x$-axis so that its position at time $t$ is given by the function $x(t)$. In Section 5.11 we defined the average velocity of the object over the time interval $[t_0, t_1]$ to be $v_{av} = \big(x(t_1) - x(t_0)\big)/(t_1 - t_0)$. Show that $v_{av}$ is, in fact, the average value of the velocity function $v(t) = dx/dt$ over the interval $[t_0, t_1]$.

**34.** If an object falls from rest under constant gravitational acceleration, show that its average height during the time $T$ of its fall is its height at time $T/\sqrt{3}$.

**35.** Find two numbers $x_1$ and $x_2$ in the interval $[0, 1]$ with $x_1 < x_2$ such that if $f(x)$ is any cubic polynomial (i.e., polynomial of degree 3), then

$$\int_0^1 f(x)\, dx = \frac{f(x_1) + f(x_2)}{2}.$$

## Challenging Problems

**1.** Evaluate the upper and lower Riemann sums, $U(f, P_n)$ and $L(f, P_n)$, for $f(x) = 1/x$ on the interval $[1, 2]$ for the partition $P_n$ with division points $x_i = 2^{i/n}$ for $0 \le i \le n$. Verify that $\lim_{n\to\infty} U(f, P_n) = \ln 2 = \lim_{n\to\infty} L(f, P_n)$.

**❗ 2. (a)** Use the addition formulas for $\cos(a + b)$ and $\cos(a - b)$ to show that

$$\cos\left(\left(j + \tfrac{1}{2}\right)t\right) - \cos\left(\left(j - \tfrac{1}{2}\right)t\right)$$
$$= -2\sin(\tfrac{1}{2}t)\sin(jt),$$

and hence deduce that if $t/(2\pi)$ is not an integer, then

$$\sum_{j=1}^{n} \sin(jt) = \frac{\cos\frac{t}{2} - \cos\left(\left(n + \tfrac{1}{2}\right)t\right)}{2\sin\frac{t}{2}}.$$

**(b)** Use the result of part (a) to evaluate $\int_0^{\pi/2} \sin x\, dx$ as a limit of a Riemann sum.

3. (a) Use the method of Problem 2 to show that if $t/(2\pi)$ is not an integer, then

$$\sum_{j=1}^{n} \cos(jt) = \frac{\sin\left((n + \frac{1}{2})t\right) - \sin\frac{t}{2}}{2\sin\frac{t}{2}}.$$

(b) Use the result to part (a) to evaluate $\int_0^{\pi/3} \cos x \, dx$ as a limit of a Riemann sum.

4. Let $f(x) = 1/x^2$ and let $1 = x_0 < x_1 < x_2 < \cdots < x_n = 2$, so that $\{x_0, x_1, x_2, \ldots, x_n\}$ is a partition of $[1, 2]$ into $n$ subintervals. Show that $c_i = \sqrt{x_{i-1}x_i}$ is in the $i$th subinterval $[x_{i-1}, x_i]$ of the partition, and evaluate the Riemann sum $\sum_{i=1}^{n} f(c_i)\,\Delta x_i$. What does this imply about $\int_1^2 (1/x^2)\,dx$?

5. (a) Use mathematical induction to verify that for every positive integer $k$, $\sum_{j=1}^{n} j^k = \dfrac{n^{k+1}}{k+1} + \dfrac{n^k}{2} + P_{k-1}(n)$, where $P_{k-1}$ is a polynomial of degree at most $k-1$. *Hint:* Start by iterating the identity

$$(j+1)^{k+1} - j^{k+1} = (k+1)j^k + \frac{(k+1)k}{2}j^{k-1}$$

$$+ \text{ lower powers of } j$$

for $j = 1, 2, 3, \ldots, k$ and adding.

(b) Deduce from (a) that $\displaystyle\int_0^a x^k\,dx = \frac{a^{k+1}}{k+1}$.

6. Let $C$ be the cubic curve $y = ax^3 + bx^2 + cx + d$, and let $P$ be any point on $C$. The tangent to $C$ at $P$ meets $C$ again at point $Q$. The tangent to $C$ at $Q$ meets $C$ again at $R$. Show that the area between $C$ and the tangent at $Q$ is 16 times the area between $C$ and the tangent at $P$.

7. Let $C$ be the cubic curve $y = ax^3 + bx^2 + cx + d$, and let $P$ be any point on $C$. The tangent to $C$ at $P$ meets $C$ again at point $Q$. Let $R$ be the inflection point of $C$. Show that $R$ lies between $P$ and $Q$ on $C$ and that $QR$ divides the area between $C$ and its tangent at $P$ in the ratio 16/11.

8. **(Double tangents)** Let line $PQ$ be tangent to the graph $C$ of the quartic polynomial $f(x) = ax^4 + bx^3 + cx^2 + dx + e$ at two distinct points: $P = (p, f(p))$ and $Q = (q, f(q))$. Let $U = (u, f(u))$ and $V = (v, f(v))$ be the other two points where the line tangent to $C$ at $T = ((p+q)/2, f((p+q)/2))$ meets $C$. If $A$ and $B$ are the two inflection points of $C$, let $R$ and $S$ be the other two points where $AB$ meets $C$. (See Figure 8.34. Also see Challenging Problem 17 in Chapter 5 for more background.)

(a) Find the ratio of the area bounded by $UV$ and $C$ to the area bounded by $PQ$ and $C$.

(b) Show that the area bounded by $RS$ and $C$ is divided at $A$ and $B$ into three parts in the ratio $1:2:1$.

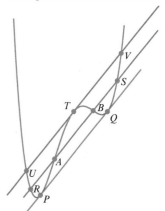

Figure 8.34

# CHAPTER 9

# Techniques of Integration

## 9.1  Integration by Parts

Our next general method for antidifferentiation is called **integration by parts**. Just as the method of substitution can be regarded as inverse to the Chain Rule for differentiation, so the method for integration by parts is inverse to the Product Rule for differentiation.

Suppose that $U(x)$ and $V(x)$ are two differentiable functions. According to the Product Rule,

$$\frac{d}{dx}\left(U(x)V(x)\right) = U(x)\frac{dV}{dx} + V(x)\frac{dU}{dx}.$$

Integrating both sides of this equation and transposing terms, we obtain

$$\int U(x)\frac{dV}{dx}\,dx = U(x)V(x) - \int V(x)\frac{dU}{dx}\,dx$$

or, more simply,

$$\int U \, dV = UV - \int V \, dU.$$

The above formula serves as a *pattern* for carrying out integration by parts, as we will see in the examples below. In each application of the method, we break up the given integrand into a product of two pieces, $U$ and $V'$, where $V'$ is readily integrated and where $\int V U' \, dx$ is usually (but not always) a *simpler* integral than $\int U V' \, dx$. The technique is called integration by parts because it replaces one integral with the sum of an integrated term and another integral that remains to be evaluated. That is, it accomplishes only *part* of the original integration.

EXAMPLE 1    $\displaystyle\int x e^x \, dx$      Let   $U = x$,    $dV = e^x \, dx$.

         Then $dU = dx$,    $V = e^x$.

$$= x e^x - \int e^x \, dx \qquad \text{(i.e., } UV - \int V \, dU\text{)}$$

$$= x e^x - e^x + C.$$

Note the form in which the integration by parts is carried out. We indicate at the side what choices we are making for $U$ and $dV$ and then calculate $dU$ and $V$ from these. However, we do not actually substitute $U$ and $V$ into the integral; instead, we use the formula $\int U \, dV = UV - \int V \, dU$ as a pattern or mnemonic device to replace the given integral by the equivalent partially integrated form on the second line.

Note also that had we included a constant of integration with $V$, for example, $V = e^x + K$, that constant would cancel out in the next step:

$$\int x e^x \, dx = x(e^x + K) - \int (e^x + K) \, dx$$

$$= x e^x + Kx - e^x - Kx + C = x e^x - e^x + C.$$

In general, do not include a constant of integration with $V$ or on the right-hand side until the last integral has been evaluated.

Study the various parts of the following example carefully; they show the various ways in which integration by parts is used, and they give some insights into what choices should be made for $U$ and $dV$ in various situations. An improper choice can result in making an integral more difficult rather than easier. Look for a factor of the integrand that is easily integrated, and include $dx$ with that factor to make up $dV$. Then $U$ is the remaining factor of the integrand. Sometimes it is necessary to take $dV = dx$ only. When breaking up an integrand using integration by parts, choose $U$ and $dV$ so that, if possible, $V \, dU$ is "simpler" (easier to integrate) than $U \, dV$.

EXAMPLE 2    Use integration by parts to evaluate

(a) $\displaystyle\int \ln x \, dx$,    (b) $\displaystyle\int x^2 \sin x \, dx$,    (c) $\displaystyle\int x \tan^{-1} x \, dx$,    (d) $\displaystyle\int \sin^{-1} x \, dx$.

**Solution**

(a)   $\displaystyle\int \ln x \, dx$        Let   $U = \ln x$,    $dV = dx$.

             Then $dU = dx/x$,    $V = x$.

$$= x \ln x - \int x \, \frac{1}{x} \, dx$$

$$= x \ln x - x + C.$$

(b) We have to integrate by parts twice this time:

$$\int x^2 \sin x \, dx \qquad\qquad \text{Let} \quad U = x^2, \qquad dV = \sin x \, dx.$$
$$\text{Then } dU = 2x \, dx, \qquad V = -\cos x.$$

$$= -x^2 \cos x + 2 \int x \cos x \, dx \qquad \text{Let} \quad U = x, \qquad dV = \cos x \, dx.$$
$$\text{Then } dU = dx, \qquad V = \sin x.$$

$$= -x^2 \cos x + 2 \left( x \sin x - \int \sin x \, dx \right)$$

$$= -x^2 \cos x + 2x \sin x + 2 \cos x + C.$$

(c) $$\int x \tan^{-1} x \, dx \qquad\qquad \text{Let} \quad U = \tan^{-1} x, \qquad dV = x \, dx.$$
$$\text{Then } dU = dx/(1 + x^2), \qquad V = \tfrac{1}{2} x^2.$$

$$= \frac{1}{2} x^2 \tan^{-1} x - \frac{1}{2} \int \frac{x^2}{1 + x^2} \, dx$$

$$= \frac{1}{2} x^2 \tan^{-1} x - \frac{1}{2} \int \left( 1 - \frac{1}{1 + x^2} \right) dx$$

$$= \frac{1}{2} x^2 \tan^{-1} x - \frac{1}{2} x + \frac{1}{2} \tan^{-1} x + C.$$

(d) $$\int \sin^{-1} x \, dx \qquad\qquad \text{Let} \quad U = \sin^{-1} x, \qquad dV = dx.$$
$$\text{Then } dU = dx/\sqrt{1 - x^2}, \qquad V = x.$$

$$= x \sin^{-1} x - \int \frac{x}{\sqrt{1 - x^2}} \, dx \qquad \text{Let } u = 1 - x^2,$$
$$du = -2x \, dx$$

$$= x \sin^{-1} x + \frac{1}{2} \int u^{-1/2} \, du$$

$$= x \sin^{-1} x + u^{1/2} + C = x \sin^{-1} x + \sqrt{1 - x^2} + C.$$

---

The following are two useful rules of thumb for choosing $U$ and $dV$:

 (i) If the integrand involves a polynomial multiplied by an exponential, a sine or a cosine, or some other readily integrable function, try $U$ equals the polynomial and $dV$ equals the rest.

 (ii) If the integrand involves a logarithm, an inverse trigonometric function, or some other function that is not readily integrable but whose derivative is readily calculated, try that function for $U$ and let $dV$ equal the rest.

(Of course, these "rules" come with no guarantee. They may fail to be helpful if "the rest" is not of a suitable form. There remain many functions that cannot be anti-differentiated by any standard techniques; e.g., $e^{x^2}$.)

The following two examples illustrate a frequently occurring and very useful phenomenon. It may happen after one or two integrations by parts, with the possible application of some known identity, that the original integral reappears on the right-hand side. Unless its coefficient there is 1, we have an equation that can be solved for that integral.

**EXAMPLE 3**    Evaluate $I = \int \sec^3 x \, dx$.

*Solution*    Start by integrating by parts:

$$I = \int \sec^3 x \, dx \qquad\qquad \text{Let} \quad U = \sec x, \qquad dV = \sec^2 x \, dx.$$
$$\text{Then } dU = \sec x \tan x \, dx, \qquad V = \tan x.$$

$$= \sec x \tan x - \int \sec x \tan^2 x \, dx$$

$$= \sec x \, \tan x - \int \sec x \, (\sec^2 x - 1) \, dx$$

$$= \sec x \, \tan x - \int \sec^3 x \, dx + \int \sec x \, dx$$

$$= \sec x \, \tan x - I + \ln |\sec x + \tan x|.$$

This is an equation that can be solved for the desired integral $I$. Since $2I = \sec x \, \tan x + \ln |\sec x + \tan x|$, we have

$$\int \sec^3 x \, dx = I = \frac{1}{2} \sec x \, \tan x + \frac{1}{2} \ln |\sec x + \tan x| + C.$$

This integral occurs frequently in applications and is worth remembering.

---

**EXAMPLE 4**    Find $I = \displaystyle\int e^{ax} \cos bx \, dx$.

*Solution*    If either $a = 0$ or $b = 0$, the integral is easy to do, so let us assume $a \neq 0$ and $b \neq 0$. We have

$$I = \int e^{ax} \cos bx \, dx \qquad \text{Let} \quad U = e^{ax}, \qquad dV = \cos bx \, dx.$$
$$\text{Then } dU = a \, e^{ax} \, dx, \qquad V = (1/b) \sin bx.$$

$$= \frac{1}{b} e^{ax} \sin bx - \frac{a}{b} \int e^{ax} \sin bx \, dx$$

$$\text{Let} \quad U = e^{ax}, \qquad dV = \sin bx \, dx.$$
$$\text{Then } dU = ae^{ax}dx, \qquad V = -(\cos bx)/b.$$

$$= \frac{1}{b} e^{ax} \sin bx - \frac{a}{b} \left( -\frac{1}{b} e^{ax} \cos bx + \frac{a}{b} \int e^{ax} \cos bx \, dx \right)$$

$$= \frac{1}{b} e^{ax} \sin bx + \frac{a}{b^2} e^{ax} \cos bx - \frac{a^2}{b^2} I.$$

Thus,

$$\left( 1 + \frac{a^2}{b^2} \right) I = \frac{1}{b} e^{ax} \sin bx + \frac{a}{b^2} e^{ax} \cos bx + C_1$$

and

$$\int e^{ax} \cos bx \, dx = I = \frac{b \, e^{ax} \sin bx + a \, e^{ax} \cos bx}{b^2 + a^2} + C.$$

---

Observe that after the first integration by parts we had an integral that was different from, but no simpler than, the original integral. At this point we might have become discouraged and given up on this method. However, perseverance proved worthwhile; a second integration by parts returned the original integral $I$ in an equation that could be solved for $I$. Having chosen to let $U$ be the exponential in the first integration by parts (we could have let it be the cosine), we made the same choice for $U$ in the second integration by parts. Had we switched horses in midstream and decided to let $U$ be the trigonometric function the second time, we would have obtained

$$I = \frac{1}{b} e^{ax} \sin bx - \frac{1}{b} e^{ax} \sin bx + I,$$

that is, we would have *undone* what we accomplished in the first step.

If we want to evaluate a definite integral by the method of integration by parts, we must remember to include the appropriate evaluation symbol with the integrated term.

EXAMPLE 5  **(A definite integral)**

$$\int_1^e x^3 (\ln x)^2 \, dx \qquad\qquad \text{Let} \quad U = (\ln x)^2, \qquad dV = x^3 \, dx.$$
$$\text{Then } dU = 2 \ln x \,(1/x) \, dx, \quad V = x^4/4.$$

$$= \frac{x^4}{4}(\ln x)^2 \Big|_1^e - \frac{1}{2} \int_1^e x^3 \ln x \, dx \qquad \text{Let} \quad U = \ln x, \qquad dV = x^3 \, dx.$$
$$\text{Then } dU = dx/x, \qquad V = x^4/4.$$

$$= \frac{e^4}{4}(1^2) - 0 - \frac{1}{2}\left( \frac{x^4}{4} \ln x \Big|_1^e - \frac{1}{4} \int_1^e x^3 \, dx \right)$$

$$= \frac{e^4}{4} - \frac{e^4}{8} + \frac{1}{8}\frac{x^4}{4}\Big|_1^e = \frac{e^4}{8} + \frac{e^4}{32} - \frac{1}{32} = \frac{5}{32}e^4 - \frac{1}{32}.$$

## Reduction Formulas

Consider the problem of finding $\int x^4 e^{-x} \, dx$. We can, as in Example 1, proceed by using integration by parts four times. Each time will reduce the power of $x$ by 1. Since this is repetitive and tedious, we prefer the following approach. For $n \geq 0$, let

$$I_n = \int x^n e^{-x} \, dx.$$

We want to find $I_4$. If we integrate by parts, we obtain a formula for $I_n$ in terms of $I_{n-1}$:

$$I_n = \int x^n e^{-x} \, dx \qquad\qquad \text{Let} \quad U = x^n, \qquad dV = e^{-x} \, dx.$$
$$\text{Then } dU = nx^{n-1} \, dx, \quad V = -e^{-x}.$$

$$= -x^n e^{-x} + n \int x^{n-1} e^{-x} \, dx = -x^n e^{-x} + nI_{n-1}.$$

The formula

$$I_n = -x^n e^{-x} + nI_{n-1}$$

is called a **reduction formula** because it gives the value of the integral $I_n$ in terms of $I_{n-1}$, an integral corresponding to a reduced value of the exponent $n$. Starting with

$$I_0 = \int x^0 e^{-x} \, dx = \int e^{-x} \, dx = -e^{-x} + C,$$

we can apply the reduction formula four times to get

$$I_1 = -xe^{-x} + I_0 = -e^{-x}(x + 1) + C_1$$
$$I_2 = -x^2 e^{-x} + 2I_1 = -e^{-x}(x^2 + 2x + 2) + C_2$$
$$I_3 = -x^3 e^{-x} + 3I_2 = -e^{-x}(x^3 + 3x^2 + 6x + 6) + C_3$$
$$I_4 = -x^4 e^{-x} + 4I_3 = -e^{-x}(x^4 + 4x^3 + 12x^2 + 24x + 24) + C_4.$$

EXAMPLE 6  Obtain and use a reduction formula to evaluate

$$I_n = \int_0^{\pi/2} \cos^n x \, dx \qquad (n = 0, 1, 2, 3, \dots).$$

*Solution*   Observe first that

$$I_0 = \int_0^{\pi/2} dx = \frac{\pi}{2} \quad \text{and} \quad I_1 = \int_0^{\pi/2} \cos x \, dx = \sin x \Big|_0^{\pi/2} = 1.$$

Now let $n \geq 2$:

$$I_n = \int_0^{\pi/2} \cos^n x \, dx = \int_0^{\pi/2} \cos^{n-1} x \cos x \, dx$$

$$U = \cos^{n-1} x, \qquad dV = \cos x \, dx$$
$$dU = -(n-1)\cos^{n-2} x \sin x \, dx, \quad V = \sin x$$

$$= \sin x \, \cos^{n-1} x \Big|_0^{\pi/2} + (n-1)\int_0^{\pi/2} \cos^{n-2} x \sin^2 x \, dx$$

$$= 0 - 0 + (n-1)\int_0^{\pi/2} \cos^{n-2} x \, (1 - \cos^2 x) \, dx$$

$$= (n-1)I_{n-2} - (n-1)I_n.$$

Transposing the term $-(n-1)I_n$, we obtain $nI_n = (n-1)I_{n-2}$, or

$$I_n = \frac{n-1}{n} I_{n-2},$$

which is the required reduction formula. It is valid for $n \geq 2$, which was needed to ensure that $\cos^{n-1}(\pi/2) = 0$. If $n \geq 2$ is an *even integer*, we have

$$I_n = \frac{n-1}{n} I_{n-2} = \frac{n-1}{n} \cdot \frac{n-3}{n-2} I_{n-4} = \cdots$$
$$= \frac{n-1}{n} \cdot \frac{n-3}{n-2} \cdot \frac{n-5}{n-4} \cdots \frac{5}{6} \cdot \frac{3}{4} \cdot \frac{1}{2} \cdot I_0$$
$$= \frac{n-1}{n} \cdot \frac{n-3}{n-2} \cdot \frac{n-5}{n-4} \cdots \frac{5}{6} \cdot \frac{3}{4} \cdot \frac{1}{2} \cdot \frac{\pi}{2}.$$

If $n \geq 3$ is an *odd* integer, we have

$$I_n = \frac{n-1}{n} \cdot \frac{n-3}{n-2} \cdot \frac{n-5}{n-4} \cdots \frac{6}{7} \cdot \frac{4}{5} \cdot \frac{2}{3} \cdot I_1$$
$$= \frac{n-1}{n} \cdot \frac{n-3}{n-2} \cdot \frac{n-5}{n-4} \cdots \frac{6}{7} \cdot \frac{4}{5} \cdot \frac{2}{3}.$$

See Exercise 38 for an interesting consequence of these formulas.

## EXERCISES 9.1

Evaluate the integrals in Exercises 1–28.

**1.** $\int x \cos x \, dx$

**2.** $\int (x+3)e^{2x} \, dx$

**3.** $\int x^2 \cos \pi x \, dx$

**4.** $\int (x^2 - 2x)e^{kx} \, dx$

**5.** $\int x^3 \ln x \, dx$

**6.** $\int x(\ln x)^3 \, dx$

**7.** $\int \tan^{-1} x \, dx$

**8.** $\int x^2 \tan^{-1} x \, dx$

**9.** $\int x \sin^{-1} x \, dx$

**10.** $\int x^5 e^{-x^2} \, dx$

**11.** $\int_0^{\pi/4} \sec^5 x \, dx$

**12.** $\int \tan^2 x \sec x \, dx$

**13.** $\int e^{2x} \sin 3x \, dx$

**14.** $\int x e^{\sqrt{x}} \, dx$

**15.** $\int_{1/2}^1 \frac{\sin^{-1} x}{x^2} \, dx$

**16.** $\int_0^1 \sqrt{x} \sin(\pi \sqrt{x}) \, dx$

**17.** $\int x \sec^2 x \, dx$

**18.** $\int x \sin^2 x \, dx$

**19.** $\int \cos(\ln x)\, dx$

**20.** $\int_1^e \sin(\ln x)\, dx$

**21.** $\int \dfrac{\ln(\ln x)}{x}\, dx$

**22.** $\int_0^4 \sqrt{x}\, e^{\sqrt{x}}\, dx$

**23.** $\int \arccos x\, dx$

**24.** $\int x\, \sec^{-1}x\, dx$

**25.** $\int_1^2 \sec^{-1}x\, dx$

**! 26.** $\int (\sin^{-1} x)^2\, dx$

**! 27.** $\int x(\tan^{-1} x)^2\, dx$

**! 28.** $\int x\, e^x\, \cos x\, dx$

**29.** Find the area below $y = e^{-x} \sin x$ and above $y = 0$ from $x = 0$ to $x = \pi$.

**30.** Find the area of the finite plane region bounded by the curve $y = \ln x$, the line $y = 1$, and the tangent line to $y = \ln x$ at $x = 1$.

**Reduction formulas**

**31.** Obtain a reduction formula for $I_n = \int (\ln x)^n\, dx$, and use it to evaluate $I_4$.

**32.** Obtain a reduction formula for $I_n = \int_0^{\pi/2} x^n \sin x\, dx$, and use it to evaluate $I_6$.

**33.** Obtain a reduction formula for $I_n = \int \sin^n x\, dx$ (where $n \geq 2$), and use it to find $I_6$ and $I_7$.

**34.** Obtain a reduction formula for $I_n = \int \sec^n x\, dx$ (where $n \geq 3$), and use it to find $I_6$ and $I_7$.

**! 35.** By writing

$$I_n = \int \frac{dx}{(x^2 + a^2)^n}$$

$$= \frac{1}{a^2} \int \frac{dx}{(x^2 + a^2)^{n-1}} - \frac{1}{a^2} \int x \frac{x}{(x^2 + a^2)^n}\, dx$$

and integrating the last integral by parts, using $U = x$, obtain a reduction formula for $I_n$. Use this formula to find $I_3$.

**! 36.** If $f$ is twice differentiable on $[a, b]$ and $f(a) = f(b) = 0$, show that

$$\int_a^b (x - a)(b - x) f''(x)\, dx = -2 \int_a^b f(x)\, dx.$$

(*Hint:* Use integration by parts on the left-hand side twice.) This formula will be used in Section 9.3 to construct an error estimate for the Trapezoid Rule approximation formula.

**! 37.** If $f$ and $g$ are two functions having continuous second derivatives on the interval $[a, b]$, and if $f(a) = g(a) = f(b) = g(b) = 0$, show that

$$\int_a^b f(x)\, g''(x)\, dx = \int_a^b f''(x)\, g(x)\, dx.$$

What other assumptions about the values of $f$ and $g$ at $a$ and $b$ would give the same result?

**! 38.** (**The Wallis Product**) Let $I_n = \int_0^{\pi/2} \cos^n x\, dx$.

(a) Use the fact that $0 \leq \cos x \leq 1$ for $0 \leq x \leq \pi/2$ to show that $I_{2n+2} \leq I_{2n+1} \leq I_{2n}$, for $n = 0, 1, 2, \ldots$.

(b) Use the reduction formula $I_n = ((n-1)/n)I_{n-2}$ obtained in Example 6, together with the result of (a), to show that

$$\lim_{n \to \infty} \frac{I_{2n+1}}{I_{2n}} = 1.$$

(c) Combine the result of (b) with the explicit formulas obtained for $I_n$ (for even and odd $n$) in Example 6 to show that

$$\lim_{n \to \infty} \frac{2}{1} \cdot \frac{2}{3} \cdot \frac{4}{3} \cdot \frac{4}{5} \cdot \frac{6}{5} \cdot \frac{6}{7} \cdots \frac{2n}{2n-1} \cdot \frac{2n}{2n+1} = \frac{\pi}{2}.$$

This interesting product formula for $\pi$ is due to the seventeenth-century English mathematician John Wallis and is referred to as the Wallis Product.

## 9.2    Improper Integrals

Up to this point, we have considered definite integrals of the form

$$I = \int_a^b f(x)\,dx,$$

where the integrand $f$ is *continuous* on the *closed, finite* interval $[a, b]$. Since such a function is necessarily *bounded*, the integral $I$ is necessarily a finite number; for positive $f$ it corresponds to the area of a **bounded region** of the plane, a region contained inside some disk of finite radius with centre at the origin. Such integrals are also called **proper integrals**. We are now going to generalize the definite integral to allow for two possibilities excluded in the situation described above:

(i)  We may have $a = -\infty$ or $b = \infty$ or both.

(ii)  $f$ may be unbounded as $x$ approaches $a$ or $b$ or both.

Integrals satisfying (i) are called **improper integrals of type I**; integrals satisfying (ii) are called **improper integrals of type II**. Either type of improper integral corresponds (for positive $f$) to the area of a region in the plane that "extends to infinity" in some direction and therefore is *unbounded*. As we will see, such integrals may or may not have finite values. The ideas involved are best introduced by examples.

### Improper Integrals of Type I

**EXAMPLE 1**    Find the area of the region $A$ lying under the curve $y = 1/x^2$ and above the $x$-axis to the right of $x = 1$. (See Figure 9.1(a).)

***Solution***    We would like to calculate the area with an integral

$$A = \int_1^\infty \frac{dx}{x^2},$$

which is improper of type I, since its interval of integration is infinite. It is not immediately obvious whether the area is finite; the region has an infinitely long "spike" along the $x$-axis, but this spike becomes infinitely thin as $x$ approaches $\infty$. In order to evaluate this improper integral, we interpret it as a limit of proper integrals over intervals $[1, R]$ as $R \to \infty$. (See Figure 9.1(b).)

$$A = \int_1^\infty \frac{dx}{x^2} = \lim_{R \to \infty} \int_1^R \frac{dx}{x^2} = \lim_{R \to \infty} \left( -\frac{1}{x} \right) \Big|_1^R$$

$$= \lim_{R \to \infty} \left( -\frac{1}{R} + 1 \right) = 1$$

Since the limit exists (is finite), we say that the improper integral *converges*. The region has finite area $A = 1$ square unit.

**Figure 9.1**

(a)  $A = \int_1^\infty \frac{1}{x^2}\,dx$

(b)  $A = \lim_{R \to \infty} \int_1^R \frac{1}{x^2}\,dx$

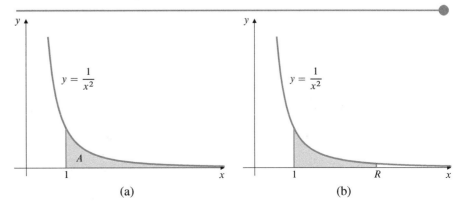

(a)                                              (b)

EXAMPLE 2    Find the area of the region under $y = 1/x$, above $y = 0$, and to the right of $x = 1$. (See Figure 9.2.)

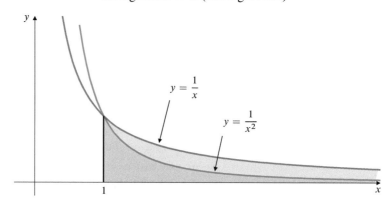

Figure 9.2    The area under the red curve is infinite. The area under the blue curve is finite.

*Solution*    This area is given by the improper integral

$$A = \int_1^\infty \frac{dx}{x} = \lim_{R\to\infty} \int_1^R \frac{dx}{x} = \lim_{R\to\infty} \ln x \Big|_1^R = \lim_{R\to\infty} \ln R = \infty.$$

We say that this improper integral *diverges to infinity*. Observe that the region has a similar shape to the region under $y = 1/x^2$ considered in the above example, but its "spike" is somewhat thicker at each value of $x > 1$. Evidently, the extra thickness makes a big difference; this region has *infinite* area.

DEFINITION

**1**

**Improper integrals of type I**

If $f$ is continuous on $[a, \infty)$, we define the improper integral of $f$ over $[a, \infty)$ as a limit of proper integrals:

$$\int_a^\infty f(x)\,dx = \lim_{R\to\infty} \int_a^R f(x)\,dx.$$

Similarly, if $f$ is continuous on $(-\infty, b]$, then we define

$$\int_{-\infty}^b f(x)\,dx = \lim_{R\to-\infty} \int_R^b f(x)\,dx.$$

In either case, if the limit exists (is a finite number), we say that the improper integral **converges**; if the limit does not exist, we say that the improper integral **diverges**. If the limit is $\infty$ (or $-\infty$), we say the improper integral **diverges to infinity** (or **diverges to negative infinity**).

The integral $\int_{-\infty}^\infty f(x)\,dx$ is, for $f$ continuous on the real line, improper of type I at both endpoints. We break it into two separate integrals:

$$\int_{-\infty}^\infty f(x)\,dx = \int_{-\infty}^0 f(x)\,dx + \int_0^\infty f(x)\,dx.$$

The integral on the left converges if and only if *both* integrals on the right converge.

EXAMPLE 3    Evaluate $\displaystyle\int_{-\infty}^\infty \frac{1}{1+x^2}\,dx.$

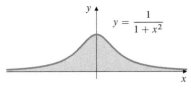

**Figure 9.3**

*Solution*  By the (even) symmetry of the integrand (see Figure 9.3), we have

$$\int_{-\infty}^{\infty} \frac{dx}{1+x^2} = \int_{-\infty}^{0} \frac{dx}{1+x^2} + \int_{0}^{\infty} \frac{dx}{1+x^2}$$

$$= 2 \lim_{R\to\infty} \int_{0}^{R} \frac{dx}{1+x^2}$$

$$= 2 \lim_{R\to\infty} \tan^{-1} R = 2\left(\frac{\pi}{2}\right) = \pi.$$

The use of symmetry here requires some justification. At the time we used it we did not know whether each of the half-line integrals was finite or infinite. However, since both are positive, even if they are infinite, their sum would still be twice one of them. If one had been positive and the other negative, we would not have been justified in cancelling them to get 0 until we knew that they were finite. ($\infty + \infty = \infty$, but $\infty - \infty$ is not defined.) In any event, the given integral converges to $\pi$.

**EXAMPLE 4**    $\displaystyle\int_{0}^{\infty} \cos x \, dx = \lim_{R\to\infty} \int_{0}^{R} \cos x \, dx = \lim_{R\to\infty} \sin R.$

This limit does not exist (and it is not $\infty$ or $-\infty$), so all we can say is that the given integral diverges. (See Figure 9.4.) As $R$ increases, the integral alternately adds and subtracts the areas of the hills and valleys but does not approach any unique limit.

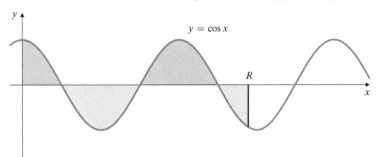

**Figure 9.4**    Not every divergent improper integral diverges to $\infty$ or $-\infty$

## Improper Integrals of Type II

**DEFINITION**

**2**

**Improper integrals of type II**

If $f$ is continuous on the interval $(a, b]$ and is possibly unbounded near $a$, we define the improper integral

$$\int_{a}^{b} f(x) \, dx = \lim_{c\to a+} \int_{c}^{b} f(x) \, dx.$$

Similarly, if $f$ is continuous on $[a, b)$ and is possibly unbounded near $b$, we define

$$\int_{a}^{b} f(x) \, dx = \lim_{c\to b-} \int_{a}^{c} f(x) \, dx.$$

These improper integrals may converge, diverge, diverge to infinity, or diverge to negative infinity.

**EXAMPLE 5**    Find the area of the region $S$ lying under $y = 1/\sqrt{x}$, above the $x$-axis, between $x = 0$ and $x = 1$.

*Solution*  The area $A$ is given by

$$A = \int_0^1 \frac{1}{\sqrt{x}}\, dx,$$

which is an improper integral of type II since the integrand is unbounded near $x = 0$. The region $S$ has a "spike" extending to infinity along the $y$-axis, a vertical asymptote of the integrand, as shown in Figure 9.5. As we did for improper integrals of type I, we express such integrals as limits of proper integrals:

$$A = \lim_{c\to 0+} \int_c^1 x^{-1/2}\, dx = \lim_{c\to 0+} 2x^{1/2}\Big|_c^1 = \lim_{c\to 0+}(2 - 2\sqrt{c}) = 2.$$

This integral converges, and $S$ has a finite area of 2 square units.

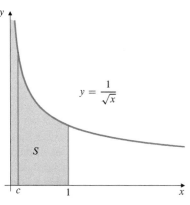

$y = \dfrac{1}{\sqrt{x}}$

**Figure 9.5**    The shaded area is finite

While improper integrals of type I are always easily recognized because of the infinite limits of integration, improper integrals of type II can be somewhat harder to spot. You should be alert for singularities of integrands and especially points where they have vertical asymptotes. It may be necessary to break an improper integral into several improper integrals if it is improper at both endpoints or at points inside the interval of integration. For example,

$$\int_{-1}^1 \frac{\ln|x|\,dx}{\sqrt{1-x}} = \int_{-1}^0 \frac{\ln|x|\,dx}{\sqrt{1-x}} + \int_0^{1/2} \frac{\ln|x|\,dx}{\sqrt{1-x}} + \int_{1/2}^1 \frac{\ln|x|\,dx}{\sqrt{1-x}}.$$

Each integral on the right is improper because of a singularity at one endpoint.

**EXAMPLE 6**    Evaluate each of the following integrals or show that it diverges:

(a)  $\displaystyle\int_0^1 \frac{1}{x}\, dx,$    (b)  $\displaystyle\int_0^2 \frac{1}{\sqrt{2x-x^2}}\, dx,$    and    (c)  $\displaystyle\int_0^1 \ln x\, dx.$

*Solution*

(a)  $\displaystyle\int_0^1 \frac{1}{x}\, dx = \lim_{c\to 0+} \int_c^1 \frac{1}{x}\, dx = \lim_{c\to 0+}(\ln 1 - \ln c) = \infty.$
This integral diverges to infinity.

(b)  $\displaystyle\int_0^2 \frac{1}{\sqrt{2x-x^2}}\, dx = \int_0^2 \frac{1}{\sqrt{1-(x-1)^2}}\, dx$    Let $u = x - 1,$
    $du = dx$

$$= \int_{-1}^1 \frac{1}{\sqrt{1-u^2}}\, du$$

$$= 2\int_0^1 \frac{1}{\sqrt{1-u^2}}\, du \qquad \text{(by symmetry)}$$

$$= 2\lim_{c\to 1-}\int_0^c \frac{1}{\sqrt{1-u^2}}\, du$$

$$= 2\lim_{c\to 1-} \sin^{-1} u\Big|_0^c = 2\lim_{c\to 1-}\sin^{-1} c = \pi.$$

This integral converges to $\pi$. Observe how a change of variable can be made even before an improper integral is expressed as a limit of proper integrals.

(c) $\displaystyle \int_0^1 \ln x \, dx = \lim_{c \to 0+} \int_c^1 \ln x \, dx$  (See Example 2(a) of Section 9.1.)

$$= \lim_{c \to 0+} (x \ln x - x) \Big|_c^1$$

$$= \lim_{c \to 0+} (0 - 1 - c \ln c + c)$$

$$= -1 + 0 - \lim_{c \to 0+} \frac{\ln c}{1/c} \qquad \left[ \frac{-\infty}{\infty} \right]$$

$$= -1 - \lim_{c \to 0+} \frac{1/c}{-(1/c^2)} \qquad \text{(by l'Hôpital's Rule)}$$

$$= -1 - \lim_{c \to 0+} (-c) = -1 + 0 = -1.$$

The integral converges to $-1$.

---

The following theorem summarizes the behaviour of improper integrals of types I and II for powers of $x$.

**THEOREM**

**2**

**$p$-integrals**

If $0 < a < \infty$, then

(a) $\displaystyle \int_a^\infty x^{-p} \, dx$ $\begin{cases} \text{converges to } \dfrac{a^{1-p}}{p-1} & \text{if } p > 1 \\ \text{diverges to } \infty & \text{if } p \leq 1 \end{cases}$

(b) $\displaystyle \int_0^a x^{-p} \, dx$ $\begin{cases} \text{converges to } \dfrac{a^{1-p}}{1-p} & \text{if } p < 1 \\ \text{diverges to } \infty & \text{if } p \geq 1. \end{cases}$

**PROOF**  We prove part (b) only. The proof of part (a) is similar and is left as an exercise. Also, the case $p = 1$ of part (b) is similar to Example 6(a) above, so we need consider only the cases $p < 1$ and $p > 1$. If $p < 1$, then we have

$$\int_0^a x^{-p} \, dx = \lim_{c \to 0+} \int_c^a x^{-p} \, dx$$

$$= \lim_{c \to 0+} \frac{x^{-p+1}}{-p+1} \Big|_c^a$$

$$= \lim_{c \to 0+} \frac{a^{1-p} - c^{1-p}}{1-p} = \frac{a^{1-p}}{1-p}$$

because $1 - p > 0$. If $p > 1$, then

$$\int_0^a x^{-p} \, dx = \lim_{c \to 0+} \int_c^a x^{-p} \, dx$$

$$= \lim_{c \to 0+} \frac{x^{-p+1}}{-p+1} \Big|_c^a$$

$$= \lim_{c \to 0+} \frac{c^{-(p-1)} - a^{-(p-1)}}{p-1} = \infty.$$

---

The integrals in Theorem 2 are called **$p$-integrals**. It is very useful to know when they converge and diverge when you have to decide whether certain other improper integrals converge or not and you can't find the appropriate antiderivatives. (See the discussion of estimating convergence below.) Note that $\int_0^\infty x^{-p} \, dx$ does not converge for any value of $p$.

**Remark**  If $f$ is continuous on the interval $[a, b]$ so that $\int_a^b f(x)\,dx$ is a proper definite integral, then treating the integral as improper will lead to the same value:

$$\lim_{c \to a+} \int_c^b f(x)\,dx = \int_a^b f(x)\,dx = \lim_{c \to b-} \int_a^c f(x)\,dx.$$

This justifies the definition of the definite integral of a piecewise continuous function that was given in Section 8.4. To integrate a function defined to be different continuous functions on different intervals, we merely add the integrals of the various component functions over their respective intervals. Any of these integrals may be proper or improper; if any are improper, all must converge or the given integral will diverge.

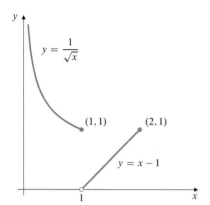

$y = \dfrac{1}{\sqrt{x}}$

$(1, 1)$    $(2, 1)$

$y = x - 1$

**Figure 9.6**    A discontinuous function

**EXAMPLE 7**    Evaluate $\int_0^2 f(x)\,dx$, where $f(x) = \begin{cases} 1/\sqrt{x} & \text{if } 0 < x \le 1 \\ x - 1 & \text{if } 1 < x \le 2. \end{cases}$

**Solution**  The graph of $f$ is shown in Figure 9.6. We have

$$\int_0^2 f(x)\,dx = \int_0^1 \frac{dx}{\sqrt{x}} + \int_1^2 (x - 1)\,dx$$

$$= \lim_{c \to 0+} \int_c^1 \frac{dx}{\sqrt{x}} + \left( \frac{x^2}{2} - x \right) \Big|_1^2 = 2 + \left( 2 - 2 - \frac{1}{2} + 1 \right) = \frac{5}{2};$$

the first integral on the right is improper but convergent (see Example 5 above), and the second is proper.

## Estimating Convergence and Divergence

When an improper integral cannot be evaluated by the Fundamental Theorem of Calculus because an antiderivative can't be found, we may still be able to determine whether the integral converges by comparing it with simpler integrals. The following theorem is central to this approach.

**THEOREM**

**3**

**A comparison theorem for integrals**

Let $-\infty \le a < b \le \infty$, and suppose that functions $f$ and $g$ are continuous on the interval $(a, b)$ and satisfy $0 \le f(x) \le g(x)$. If $\int_a^b g(x)\,dx$ converges, then so does $\int_a^b f(x)\,dx$, and

$$\int_a^b f(x)\,dx \le \int_a^b g(x)\,dx.$$

Equivalently, if $\int_a^b f(x)\,dx$ diverges to $\infty$, then so does $\int_a^b g(x)\,dx$.

**PROOF**    Since both integrands are nonnegative, there are only two possibilities for each integral: it can either converge to a nonnegative number or diverge to $\infty$. Since $f(x) \le g(x)$ on $(a, b)$, it follows by Theorem 3(e) of Section 8.4 that if $a < r < s < b$, then

$$\int_r^s f(x)\,dx \le \int_r^s g(x)\,dx.$$

This theorem now follows by taking limits as $r \to a+$ and $s \to b-$.

**EXAMPLE 8**    Show that $\int_0^\infty e^{-x^2}\,dx$ converges, and find an upper bound for its value.

**Solution**   We can't integrate $e^{-x^2}$, but we can integrate $e^{-x}$. We would like to use the inequality $e^{-x^2} \leq e^{-x}$, but this is only valid for $x \geq 1$. (See Figure 9.7.) Therefore, we break the integral into two parts.

On $[0, 1]$ we have $0 < e^{-x^2} \leq 1$, so

$$0 < \int_0^1 e^{-x^2}\, dx \leq \int_0^1 dx = 1.$$

On $[1, \infty)$ we have $x^2 \geq x$, so $-x^2 \leq -x$ and $0 < e^{-x^2} \leq e^{-x}$. Thus,

$$0 < \int_1^\infty e^{-x^2}\, dx \leq \int_1^\infty e^{-x}\, dx = \lim_{R \to \infty} \frac{e^{-x}}{-1}\Big|_1^R$$

$$= \lim_{R \to \infty}\left(\frac{1}{e} - \frac{1}{e^R}\right) = \frac{1}{e}.$$

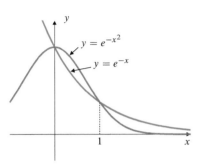

**Figure 9.7**    Comparing $e^{-x^2}$ and $e^{-x}$

Hence, $\displaystyle\int_0^\infty e^{-x^2}\, dx$ converges and its value is less than $1 + (1/e)$.

We remark that the above integral is, in fact, equal to $\frac{1}{2}\sqrt{\pi}$, although we cannot prove this now.

For large or small values of $x$ many integrands behave like powers of $x$. If so, they can be compared with $p$-integrals.

**EXAMPLE 9**    Determine whether $\displaystyle\int_0^\infty \frac{dx}{\sqrt{x + x^3}}$ converges.

**Solution**   The integral is improper of both types, so we write

$$\int_0^\infty \frac{dx}{\sqrt{x + x^3}} = \int_0^1 \frac{dx}{\sqrt{x + x^3}} + \int_1^\infty \frac{dx}{\sqrt{x + x^3}} = I_1 + I_2.$$

On $(0, 1]$ we have $\sqrt{x + x^3} > \sqrt{x}$, so

$$I_1 < \int_0^1 \frac{dx}{\sqrt{x}} = 2 \qquad \text{(by Theorem 2)}.$$

On $[1, \infty)$ we have $\sqrt{x + x^3} > \sqrt{x^3}$, so

$$I_2 < \int_1^\infty x^{-3/2}\, dx = 2 \qquad \text{(by Theorem 2)}.$$

Hence, the given integral converges, and its value is less than 4.

We introduced big-O notation as a way of conveying growth-rate information in limit situations. We wrote $f(x) = O\big(g(x)\big)$ as $x \to a$ to mean the same thing as $|f(x)| \leq K|g(x)|$ for some constant $K$ on some open interval containing $a$. Similarly, we can say that $f(x) = O\big(g(x)\big)$ as $x \to \infty$ if for some constants $a$ and $K$ we have $|f(x)| \leq K|g(x)|$ for all $x \geq a$.

**EXAMPLE 10**    $\dfrac{1 + x^2}{1 + x^4} = O\left(\dfrac{1}{x^2}\right)$ as $x \to \infty$ because, for $x \geq 1$ we have

$$\left|\frac{1 + x^2}{1 + x^4}\right| < \frac{2x^2}{x^4} = \frac{2}{x^2}.$$

EXAMPLE 11     Show that if $p > 1$ and $f$ is continuous on $[1, \infty)$ and satisfies
$$f(x) = O(x^{-p}), \text{ then } \int_1^\infty f(x)\, dx \text{ converges, and the error } E(R)$$
in the approximation

$$\int_1^\infty f(x)\, dx \approx \int_1^R f(x)\, dx$$

satisfies $E(R) = O(R^{1-p})$ as $R \to \infty$.

**Solution**   Since $f(x) = O(x^{-p})$ as $x \to \infty$, we have, for some $a \geq 1$ and some $K$, $f(x) \leq K x^{-p}$ for all $x \geq a$. Thus,

$$|E(R)| = \left| \int_R^\infty f(x)\, dx \right|$$

$$\leq K \int_R^\infty x^{-p}\, dx = K \left. \frac{x^{-p+1}}{-p+1} \right|_R^\infty = \frac{K}{p-1} R^{1-p},$$

so $E(R) = O(R^{1-p})$ as $R \to \infty$.

## EXERCISES 9.2

In Exercises 1–22, evaluate the given integral or show that it diverges.

**1.** $\displaystyle\int_2^\infty \frac{1}{(x-1)^3}\, dx$

**2.** $\displaystyle\int_3^\infty \frac{1}{(2x-1)^{2/3}}\, dx$

**3.** $\displaystyle\int_0^\infty e^{-2x}\, dx$

**4.** $\displaystyle\int_{-\infty}^{-1} \frac{dx}{x^2+1}$

**5.** $\displaystyle\int_{-1}^1 \frac{dx}{(x+1)^{2/3}}$

**6.** $\displaystyle\int_0^a \frac{dx}{a^2-x^2}$

**7.** $\displaystyle\int_0^1 \frac{1}{(1-x)^{1/3}}\, dx$

**8.** $\displaystyle\int_0^1 \frac{1}{x\sqrt{1-x}}\, dx$

**9.** $\displaystyle\int_0^{\pi/2} \frac{\cos x\, dx}{(1-\sin x)^{2/3}}$

**10.** $\displaystyle\int_0^\infty x\, e^{-x}\, dx$

**11.** $\displaystyle\int_0^1 \frac{dx}{\sqrt{x(1-x)}}$

**12.** $\displaystyle\int_0^\infty \frac{x}{1+2x^2}\, dx$

**13.** $\displaystyle\int_0^\infty \frac{x\, dx}{(1+2x^2)^{3/2}}$

**14.** $\displaystyle\int_0^{\pi/2} \sec x\, dx$

**15.** $\displaystyle\int_0^{\pi/2} \tan x\, dx$

**16.** $\displaystyle\int_e^\infty \frac{dx}{x \ln x}$

**17.** $\displaystyle\int_1^e \frac{dx}{x\sqrt{\ln x}}$

**18.** $\displaystyle\int_e^\infty \frac{dx}{x(\ln x)^2}$

**19.** $\displaystyle\int_{-\infty}^\infty \frac{x}{1+x^2}\, dx$

**20.** $\displaystyle\int_{-\infty}^\infty \frac{x}{1+x^4}\, dx$

**21.** $\displaystyle\int_{-\infty}^\infty x\, e^{-x^2}\, dx$

**22.** $\displaystyle\int_{-\infty}^\infty e^{-|x|}\, dx$

**23.** Find the area below $y = 0$, above $y = \ln x$, and to the right of $x = 0$.

**24.** Find the area below $y = e^{-x}$, above $y = e^{-2x}$, and to the right of $x = 0$.

**25.** Find the area of a region that lies above $y = 0$, to the right of $x = 1$, and under the curve $y = \dfrac{4}{2x+1} - \dfrac{2}{x+2}$.

**26.** Find the area of the plane region that lies under the graph of $y = x^{-2} e^{-1/x}$, above the $x$-axis, and to the right of the $y$-axis.

**27.** Prove Theorem 2(a) by directly evaluating the integrals involved.

**28.** Evaluate $\int_{-1}^1 (x \operatorname{sgn} x)/(x+2)\, dx$. Recall that $\operatorname{sgn} x = x/|x|$.

**29.** Evaluate $\int_0^2 x^2 \operatorname{sgn}(x-1)\, dx$.

In Exercises 30–41, state whether the given integral converges or diverges, and justify your claim.

**30.** $\displaystyle\int_0^\infty \frac{x^2}{x^5+1}\, dx$

**31.** $\displaystyle\int_0^\infty \frac{dx}{1+\sqrt{x}}$

**32.** $\displaystyle\int_2^\infty \frac{x\sqrt{x}\, dx}{x^2-1}$

**33.** $\displaystyle\int_0^\infty e^{-x^3}\, dx$

**34.** $\displaystyle\int_0^\infty \frac{dx}{\sqrt{x}+x^2}$

**35.** $\displaystyle\int_{-1}^1 \frac{e^x}{x+1}\, dx$

**36.** $\displaystyle\int_0^\pi \frac{\sin x}{x}\, dx$

**37.** $\displaystyle\int_0^\infty \frac{|\sin x|}{x^2}\, dx$

**38.** $\displaystyle\int_0^{\pi^2} \frac{dx}{1-\cos\sqrt{x}}$

**39.** $\displaystyle\int_{-\pi/2}^{\pi/2} \csc x\, dx$

**40.** $\displaystyle\int_2^\infty \frac{dx}{\sqrt{x} \ln x}$

**41.** $\displaystyle\int_0^\infty \frac{dx}{x e^x}$

**42.** Given that $\int_0^\infty e^{-x^2}\,dx = \frac{1}{2}\sqrt{\pi}$, evaluate

(a) $\displaystyle\int_0^\infty x^2 e^{-x^2}\,dx$ and (b) $\displaystyle\int_0^\infty x^4 e^{-x^2}\,dx$.

**43.** Suppose $f$ is continuous on the interval $(0, 1]$ and satisfies $f(x) = O(x^p)$ as $x \to 0+$, where $p > -1$. Show that

$$\int_0^1 f(x)\,dx$$ converges, and that if $0 < \epsilon < 1$, then the error $E(\epsilon)$ in the approximation

$$\int_0^1 f(x)\,dx \approx \int_\epsilon^1 f(x)\,dx$$

satisfies $E(\epsilon) = O(\epsilon^{p+1})$ as $\epsilon \to 0+$.

**44.** What is the largest value of $k$ such that the error $E(\epsilon)$ in the approximation

$$\int_0^\infty \frac{dx}{\sqrt{x}+x^2} \approx \int_\epsilon^{1/\epsilon} \frac{dx}{\sqrt{x}+x^2},$$

where $0 < \epsilon < 1$, satisfies $E(\epsilon) = O(\epsilon^k)$ as $\epsilon \to 0+$.

**45.** If $f$ is continuous on $[a, b]$, show that

$$\lim_{c \to a+} \int_c^b f(x)\,dx = \int_a^b f(x)\,dx.$$

*Hint:* A continuous function on a closed, finite interval is *bounded*: there exists a positive constant $K$ such that $|f(x)| \le K$ for all $x$ in $[a, b]$. Use this fact, together with parts (d) and (f) of Theorem 3 of Section 8.4, to show that

$$\lim_{c \to a+} \left( \int_a^b f(x)\,dx - \int_c^b f(x)\,dx \right) = 0.$$

Similarly, show that

$$\lim_{c \to b-} \int_a^c f(x)\,dx = \int_a^b f(x)\,dx.$$

**46.** (**The gamma function**) The gamma function $\Gamma(x)$ is defined by the improper integral

$$\Gamma(x) = \int_0^\infty t^{x-1} e^{-t}\,dt.$$

($\Gamma$ is the Greek capital letter gamma.)

(a) Show that the integral converges for $x > 0$.

(b) Use integration by parts to show that $\Gamma(x+1) = x\Gamma(x)$ for $x > 0$.

(c) Show that $\Gamma(n+1) = n!$ for $n = 0, 1, 2, \ldots$.

(d) Given that $\int_0^\infty e^{-x^2}\,dx = \frac{1}{2}\sqrt{\pi}$, show that $\Gamma(\frac{1}{2}) = \sqrt{\pi}$ and $\Gamma(\frac{3}{2}) = \frac{1}{2}\sqrt{\pi}$.

In view of (c), $\Gamma(x+1)$ is often written $x!$ and regarded as a real-valued extension of the factorial function. Some scientific calculators (in particular, HP calculators) with the factorial function $n!$ built in actually calculate the gamma function rather than just the integral factorial. Check whether your calculator does this by asking it for 0.5!. If you get an error message, it's not using the gamma function.

## 9.3 The Trapezoid and Midpoint Rules

Most of the applications of integration, within and outside of mathematics, involve the definite integral

$$I = \int_a^b f(x)\,dx.$$

Thanks to the Fundamental Theorem of Calculus, we can evaluate such definite integrals by first finding an antiderivative of $f$. This is why we have spent considerable time developing techniques of integration. There are, however, two obstacles that can prevent our calculating $I$ in this way:

(i) Finding an antiderivative of $f$ in terms of familiar functions may be impossible, or at least very difficult.

(ii) We may not be given a formula for $f(x)$ as a function of $x$; for instance, $f(x)$ may be an unknown function whose values at certain points of the interval $[a, b]$ have been determined by experimental measurement.

In the next two sections we investigate the problem of approximating the value of the definite integral $I$ using only the values of $f(x)$ at finitely many points of $[a, b]$. Obtaining such an approximation is called **numerical integration**. Upper and lower sums (or, indeed, any Riemann sum) can be used for this purpose, but these usually require much more calculation to yield a desired precision than the methods we will develop here. We will develop three methods for evaluating definite integrals numerically: the Trapezoid Rule, the Midpoint Rule, and Simpson's Rule (see Section 9.4). All of these methods can be easily implemented on a small computer or using a scientific calculator. The wide availability of these devices makes numerical integration a steadily more important tool for the user of mathematics. Some of the more advanced calculators have built-in routines for numerical integration.

All the techniques we consider require us to calculate the values of $f(x)$ at a set of equally spaced points in $[a, b]$. The computational "expense" involved in determining an approximate value for the integral $I$ will be roughly proportional to the number of function values required, so that the fewer function evaluations needed to achieve a desired degree of accuracy for the integral, the better we will regard the technique. Time is money, even in the world of computers.

## The Trapezoid Rule

We assume that $f(x)$ is continuous on $[a, b]$ and subdivide $[a, b]$ into $n$ subintervals of equal length $h = (b - a)/n$ using the $n + 1$ points

$$x_0 = a, \quad x_1 = a + h, \quad x_2 = a + 2h, \quad \dots, \quad x_n = a + nh = b.$$

We assume that the value of $f(x)$ at each of these points is known:

$$y_0 = f(x_0), \quad y_1 = f(x_1), \quad y_2 = f(x_2), \quad \dots, \quad y_n = f(x_n).$$

The Trapezoid Rule approximates $\int_a^b f(x)\,dx$ by using straight line segments between the points $(x_{j-1}, y_{j-1})$ and $(x_j, y_j)$, $(1 \le j \le n)$, to approximate the graph of $f$, as shown in Figure 9.8, and summing the areas of the resulting $n$ *trapezoids*. A **trapezoid** is a four-sided polygon with one pair of parallel sides. (For our discussion we assume $f$ is positive so we can talk about "areas," but the resulting formulas apply to any continuous function $f$.)

The first trapezoid has vertices $(x_0, 0)$, $(x_0, y_0)$, $(x_1, y_1)$, and $(x_1, 0)$. The two parallel sides are vertical and have lengths $y_0$ and $y_1$. The perpendicular distance between them is $h = x_1 - x_0$. The area of this trapezoid is $h$ times the average of the parallel sides:

$$h \frac{y_0 + y_1}{2} \text{ square units.}$$

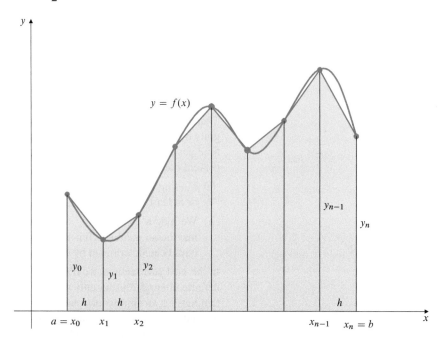

Figure 9.8    The area under $y = f(x)$ is approximated by the sum of the areas of $n$ trapezoids

This can be seen geometrically by considering the trapezoid as the nonoverlapping union of a rectangle and a triangle; see Figure 9.9. We use this trapezoidal area to approximate the integral of $f$ over the first subinterval $[x_0, x_1]$:

$$\int_{x_0}^{x_1} f(x)\, dx \approx h\, \frac{y_0 + y_1}{2}.$$

We can approximate the integral of $f$ over any subinterval in the same way:

$$\int_{x_{j-1}}^{x_j} f(x)\, dx \approx h\, \frac{y_{j-1} + y_j}{2}, \qquad (1 \le j \le n).$$

It follows that the original integral $I$ can be approximated by the sum of these trapezoidal areas:

$$\int_a^b f(x)\, dx \approx h \left( \frac{y_0 + y_1}{2} + \frac{y_1 + y_2}{2} + \frac{y_2 + y_3}{2} + \cdots + \frac{y_{n-1} + y_n}{2} \right)$$

$$= h \left( \frac{1}{2} y_0 + y_1 + y_2 + y_3 + \cdots + y_{n-1} + \frac{1}{2} y_n \right).$$

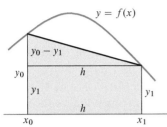

**Figure 9.9**    The trapezoid has area
$y_1 h + \frac{1}{2}(y_0 - y_1)h = \frac{1}{2}h(y_0 + y_1)$

**DEFINITION**

**3**

**The Trapezoid Rule**

The $n$-subinterval **Trapezoid Rule** approximation to $\int_a^b f(x)\, dx$, denoted $T_n$, is given by

$$T_n = h \left( \frac{1}{2} y_0 + y_1 + y_2 + y_3 + \cdots + y_{n-1} + \frac{1}{2} y_n \right).$$

We now illustrate the Trapezoid Rule by using it to approximate an integral whose value we already know:

$$I = \int_1^2 \frac{1}{x}\, dx = \ln 2 = 0.693\,147\,18\ldots.$$

(This value, and those of all the approximations quoted in these sections, were calculated using a scientific calculator.) We will use the same integral to illustrate other methods for approximating definite integrals later.

**EXAMPLE 1**    Calculate the Trapezoid Rule approximations $T_4$, $T_8$, and $T_{16}$ for

$$I = \int_1^2 \frac{1}{x}\, dx.$$

**Solution**    For $n = 4$ we have $h = (2-1)/4 = 1/4$; for $n = 8$ we have $h = 1/8$; for $n = 16$ we have $h = 1/16$. Therefore,

$$T_4 = \frac{1}{4} \left[ \frac{1}{2}(1) + \frac{4}{5} + \frac{2}{3} + \frac{4}{7} + \frac{1}{2}\left(\frac{1}{2}\right) \right] = 0.697\,023\,81\ldots$$

$$T_8 = \frac{1}{8} \left[ \frac{1}{2}(1) + \frac{8}{9} + \frac{4}{5} + \frac{8}{11} + \frac{2}{3} + \frac{8}{13} + \frac{4}{7} + \frac{8}{15} + \frac{1}{2}\left(\frac{1}{2}\right) \right]$$

$$= \frac{1}{8} \left[ 4\,T_4 + \frac{8}{9} + \frac{8}{11} + \frac{8}{13} + \frac{8}{15} \right] = 0.694\,121\,85\ldots$$

$$T_{16} = \frac{1}{16} \left[ 8\,T_8 + \frac{16}{17} + \frac{16}{19} + \frac{16}{21} + \frac{16}{23} + \frac{16}{25} + \frac{16}{27} + \frac{16}{29} + \frac{16}{31} \right]$$

$$= 0.693\,391\,20\ldots.$$

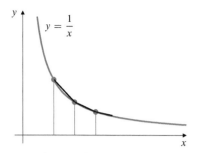

**Figure 9.10** The trapezoid areas are greater than the area under the curve if the curve is concave upward

Note how the function values used to calculate $T_4$ were reused in the calculation of $T_8$, and similarly how those in $T_8$ were reused for $T_{16}$. When several approximations are needed, it is very useful to double the number of subintervals for each new calculation so that previously calculated values of $f$ can be reused.

All Trapezoid Rule approximations to $I = \int_1^2 (1/x)\,dx$ are greater than the true value of $I$. This is because the graph of $y = 1/x$ is concave up on $[1, 2]$, and therefore the tops of the approximating trapezoids lie above the curve. (See Figure 9.10.)

We can calculate the exact errors in the three approximations since we know that $I = \ln 2 = 0.69314718\ldots$ (We always take the error in an approximation to be the true value minus the approximate value.)

$$I - T_4 = 0.693\,147\,18\ldots - 0.697\,023\,81\ldots = -0.003\,876\,63\ldots$$
$$I - T_8 = 0.693\,147\,18\ldots - 0.694\,121\,85\ldots = -0.000\,974\,67\ldots$$
$$I - T_{16} = 0.693\,147\,18\ldots - 0.693\,391\,20\ldots = -0.000\,244\,02\ldots.$$

Observe that the size of the error decreases to about a quarter of its previous value each time we double $n$. We will show below that this is to be expected for a "well-behaved" function like $1/x$.

Example 1 is somewhat artificial in the sense that we know the actual value of the integral so we really don't need an approximation. In practical applications of numerical integration we do not know the actual value. It is tempting to calculate several approximations for increasing values of $n$ until the two most recent ones agree to within a prescribed error tolerance. For example, we might be inclined to claim that $\ln 2 \approx 0.69\ldots$ from a comparison of $T_4$ and $T_8$, and further comparison of $T_{16}$ and $T_8$ suggests that the third decimal place is probably 3: $I \approx 0.693\ldots$. Although this approach cannot be justified in general, it is frequently used in practice.

### The Midpoint Rule

A somewhat simpler approximation to $\int_a^b f(x)\,dx$, based on the partition of $[a, b]$ into $n$ equal subintervals, involves forming a Riemann sum of the areas of rectangles whose heights are taken at the midpoints of the $n$ subintervals. (See Figure 9.11.)

**DEFINITION**

**4**

**The Midpoint Rule**

If $h = (b - a)/n$, let $m_j = a + \left(j - \frac{1}{2}\right)h$ for $1 \le j \le n$. The **Midpoint Rule** approximation to $\int_a^b f(x)\,dx$, denoted $M_n$, is given by

$$M_n = h\big(f(m_1) + f(m_2) + \cdots + f(m_n)\big) = h\sum_{j=1}^{n} f(m_j).$$

**EXAMPLE 2**    Find the Midpoint Rule approximations $M_4$ and $M_8$ for the integral $I = \displaystyle\int_1^2 \frac{1}{x}\,dx$, and compare their actual errors with those obtained for the Trapezoid Rule approximations above.

*Solution*    To find $M_4$, the interval $[1, 2]$ is divided into four equal subintervals,

$$\left[1, \frac{5}{4}\right], \quad \left[\frac{5}{4}, \frac{3}{2}\right], \quad \left[\frac{3}{2}, \frac{7}{4}\right], \quad \text{and} \quad \left[\frac{7}{4}, 2\right].$$

The midpoints of these intervals are $9/8$, $11/8$, $13/8$, and $15/8$, respectively. The midpoints of the subintervals for $M_8$ are obtained in a similar way. The required Midpoint Rule approximations are

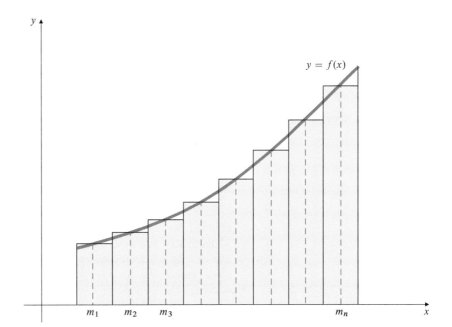

**Figure 9.11**    The Midpoint Rule approximation $M_n$ to $\int_a^b f(x)\,dx$ is the Riemann sum based on the heights to the graph of $f$ at the midpoints of the subintervals of the partition

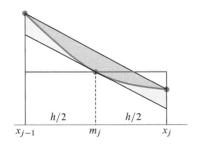

**Figure 9.12**    The Midpoint Rule error (the yellow area) is opposite in sign and about half the size of the Trapezoid Rule error (shaded in green)

$$M_4 = \frac{1}{4}\left[\frac{8}{9} + \frac{8}{11} + \frac{8}{13} + \frac{8}{15}\right] = 0.691\,219\,89\ldots$$

$$M_8 = \frac{1}{8}\left[\frac{16}{17} + \frac{16}{19} + \frac{16}{21} + \frac{16}{23} + \frac{16}{25} + \frac{16}{27} + \frac{16}{29} + \frac{16}{31}\right] = 0.692\,660\,55\ldots$$

The errors in these approximations are

$$I - M_4 = 0.693\,147\,18\ldots - 0.691\,219\,89\ldots = 0.001\,927\,29\ldots$$
$$I - M_8 = 0.693\,147\,18\ldots - 0.692\,660\,55\ldots = 0.000\,486\,63\ldots$$

These errors are of opposite sign and about *half the size* of the corresponding Trapezoid Rule errors $I - T_4$ and $I - T_8$. Figure 9.12 suggests the reason for this. The rectangular area $hf(m_j)$ is equal to the area of the trapezoid formed by the tangent line to $y = f(x)$ at $(m_j, f(m_j))$. The shaded region above the curve is the part of the Trapezoid Rule error due to the $j$th subinterval. The shaded area below the curve is the corresponding Midpoint Rule error.

One drawback of the Midpoint Rule is that we cannot reuse values of $f$ calculated for $M_n$ when we calculate $M_{2n}$. However, to calculate $T_{2n}$ we can use the data values already calculated for $T_n$ and $M_n$. Specifically,

$$T_{2n} = \tfrac{1}{2}(T_n + M_n).$$

A good strategy for using these methods to obtain a value for an integral $I$ to a desired degree of accuracy is to calculate successively

$$T_n, \quad M_n, \quad T_{2n} = \frac{T_n + M_n}{2}, \quad M_{2n}, \quad T_{4n} = \frac{T_{2n} + M_{2n}}{2}, \quad M_{4n}, \quad \cdots$$

until two consecutive terms agree sufficiently closely. If a single quick approximation is needed, $M_n$ is a better choice than $T_n$.

## Error Estimates

The following theorem provides a bound for the error in the Trapezoid and Midpoint Rule approximations in terms of the second derivative of the integrand.

THEOREM

4

**Error estimates for the Trapezoid and Midpoint Rules**

If $f$ has a continuous second derivative on $[a, b]$ and satisfies $|f''(x)| \leq K$ there, then

$$\left| \int_a^b f(x)\, dx - T_n \right| \leq \frac{K(b-a)}{12} h^2 = \frac{K(b-a)^3}{12n^2},$$

$$\left| \int_a^b f(x)\, dx - M_n \right| \leq \frac{K(b-a)}{24} h^2 = \frac{K(b-a)^3}{24n^2},$$

where $h = (b-a)/n$. Note that these error bounds decrease like the square of the subinterval length as $n$ increases.

*PROOF*  We will prove only the Trapezoid Rule error estimate here. (The one for the Midpoint Rule is a little easier to prove; the method is suggested in Exercise 14 below.) The straight line approximating $y = f(x)$ in the first subinterval $[x_0, x_1] = [a, a+h]$ passes through the two points $(x_0, y_0)$ and $(x_1, y_1)$. Its equation is $y = A + B(x - x_0)$, where

$$A = y_0 \qquad \text{and} \qquad B = \frac{y_1 - y_0}{x_1 - x_0} = \frac{y_1 - y_0}{h}.$$

Let the function $g(x)$ be the vertical distance between the graph of $f$ and this line:

$$g(x) = f(x) - A - B(x - x_0).$$

Since the integral of $A + B(x - x_0)$ over $[x_0, x_1]$ is the area of the first trapezoid, which is $h(y_0 + y_1)/2$ (see Figure 9.13), the integral of $g(x)$ over $[x_0, x_1]$ is the error in the approximation of $\int_{x_0}^{x_1} f(x)\, dx$ by the area of the trapezoid:

$$\int_{x_0}^{x_1} f(x)\, dx - h \frac{y_0 + y_1}{2} = \int_{x_0}^{x_1} g(x)\, dx.$$

Now $g$ is twice differentiable, and $g''(x) = f''(x)$. Also $g(x_0) = g(x_1) = 0$. Two integrations by parts (see Exercise 36 of Section 9.1) show that

$$\int_{x_0}^{x_1} (x - x_0)(x_1 - x)\, f''(x)\, dx = \int_{x_0}^{x_1} (x - x_0)(x_1 - x)\, g''(x)\, dx$$

$$= -2 \int_{x_0}^{x_1} g(x)\, dx.$$

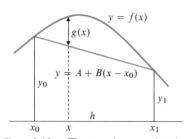

y = f(x)

g(x)

$y = A + B(x - x_0)$

$y_0$

$y_1$

$h$

$x_0 \quad x \quad x_1$

**Figure 9.13**  The error in approximating the area under the curve by that of the trapezoid is $\int_{x_0}^{x_1} g(x)\, dx$

By the triangle inequality for definite integrals (Theorem 3(f) of Section 8.4),

$$\left| \int_{x_0}^{x_1} f(x)\, dx - h \frac{y_0 + y_1}{2} \right| \leq \frac{1}{2} \int_{x_0}^{x_1} (x - x_0)(x_1 - x)\, |f''(x)|\, dx$$

$$\leq \frac{K}{2} \int_{x_0}^{x_1} \left( -x^2 + (x_0 + x_1)x - x_0 x_1 \right) dx$$

$$= \frac{K}{12} (x_1 - x_0)^3 = \frac{K}{12} h^3.$$

A similar estimate holds on each subinterval $[x_{j-1}, x_j]$ $(1 \leq j \leq n)$. Therefore,

$$\left| \int_a^b f(x)\, dx - T_n \right| = \left| \sum_{j=1}^n \left( \int_{x_{j-1}}^{x_j} f(x)\, dx - h \frac{y_{j-1} + y_j}{2} \right) \right|$$

$$\leq \sum_{j=1}^n \left| \int_{x_{j-1}}^{x_j} f(x)\, dx - h \frac{y_{j-1} + y_j}{2} \right|$$

$$= \sum_{j=1}^n \frac{K}{12} h^3 = \frac{K}{12} n h^3 = \frac{K(b-a)}{12} h^2,$$

since $nh = b - a$.

We illustrate this error estimate for the approximations of Examples 1 and 2 above.

**EXAMPLE 3**    Obtain bounds for the errors for $T_4$, $T_8$, $T_{16}$, $M_4$, and $M_8$ for

$$I = \int_1^2 \frac{1}{x}\, dx.$$

***Solution***    If $f(x) = 1/x$, then $f'(x) = -1/x^2$ and $f''(x) = 2/x^3$. On $[1, 2]$ we have $|f''(x)| \le 2$, so we may take $K = 2$ in the estimate. Thus,

$$|I - T_4| \le \frac{2(2-1)}{12}\left(\frac{1}{4}\right)^2 = 0.010\,4\ldots,$$

$$|I - M_4| \le \frac{2(2-1)}{24}\left(\frac{1}{4}\right)^2 = 0.005\,2\ldots,$$

$$|I - T_8| \le \frac{2(2-1)}{12}\left(\frac{1}{8}\right)^2 = 0.002\,6\ldots,$$

$$|I - M_8| \le \frac{2(2-1)}{24}\left(\frac{1}{8}\right)^2 = 0.001\,3\ldots,$$

$$|I - T_{16}| \le \frac{2(2-1)}{12}\left(\frac{1}{16}\right)^2 = 0.000\,65\ldots.$$

The actual errors calculated earlier are considerably smaller than these bounds, because $|f''(x)|$ is rather smaller than $K = 2$ over most of the interval $[1, 2]$.

***Remark***    Error bounds are not usually as easily obtained as they are in Example 3. In particular, if an exact formula for $f(x)$ is not known (as is usually the case if the values of $f$ are obtained from experimental data), then we have no method of calculating $f''(x)$, so we can't determine $K$. Theorem 4 is of more theoretical than practical importance. It shows us that, for a "well-behaved" function $f$, the Midpoint Rule error is typically about half as large as the Trapezoid Rule error and that both the Trapezoid Rule and Midpoint Rule errors can be expected to decrease like $1/n^2$ as $n$ increases; in terms of big-O notation,

$$I = T_n + O\left(\frac{1}{n^2}\right) \quad \text{and} \quad I = M_n + O\left(\frac{1}{n^2}\right) \qquad \text{as } n \to \infty.$$

Of course, actual errors are not equal to the error bounds, so they won't always be cut to exactly a quarter of their size when we double $n$.

## EXERCISES 9.3

In Exercises 1–4, calculate the approximations $T_4$, $M_4$, $T_8$, $M_8$, and $T_{16}$ for the given integrals. (Use a scientific calculator or computer spreadsheet program.) Also calculate the exact value of each integral, and so determine the exact error in each approximation. Compare these exact errors with the bounds for the size of the error supplied by Theorem 4.

**1.** $I = \displaystyle\int_0^2 (1 + x^2)\, dx$     **2.** $I = \displaystyle\int_0^1 e^{-x}\, dx$

**3.** $I = \displaystyle\int_0^{\pi/2} \sin x\, dx$     **4.** $I = \displaystyle\int_0^1 \frac{dx}{1 + x^2}$

**5.** Figure 9.14 shows the graph of a function $f$ over the interval $[1, 9]$. Using values from the graph, find the Trapezoid Rule estimates $T_4$ and $T_8$ for $\int_1^9 f(x)\, dx$.

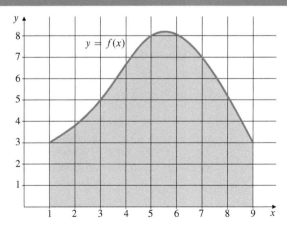

Figure  9.14

**6.** Obtain the best Midpoint Rule approximation that you can for $\int_1^9 f(x)\,dx$ from the data in Figure 9.14.

**7.** The map of a region is traced on the grid in Figure 9.15, where 1 unit in both the vertical and horizontal directions represents 10 km. Use the Trapezoid Rule to obtain two estimates for the area of the region.

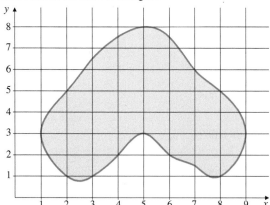

Figure 9.15

**8.** Find a Midpoint Rule estimate for the area of the region in Exercise 7.

**9.** Find $T_4$, $M_4$, $T_8$, $M_8$, and $T_{16}$ for $\int_0^{1.6} f(x)\,dx$ for the function $f$ whose values are given in Table 1.

Table 1.

| $x$ | $f(x)$ | $x$ | $f(x)$ |
|-----|--------|-----|--------|
| 0.0 | 1.4142 | 0.1 | 1.4124 |
| 0.2 | 1.4071 | 0.3 | 1.3983 |
| 0.4 | 1.3860 | 0.5 | 1.3702 |
| 0.6 | 1.3510 | 0.7 | 1.3285 |
| 0.8 | 1.3026 | 0.9 | 1.2734 |
| 1.0 | 1.2411 | 1.1 | 1.2057 |
| 1.2 | 1.1772 | 1.3 | 1.1258 |
| 1.4 | 1.0817 | 1.5 | 1.0348 |
| 1.6 | 0.9853 |     |        |

**10.** Find the approximations $M_8$ and $T_{16}$ for $\int_0^1 e^{-x^2}\,dx$. Quote a value for the integral to as many decimal places as you feel are justified.

**11.** Repeat Exercise 10 for $\int_0^{\pi/2} \dfrac{\sin x}{x}\,dx$. (Assume the integrand is 1 at $x = 0$.)

**12.** Compute the actual error in the approximation $\int_0^1 x^2\,dx \approx T_1$ and use it to show that the constant 12 in the estimate of Theorem 4 cannot be improved. That is, show that the absolute value of the actual error is as large as allowed by that estimate.

**13.** Repeat Exercise 12 for $M_1$.

**14.** Prove the error estimate for the Midpoint Rule in Theorem 4 as follows: If $x_1 - x_0 = h$ and $m_1$ is the midpoint of $[x_0, x_1]$, use the error estimate for the tangent line approximation (Theorem 11 of Section 7.7) to show that

$$|f(x) - f(m_1) - f'(m_1)(x - m_1)| \le \frac{K}{2}(x - m_1)^2.$$

Use this inequality to show that

$$\left| \int_{x_0}^{x_1} f(x)\,dx - f(m_1)h \right|$$
$$= \left| \int_{x_0}^{x_1} \Big( f(x) - f(m_1) - f'(m_1)(x - m_1) \Big)dx \right|$$
$$\le \frac{K}{24} h^3.$$

Complete the proof the same way used for the Trapezoid Rule estimate in Theorem 4.

## 9.4    Simpson's Rule

The Trapezoid Rule approximation to $\int_a^b f(x)\,dx$ results from approximating the graph of $f$ by straight line segments through adjacent pairs of data points on the graph. Intuitively, we would expect to do better if we approximate the graph by more general curves. Since straight lines are the graphs of linear functions, the simplest obvious generalization is to use the class of quadratic functions, that is, to approximate the graph of $f$ by segments of parabolas. This is the basis of Simpson's Rule.

Suppose that we are given three points in the plane, one on each of three equally spaced vertical lines, spaced, say, $h$ units apart. If we choose the middle of these lines as the $y$-axis, then the coordinates of the three points will be, say, $(-h, y_L)$, $(0, y_M)$, and $(h, y_R)$, as illustrated in Figure 9.16.

Constants $A$, $B$, and $C$ can be chosen so that the parabola $y = A + Bx + Cx^2$ passes through these points; substituting the coordinates of the three points into the equation of the parabola, we get

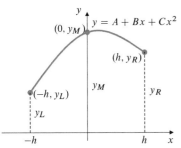

$$\left. \begin{aligned} y_L &= A - Bh + Ch^2 \\ y_M &= A \\ y_R &= A + Bh + Ch^2 \end{aligned} \right\} \quad \Rightarrow \quad A = y_M \quad \text{and} \quad 2Ch^2 = y_L - 2y_M + y_R.$$

Now we have

$$\int_{-h}^{h} (A + Bx + Cx^2)\, dx = \left( Ax + \frac{B}{2} x^2 + \frac{C}{3} x^3 \right) \Big|_{-h}^{h} = 2Ah + \frac{2}{3} Ch^3$$

$$= h \left( 2y_M + \frac{1}{3} (y_L - 2y_M + y_R) \right)$$

$$= \frac{h}{3} (y_L + 4y_M + y_R).$$

Figure 9.16    Fitting a quadratic graph through three points with equal horizontal spacing

Thus, the area of the plane region bounded by the parabolic arc, the interval of length $2h$ on the $x$-axis, and the left and right vertical lines is equal to $(h/3)$ times the sum of the heights of the region at the left and right edges and four times the height at the middle. (It is independent of the position of the $y$-axis.)

Now suppose that we are given the same data for $f$ as we were given for the Trapezoid Rule; that is, we know the values $y_j = f(x_j)$ ($0 \le j \le n$) at $n+1$ equally spaced points

$$x_0 = a, \quad x_1 = a + h, \quad x_2 = a + 2h, \quad \ldots, \quad x_n = a + nh = b,$$

where $h = (b - a)/n$. We can approximate the graph of $f$ over *pairs* of the subintervals $[x_{j-1}, x_j]$ using parabolic segments and use the integrals of the corresponding quadratic functions to approximate the integrals of $f$ over these subintervals. Since we need to use the subintervals two at a time, we must assume that $n$ is *even*. Using the integral computed for the parabolic segment above, we have

$$\int_{x_0}^{x_2} f(x)\, dx \approx \frac{h}{3} (y_0 + 4y_1 + y_2)$$

$$\int_{x_2}^{x_4} f(x)\, dx \approx \frac{h}{3} (y_2 + 4y_3 + y_4)$$

$$\vdots$$

$$\int_{x_{n-2}}^{x_n} f(x)\, dx \approx \frac{h}{3} (y_{n-2} + 4y_{n-1} + y_n).$$

Adding these $n/2$ individual approximations, we get the Simpson's Rule approximation to the integral $\int_a^b f(x)\, dx$.

**DEFINITION**

**5**

**Simpson's Rule**

The **Simpson's Rule** approximation to $\int_a^b f(x)\, dx$ based on a subdivision of $[a, b]$ into an even number $n$ of subintervals of equal length $h = (b - a)/n$ is denoted $S_n$ and is given by:

$$\int_a^b f(x)\, dx \approx S_n$$

$$= \frac{h}{3} \left( y_0 + 4y_1 + 2y_2 + 4y_3 + 2y_4 + \cdots + 2y_{n-2} + 4y_{n-1} + y_n \right)$$

$$= \frac{h}{3} \left( \sum y_{\text{"ends"}} + 4 \sum y_{\text{"odds"}} + 2 \sum y_{\text{"evens"}} \right).$$

Note that the Simpson's Rule approximation $S_n$ requires no more data than does the Trapezoid Rule approximation $T_n$; both require the values of $f(x)$ at $n + 1$ equally spaced points. However, Simpson's Rule treats the data differently, weighting successive values either 1/3, 2/3, or 4/3. As we will see, this can produce a much better approximation to the integral of $f$.

---

**EXAMPLE 1**    Calculate the approximations $S_4$, $S_8$, and $S_{16}$ for $I = \displaystyle\int_1^2 \frac{1}{x}\,dx$

and compare them with the actual value $I = \ln 2 = 0.693\,147\,18\ldots$, and with the values of $T_4$, $T_8$, and $T_{16}$ obtained in Example 1 of Section 9.3.

*Solution*    We calculate

$$S_4 = \frac{1}{12}\left[1 + 4\left(\frac{4}{5}\right) + 2\left(\frac{2}{3}\right) + 4\left(\frac{4}{7}\right) + \frac{1}{2}\right] = 0.693\,253\,97\ldots,$$

$$S_8 = \frac{1}{24}\left[1 + \frac{1}{2} + 4\left(\frac{8}{9} + \frac{8}{11} + \frac{8}{13} + \frac{8}{15}\right)\right.$$
$$\left. + 2\left(\frac{4}{5} + \frac{2}{3} + \frac{4}{7}\right)\right] = 0.693\,154\,53\ldots,$$

$$S_{16} = \frac{1}{48}\left[1 + \frac{1}{2}\right.$$
$$+ 4\left(\frac{16}{17} + \frac{16}{19} + \frac{16}{21} + \frac{16}{23} + \frac{16}{25} + \frac{16}{27} + \frac{16}{29} + \frac{16}{31}\right)$$
$$\left. + 2\left(\frac{8}{9} + \frac{4}{5} + \frac{8}{11} + \frac{2}{3} + \frac{8}{13} + \frac{4}{7} + \frac{8}{15}\right)\right] = 0.693\,147\,65\ldots.$$

The errors are

$$I - S_4 = 0.693\,147\,18\ldots - 0.693\,253\,97\ldots = -0.000\,106\,79,$$
$$I - S_8 = 0.693\,147\,18\ldots - 0.693\,154\,53\ldots = -0.000\,007\,35,$$
$$I - S_{16} = 0.693\,147\,18\ldots - 0.693\,147\,65\ldots = -0.000\,000\,47.$$

These errors are evidently much smaller than the corresponding errors for the Trapezoid or Midpoint Rule approximations.

---

*Remark*    Simpson's Rule $S_{2n}$ makes use of the same $2n + 1$ data values that $T_n$ and $M_n$ together use. It is not difficult to verify that

$$S_{2n} = \frac{T_n + 2M_n}{3}, \qquad S_{2n} = \frac{2T_{2n} + M_n}{3}, \qquad \text{and} \qquad S_{2n} = \frac{4T_{2n} - T_n}{3}.$$

Figure 6.19 and Theorem 4 in Section 9.3 suggest why the first of these formulas ought to yield a particularly good approximation to $I$.

Obtaining an error estimate for Simpson's Rule is more difficult than for the Trapezoid Rule. We state the appropriate estimate in the following theorem, but we do not attempt any proof. Proofs can be found in textbooks on numerical analysis.

**THEOREM**

**5**

**Error estimate for Simpson's Rule**

If $f$ has a continuous fourth derivative on the interval $[a, b]$, satisfying $|f^{(4)}(x)| \le K$ there, then

$$\left| \int_a^b f(x)\, dx - S_n \right| \le \frac{K(b-a)}{180} h^4 = \frac{K(b-a)^5}{180 n^4},$$

where $h = (b-a)/n$.

Observe that, as $n$ increases, the error decreases as the fourth power of $h$ and, hence, as $1/n^4$. Using the big-O notation we have

$$\int_a^b f(x)\, dx = S_n + O\left( \frac{1}{n^4} \right) \qquad \text{as } n \to \infty.$$

This accounts for the fact that $S_n$ is a much better approximation than is $T_n$, provided that $h$ is small and $|f^{(4)}(x)|$ is not unduly large compared with $|f''(x)|$. Note also that for any (even) $n$, $S_n$ gives the exact value of the integral of any *cubic* function $f(x) = A + Bx + Cx^2 + Dx^3$; $f^{(4)}(x) = 0$ identically for such $f$, so we can take $K = 0$ in the error estimate.

---

**EXAMPLE 2**    Obtain bounds for the absolute values of the errors in the approximations of Example 1.

**Solution**    If $f(x) = 1/x$, then

$$f'(x) = -\frac{1}{x^2}, \qquad f''(x) = \frac{2}{x^3}, \qquad f^{(3)}(x) = -\frac{6}{x^4}, \qquad f^{(4)}(x) = \frac{24}{x^5}.$$

Clearly, $|f^{(4)}(x)| \le 24$ on $[1, 2]$, so we can take $K = 24$ in the estimate of Theorem 5. We have

$$|I - S_4| \le \frac{24(2-1)}{180} \left( \frac{1}{4} \right)^4 \approx 0.000\,520\,83,$$

$$|I - S_8| \le \frac{24(2-1)}{180} \left( \frac{1}{8} \right)^4 \approx 0.000\,032\,55,$$

$$|I - S_{16}| \le \frac{24(2-1)}{180} \left( \frac{1}{16} \right)^4 \approx 0.000\,002\,03.$$

Again we observe that the actual errors are well within these bounds.

---

**EXAMPLE 3**    A function $f$ satisfies $|f^{(4)}(x)| \le 7$ on the interval $[1, 3]$, and the values $f(1.0) = 0.1860$, $f(1.5) = 0.9411$, $f(2.0) = 1.1550$, $f(2.5) = 1.4511$, and $f(3.0) = 1.2144$. Find the best possible Simpson's Rule approximation to $I = \int_1^3 f(x)\, dx$ based on these data. Give a bound for the size of the error, and specify the smallest interval you can that must contain the value of $I$.

**Solution**    We take $n = 4$, so that $h = (3-1)/4 = 0.5$, and we obtain

$$I = \int_1^3 f(x)\, dx$$

$$\approx S_4 = \frac{0.5}{3}(0.1860 + 4(0.9411 + 1.4511) + 2(1.1550) + 1.2144)$$

$$= 2.2132.$$

Since $|f^{(4)}(x)| \leq 7$ on $[1, 3]$, we have

$$|I - S_4| \leq \frac{7(3-1)}{180} (0.5)^4 < 0.0049.$$

$I$ must therefore satisfy

$$2.2132 - 0.0049 < I < 2.2132 + 0.0049 \quad \text{or} \quad 2.2083 < I < 2.2181.$$

## EXERCISES 9.4

In Exercises 1–4, find Simpson's Rule approximations $S_4$ and $S_8$ for the given functions. Compare your results with the actual values of the integrals and with the corresponding Trapezoid Rule approximations obtained in Exercises 1–4 of Section 9.3.

**1.** $I = \displaystyle\int_0^2 (1 + x^2)\, dx$

**2.** $I = \displaystyle\int_0^1 e^{-x}\, dx$

**3.** $I = \displaystyle\int_0^{\pi/2} \sin x\, dx$

**4.** $I = \displaystyle\int_0^1 \frac{dx}{1 + x^2}$

**5.** Find the Simpson's Rule approximation $S_8$ for the integral in Exercise 5 of Section 9.3.

**6.** Find the best Simpson's Rule approximation that you can for the area of the region in Exercise 7 of Section 9.3.

**7.** Use Theorem 5 to obtain bounds for the errors in the approximations obtained in Exercises 2 and 3 above.

**8.** Verify that $S_{2n} = \dfrac{T_n + 2M_n}{3} = \dfrac{2T_{2n} + M_n}{3}$, where $T_n$ and

$M_n$ refer to the appropriate Trapezoid and Midpoint Rule approximations. Deduce that $S_{2n} = \dfrac{4T_{2n} - T_n}{3}$.

**9.** Find $S_4$, $S_8$, and $S_{16}$ for $\int_0^{1.6} f(x)\, dx$ for the function $f$ whose values are tabulated in Exercise 9 of Section 9.3.

**10.** Find the Simpson's Rule approximations $S_8$ and $S_{16}$ for $\int_0^1 e^{-x^2}\, dx$. Quote a value for the integral to the number of decimal places you feel is justified based on comparing the two approximations.

**11.** Compute the actual error in the approximation $\int_0^1 x^4\, dx \approx S_2$ and use it to show that the constant 180 in the estimate of Theorem 5 cannot be improved.

**12.** Since Simpson's Rule is based on quadratic approximation, it is not surprising that it should give an exact value for an integral of $A + Bx + Cx^2$. It is more surprising that it is exact for a cubic function as well. Verify by direct calculation that $\int_0^1 x^3\, dx = S_2$.

# CHAPTER 10

# Applications of Integration

Volumes by Slicing—Solids of Revolution

In this section we show how volumes of certain three-dimensional regions (or *solids*) can be expressed as definite integrals and thereby determined. We will not attempt to give a definition of *volume* but will rely on our intuition and experience with solid objects to provide enough insight for us to specify the volumes of certain simple solids. For example, if the base of a rectangular box is a rectangle of length $l$ and width $w$ (and therefore area $A = lw$), and if the box has height $h$, then its volume is $V = Ah = lwh$. If $l$, $w$, and $h$ are measured in *units* (e.g., centimetres), then the volume is expressed in *cubic units* (cubic centimetres, or cm$^3$).

A rectangular box is a special case of a solid called a **cylinder**. (See Figure 10.1.) Such a solid has a flat base occupying a region $R$ in a plane, and consists of all points on parallel straight line segments having one end in $R$ and the other end in a (necessarily congruent) region in a second plane parallel to the plane of the base. Either of these regions can be called the **base** of the cylinder. The **cylindrical wall** is the surface consisting of the parallel line segments joining corresponding points on the boundaries of the two bases. A cylinder having a polygonal base (i.e., one bounded by straight lines) is usually called a **prism**. The height of any cylinder or prism is the perpendicular distance between the parallel planes containing the two bases. If this height is $h$ units and the area of a base is $A$ square units, then the volume of the cylinder or prism is $V = Ah$ cubic units.

We use the adjective **right** to describe a cylinder or prism if the parallel line segments that constitute it are perpendicular to the base planes; otherwise, the cylinder or prism is called **oblique**. For example, a right cylinder whose bases are circular disks of radius $r$ units and whose height is $h$ units is called a **right circular cylinder**; its volume is $V = \pi r^2 h$ cubic units. Obliqueness has no effect on the volume $V = Ah$ of a prism or cylinder since $h$ is always measured in a direction perpendicular to the base.

**What is a cylinder?** The word "cylinder" has two different but related meanings in Mathematics. As used in this Section, it is a *solid object* lying between congruent bases in two parallel planes and inside a surface (the cylindrical wall) consisting of parallel line segments joining corresponding points on the boundaries of those bases. The second meaning for "cylinder" that we will encounter in Chapter 10 and later, extends the concept of the cylindrical wall of a solid cylinder. It is a *surface* consisting of a family of parallel straight lines in three dimensional space that intersect a plane perpendicular to those lines in a curve $\mathcal{C}$. In this case the cylinder is circular if $\mathcal{C}$ is a circle.

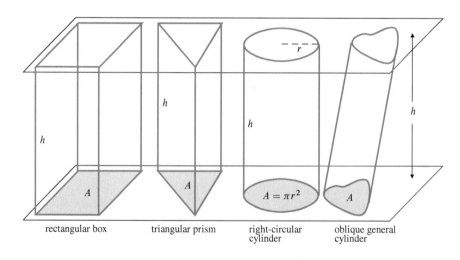

**Figure 10.1**   The volume of any prism or cylinder is the area $A$ of its base times its height $h$ (measured perpendicularly to the base): $V = Ah$

rectangular box          triangular prism          right-circular cylinder          oblique general cylinder

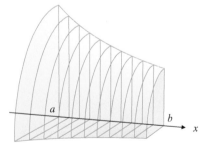

**Figure 10.2**   Slicing a solid perpendicularly to an axis

## Volumes by Slicing

Knowing the volume of a cylinder enables us to determine the volumes of some more general solids. We can divide solids into thin "slices" by parallel planes. (Think of a loaf of sliced bread.) Each slice is approximately a cylinder of very small "height"; the height is the thickness of the slice. See Figure 10.2, where the height is measured horizontally in the $x$ direction. If we know the cross-sectional area of each slice, we can determine its volume and sum these volumes to find the volume of the solid.

To be specific, suppose that the solid $S$ lies between planes perpendicular to the $x$-axis at positions $x = a$ and $x = b$ and that the cross-sectional area of $S$ in the plane perpendicular to the $x$-axis at $x$ is a known function $A(x)$, for $a \le x \le b$. We assume that $A(x)$ is continuous on $[a, b]$. If $a = x_0 < x_1 < x_2 < \cdots < x_{n-1} < x_n = b$, then $P = \{x_0, x_1, x_2, \ldots, x_{n-1}, x_n\}$ is a partition of $[a, b]$ into $n$ subintervals, and the planes perpendicular to the $x$-axis at $x_1, x_2, \ldots, x_{n-1}$ divide the solid into $n$ slices of which the $i$th has thickness $\Delta x_i = x_i - x_{i-1}$. The volume $\Delta V_i$ of that slice lies between the maximum and minimum values of $A(x)\,\Delta x_i$ for values of $x$ in $[x_{i-1}, x_i]$ (Figure 10.3), so, by the Intermediate-Value Theorem, for some $c_i$ in $[x_{i-1}, x_i]$,

$$\Delta V_i = A(c_i)\,\Delta x_i.$$

The volume of the solid is therefore given by the Riemann sum

$$V = \sum_{i=1}^{n} \Delta V_i = \sum_{i=1}^{n} A(c_i)\,\Delta x_i.$$

Letting $n$ approach infinity in such a way that $\max \Delta x_i$ approaches 0, we obtain the definite integral of $A(x)$ over $[a, b]$ as the limit of this Riemann sum. Therefore:

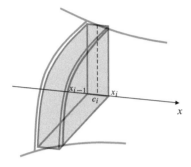

Figure 10.3   The volume of a slice

> The volume $V$ of a solid between $x = a$ and $x = b$ having cross-sectional area $A(x)$ at position $x$ is
>
> $$V = \int_a^b A(x)\,dx.$$

There is another way to obtain this formula and others of a similar nature. Consider a slice of the solid between the planes perpendicular to the $x$-axis at positions $x$ and $x + \Delta x$. Since $A(x)$ is continuous, it doesn't change much in a short interval, so if $\Delta x$ is small, then the slice has volume $\Delta V$ approximately equal to the volume of a cylinder of base area $A(x)$ and height $\Delta x$:

$$\Delta V \approx A(x)\,\Delta x.$$

The error in this approximation is small compared to the size of $\Delta V$. This suggests, correctly, that the **volume element**, that is, the volume of an infinitely thin slice of thickness $dx$ is $dV = A(x)\,dx$, and that the volume of the solid is the "sum" (i.e., the integral) of these volume elements between the two ends of the solid, $x = a$ and $x = b$ (see Figure 10.4):

$$V = \int_{x=a}^{x=b} dV, \qquad \text{where} \qquad dV = A(x)\,dx.$$

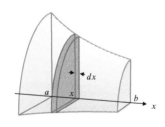

Figure 10.4   The volume element

We will use this *differential element* approach to model other applications that result in integrals rather than setting up explicit Riemann sums each time. Even though this argument does *not* constitute a proof of the formula, you are strongly encouraged to think of the formula this way; the volume is the integral of the volume elements.

## Solids of Revolution

Many common solids have circular cross-sections in planes perpendicular to some axis. Such solids are called **solids of revolution** because they can be generated by rotating a plane region about an axis in that plane so that it sweeps out the solid. For example, a solid ball is generated by rotating a half-disk about the diameter of that half-disk (Figure 10.5(a)). Similarly, a solid right-circular cone is generated by rotating a right-angled triangle about one of its legs (Figure 10.5(b)).

If the region $R$ bounded by $y = f(x)$, $y = 0$, $x = a$, and $x = b$ is rotated about the $x$-axis, then the cross-section of the solid generated in the plane perpendicular to the $x$-axis at $x$ is a circular disk of radius $|f(x)|$. The area of this cross-section is $A(x) = \pi \big(f(x)\big)^2$, so the volume of the solid of revolution is

$$V = \pi \int_a^b (f(x))^2 \, dx.$$

EXAMPLE 1    (**The volume of a ball**)  Find the volume of a solid ball having radius $a$.

*Solution*    The ball can be generated by rotating the half-disk, $0 \le y \le \sqrt{a^2 - x^2}$, $-a \le x \le a$ about the $x$-axis. See the cutaway view in Figure 10.5(a). Therefore, its volume is

$$V = \pi \int_{-a}^a (\sqrt{a^2 - x^2})^2 \, dx = 2\pi \int_0^a (a^2 - x^2) \, dx$$

$$= 2\pi \left( a^2 x - \frac{x^3}{3} \right) \Big|_0^a = 2\pi \left( a^3 - \frac{1}{3} a^3 \right) = \frac{4}{3} \pi a^3 \text{ cubic units.}$$

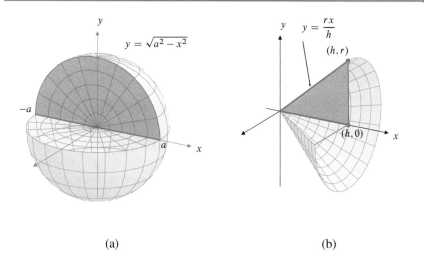

**Figure 10.5**

(a) The ball is generated by rotating the red half-disk $0 \le y \le \sqrt{a^2 - x^2}$ about the $x$-axis

(b) The cone of base radius $r$ and height $h$ is generated by rotating the red triangle $0 \le x \le h$, $0 \le y \le rx/h$ about the $x$-axis

(a)

(b)

EXAMPLE 2    (**The volume of a right-circular cone**)  Find the volume of the right-circular cone of base radius $r$ and height $h$ that is generated by rotating the triangle with vertices $(0, 0)$, $(h, 0)$, and $(h, r)$ about the $x$-axis.

*Solution*    The line from $(0, 0)$ to $(h, r)$ has equation $y = rx/h$. Thus, the volume of the cone (see the cutaway view in Figure 10.5(b)) is

$$V = \pi \int_0^h \left( \frac{rx}{h} \right)^2 \, dx = \pi \left( \frac{r}{h} \right)^2 \frac{x^3}{3} \Big|_0^h = \frac{1}{3} \pi r^2 h \text{ cubic units.}$$

Improper integrals can represent volumes of unbounded solids. If the improper integral converges, the unbounded solid has a finite volume.

EXAMPLE 3    Find the volume of the infinitely long horn that is generated by rotating the region bounded by $y = 1/x$ and $y = 0$ and lying to the right of $x = 1$ about the $x$-axis. The horn is illustrated in Figure 10.6.

*Solution*    The volume of the horn is

$$V = \pi \int_1^\infty \left( \frac{1}{x} \right)^2 \, dx = \pi \lim_{R \to \infty} \int_1^R \frac{1}{x^2} \, dx$$

$$= -\pi \lim_{R \to \infty} \frac{1}{x} \Big|_1^R = -\pi \lim_{R \to \infty} \left( \frac{1}{R} - 1 \right) = \pi \text{ cubic units.}$$

It is interesting to note that this finite volume arises from rotating a region that itself has infinite area: $\int_1^\infty dx/x = \infty$. We have a paradox: it takes an infinite amount of paint to paint the region but only a finite amount to fill the horn obtained by rotating the region. (How can you resolve this paradox?)

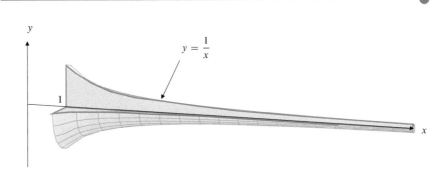

Figure 10.6    Cutaway view of an infinitely long horn

The following example shows how to deal with a problem where the axis of rotation is not the $x$-axis. Just rotate a suitable area element about the axis to form a volume element.

**EXAMPLE 4**    A ring-shaped solid is generated by rotating the finite plane region $R$ bounded by the curve $y = x^2$ and the line $y = 1$ about the line $y = 2$. Find its volume.

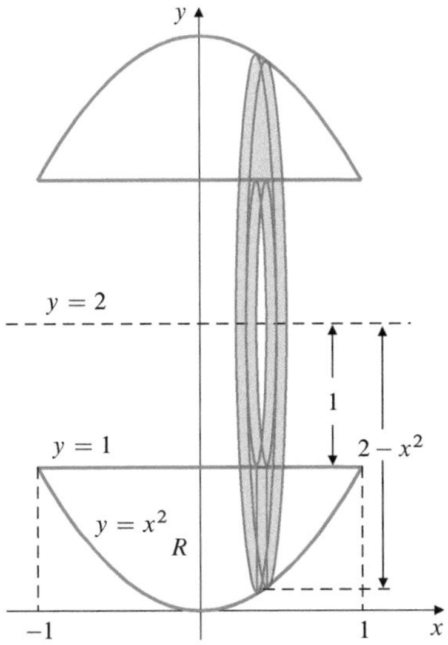

*Solution*    First, we solve the pair of equations $y = x^2$ and $y = 1$ to obtain the intersections at $x = -1$ and $x = 1$. The solid lies between these two values of $x$. The area element of $R$ at position $x$ is a vertical strip of width $dx$ extending upward from $y = x^2$ to $y = 1$. When $R$ is rotated about the line $y = 2$, this area element sweeps out a thin, washer-shaped volume element of thickness $dx$ and radius $2 - x^2$, having a hole of radius 1 through the middle. (See Figure 10.7.) The cross-sectional area of this element is the area of a circle of radius $2 - x^2$ minus the area of the hole, a circle of radius 1. Thus,

$$dV = \left(\pi(2 - x^2)^2 - \pi(1)^2\right) dx = \pi(3 - 4x^2 + x^4) \, dx.$$

Since the solid extends from $x = -1$ to $x = 1$, its volume is

$$V = \pi \int_{-1}^{1} (3 - 4x^2 + x^4) \, dx = 2\pi \int_{0}^{1} (3 - 4x^2 + x^4) \, dx$$

$$= 2\pi \left( 3x - \frac{4x^3}{3} + \frac{x^5}{5} \right)\Big|_{0}^{1} = 2\pi \left( 3 - \frac{4}{3} + \frac{1}{5} \right) = \frac{56\pi}{15} \text{ cubic units.}$$

Figure 10.7    The volume element for Example 4

Sometimes we want to rotate a region bounded by curves with equations of the form $x = g(y)$ about the $y$-axis. In this case, the roles of $x$ and $y$ are reversed, and we use horizontal slices instead of vertical ones.

**EXAMPLE 5**    Find the volume of the solid generated by rotating the region to the right of the $y$-axis and to the left of the curve $x = 2y - y^2$ about the $y$-axis.

*Solution*    For intersections of $x = 2y - y^2$ and $x = 0$, we have

$$2y - y^2 = 0 \quad \Longrightarrow \quad y = 0 \quad \text{or} \quad y = 2.$$

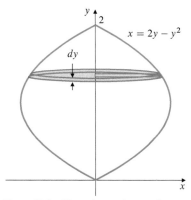

**Figure 10.8** The volume element for Example 5

The solid lies between the horizontal planes at $y = 0$ and $y = 2$. A horizontal area element at height $y$ and having thickness $dy$ rotates about the $y$-axis to generate a thin disk-shaped volume element of radius $2y - y^2$ and thickness $dy$. (See Figure 10.8.) Its volume is

$$dV = \pi(2y - y^2)^2 \, dy = \pi(4y^2 - 4y^3 + y^4) \, dy.$$

Thus, the volume of the solid is

$$
\begin{aligned}
V &= \pi \int_0^2 (4y^2 - 4y^3 + y^4) \, dy \\
&= \pi \left( \frac{4y^3}{3} - y^4 + \frac{y^5}{5} \right) \Big|_0^2 \\
&= \pi \left( \frac{32}{3} - 16 + \frac{32}{5} \right) = \frac{16\pi}{15} \text{ cubic units.}
\end{aligned}
$$

## Cylindrical Shells

Suppose that the region $R$ bounded by $y = f(x) \geq 0$, $y = 0$, $x = a \geq 0$, and $x = b > a$ is rotated about the $y$-axis to generate a solid of revolution. In order to find the volume of the solid using (plane) slices, we would need to know the cross-sectional area $A(y)$ in each plane of height $y$, and this would entail solving the equation $y = f(x)$ for one or more solutions of the form $x = g(y)$. In practice this can be inconvenient or impossible.

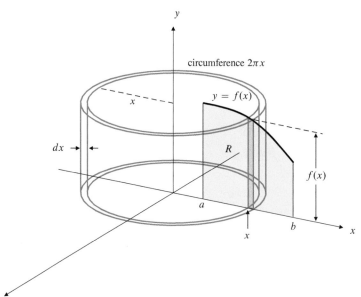

**Figure 10.9** When rotated around the $y$-axis, the area element of width $dx$ under $y = f(x)$ at $x$ generates a cylindrical shell of height $f(x)$, circumference $2\pi x$, and hence volume $dV = 2\pi x \, f(x) \, dx$

The standard area element of $R$ at position $x$ is a vertical strip of width $dx$, height $f(x)$, and area $dA = f(x) \, dx$. When $R$ is rotated about the $y$-axis, this strip sweeps out a volume element in the shape of a circular **cylindrical shell** having radius $x$, height $f(x)$, and thickness $dx$. (See Figure 10.9.) Regard this shell as a rolled-up rectangular slab with dimensions $2\pi x$, $f(x)$, and $dx$; evidently, it has volume

$$dV = 2\pi x \, f(x) \, dx.$$

The volume of the solid of revolution is the sum *(integral)* of the volumes of such shells with radii ranging from $a$ to $b$:

The volume of the solid obtained by rotating the plane region $0 \le y \le f(x), 0 \le a < x < b$ about the $y$-axis is

$$V = 2\pi \int_a^b x \, f(x) \, dx.$$

---

**EXAMPLE 6** **(The volume of a torus)** A disk of radius $a$ has centre at the point $(b, 0)$, where $b > a > 0$. The disk is rotated about the $y$-axis to generate a **torus** (a doughnut-shaped solid), illustrated in Figure 10.10. Find its volume.

*Solution* The circle with centre at $(b, 0)$ and having radius $a$ has equation $(x - b)^2 + y^2 = a^2$, so its upper semicircle is the graph of the function

$$f(x) = \sqrt{a^2 - (x - b)^2}.$$

We will double the volume of the upper half of the torus, which is generated by rotating the half-disk $0 \le y \le \sqrt{a^2 - (x-b)^2}$, $b - a \le x \le b + a$ about the $y$-axis. The volume of the complete torus is

$$
\begin{aligned}
V &= 2 \times 2\pi \int_{b-a}^{b+a} x \sqrt{a^2 - (x-b)^2} \, dx \qquad \text{Let } u = x - b, \\
&\hspace{6.5cm} du = dx \\
&= 4\pi \int_{-a}^{a} (u + b)\sqrt{a^2 - u^2} \, du \\
&= 4\pi \int_{-a}^{a} u \sqrt{a^2 - u^2} \, du + 4\pi b \int_{-a}^{a} \sqrt{a^2 - u^2} \, du \\
&= 0 + 4\pi b \frac{\pi a^2}{2} = 2\pi^2 a^2 b \text{ cubic units.}
\end{aligned}
$$

(The first of the final two integrals is 0 because the integrand is odd and the interval is symmetric about 0; the second is the area of a semicircle of radius $a$.) Note that the volume of the torus is $(\pi a^2)(2\pi b)$, that is, the area of the disk being rotated times the distance travelled by the centre of that disk as it rotates about the $y$-axis. This result will be generalized by Pappus's Theorem in Section 10.5.

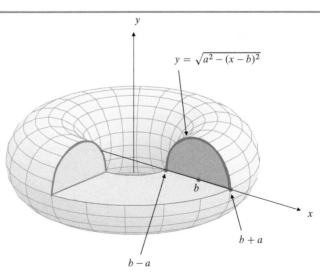

**Figure 10.10** Cutaway view of a torus

---

**EXAMPLE 7** Find the volume of a bowl obtained by revolving the parabolic arc $y = x^2, 0 \le x \le 1$ about the $y$-axis.

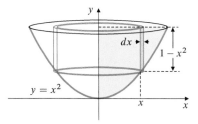

Figure 10.11    A parabolic bowl

*Solution*    The interior of the bowl corresponds to revolving the region given by $x^2 \leq y \leq 1$, $0 \leq x \leq 1$ about the $y$-axis. The area element at position $x$ has height $1 - x^2$ and generates a cylindrical shell of volume $dV = 2\pi x(1 - x^2)\,dx$. (See Figure 10.11.) Thus, the volume of the bowl is

$$V = 2\pi \int_0^1 x(1 - x^2)\,dx$$

$$= 2\pi \left( \frac{x^2}{2} - \frac{x^4}{4} \right) \Bigg|_0^1 = \frac{\pi}{2} \text{ cubic units.}$$

We have described two methods for determining the volume of a solid of revolution, slicing and cylindrical shells. The choice of method for a particular solid is usually dictated by the form of the equations defining the region being rotated and by the axis of rotation. The volume element $dV$ can always be determined by rotating a suitable area element $dA$ about the axis of rotation. If the region is bounded by vertical lines and one or more graphs of the form $y = f(x)$, the appropriate area element is a vertical strip of width $dx$. If the rotation is about the $x$-axis or any other horizontal line, this strip generates a disk- or washer-shaped slice of thickness $dx$. If the rotation is about the $y$-axis or any other vertical line, the strip generates a cylindrical shell of thickness $dx$. On the other hand, if the region being rotated is bounded by horizontal lines and one or more graphs of the form $x = g(y)$, it is easier to use a horizontal strip of width $dy$ as the area element, and this generates a slice if the rotation is about a vertical line and a cylindrical shell if the rotation is about a horizontal line. For very simple regions either method can be made to work easily. See the following table.

Table 1.    Volumes of solids of revolution

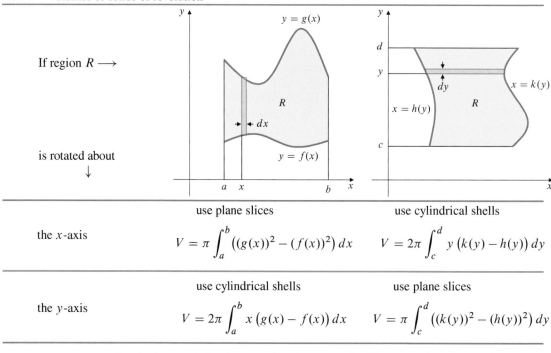

| If region $R \longrightarrow$ is rotated about $\downarrow$ | | |
|---|---|---|
| | use plane slices | use cylindrical shells |
| the $x$-axis | $V = \pi \int_a^b \left( (g(x))^2 - (f(x))^2 \right) dx$ | $V = 2\pi \int_c^d y \left( k(y) - h(y) \right) dy$ |
| | use cylindrical shells | use plane slices |
| the $y$-axis | $V = 2\pi \int_a^b x \left( g(x) - f(x) \right) dx$ | $V = \pi \int_c^d \left( (k(y))^2 - (h(y))^2 \right) dy$ |

Our final example involves rotation about a vertical line other than the $y$-axis.

**EXAMPLE 8**    The triangular region bounded by $y = x$, $y = 0$, and $x = a > 0$ is rotated about the line $x = b > a$. (See Figure 10.12.) Find the volume of the solid so generated.

*Solution*    Here the vertical area element at $x$ generates a cylindrical shell of radius $b - x$, height $x$, and thickness $dx$. Its volume is $dV = 2\pi(b - x)\,x\,dx$, and the volume of the solid is

$$V = 2\pi \int_0^a (b-x)\, x\, dx = 2\pi \left( \frac{bx^2}{2} - \frac{x^3}{3} \right)\Bigg|_0^a = \pi \left( a^2 b - \frac{2a^3}{3} \right) \text{ cubic units.}$$

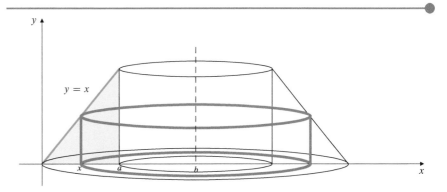

**Figure 10.12**   The volume element for Example 8

## EXERCISES 10.1

Find the volume of each solid $S$ in Exercises 1–4 in two ways, using the method of slicing and the method of cylindrical shells.

1. $S$ is generated by rotating about the $x$-axis the region bounded by $y = x^2$, $y = 0$, and $x = 1$.

2. $S$ is generated by rotating the region of Exercise 1 about the $y$-axis.

3. $S$ is generated by rotating about the $x$-axis the region bounded by $y = x^2$ and $y = \sqrt{x}$ between $x = 0$ and $x = 1$.

4. $S$ is generated by rotating the region of Exercise 3 about the $y$-axis.

Find the volumes of the solids obtained if the plane regions $R$ described in Exercises 5–10 are rotated about (a) the $x$-axis and (b) the $y$-axis.

5. $R$ is bounded by $y = x(2 - x)$ and $y = 0$ between $x = 0$ and $x = 2$.

6. $R$ is the finite region bounded by $y = x$ and $y = x^2$.

7. $R$ is the finite region bounded by $y = x$ and $x = 4y - y^2$.

8. $R$ is bounded by $y = 1 + \sin x$ and $y = 1$ from $x = 0$ to $x = \pi$.

9. $R$ is bounded by $y = 1/(1 + x^2)$, $y = 2$, $x = 0$, and $x = 1$.

10. $R$ is the finite region bounded by $y = 1/x$ and $3x + 3y = 10$.

11. The triangular region with vertices $(0, -1)$, $(1, 0)$, and $(0, 1)$ is rotated about the line $x = 2$. Find the volume of the solid so generated.

12. Find the volume of the solid generated by rotating the region $0 \le y \le 1 - x^2$ about the line $y = 1$.

13. What percentage of the volume of a ball of radius 2 is removed if a hole of radius 1 is drilled through the centre of the ball?

14. A cylindrical hole is bored through the centre of a ball of radius $R$. If the length of the hole is $L$, show that the volume of the remaining part of the ball depends only on $L$ and not on $R$.

15. A cylindrical hole of radius $a$ is bored through a solid

right-circular cone of height $h$ and base radius $b > a$. If the axis of the hole lies along that of the cone, find the volume of the remaining part of the cone.

16. Find the volume of the solid obtained by rotating a circular disk about one of its tangent lines.

17. A plane slices a ball of radius $a$ into two pieces. If the plane passes $b$ units away from the centre of the ball (where $b < a$), find the volume of the smaller piece.

18. Water partially fills a hemispherical bowl of radius 30 cm so that the maximum depth of the water is 20 cm. What volume of water is in the bowl?

19. Find the volume of the ellipsoid of revolution obtained by rotating the ellipse $(x^2/a^2) + (y^2/b^2) = 1$ about the $x$-axis.

20. Recalculate the volume of the torus of Example 6 by slicing perpendicular to the $y$-axis rather than using cylindrical shells.

21. The region $R$ bounded by $y = e^{-x}$ and $y = 0$ and lying to the right of $x = 0$ is rotated (a) about the $x$-axis and (b) about the $y$-axis. Find the volume of the solid of revolution generated in each case.

22. The region $R$ bounded by $y = x^{-k}$ and $y = 0$ and lying to the right of $x = 1$ is rotated about the $x$-axis. Find all real values of $k$ for which the solid so generated has finite volume.

23. Repeat Exercise 22 with rotation about the $y$-axis.

24. Early editions of this text incorrectly defined a prism or cylinder as being a solid for which cross-sections parallel to the base were congruent to the base. Does this define a larger or smaller set of solids than the definition given in this section? What does the older definition say about the volume of a cylinder or prism having base area $A$ and height $h$?

25. Continuing Exercise 24, consider the solid $S$ whose cross-section in the plane perpendicular to the $x$-axis at $x$ is an isosceles right-angled triangle having equal sides of length $a$ cm with one end of the hypotenuse on the $x$-axis and with hypotenuse making angle $x$ with a fixed direction. Is $S$ a

prism according to the definition given in early editions? Is it a prism according to the definition in this edition? If the height of $S$ is $b$ cm, what is the volume of $S$?

**26.** Find the volume of the solid generated by rotating the finite region in the first quadrant bounded by the coordinate axes and the curve $x^{2/3} + y^{2/3} = 4$ about either of the coordinate axes. (Both volumes are the same. Why?)

**27.** Given that the surface area of a sphere of radius $r$ is $kr^2$, where $k$ is a constant independent of $r$, express the volume of a ball of radius $R$ as an integral of volume elements that are the volumes of spherical shells of thickness $dr$ and varying radii $r$. Hence find $k$.

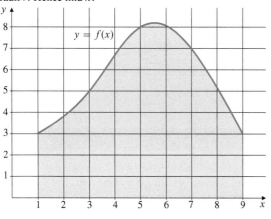

Figure 10.13

**28.** The region shaded in Figure 10.13 is rotated about the $x$-axis. Use Simpson's Rule to find the volume of the resulting solid.

**29.** The region shaded in Figure 10.13 is rotated about the $y$-axis.

Use Simpson's Rule to find the volume of the resulting solid.

**30.** The region shaded in Figure 10.13 is rotated about the line $x = -1$. Use Simpson's Rule to find the volume of the resulting solid.

The following problems are *very difficult*. You will need some ingenuity and a lot of hard work to solve them by the techniques available to you now.

**31.** A martini glass in the shape of a right-circular cone of height $h$ and semi-vertical angle $\alpha$ (see Figure 10.14) is filled with liquid. Slowly a ball is lowered into the glass, displacing liquid and causing it to overflow. Find the radius $R$ of the ball that causes the greatest volume of liquid to overflow out of the glass.

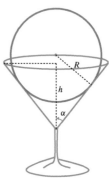

Figure 10.14

**32.** The finite plane region bounded by the curve $xy = 1$ and the straight line $2x + 2y = 5$ is rotated about that line to generate a solid of revolution. Find the volume of that solid.

---

## 10.2 More Volumes by Slicing

The method of slicing introduced in Section 10.1 can be used to determine volumes of solids that are not solids of revolution. All we need to know is the area of cross-section of the solid in every plane perpendicular to some fixed axis. If that axis is the $x$-axis, if the solid lies between the planes at $x = a$ and $x = b > a$, and if the cross-sectional area in the plane at $x$ is the continuous (or even piecewise continuous) function $A(x)$, then the volume of the solid is

$$V = \int_a^b A(x)\,dx.$$

In this section we consider some examples that are not solids of revolution.

**Pyramids** and **cones** are solids consisting of all points on line segments that join a fixed point, the **vertex**, to all the points in a region lying in a plane not containing the vertex. The region is called the **base** of the pyramid or cone. Some pyramids and cones are shown in Figure 10.15. If the base is bounded by straight lines, the solid is called a **pyramid**; if the base has a curved boundary the solid is called a **cone**. All pyramids and cones have volume

$$V = \frac{1}{3}Ah,$$

where $A$ is the area of the base region, and $h$ is the height from the vertex to the plane of the base, measured in the direction perpendicular to that plane. For the time being, we verify it for the case of a rectangular base.

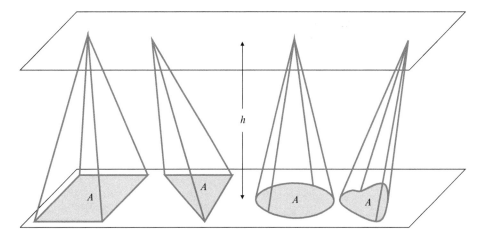

Figure 10.15   Some pyramids and cones. Each has volume $V = \frac{1}{3}Ah$, where $A$ is the area of the base, and $h$ is the height measured perpendicular to the base

---

**EXAMPLE 1**   Verify the formula for the volume of a pyramid with rectangular base of area $A$ and height $h$.

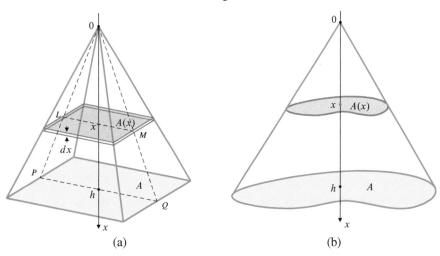

Figure 10.16

(a) A rectangular pyramid

(b) A general cone

(a)                              (b)

**Solution**   Cross-sections of the pyramid in planes parallel to the base are similar rectangles. If the origin is at the vertex of the pyramid and the $x$-axis is perpendicular to the base, then the cross-section at position $x$ is a rectangle whose dimensions are $x/h$ times the corresponding dimensions of the base. For example, in Figure 10.16(a), the length $LM$ is $x/h$ times the length $PQ$, as can be seen from the similar triangles $OLM$ and $OPQ$. Thus, the area of the rectangular cross-section at $x$ is

$$A(x) = \left(\frac{x}{h}\right)^2 A.$$

The volume of the pyramid is therefore

$$V = \int_0^h \left(\frac{x}{h}\right)^2 A\,dx = \frac{A}{h^2}\frac{x^3}{3}\bigg|_0^h = \frac{1}{3}Ah \text{ cubic units.}$$

---

A similar argument, resulting in the same formula for the volume, holds for a cone, that is, a pyramid with a more general (curved) shape to its base, such as that in Figure 10.16(b). Although it is not as obvious as in the case of the pyramid, the cross-section at $x$ still has area $(x/h)^2$ times that of the base.

**EXAMPLE 2**    A tent has a circular base of radius $a$ metres and is supported by a horizontal ridge bar held at height $b$ metres above a diameter of the base by vertical supports at each end of the diameter. The material of the tent is stretched tight so that each cross-section perpendicular to the ridge bar is an isosceles triangle. (See Figure 10.17.) Find the volume of the tent.

*Solution*    Let the $x$-axis be the diameter of the base under the ridge bar. The cross-section at position $x$ has base length $2\sqrt{a^2 - x^2}$, so its area is

$$A(x) = \frac{1}{2}\left(2\sqrt{a^2 - x^2}\right)b = b\sqrt{a^2 - x^2}.$$

Thus, the volume of the solid is

$$V = \int_{-a}^{a} b\sqrt{a^2 - x^2}\, dx = b \int_{-a}^{a} \sqrt{a^2 - x^2}\, dx = b\frac{\pi a^2}{2} = \frac{\pi}{2}a^2 b \text{ m}^3.$$

Note that we evaluated the last integral by inspection. It is the area of a half-disk of radius $a$.

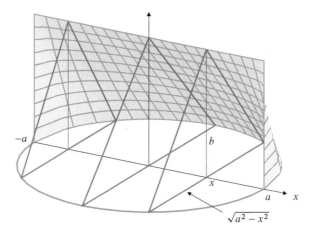

Figure 10.17    The tent of Example 2 with the front covering removed to show the shape more clearly

**EXAMPLE 3**    Two circular cylinders, each having radius $a$, intersect so that their axes meet at right angles. Find the volume of the region lying inside both cylinders.

*Solution*    We represent the cylinders in a three-dimensional Cartesian coordinate system where the plane containing the $x$- and $y$-axes is horizontal and the $z$-axis is vertical. One-eighth of the solid is represented in Figure 10.18, that part corresponding to all three coordinates being positive. The two cylinders have axes along the $x$- and $y$-axes, respectively. The cylinder with axis along the $x$-axis intersects the plane of the $y$- and $z$-axes in a circle of radius $a$.

Similarly, the other cylinder meets the plane of the $x$- and $z$-axes in a circle of radius $a$. It follows that if the region lying inside both cylinders (and having $x \geq 0$, $y \geq 0$, and $z \geq 0$) is sliced horizontally, then the slice at height $z$ above the $xy$-plane is a square of side $\sqrt{a^2 - z^2}$ and has area $A(z) = a^2 - z^2$. The volume $V$ of the whole region, being eight times that of the part shown, is

$$V = 8 \int_{0}^{a} (a^2 - z^2)\, dz = 8\left(a^2 z - \frac{z^3}{3}\right)\Bigg|_{0}^{a} = \frac{16}{3}a^3 \text{ cubic units.}$$

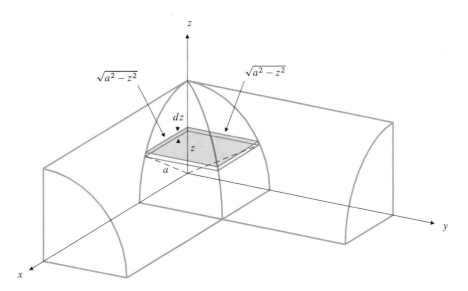

**Figure 10.18**    One-eighth of the solid lying inside two perpendicular cylindrical pipes. The horizontal slice shown is square

## EXERCISES 10.2

**1.** A solid is 2 m high. The cross-section of the solid at height $x$ above its base has area $3x$ square metres. Find the volume of the solid.

**2.** The cross-section at height $z$ of a solid of height $h$ is a rectangle with dimensions $z$ and $h - z$. Find the volume of the solid.

**3.** Find the volume of a solid of height 1 whose cross-section at height $z$ is an ellipse with semi-axes $z$ and $\sqrt{1 - z^2}$.

**4.** A solid extends from $x = 1$ to $x = 3$. The cross-section of the solid in the plane perpendicular to the $x$-axis at $x$ is a square of side $x$. Find the volume of the solid.

**5.** A solid is 6 ft high. Its horizontal cross-section at height $z$ ft above its base is a rectangle with length $2 + z$ ft and width $8 - z$ ft. Find the volume of the solid.

**6.** A solid extends along the $x$-axis from $x = 1$ to $x = 4$. Its cross-section at position $x$ is an equilateral triangle with edge length $\sqrt{x}$. Find the volume of the solid.

**7.** Find the volume of a solid that is $h$ cm high if its horizontal cross-section at any height $y$ above its base is a circular sector having radius $a$ cm and angle $2\pi\left(1 - (y/h)\right)$ radians.

**8.** The opposite ends of a solid are at $x = 0$ and $x = 2$. The area of cross-section of the solid in a plane perpendicular to the $x$-axis at $x$ is $kx^3$ square units. The volume of the solid is 4 cubic units. Find $k$.

**9.** Find the cross-sectional area of a solid in any horizontal plane at height $z$ above its base if the volume of that part of the solid lying below any such plane is $z^3$ cubic units.

**10.** All the cross-sections of a solid in horizontal planes are squares. The volume of the part of the solid lying below any plane of height $z$ is $4z$ cubic units, where $0 < z < h$, the height of the solid. Find the edge length of the square cross-section at height $z$ for $0 < z < h$.

**11.** A solid has a circular base of radius $r$. All sections of the solid perpendicular to a particular diameter of the base are squares. Find the volume of the solid.

**12.** Repeat Exercise 11 but with sections that are equilateral triangles instead of squares.

**13.** The base of a solid is an isosceles right-angled triangle with equal legs measuring 12 cm. Each cross-section perpendicular to one of these legs is half of a circular disk. Find the volume of the solid.

**14.** (**Cavalieri's Principle**) Two solids have equal cross-sectional areas at equal heights above their bases. If both solids have the same height, show that they both have the same volume.

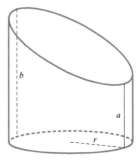

**Figure 10.19**

**15.** The top of a circular cylinder of radius $r$ is a plane inclined at an angle to the horizontal. (See Figure 10.19.) If the lowest and highest points on the top are at heights $a$ and $b$, respectively, above the base, find the volume of the cylinder. (Note that there is an easy geometric way to get the answer, but you should also try to do it by slicing. You can use either rectangular or trapezoidal slices.)

16. **(Volume of an ellipsoid)** Find the volume enclosed by the ellipsoid

$$\frac{x^2}{a^2} + \frac{y^2}{b^2} + \frac{z^2}{c^2} = 1.$$

*Hint:* This is not a solid of revolution. As in Example 3, the $z$-axis is perpendicular to the plane of the $x$- and $y$-axes. Each horizontal plane $z = k$ ($-c \le k \le c$) intersects the ellipsoid in an ellipse $(x/a)^2 + (y/b)^2 = 1 - (k/c)^2$. Thus, $dV = dz \times$ the area of this ellipse. The area of the ellipse $(x/a)^2 + (y/b)^2 = 1$ is $\pi ab$.

Figure 10.20

17. **(Notching a log)** A $45°$ notch is cut to the centre of a cylindrical log having radius 20 cm, as shown in Figure 10.20.

One plane face of the notch is perpendicular to the axis of the log. What volume of wood was removed from the log by cutting the notch?

18. **(A smaller notch)** Repeat Exercise 17, but assume that the notch penetrates only one quarter way (10 cm) into the log.

19. What volume of wood is removed from a 3-in-thick board if a circular hole of radius 2 in is drilled through it with the axis of the hole tilted at an angle of $45°$ to board?

20. **(More intersecting cylinders)** The axes of two circular cylinders intersect at right angles. If the radii of the cylinders are $a$ and $b$ ($a > b > 0$), show that the region lying inside both cylinders has volume

$$V = 8 \int_0^b \sqrt{b^2 - z^2} \sqrt{a^2 - z^2}\, dz.$$

*Hint:* Review Example 3. Try to make a similar diagram, showing only one-eighth of the region. The integral is not easily evaluated.

21. A circular hole of radius 2 cm is drilled through the middle of a circular log of radius 4 cm, with the axis of the hole perpendicular to the axis of the log. Find the volume of wood removed from the log. *Hint:* This is very similar to Exercise 20. You will need to use numerical methods or a calculator with a numerical integration function to get the answer.

## 10.3  Arc Length and Surface Area

In this section we consider how integrals can be used to find the lengths of curves and the areas of the surfaces of solids of revolution.

### Arc Length

If $A$ and $B$ are two points in the plane, let $|AB|$ denote the distance between $A$ and $B$, that is, the length of the straight line segment $AB$.

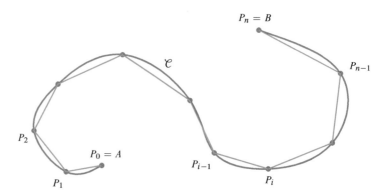

Figure 10.21   A polygonal approximation to a curve $\mathcal{C}$

Given a curve $\mathcal{C}$ joining the two points $A$ and $B$, we would like to define what is meant by the *length* of the curve $\mathcal{C}$ from $A$ to $B$. Suppose we choose points $A = P_0$, $P_1$, $P_2$, $\ldots$, $P_{n-1}$, and $P_n = B$ in order along the curve, as shown in Figure 10.21. The polygonal line $P_0 P_1 P_2 \ldots P_{n-1} P_n$ constructed by joining adjacent pairs of these points with straight line segments forms a *polygonal approximation* to $\mathcal{C}$, having length

$$L_n = |P_0 P_1| + |P_1 P_2| + \cdots + |P_{n-1} P_n| = \sum_{i=1}^{n} |P_{i-1} P_i|.$$

Intuition tells us that the shortest curve joining two points is a straight line segment, so the length $L_n$ of any such polygonal approximation to $\mathcal{C}$ cannot exceed the length of $\mathcal{C}$. If we increase $n$ by adding more vertices to the polygonal line between existing vertices, $L_n$ cannot get smaller and may increase. If there exists a finite number $K$ such that $L_n \leq K$ for every polygonal approximation to $\mathcal{C}$, then there will be a smallest such number $K$ (by the completeness of the real numbers), and we call this smallest $K$ the arc length of $\mathcal{C}$.

**DEFINITION**

**1**

> The **arc length** of the curve $\mathcal{C}$ from $A$ to $B$ is the smallest real number $s$ such that the length $L_n$ of every polygonal approximation to $\mathcal{C}$ satisfies $L_n \leq s$.

A curve with a finite arc length is said to be **rectifiable**. Its arc length $s$ is the limit of the lengths $L_n$ of polygonal approximations as $n \to \infty$ in such a way that the maximum segment length $|P_{i-1} P_i| \to 0$.

It is possible to construct continuous curves that are bounded (they do not go off to infinity anywhere) but are not rectifiable; they have infinite length. To avoid such pathological examples, we will assume that our curves are **smooth**; they will be defined by functions having continuous derivatives.

## The Arc Length of the Graph of a Function

Let $f$ be a function defined on a closed, finite interval $[a, b]$ and having a continuous derivative $f'$ there. If $\mathcal{C}$ is the graph of $f$, that is, the graph of the equation $y = f(x)$, then any partition of $[a, b]$ provides a polygonal approximation to $\mathcal{C}$. For the partition

$$\{a = x_0 < x_1 < x_2 < \cdots < x_n = b\},$$

let $P_i$ be the point $(x_i, f(x_i))$, $(0 \leq i \leq n)$. The length of the polygonal line $P_0 P_1 P_2 \ldots P_{n-1} P_n$ is

$$L_n = \sum_{i=1}^{n} |P_{i-1} P_i| = \sum_{i=1}^{n} \sqrt{(x_i - x_{i-1})^2 + \left(f(x_i) - f(x_{i-1})\right)^2}$$

$$= \sum_{i=1}^{n} \sqrt{1 + \left(\frac{f(x_i) - f(x_{i-1})}{x_i - x_{i-1}}\right)^2} \, \Delta x_i,$$

where $\Delta x_i = x_i - x_{i-1}$. By the Mean-Value Theorem there exists a number $c_i$ in the interval $[x_{i-1}, x_i]$ such that

$$\frac{f(x_i) - f(x_{i-1})}{x_i - x_{i-1}} = f'(c_i),$$

so we have $L_n = \sum_{i=1}^{n} \sqrt{1 + \left(f'(c_i)\right)^2} \, \Delta x_i.$

Thus, $L_n$ is a Riemann sum for $\int_a^b \sqrt{1 + (f'(x))^2} \, dx$. Being the limit of such Riemann sums as $n \to \infty$ in such a way that $\max(\Delta x_i) \to 0$, that integral is the length of the curve $\mathcal{C}$.

> The arc length $s$ of the curve $y = f(x)$ from $x = a$ to $x = b$ is given by
>
> $$s = \int_a^b \sqrt{1 + \left(f'(x)\right)^2} \, dx = \int_a^b \sqrt{1 + \left(\frac{dy}{dx}\right)^2} \, dx.$$

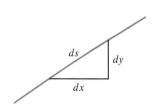

Figure 10.22   A differential triangle

You can regard the integral formula above as giving the arc length $s$ of $\mathcal{C}$ as a "sum" of **arc length elements**:

$$s = \int_{x=a}^{x=b} ds, \qquad \text{where} \qquad ds = \sqrt{1 + (f'(x))^2}\, dx.$$

Figure 10.22 provides a convenient way to remember this; it also suggests how we can arrive at similar formulas for arc length elements of other kinds of curves. The *differential triangle* in the figure suggests that

$$(ds)^2 = (dx)^2 + (dy)^2.$$

Dividing this equation by $(dx)^2$ and taking the square root, we get

$$\left(\frac{ds}{dx}\right)^2 = 1 + \left(\frac{dy}{dx}\right)^2$$

$$\frac{ds}{dx} = \sqrt{1 + \left(\frac{dy}{dx}\right)^2}$$

$$ds = \sqrt{1 + \left(\frac{dy}{dx}\right)^2}\, dx = \sqrt{1 + (f'(x))^2}\, dx.$$

A similar argument shows that for a curve specified by an equation of the form $x = g(y)$, $(c \le y \le d)$, the arc length element is

$$ds = \sqrt{1 + \left(\frac{dx}{dy}\right)^2}\, dy = \sqrt{1 + (g'(y))^2}\, dy.$$

**EXAMPLE 1**   Find the length of the curve $y = x^{2/3}$ from $x = 1$ to $x = 8$.

**Solution**   Since $dy/dx = \frac{2}{3}x^{-1/3}$ is continuous between $x = 1$ and $x = 8$ and $x^{1/3} > 0$ there, the length of the curve is given by

$$s = \int_1^8 \sqrt{1 + \frac{4}{9}x^{-2/3}}\, dx = \int_1^8 \sqrt{\frac{9x^{2/3} + 4}{9x^{2/3}}}\, dx$$

$$= \int_1^8 \frac{\sqrt{9x^{2/3} + 4}}{3x^{1/3}}\, dx \qquad \text{Let } u = 9x^{2/3} + 4,$$
$$du = 6x^{-1/3}\, dx$$

$$= \frac{1}{18}\int_{13}^{40} u^{1/2}\, du = \frac{1}{27}u^{3/2}\Big|_{13}^{40} = \frac{40\sqrt{40} - 13\sqrt{13}}{27}\ \text{units.}$$

**EXAMPLE 2**   Find the length of the curve $y = x^4 + \dfrac{1}{32x^2}$ from $x = 1$ to $x = 2$.

**Solution**   Here $\dfrac{dy}{dx} = 4x^3 - \dfrac{1}{16x^3}$ and

$$1 + \left(\frac{dy}{dx}\right)^2 = 1 + \left(4x^3 - \frac{1}{16x^3}\right)^2$$

$$= 1 + (4x^3)^2 - \frac{1}{2} + \left(\frac{1}{16x^3}\right)^2$$

$$= (4x^3)^2 + \frac{1}{2} + \left(\frac{1}{16x^3}\right)^2 = \left(4x^3 + \frac{1}{16x^3}\right)^2.$$

The expression in the last set of parentheses is positive for $1 \le x \le 2$, so the length of the curve is

$$s = \int_1^2 \left( 4x^3 + \frac{1}{16x^3} \right) dx = \left. \left( x^4 - \frac{1}{32x^2} \right) \right|_1^2$$

$$= 16 - \frac{1}{128} - \left( 1 - \frac{1}{32} \right) = 15 + \frac{3}{128} \text{ units.}$$

The examples above are deceptively simple; the curves were chosen so that the arc length integrals could be easily evaluated. For instance, the number 32 in the curve in Example 2 was chosen so the expression $1 + (dy/dx)^2$ would turn out to be a perfect square and its square root would cause no problems. Because of the square root in the formula, arc length problems for most curves lead to integrals that are difficult or impossible to evaluate without using numerical techniques.

**EXAMPLE 3**  **(Manufacturing corrugated panels)**  Flat rectangular sheets of metal 2 m wide are to be formed into corrugated roofing panels 2 m wide by bending them into the sinusoidal shape shown in Figure 10.23. The period of the cross-sectional sine curve is 20 cm. Its amplitude is 5 cm, so the panel is 10 cm thick. How long should the flat sheets be cut if the resulting panels must be 5 m long?

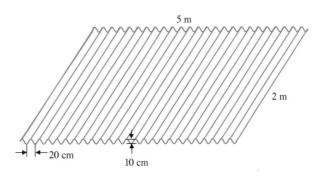

**Figure 10.23**  A corrugated roofing panel

*Solution*  One period of the sinusoidal cross-section is shown in Figure 10.24. The distances are all in metres; the 5 cm amplitude is shown as 1/20 m, and the 20 cm period is shown as 2/10 m. The curve has equation

$$y = \frac{1}{20} \sin(10\pi x).$$

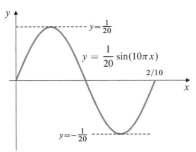

**Figure 10.24**  One period of the panel's cross-section

Note that 25 periods are required to produce a 5 m long panel. The length of the flat sheet required is 25 times the length of one period of the sine curve:

$$s = 25 \int_0^{2/10} \sqrt{1 + \left( \frac{\pi}{2} \cos(10\pi x) \right)^2} \, dx \qquad \text{Let } t = 10\pi x,$$
$$dt = 10\pi \, dx$$
$$= \frac{5}{2\pi} \int_0^{2\pi} \sqrt{1 + \frac{\pi^2}{4} \cos^2 t} \, dt = \frac{10}{\pi} \int_0^{\pi/2} \sqrt{1 + \frac{\pi^2}{4} \cos^2 t} \, dt.$$

The integral can be evaluated numerically using the techniques of the previous chapter or by using the definite integral function on an advanced scientific calculator or a computer. The value is $s \approx 7.32$. The flat metal sheet should be about 7.32 m long to yield a 5 m long finished panel.

If integrals needed for standard problems such as arc lengths of simple curves cannot be evaluated exactly, they are sometimes used to define new functions whose values are tabulated or built into computer programs. An example of this is the complete elliptic integral function that arises in the next example.

EXAMPLE 4    (**The circumference of an ellipse**)  Find the circumference of the ellipse

$$\frac{x^2}{a^2} + \frac{y^2}{b^2} = 1,$$

where $a \geq b > 0$. See Figure 10.25.

*Solution*  The upper half of the ellipse has equation $y = b\sqrt{1 - \frac{x^2}{a^2}} = \frac{b}{a}\sqrt{a^2 - x^2}$. Hence,

$$\frac{dy}{dx} = -\frac{b}{a}\frac{x}{\sqrt{a^2 - x^2}},$$

so

$$1 + \left(\frac{dy}{dx}\right)^2 = 1 + \frac{b^2}{a^2}\frac{x^2}{a^2 - x^2}$$

$$= \frac{a^4 - (a^2 - b^2)x^2}{a^2(a^2 - x^2)}.$$

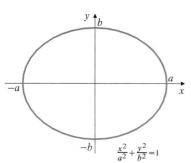

Figure 10.25    The ellipse of Example 4

The circumference of the ellipse is four times the arc length of the part lying in the first quadrant, so

$$s = 4\int_0^a \frac{\sqrt{a^4 - (a^2 - b^2)x^2}}{a\sqrt{a^2 - x^2}}\,dx \qquad \text{Let } x = a\sin t,$$
$$\qquad\qquad\qquad\qquad\qquad\qquad dx = a\cos t\,dt$$

$$= 4\int_0^{\pi/2} \frac{\sqrt{a^4 - (a^2 - b^2)a^2\sin^2 t}}{a(a\cos t)}\,a\cos t\,dt$$

$$= 4\int_0^{\pi/2} \sqrt{a^2 - (a^2 - b^2)\sin^2 t}\,dt$$

$$= 4a\int_0^{\pi/2} \sqrt{1 - \frac{a^2 - b^2}{a^2}\sin^2 t}\,dt$$

$$= 4a\int_0^{\pi/2} \sqrt{1 - \varepsilon^2\sin^2 t}\,dt \text{ units,}$$

where $\varepsilon = (\sqrt{a^2 - b^2})/a$ is the *eccentricity* of the ellipse. Note that $0 \leq \varepsilon < 1$. The function $E(\varepsilon)$, defined by

$$E(\varepsilon) = \int_0^{\pi/2} \sqrt{1 - \varepsilon^2\sin^2 t}\,dt,$$

is called the **complete elliptic integral of the second kind**. The integral cannot be evaluated by elementary techniques for general $\varepsilon$, although numerical methods can be applied to find approximate values for any given value of $\varepsilon$. Tables of values of $E(\varepsilon)$ for various values of $\varepsilon$ can be found in collections of mathematical tables. As shown above, the circumference of the ellipse is given by $4aE(\varepsilon)$. Note that for $a = b$ we have $\varepsilon = 0$, and the formula returns the circumference of a circle; $s = 4a(\pi/2) = 2\pi a$ units.

## Areas of Surfaces of Revolution

When a plane curve is rotated (in three dimensions) about a line in the plane of the curve, it sweeps out a **surface of revolution**. For instance, a sphere of radius $a$ is generated by rotating a semicircle of radius $a$ about the diameter of that semicircle.

The area of a surface of revolution can be found by integrating an area element $dS$ constructed by rotating the arc length element $ds$ of the curve about the given line. If the radius of rotation of the element $ds$ is $r$, then it generates, on rotation, a circular band of width $ds$ and length (circumference) $2\pi r$. The area of this band is, therefore,

$$dS = 2\pi r\, ds,$$

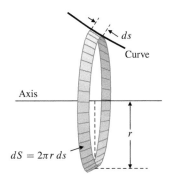

$$dS = 2\pi r\, ds$$

**Figure 10.26**   The circular band generated by rotating arc length element $ds$ about the axis

as shown in Figure 10.26. The areas of surfaces of revolution around various lines can be obtained by integrating $dS$ with appropriate choices of $r$. Here are some important special cases:

---

**Area of a surface of revolution**

If $f'(x)$ is continuous on $[a, b]$ and the curve $y = f(x)$ is rotated about the $x$-axis, the area of the surface of revolution so generated is

$$S = 2\pi \int_{x=a}^{x=b} |y|\, ds = 2\pi \int_a^b |f(x)| \sqrt{1 + (f'(x))^2}\, dx.$$

If the rotation is about the $y$-axis, the surface area is

$$S = 2\pi \int_{x=a}^{x=b} |x|\, ds = 2\pi \int_a^b |x| \sqrt{1 + (f'(x))^2}\, dx.$$

If $g'(y)$ is continuous on $[c, d]$ and the curve $x = g(y)$ is rotated about the $x$-axis, the area of the surface of revolution so generated is

$$S = 2\pi \int_{y=c}^{y=d} |y|\, ds = 2\pi \int_c^d |y| \sqrt{1 + (g'(y))^2}\, dy.$$

If the rotation is about the $y$-axis, the surface area is

$$S = 2\pi \int_{y=c}^{y=d} |x|\, ds = 2\pi \int_c^d |g(y)| \sqrt{1 + (g'(y))^2}\, dy.$$

---

*Remark*   Students sometimes wonder whether such complicated formulas are actually necessary. Why not just use $dS = 2\pi|y|\, dx$ for the area element when $y = f(x)$ is rotated about the $x$-axis instead of the more complicated area element $dS = 2\pi|y|\, ds$? After all, we are regarding $dx$ and $ds$ as both being infinitely small, and we certainly used $dx$ for the width of the disk-shaped volume element when we rotated the region under $y = f(x)$ about the $x$-axis to generate a solid of revolution. The reason is somewhat subtle. For small thickness $\Delta x$, the volume of a slice of the solid of revolution is only approximately $\pi y^2\, \Delta x$, but the error is *small compared to the volume of this slice.* On the other hand, if we use $2\pi|y|\, \Delta x$ as an approximation to the area of a thin band of the surface of revolution corresponding to an $x$ interval of width $\Delta x$, the error is *not small compared to the area of that band.* If, for instance, the curve $y = f(x)$ has slope 1 at $x$, then the width of the band is really $\Delta s = \sqrt{2}\, \Delta x$, so that the area of the band is $\Delta S = 2\pi \sqrt{2}|y|\, \Delta x$, not just $2\pi|y|\, \Delta x$. Always use the appropriate arc length element along the curve when you rotate a curve to find the area of a surface of revolution.

---

**EXAMPLE 5**   **(Surface area of a sphere)** Find the area of the surface of a sphere of radius $a$.

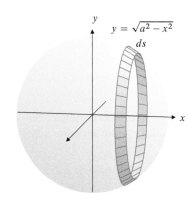

**Figure 10.27**    An area element on a sphere

*Solution*  Such a sphere can be generated by rotating the semicircle with equation $y = \sqrt{a^2 - x^2}$, $(-a \le x \le a)$, about the $x$-axis. (See Figure 10.27.) Since

$$\frac{dy}{dx} = -\frac{x}{\sqrt{a^2 - x^2}} = -\frac{x}{y},$$

the area of the sphere is given by

$$S = 2\pi \int_{-a}^{a} y \sqrt{1 + \left(\frac{x}{y}\right)^2}\, dx$$

$$= 4\pi \int_{0}^{a} \sqrt{y^2 + x^2}\, dx$$

$$= 4\pi \int_{0}^{a} \sqrt{a^2}\, dx = 4\pi a x \Big|_{0}^{a} = 4\pi a^2 \text{ square units.}$$

---

**EXAMPLE 6**    **(Surface area of a parabolic dish)**  Find the surface area of a parabolic reflector whose shape is obtained by rotating the parabolic arc $y = x^2$, $(0 \le x \le 1)$, about the $y$-axis, as illustrated in Figure 10.28.

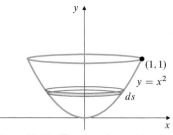

**Figure 10.28**    The area element is a horizontal band here

*Solution*  The arc length element for the parabola $y = x^2$ is $ds = \sqrt{1 + 4x^2}\, dx$, so the required surface area is

$$S = 2\pi \int_{0}^{1} x \sqrt{1 + 4x^2}\, dx \qquad \text{Let } u = 1 + 4x^2,$$
$$du = 8x\, dx$$

$$= \frac{\pi}{4} \int_{1}^{5} u^{1/2}\, du$$

$$= \frac{\pi}{6} u^{3/2} \Big|_{1}^{5} = \frac{\pi}{6}(5\sqrt{5} - 1) \text{ square units.}$$

---

# EXERCISES 10.3

In Exercises 1–16, find the lengths of the given curves.

**1.** $y = 2x - 1$ from $x = 1$ to $x = 3$

**2.** $y = ax + b$ from $x = A$ to $x = B$

**3.** $y = \frac{2}{3} x^{3/2}$ from $x = 0$ to $x = 8$

**4.** $y^2 = (x - 1)^3$ from $(1, 0)$ to $(2, 1)$

**5.** $y^3 = x^2$ from $(-1, 1)$ to $(1, 1)$

**6.** $2(x + 1)^3 = 3(y - 1)^2$ from $(-1, 1)$ to $(0, 1 + \sqrt{2/3})$

**7.** $y = \frac{x^3}{12} + \frac{1}{x}$ from $x = 1$ to $x = 4$

**8.** $y = \frac{x^3}{3} + \frac{1}{4x}$ from $x = 1$ to $x = 2$

**9.** $4y = 2 \ln x - x^2$ from $x = 1$ to $x = e$

**10.** $y = x^2 - \frac{\ln x}{8}$ from $x = 1$ to $x = 2$

**11.** $y = \frac{e^x + e^{-x}}{2}$ $(= \cosh x)$ from $x = 0$ to $x = a$

**12.** $y = \ln(1 - x^2)$ from $x = -(1/2)$ to $x = 1/2$

**13.** $y = \ln \cos x$ from $x = \pi/6$ to $x = \pi/4$

**14.** $y = x^2$ from $x = 0$ to $x = 2$

**15.** $y = \ln \frac{e^x - 1}{e^x + 1}$ from $x = 2$ to $x = 4$

**16.** $y = \ln x$ from $x = 1$ to $x = e$

**17.** Find the circumference of the closed curve $x^{2/3} + y^{2/3} = a^{2/3}$. *Hint:* The curve is symmetric about both coordinate axes (why?), so one-quarter of it lies in the first quadrant.

Use numerical methods (or a calculator with an integration function, or computer software like Maple) to find the lengths of the curves in Exercises 18–21 to 4 decimal places.

**18.** $y = x^4$ from $x = 0$ to $x = 1$

**19.** $y = x^{1/3}$ from $x = 1$ to $x = 2$

**20.** The circumference of the ellipse $3x^2 + y^2 = 3$

**21.** The shorter arc of the ellipse $x^2 + 2y^2 = 2$ between $(0, 1)$ and $(1, 1/\sqrt{2})$

In Exercises 22–29, find the areas of the surfaces obtained by rotating the given curve about the indicated lines.

**22.** $y = x^2$, $(0 \le x \le 2)$, about the $y$-axis

**23.** $y = x^3$, $(0 \le x \le 1)$, about the $x$-axis

**24.** $y = x^{3/2}$, $(0 \le x \le 1)$, about the $x$-axis

**25.** $y = x^{3/2}$, $(0 \le x \le 1)$, about the $y$-axis

**26.** $y = e^x$, $(0 \le x \le 1)$, about the $x$-axis

**27.** $y = \sin x$, $(0 \le x \le \pi)$, about the $x$-axis

**28.** $y = \dfrac{x^3}{12} + \dfrac{1}{x}$, $(1 \le x \le 4)$, about the $x$-axis

**29.** $y = \dfrac{x^3}{12} + \dfrac{1}{x}$, $(1 \le x \le 4)$, about the $y$-axis

**30.** (**Surface area of a cone**) Find the area of the curved surface of a right-circular cone of base radius $r$ and height $h$ by rotating the straight line segment from $(0,0)$ to $(r,h)$ about the $y$-axis.

**31.** (**How much icing on a doughnut?**) Find the surface area of the torus (doughnut) obtained by rotating the circle $(x - b)^2 + y^2 = a^2$ about the $y$-axis.

**32.** (**Area of a prolate spheroid**) Find the area of the surface obtained by rotating the ellipse $x^2 + 4y^2 = 4$ about the $x$-axis.

**33.** (**Area of an oblate spheroid**) Find the area of the surface obtained by rotating the ellipse $x^2 + 4y^2 = 4$ about the $y$-axis.

**34.** The ellipse of Example 4 is rotated about the line $y = c > b$ to generate a doughnut with elliptical cross-sections. Express the surface area of this doughnut in terms of the complete elliptic integral function $E(\varepsilon)$ introduced in that example.

**35.** Express the integral formula obtained for the length of the metal sheet in Example 3 in terms of the complete elliptic integral function $E(\epsilon)$ introduced in Example 4.

**36.** (**An interesting property of spheres**) If two parallel planes intersect a sphere, show that the surface area of that part of the sphere lying between the two planes depends only on the radius of the sphere and the distance between the planes, and not on the position of the planes.

**37.** For what real values of $k$ does the surface generated by rotating the curve $y = x^k$, $(0 < x \le 1)$, about the $y$-axis have a finite surface area?

**38.** The curve $y = \ln x$, $(0 < x \le 1)$, is rotated about the $y$-axis. Find the area of the horn-shaped surface so generated.

**39.** A hollow container in the shape of an infinitely long horn is generated by rotating the curve $y = 1/x$, $(1 \le x < \infty)$, about the $x$-axis.

(a) Find the volume of the container.

(b) Show that the container has infinite surface area.

(c) How do you explain the "paradox" that the container can be filled with a finite volume of paint but requires an infinite amount of paint to cover its surface?

## 10.4  Mass, Moments, and Centre of Mass

Many quantities of interest in physics, mechanics, ecology, finance, and other disciplines are described in terms of densities over regions of space, the plane, or even the real line. To determine the total value of such a quantity we must add up (integrate) the contributions from the various places where the quantity is distributed.

### Mass and Density

If a solid object is made of a homogeneous material, we would expect different parts of the solid that have the same volume to have the same mass as well. We express this homogeneity by saying that the object has constant density, that density being the mass divided by the volume for the whole object or for any part of it. Thus, for example, a rectangular brick with dimensions 20 cm, 10 cm, and 8 cm would have volume $V = 20 \times 10 \times 8 = 1{,}600$ cm$^3$, and if it was made of material having constant density $\rho = 3$ g/cm$^3$, it would have mass $m = \rho V = 3 \times 1{,}600 = 4{,}800$ g. (We will use the lowercase Greek letter rho ($\rho$) to represent density.)

If the density of the material constituting a solid object is not constant but varies from point to point in the object, no such simple relationship exists between mass and volume. If the density $\rho = \rho(P)$ is a *continuous* function of position $P$, we can subdivide the solid into many small volume elements and, by regarding $\rho$ as approximately constant over each such element, determine the masses of all the elements and add them up to get the mass of the solid. The mass $\Delta m$ of a volume element $\Delta V$ containing the point $P$ would satisfy

$$\Delta m \approx \rho(P)\,\Delta V,$$

By "density at a point $P$" of a solid object, we mean the limit $\rho(P)$ of mass/volume for the part of the solid lying in small regions containing $P$ (e.g., balls centred at $P$) as the dimensions of the regions approach zero. Such a density $\rho$ is continuous at $P$ if we can ensure that $|\rho(Q) - \rho(P)|$ is as small as we want by taking $Q$ close enough to $P$.

so the mass $m$ of the solid can be approximated:

$$m = \sum \Delta m \approx \sum \rho(P) \Delta V.$$

Such approximations become exact as we pass to the limit of differential mass and volume elements, $dm = \rho(P) dV$, so we expect to be able to calculate masses as integrals, that is, as the limits of such sums:

$$m = \int dm = \int \rho(P) dV.$$

**EXAMPLE 1**    The density of a solid vertical cylinder of height $H$ cm and base area $A$ cm$^2$ is $\rho = \rho_0(1 + h)$ g/cm$^3$, where $h$ is the height in centimetres above the base and $\rho_0$ is a constant. Find the mass of the cylinder.

**Solution**    See Figure 10.29(a). A slice of the solid at height $h$ above the base and having thickness $dh$ is a circular disk of volume $dV = A\,dh$. Since the density is constant over this disk, the mass of the volume element is

$$dm = \rho\,dV = \rho_0(1 + h)\,A\,dh.$$

Therefore, the mass of the whole cylinder is

$$m = \int_0^H \rho_0 A(1 + h)\,dh = \rho_0 A \left( H + \frac{H^2}{2} \right) \text{ g.}$$

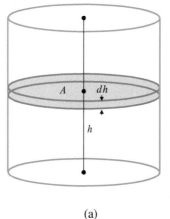 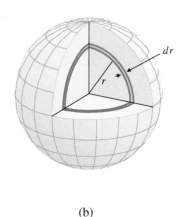

**Figure 10.29**

(a) A solid cylinder whose density varies with height

(b) Cutaway view of a planet whose density depends on distance from the centre

(a)                          (b)

**EXAMPLE 2**    **(Using spherical shells)** The density of a certain spherical planet of radius $R$ m varies with distance $r$ from the centre according to the formula

$$\rho = \frac{\rho_0}{1 + r^2} \text{ kg/m}^3.$$

Find the mass of the planet.

**Solution**    Recall that the surface area of a sphere of radius $r$ is $4\pi r^2$. The planet can be regarded as being composed of concentric spherical shells having radii between 0 and $R$. The volume of a shell of radius $r$ and thickness $dr$ (see Figure 10.29(b)) is equal to its surface area times its thickness, and its mass is its volume times its density:

$$dV = 4\pi r^2\,dr; \qquad dm = \rho\,dV = 4\pi\rho_0 \frac{r^2}{1 + r^2}\,dr.$$

We add the masses of these shells to find the mass of the whole planet:

$$m = 4\pi\rho_0 \int_0^R \frac{r^2}{1+r^2}\,dr = 4\pi\rho_0 \int_0^R \left(1 - \frac{1}{1+r^2}\right)\,dr$$

$$= 4\pi\rho_0 (r - \tan^{-1} r)\Big|_0^R = 4\pi\rho_0(R - \tan^{-1} R) \text{ kg.}$$

Similar techniques can be applied to find masses of one- and two-dimensional objects, such as wires and thin plates, that have variable densities of the forms mass/unit length (**line density**, which we will usually denote by $\delta$) and $\sigma =$ mass/unit area (**areal density**, which we will denote by $\sigma$).

**EXAMPLE 3**   A wire of variable composition is stretched along the $x$-axis from $x = 0$ to $x = L$ cm. Find the mass of the wire if the line density at position $x$ is $\delta(x) = kx$ g/cm, where $k$ is a positive constant.

**Solution**   The mass of a length element $dx$ of the wire located at position $x$ is given by $dm = \delta(x)\,dx = kx\,dx$. Thus, the mass of the wire is

$$m = \int_0^L kx\,dx = \left(\frac{kx^2}{2}\right)\Big|_0^L = \frac{kL^2}{2} \text{ g.}$$

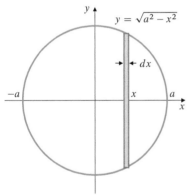

**EXAMPLE 4**   Find the mass of a disk of radius $a$ cm whose centre is at the origin in the $xy$-plane if the areal density at position $(x, y)$ is $\sigma = k(2a + x)$ g/cm$^2$. Here $k$ is a constant.

**Solution**   The areal density depends only on the horizontal coordinate $x$, so it is constant along vertical lines on the disk. This suggests that thin vertical strips should be used as area elements. A vertical strip of thickness $dx$ at $x$ has area $dA = 2\sqrt{a^2 - x^2}\,dx$ (see Figure 10.30); its mass is therefore

$$dm = \sigma\,dA = 2k(2a + x)\sqrt{a^2 - x^2}\,dx.$$

Hence, the mass of the disk is

$$m = \int_{x=-a}^{x=a} dm = 2k \int_{-a}^a (2a + x)\sqrt{a^2 - x^2}\,dx$$

$$= 4ak \int_{-a}^a \sqrt{a^2 - x^2}\,dx + 2k \int_{-a}^a x\sqrt{a^2 - x^2}\,dx$$

$$= 4ak\,\frac{\pi a^2}{2} + 0 = 2\pi k a^3 \text{ g.}$$

**Figure 10.30**   The area element of Example 4

We used the area of a semicircle to evaluate the first integral. The second integral is zero because the integrand is odd and the interval is symmetric about $x = 0$.

Distributions of mass along one-dimensional structures (lines or curves) necessarily lead to integrals of functions of one variable, but distributions of mass on a surface or in space can lead to integrals involving functions of more than one variable. Such integrals are studied in multivariable calculus. In the examples above, the given densities were functions of only one variable, so these problems, although higher dimensional in nature, led to integrals of functions of only one variable and could be solved by the methods at hand.

## Moments and Centres of Mass

The **moment** about the point $x = x_0$ of a mass $m$ located at position $x$ on the $x$-axis is the product $m(x - x_0)$ of the mass and its (signed) distance from $x_0$. If the $x$-axis is a horizontal arm hinged at $x_0$, the moment about $x_0$ measures the tendency of the weight of the mass $m$ to cause the arm to rotate. If several masses $m_1, m_2, m_3, \ldots,$ $m_n$ are located at the points $x_1, x_2, x_3, \ldots, x_n$, respectively, then the total moment of the system of masses about the point $x = x_0$ is the sum of the individual moments (see Figure 10.31):

$$M_{x=x_0} = (x_1 - x_0)m_1 + (x_2 - x_0)m_2 + \cdots + (x_n - x_0)m_n = \sum_{j=1}^{n}(x_j - x_0)m_j.$$

**Figure 10.31**   A system of discrete masses on a line

The **centre of mass** of the system of masses is the point $\bar{x}$ about which the total moment of the system is zero. Thus,

$$0 = \sum_{j=1}^{n}(x_j - \bar{x})m_j = \sum_{j=1}^{n}x_j m_j - \bar{x}\sum_{j=1}^{n}m_j.$$

The centre of mass of the system is therefore given by

$$\bar{x} = \frac{\displaystyle\sum_{j=1}^{n}x_j m_j}{\displaystyle\sum_{j=1}^{n}m_j} = \frac{M_{x=0}}{m},$$

where $m$ is the total mass of the system and $M_{x=0}$ is the total moment about $x = 0$. If you think of the $x$-axis as being a weightless wire supporting the masses, then $\bar{x}$ is the point at which the wire could be supported and remain in perfect balance (equilibrium), not tipping either way. Even if the axis represents a nonweightless support, say a seesaw, supported at $x = \bar{x}$, it will remain balanced after the masses are added, provided it was balanced beforehand. For many purposes a system of masses behaves as though its total mass were concentrated at its centre of mass.

Now suppose that a one-dimensional distribution of mass with continuously variable line density $\delta(x)$ lies along the interval $[a, b]$ of the $x$-axis. An element of length $dx$ at position $x$ contains mass $dm = \delta(x)\,dx$, so its moment is $dM_{x=0} = x\,dm = x\delta(x)\,dx$ about $x = 0$. The total moment about $x = 0$ is the *sum* (integral) of these moment elements:

$$M_{x=0} = \int_{a}^{b} x\delta(x)\,dx.$$

Since the total mass is

$$m = \int_{a}^{b} \delta(x)\,dx,$$

we obtain the following formula for the centre of mass:

The centre of mass of a distribution of mass with line density $\delta(x)$ on the interval $[a, b]$ is given by

$$\bar{x} = \frac{M_{x=0}}{m} = \frac{\displaystyle\int_a^b x\delta(x)\,dx}{\displaystyle\int_a^b \delta(x)\,dx}.$$

**EXAMPLE 5**  At what point can the wire of Example 3 be suspended so that it will balance?

*Solution*  In Example 3 we evaluated the mass of the wire to be $kL^2/2$ g. Its moment about $x = 0$ is

$$M_{x=0} = \int_0^L x\delta(x)\,dx$$

$$= \int_0^L kx^2\,dx = \left(\frac{kx^3}{3}\right)\Big|_0^L = \frac{kL^3}{3} \text{ g·cm.}$$

(Note that the appropriate units for the moment are units of mass times units of distance: in this case gram-centimetres.) The centre of mass of the wire is

$$\bar{x} = \frac{kL^3/3}{kL^2/2} = \frac{2L}{3}.$$

The wire will be balanced if suspended at position $x = 2L/3$ cm.

## Two- and Three-Dimensional Examples

The system of mass considered in Example 5 is one-dimensional and lies along a straight line. If mass is distributed in a plane or in space, similar considerations prevail. For a system of masses $m_1$ at $(x_1, y_1)$, $m_2$ at $(x_2, y_2)$, ..., $m_n$ at $(x_n, y_n)$, the **moment about** $x = 0$ is

$$M_{x=0} = x_1 m_1 + x_2 m_2 + \cdots + x_n m_n = \sum_{j=1}^n x_j m_j,$$

and the **moment about** $y = 0$ is

$$M_{y=0} = y_1 m_1 + y_2 m_2 + \cdots + y_n m_n = \sum_{j=1}^n y_j m_j.$$

The **centre of mass** is the point $(\bar{x}, \bar{y})$ where

$$\bar{x} = \frac{M_{x=0}}{m} = \frac{\displaystyle\sum_{j=1}^n x_j m_j}{\displaystyle\sum_{j=1}^n m_j} \quad \text{and} \quad \bar{y} = \frac{M_{y=0}}{m} = \frac{\displaystyle\sum_{j=1}^n y_j m_j}{\displaystyle\sum_{j=1}^n m_j}.$$

For continuous distributions of mass, the sums become appropriate integrals.

**EXAMPLE 6**  Find the centre of mass of a rectangular plate that occupies the region $0 \le x \le a$, $0 \le y \le b$, if the areal density of the material in the plate at position $(x, y)$ is $\sigma = ky$.

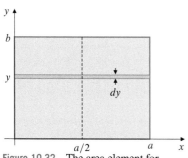

**Figure 10.32**  The area element for Example 6

**Solution**  Since the areal density is independent of $x$ and the rectangle is symmetric about the line $x = a/2$, the $x$-coordinate of the centre of mass must be $\bar{x} = a/2$. A thin horizontal strip of width $dy$ at height $y$ (see Figure 10.32) has mass $dm = aky\,dy$. The moment of this strip about $y = 0$ is $dM_{y=0} = y\,dm = kay^2\,dy$. Hence, the mass and moment about $y = 0$ of the whole plate are

$$m = ka \int_0^b y\,dy = \frac{kab^2}{2},$$

$$M_{y=0} = ka \int_0^b y^2\,dy = \frac{kab^3}{3}.$$

Therefore, $\bar{y} = M_{y=0}/m = 2b/3$, and the centre of mass of the plate is $(a/2, 2b/3)$. The plate would be balanced if supported at this point.

For distributions of mass in three-dimensional space one defines, analogously, the moments $M_{x=0}$, $M_{y=0}$, and $M_{z=0}$ of the system of mass about the planes $x = 0$, $y = 0$, and $z = 0$, respectively. The centre of mass is $(\bar{x}, \bar{y}, \bar{z})$ where

$$\bar{x} = \frac{M_{x=0}}{m}, \qquad \bar{y} = \frac{M_{y=0}}{m}, \qquad \text{and} \qquad \bar{z} = \frac{M_{z=0}}{m},$$

$m$ being the total mass: $m = m_1 + m_2 + \cdots + m_n$. Again, the sums are replaced with integrals for continuous distributions of mass.

**EXAMPLE 7**  Find the centre of mass of a solid hemisphere of radius $R$ ft if its density at height $z$ ft above the base plane of the hemisphere is $\rho_0 z$ lb/ft$^3$.

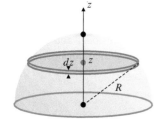

**Figure 10.33**  Mass element of a solid hemisphere with density depending on height

**Solution**  The solid is symmetric about the vertical axis (let us call it the $z$-axis), and the density is constant in planes perpendicular to this axis. Therefore, the centre of mass must lie somewhere on this axis. A slice of the solid at height $z$ above the base, and having thickness $dz$, is a disk of radius $\sqrt{R^2 - z^2}$. (See Figure 10.33.) Its volume is $dV = \pi(R^2 - z^2)\,dz$, and its mass is $dm = \rho_0 z\,dV = \rho_0 \pi(R^2 z - z^3)\,dz$. Its moment about the base plane $z = 0$ is $dM_{z=0} = z\,dm = \rho_0 \pi(R^2 z^2 - z^4)\,dz$. The mass of the solid is

$$m = \rho_0 \pi \int_0^R (R^2 z - z^3)\,dz = \rho_0 \pi \left( \frac{R^2 z^2}{2} - \frac{z^4}{4} \right)\Bigg|_0^R = \frac{\pi}{4}\rho_0 R^4 \text{ lb.}$$

The moment of the hemisphere about the plane $z = 0$ is

$$M_{z=0} = \rho_0 \pi \int_0^R (R^2 z^2 - z^4)\,dz = \rho_0 \pi \left( \frac{R^2 z^3}{3} - \frac{z^5}{5} \right)\Bigg|_0^R = \frac{2\pi}{15}\rho_0 R^5 \text{ lb·ft.}$$

The centre of mass therefore lies along the axis of symmetry of the hemisphere at height $\bar{z} = M_{z=0}/m = 8R/15$ ft above the base of the hemisphere.

**EXAMPLE 8**  Find the centre of mass of a plate that occupies the region $a \le x \le b, 0 \le y \le f(x)$, if the density at any point $(x, y)$ is $\sigma(x)$.

**Solution**  The appropriate area element is shown in Figure 10.34. It has area $f(x)\,dx$, mass

$$dm = \sigma(x) f(x)\,dx,$$

and moment about $x = 0$

$$dM_{x=0} = x\sigma(x)f(x)\,dx.$$

Since the density depends only on $x$, the mass element $dm$ has constant density, so the $y$-coordinate of *its* centre of mass is at its midpoint: $\bar{y}_{dm} = \frac{1}{2}f(x)$. Therefore, the moment of the mass element $dm$ about $y = 0$ is

$$dM_{y=0} = \bar{y}_{dm}\,dm = \frac{1}{2}\sigma(x)\big(f(x)\big)^2\,dx.$$

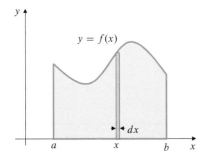

$y = f(x)$

$dx$

$a \qquad x \qquad b \qquad x$

**Figure 10.34**   Mass element of a plate

The coordinates of the centre of mass of the plate are $\bar{x} = \dfrac{M_{x=0}}{m}$ and $\bar{y} = \dfrac{M_{y=0}}{m}$, where

$$m = \int_a^b \sigma(x)f(x)\,dx,$$

$$M_{x=0} = \int_a^b x\sigma(x)f(x)\,dx,$$

$$M_{y=0} = \frac{1}{2}\int_a^b \sigma(x)\big(f(x)\big)^2\,dx.$$

---

**Remark**   Similar formulas can be obtained if the density depends on $y$ instead of $x$, provided that the region admits a suitable horizontal area element (e.g., the region might be specified by $c \le y \le d$, $0 \le x \le g(y)$). Finding centres of mass for plates that occupy regions specified by functions of $x$, but where the density depends on $y$, generally requires the use of "double integrals." Such problems are therefore studied in multivariable calculus.

## EXERCISES 10.4

Find the mass and centre of mass for the systems in Exercises 1–16. Be alert for symmetries.

1. A straight wire of length $L$ cm, where the density at distance $s$ cm from one end is $\delta(s) = \sin \pi s/L$ g/cm

2. A straight wire along the $x$-axis from $x = 0$ to $x = L$ if the density is constant $\delta_0$, but the cross-sectional radius of the wire varies so that its value at $x$ is $a + bx$

3. A quarter-circular plate having radius $a$, constant areal density $\sigma_0$, and occupying the region $x^2 + y^2 \le a^2$, $x \ge 0$, $y \ge 0$

4. A quarter-circular plate of radius $a$ occupying the region $x^2 + y^2 \le a^2$, $x \ge 0$, $y \ge 0$, having areal density $\sigma(x) = \sigma_0 x$

5. A plate occupying the region $0 \le y \le 4 - x^2$ if the areal density at $(x, y)$ is $ky$

6. A right-triangular plate with legs 2 m and 3 m if the areal density at any point $P$ is $5h$ kg/m$^2$, $h$ being the distance of $P$ from the shorter leg

7. A square plate of edge $a$ cm if the areal density at $P$ is $kx$ g/cm$^2$, where $x$ is the distance from $P$ to one edge of the square

8. The plate in Exercise 7, but with areal density $kr$ g/cm$^2$,

where $r$ is the distance (in centimetres) from $P$ to one of the diagonals of the square

9. A plate of areal density $\sigma(x)$ occupying the region $a \le x \le b$, $f(x) \le y \le g(x)$

10. A rectangular brick with dimensions 20 cm, 10 cm, and 5 cm if the density at $P$ is $kx$ g/cm$^3$, where $x$ is the distance from $P$ to one of the $10 \times 5$ faces

11. A solid ball of radius $R$ m if the density at $P$ is $z$ kg/m$^3$, where $z$ is the distance from $P$ to a plane at distance $2R$ m from the centre of the ball

12. A right-circular cone of base radius $a$ cm and height $b$ cm if the density at point $P$ is $kz$ g/cm$^3$, where $z$ is the distance of $P$ from the base of the cone

**!** 13. The solid occupying the quarter of a ball of radius $a$ centred at the origin having as base the region $x^2 + y^2 \le a^2$, $x \ge 0$ in the $xy$-plane, if the density at height $z$ above the base is $\rho_0 z$

**!** 14. The cone of Exercise 12, but with density at $P$ equal to $kx$ g/cm$^3$, where $x$ is the distance of $P$ from the axis of symmetry of the cone. *Hint:* Use a cylindrical shell centred on the axis of symmetry as a volume element. This element has constant density, so its centre of mass is known, and its moment can be determined from its mass.

**15.** A semicircular plate occupying the region $x^2 + y^2 \leq a^2$, $y \geq 0$, if the density at distance $s$ from the origin is $ks$ g/cm$^2$

**16.** The wire in Exercise 1 if it is bent in a semicircle

**17.** It is estimated that the density of matter in the neighbourhood of a gas giant star is given by $\rho(r) = Ce^{-kr^2}$, where $C$ and $k$ are positive constants, and $r$ is the distance from the centre of

the star. The radius of the star is indeterminate but can be taken to be infinite since $\rho(r)$ decreases very rapidly for large $r$. Find the approximate mass of the star in terms of $C$ and $k$.

**18.** Find the average distance $\bar{r}$ of matter in the star of Exercise 17 from the centre of the star. $\bar{r}$ is given by $\int_0^\infty r\, dm / \int_0^\infty dm$, where $dm$ is the mass element at distance $r$ from the centre of the star.

## 10.5 Centroids

If matter is distributed uniformly in a system so that the density $\delta$ is constant, then that density cancels out of the numerator and denominator in sum or integral expressions for coordinates of the centre of mass. In such cases the centre of mass depends only on the *shape* of the object, that is, on geometric properties of the region occupied by the object, and we call it the **centroid** of the region.

Centroids are calculated using the same formulas as those used for centres of mass, except that the density (being constant) is taken to be unity, so the mass is just the length, area, or volume of the region, and the moments are referred to as **moments of the region**, rather than of any mass occupying the region. If we set $\sigma(x) = 1$ in the formulas obtained in Example 8 of Section 10.4, we obtain the following result:

> **The centroid of a standard plane region**
>
> The centroid of the plane region $a \leq x \leq b, 0 \leq y \leq f(x)$, is $(\bar{x}, \bar{y})$, where
>
> $$\bar{x} = \frac{M_{x=0}}{A}, \quad \bar{y} = \frac{M_{y=0}}{A}, \quad \text{and)}$$
>
> $$A = \int_a^b f(x)\, dx, \quad M_{x=0} = \int_a^b x f(x)\, dx, \quad M_{y=0} = \frac{1}{2}\int_a^b \left(f(x)\right)^2 dx.$$

Thus, for example, $\bar{x}$ is the *average value* of the function $x$ over the region.

The centroids of some regions are obvious by symmetry. The centroid of a circular disk or an elliptical disk is at the centre of the disk. The centroid of a rectangle is at the centre also; the centre is the point of intersection of the diagonals. The centroid of any region lies on any axes of symmetry of the region.

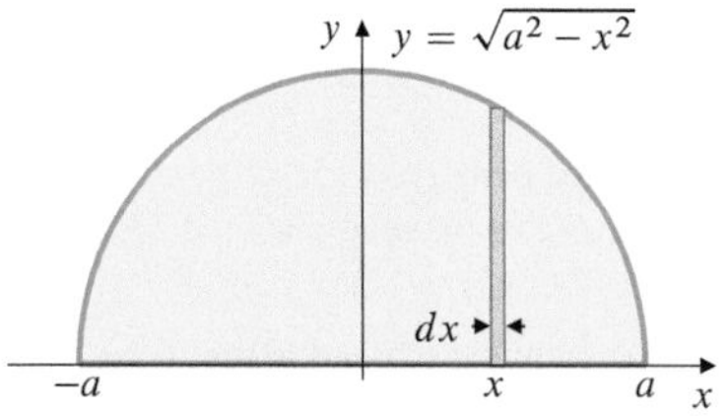

Figure 10.35    The half-disk of Example 1

**EXAMPLE 1**    What is the average value of $y$ over the half-disk $-a \leq x \leq a$, $0 \leq y \leq \sqrt{a^2 - x^2}$? Find the centroid of the half-disk.

*Solution*    By symmetry, the centroid lies on the $y$-axis, so its $x$-coordinate is $\bar{x} = 0$. (See Figure 10.35.) Since the area of the half-disk is $A = \frac{1}{2}\pi a^2$, the average value of $y$ over the half-disk is

$$\bar{y} = \frac{M_{y=0}}{A} = \frac{2}{\pi a^2}\frac{1}{2}\int_{-a}^a (a^2 - x^2)\, dx = \frac{2}{\pi a^2}\frac{2a^3}{3} = \frac{4a}{3\pi}.$$

The centroid of the half-disk is $\left(0, \dfrac{4a}{3\pi}\right)$.

**EXAMPLE 2**    Find the centroid of the semicircle $y = \sqrt{a^2 - x^2}$.

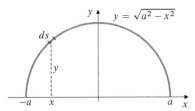

**Figure 10.36**    The semicircle of Example 2

*Solution*  Here, the "region" is a one-dimensional curve, having length rather than area. Again $\bar{x} = 0$ by symmetry. A short arc of length $ds$ at height $y$ on the semicircle has moment $dM_{y=0} = y\, ds$ about $y = 0$. (See Figure 10.36.) Since

$$ds = \sqrt{1 + \left(\frac{dy}{dx}\right)^2}\, dx = \sqrt{1 + \frac{x^2}{a^2 - x^2}}\, dx = \frac{a\, dx}{\sqrt{a^2 - x^2}},$$

and since $y = \sqrt{a^2 - x^2}$ on the semicircle, we have

$$M_{y=0} = \int_{-a}^{a} \sqrt{a^2 - x^2}\, \frac{a\, dx}{\sqrt{a^2 - x^2}} = a \int_{-a}^{a} dx = 2a^2.$$

Since the length of the semicircle is $\pi a$, we have $\bar{y} = \dfrac{M_{y=0}}{\pi a} = \dfrac{2a}{\pi}$, and the centroid of the semicircle is $\left(0, \dfrac{2a}{\pi}\right)$. Note that the centroid of a semicircle of radius $a$ is not the same as that of half-disk of radius $a$. Note also that the centroid of the semicircle does not lie on the semicircle itself.

**THEOREM**

**1**

**The centroid of a triangle**

The centroid of a triangle is the point at which all three medians of the triangle intersect.

*PROOF*  Recall that a median of a triangle is a straight line joining one vertex of the triangle to the midpoint of the opposite side. Given any median of a triangle, we will show that the centroid lies on that median. Thus, the centroid must lie on all three medians.

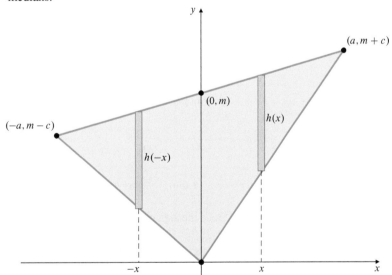

**Figure 10.37**    The axes of Theorem 1

Adopt a coordinate system where the median in question lies along the $y$-axis and such that a vertex of the triangle is at the origin. (See Figure 10.37.) Let the midpoint of the opposite side be $(0, m)$. Then the other two vertices of the triangle must have coordinates of the form $(-a, m - c)$ and $(a, m + c)$ so that $(0, m)$ will be the midpoint between them. The two vertical area elements shown in the figure are at the same distance on opposite sides of the $y$-axis, so they have the same heights $h(-x) = h(x)$ (by similar triangles) and the same area. The sum of the moments about $x = 0$ of these area elements is

$$dM_{x=0} = -xh(-x)\, dx + xh(x)\, dx = 0,$$

so the moment of the whole triangle about $x = 0$ is

$$M_{x=0} = \int_{x=-a}^{x=a} dM_{x=0} = 0.$$

Therefore, the centroid of the triangle lies on the $y$-axis.

**Remark**   By simultaneously solving the equations of any two medians of a triangle, we can verify the following formula:

> **Coordinates of the centroid of a triangle**
>
> The coordinates of the centroid of a triangle are the averages of the corresponding coordinates of the three vertices of the triangle. The triangle with vertices $(x_1, y_1)$, $(x_2, y_2)$, and $(x_3, y_3)$ has centroid
>
> $$(\bar{x}, \bar{y}) = \left( \frac{x_1 + x_2 + x_3}{3}, \frac{y_1 + y_2 + y_3}{3} \right).$$

If a region is a union of nonoverlapping subregions, then any moment of the region is the sum of the corresponding moments of the subregions. This fact enables us to calculate the centroid of the region if we know the centroids and areas of all the subregions.

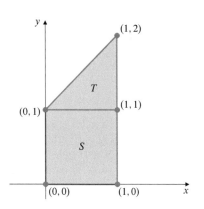

Figure 10.38   The trapezoid of Example 3

**EXAMPLE 3**   Find the centroid of the trapezoid with vertices $(0, 0)$, $(1, 0)$, $(1, 2)$, and $(0, 1)$.

**Solution**   The trapezoid is the union of a square and a (nonoverlapping) triangle, as shown in Figure 10.38. By symmetry, the square has centroid $(\bar{x}_S, \bar{y}_S) = \left( \frac{1}{2}, \frac{1}{2} \right)$, and its area is $A_S = 1$. The triangle has area $A_T = \frac{1}{2}$, and its centroid is $(\bar{x}_T, \bar{y}_T)$, where

$$\bar{x}_T = \frac{0 + 1 + 1}{3} = \frac{2}{3} \qquad \text{and} \qquad \bar{y}_T = \frac{1 + 1 + 2}{3} = \frac{4}{3}.$$

Continuing to use subscripts $S$ and $T$ to denote the square and triangle, respectively, we calculate

$$M_{x=0} = M_{S;x=0} + M_{T;x=0} = A_S \bar{x}_S + A_T \bar{x}_T = 1 \times \frac{1}{2} + \frac{1}{2} \times \frac{2}{3} = \frac{5}{6},$$

$$M_{y=0} = M_{S;y=0} + M_{T;y=0} = A_S \bar{y}_S + A_T \bar{y}_T = 1 \times \frac{1}{2} + \frac{1}{2} \times \frac{4}{3} = \frac{7}{6}.$$

Since the area of the trapezoid is $A = A_S + A_T = \frac{3}{2}$, its centroid is

$$(\bar{x}, \bar{y}) = \left( \frac{5}{6} \bigg/ \frac{3}{2}, \frac{7}{6} \bigg/ \frac{3}{2} \right) = \left( \frac{5}{9}, \frac{7}{9} \right).$$

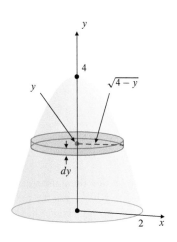

Figure 10.39   A parabolic solid

**EXAMPLE 4**   Find the centroid of the solid region obtained by rotating about the $y$-axis the first quadrant region lying between the $x$-axis and the parabola $y = 4 - x^2$.

**Solution**   By symmetry, the centroid of the parabolic solid will lie on its axis of symmetry, the $y$-axis. A thin, disk-shaped slice of the solid at height $y$ and having thickness $dy$ (see Figure 10.39) has volume

$$dV = \pi x^2 \, dy = \pi (4 - y) \, dy$$

and moment about the base plane

$$dM_{y=0} = y\,dV = \pi(4y - y^2)\,dy.$$

Hence, the volume of the solid is

$$V = \pi \int_0^4 (4 - y)\,dy = \pi \left( 4y - \frac{y^2}{2} \right) \Big|_0^4 = \pi(16 - 8) = 8\pi,$$

and its moment about $y = 0$ is

$$M_{y=0} = \pi \int_0^4 (4y - y^2)\,dy = \pi \left( 2y^2 - \frac{y^3}{3} \right) \Big|_0^4 = \pi \left( 32 - \frac{64}{3} \right) = \frac{32}{3}\pi.$$

Hence, the centroid is located at $\bar{y} = \dfrac{32\pi}{3} \times \dfrac{1}{8\pi} = \dfrac{4}{3}.$

## Pappus's Theorem

The following theorem relates volumes or surface areas of revolution to the centroid of the region or curve being rotated.

**THEOREM**

**2**

**Pappus's Theorem**

(a) If a plane region $R$ lies on one side of a line $L$ in that plane and is rotated about $L$ to generate a solid of revolution, then the volume $V$ of that solid is the product of the area of $R$ and the distance travelled by the centroid of $R$ under the rotation; that is,

$$V = 2\pi \bar{r} A,$$

where $A$ is the area of $R$, and $\bar{r}$ is the perpendicular distance from the centroid of $R$ to $L$.

(b) If a plane curve $\mathcal{C}$ lies on one side of a line $L$ in that plane and is rotated about that line to generate a surface of revolution, then the area $S$ of that surface is the length of $\mathcal{C}$ times the distance travelled by the centroid of $\mathcal{C}$:

$$S = 2\pi \bar{r} s,$$

where $s$ is the length of the curve $\mathcal{C}$, and $\bar{r}$ is the perpendicular distance from the centroid of $\mathcal{C}$ to the line $L$.

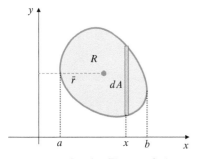

**Figure 10.40**   Proving Theorem 2(a)

**PROOF**   We prove part (a). The proof of (b) is similar and is left as an exercise.

Let us take $L$ to be the $y$-axis and suppose that $R$ lies between $x = a$ and $x = b$ where $0 \le a < b$. Thus $\bar{r} = \bar{x}$, the $x$-coordinate of the centroid of $R$. Let $dA$ denote the area of a thin strip of $R$ at position $x$ and having width $dx$. (See Figure 10.40.) This strip generates, on rotation about $L$, a cylindrical shell of volume $dV = 2\pi x\,dA$, so the volume of the solid of revolution is

$$V = 2\pi \int_{x=a}^{x=b} x\,dA = 2\pi M_{x=0} = 2\pi \bar{x} A = 2\pi \bar{r} A.$$

As the following examples illustrate, Pappus's Theorem can be used in two ways: either the centroid can be determined when the appropriate volume or surface area is known, or the volume or surface area can be determined if the centroid of the rotating region or curve is known.

**EXAMPLE 5**    Use Pappus's Theorem to find the centroid of the semicircle
$y = \sqrt{a^2 - x^2}$.

*Solution*    The centroid of the semicircle lies on its axis of symmetry, the $y$-axis, so it is located at a point with coordinates $(0, \bar{y})$. Since the semicircle has length $\pi a$ units and generates, on rotation about the $x$-axis, a sphere having area $4\pi a^2$ square units, we obtain, using part (b) of Pappus's Theorem,

$$4\pi a^2 = 2\pi(\pi a)\bar{y}.$$

Thus $\bar{y} = 2a/\pi$, as shown previously in Example 2.

**EXAMPLE 6**    Use Pappus's Theorem to find the volume and surface area of the torus (doughnut) obtained by rotating the disk $(x - b)^2 + y^2 \leq a^2$ about the $y$-axis. Here $0 < a < b$. (See Figure 10.10 in Section 10.1.)

*Solution*    The centroid of the disk is at $(b, 0)$, which is at distance $\bar{r} = b$ units from the axis of rotation. Since the disk has area $\pi a^2$ square units, the volume of the torus is

$$V = 2\pi b(\pi a^2) = 2\pi^2 a^2 b \text{ cubic units.}$$

To find the surface area $S$ of the torus (in case you want to have icing on the doughnut), rotate the circular boundary of the disk, which has length $2\pi a$, about the $y$-axis and obtain

$$S = 2\pi b(2\pi a) = 4\pi^2 ab \text{ square units.}$$

## EXERCISES 10.5

Find the centroids of the geometric structures in Exercises 1–21. Be alert for symmetries and opportunities to use Pappus's Theorem.

**1.** The quarter-disk $x^2 + y^2 \leq r^2, x \geq 0, y \geq 0$

**2.** The region $0 \leq y \leq 9 - x^2$

**3.** The region $0 \leq x \leq 1, 0 \leq y \leq \dfrac{1}{\sqrt{1 + x^2}}$

**4.** The circular disk sector $x^2 + y^2 \leq r^2, 0 \leq y \leq x$

**5.** The circular disk segment $0 \leq y \leq \sqrt{4 - x^2} - 1$

**6.** The semi-elliptic disk $0 \leq y \leq b\sqrt{1 - (x/a)^2}$

**7.** The quadrilateral with vertices (in clockwise order) $(0, 0)$, $(3, 1)$, $(4, 0)$, and $(2, -2)$

**8.** The region bounded by the semicircle $y = \sqrt{1 - (x - 1)^2}$, the $y$-axis, and the line $y = x - 2$

**9.** A hemispherical surface of radius $r$

**10.** A solid half ball of radius $r$

**11.** A solid cone of base radius $r$ and height $h$

**12.** A conical surface of base radius $r$ and height $h$

**13.** The plane region $0 \leq y \leq \sin x, \ 0 \leq x \leq \pi$

**14.** The plane region $0 \leq y \leq \cos x, \ 0 \leq x \leq \pi/2$

**15.** The quarter-circle arc $x^2 + y^2 = r^2, x \geq 0, \ y \geq 0$

**16.** The solid obtained by rotating the region in Figure 10.41(a) about the $y$-axis

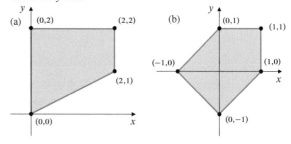

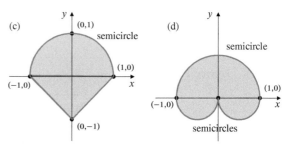

**Figure 10.41**

17. The region in Figure 10.41(a)

18. The region in Figure 10.41(b)

19. The region in Figure 10.41(c)

20. The region in Figure 10.41(d)

21. The solid obtained by rotating the plane region $0 \le y \le 2x - x^2$ about the line $y = -2$

22. The line segment from $(1, 0)$ to $(0, 1)$ is rotated about the line $x = 2$ to generate part of a conical surface. Find the area of that surface.

23. The triangle with vertices $(0, 0)$, $(1, 0)$, and $(0, 1)$ is rotated about the line $x = 2$ to generate a certain solid. Find the volume of that solid.

24. An equilateral triangle of edge $s$ cm is rotated about one of its edges to generate a solid. Find the volume and surface area of that solid.

25. Find to 5 decimal places the coordinates of the centroid of the region $0 \le x \le \pi/2, 0 \le y \le \sqrt{x} \cos x$.

26. Find to 5 decimal places the coordinates of the centroid of the region $0 < x \le \pi/2, \ln(\sin x) \le y \le 0$.

27. Find the centroid of the infinitely long spike-shaped region lying between the $x$-axis and the curve $y = (x + 1)^{-3}$ and to the right of the $y$-axis.

28. Show that the curve $y = e^{-x^2}$ $(-\infty < x < \infty)$ generates a surface of finite area when rotated about the $x$-axis. What does this imply about the location of the centroid of this infinitely long curve?

29. Obtain formulas for the coordinates of the centroid of the plane region $c \le y \le d, 0 < f(y) \le x \le g(y)$.

30. Prove part (b) of Pappus's Theorem (Theorem 2).

31. **(Stability of a floating object)** Determining the orientation that a floating object will assume is a problem of critical importance to ship designers. Boats must be designed to float stably in an upright position; if the boat tilts somewhat from upright, the forces on it must be such as to right it again. The two forces on a floating object that need to be taken into account are its weight **W** and the balancing buoyant force **B** = −**W**. The weight **W** must be treated for mechanical purposes as being applied at the centre of mass (CM) of the object. The buoyant force, however, acts at the *centre of buoyancy* (CB), which is the centre of mass of the water displaced by the object, and is therefore the centroid of the "hole in the water" made by the object.

For example, consider a channel marker buoy consisting of a hemispherical hull surmounted by a conical tower supporting a navigation light. The buoy has a vertical axis of symmetry. If it is upright, both the CM and the CB lie on this line, as shown in the left half of Figure 10.42.

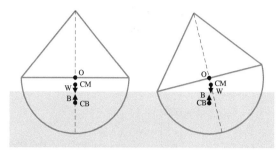

Figure 10.42

Is this upright flotation of the buoy stable? It is if the CM lies below the centre O of the hemispherical hull, as shown in the right half of the figure. To see why, imagine the buoy tilted slightly from the vertical as shown in the right half of the figure. Observe that the CM still lies on the axis of symmetry of the buoy, but the CB lies on the vertical line through O. The forces **W** and **B** no longer act along the same line, but their torques are such as to rotate the buoy back to a vertical upright position. If CM had been above O in the left figure, the torques would have been such as to tip the buoy over once it was displaced even slightly from the vertical.

A wooden beam has a square cross-section and specific gravity 0.5, so that it will float with half of its volume submerged. (See Figure 10.43.) Assuming it will float horizontally in the water, what is the stable orientation of the square cross-section with respect to the surface of the water? In particular, will the beam float with a flat face upward or an edge upward? Prove your assertions. You may find Maple or another symbolic algebra program useful.

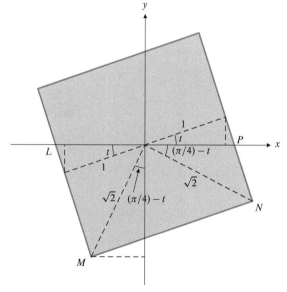

Figure 10.43

---

## 10.6  Other Physical Applications

In this section we present some examples of the use of integration to calculate quantities arising in physics and mechanics.

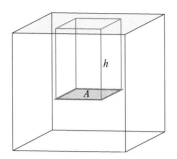

Figure 10.44 The volume of liquid above the area $A$ is $V = Ah$. The weight of this liquid is $\rho V g = \rho g h A$, so the pressure (force per unit area) at depth $h$ is $p = \rho g h$

## Hydrostatic Pressure

The **pressure** $p$ at depth $h$ beneath the surface of a liquid is the *force per unit area* exerted on a horizontal plane surface at that depth due to the weight of the liquid above it. Hence, $p$ is given by

$$p = \rho g h,$$

where $\rho$ is the density of the liquid, and $g$ is the acceleration produced by gravity where the fluid is located. (See Figure 10.44.) For water at the surface of the earth we have, approximately, $\rho = 1{,}000$ kg/m$^3$ and $g = 9.8$ m/s$^2$, so the pressure at depth $h$ m is

$$p = 9{,}800h \text{ N/m}^2.$$

The unit of force used here is the newton (N); 1 N = 1 kg·m/s$^2$, the force that imparts an acceleration of 1 m/s$^2$ to a mass of 1 kg.

The molecules in a liquid interact in such a way that the pressure at any depth acts equally in all directions; the pressure against a vertical surface is the same as that against a horizontal surface at the same depth. This is **Pascal's principle**.

The total force exerted by a liquid on a horizontal surface (say, the bottom of a tank holding the liquid) is found by multiplying the area of that surface by the pressure at the depth of the surface below the top of the liquid. For nonhorizontal surfaces, however, the pressure is not constant over the whole surface, and the total force cannot be determined so easily. In this case we divide the surface into area elements $dA$, each at some particular depth $h$, and we then sum (i.e., integrate) the corresponding force elements $dF = \rho g h \, dA$ to find the total force.

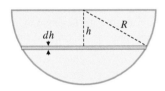

Figure 10.45 An end plate of the water trough

**EXAMPLE 1**    One vertical wall of a water trough is a semicircular plate of radius $R$ m with curved edge downward. If the trough is full, so that the water comes up to the top of the plate, find the total force of the water on the plate.

*Solution*    A horizontal strip of the surface of the plate at depth $h$ m and having width $dh$ m (see Figure 10.45) has length $2\sqrt{R^2 - h^2}$ m; hence, its area is $dA = 2\sqrt{R^2 - h^2}\, dh$ m$^2$. The force of the water on this strip is

$$dF = \rho g h \, dA = 2\rho g h \sqrt{R^2 - h^2}\, dh.$$

Thus, the total force on the plate is

$$F = \int_{h=0}^{h=R} dF = 2\rho g \int_0^R h\sqrt{R^2 - h^2}\, dh \qquad \text{Let } u = R^2 - h^2,$$
$$\qquad\qquad\qquad\qquad\qquad\qquad\qquad\qquad du = -2h\, dh$$

$$= \rho g \int_0^{R^2} u^{1/2}\, du = \rho g\, \frac{2}{3}u^{3/2}\Big|_0^{R^2}$$

$$\approx \frac{2}{3} \times 9{,}800 R^3 \approx 6{,}533 R^3 \text{ N}.$$

**EXAMPLE 2**    **(Force on a dam)** Find the total force on a section of a dam 100 m long and having a vertical height of 10 m, if the surface holding back the water is inclined at an angle of 30° to the vertical and the water comes up to the top of the dam.

*Solution*    The water in a horizontal layer of thickness $dh$ m at depth $h$ m makes contact with the dam along a slanted strip of width $dh \sec 30° = (2/\sqrt{3})\, dh$ m. (See Figure 10.46.) The area of this strip is $dA = (200/\sqrt{3})\, dh$ m$^2$, and the force of water against the strip is

$$dF = \rho g h \, dA = \frac{200}{\sqrt{3}} \times 1{,}000 \times 9.8h\, dh \approx 1{,}131{,}600h\, dh \text{ N}.$$

The total force on the dam section is therefore

$$F \approx 1{,}131{,}600 \int_0^{10} h \, dh = 1{,}131{,}600 \times \frac{10^2}{2} \approx 5.658 \times 10^7 \text{ N.}$$

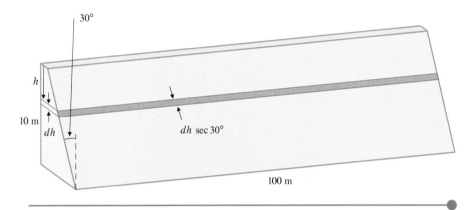

30°

$h$

10 m

$dh$

$dh \sec 30°$

100 m

Figure 10.46   The dam of Example 2

## Work

When a force acts on an object to move that object, it is said to have done **work** on the object. The amount of work done by a constant force is measured by the product of the force and the distance through which it moves the object. This assumes that the force is in the direction of the motion.

work = force × distance

Work is always related to a particular force. If other forces acting on an object cause it to move in a direction opposite to the force $F$, then work is said to have been done *against* the force $F$.

Suppose that a force in the direction of the $x$-axis moves an object from $x = a$ to $x = b$ on that axis and that the force varies continuously with the position $x$ of the object; that is, $F = F(x)$ is a continuous function. The element of work done by the force in moving the object through a very short distance from $x$ to $x + dx$ is $dW = F(x) \, dx$, so the total work done by the force is

$$W = \int_{x=a}^{x=b} dW = \int_a^b F(x) \, dx.$$

---

**EXAMPLE 3**   (**Stretching or compressing a spring**)  By **Hooke's Law**, the force $F(x)$ required to extend (or compress) an elastic spring to $x$ units longer (or shorter) than its natural length is proportional to $x$:

$$F(x) = kx,$$

where $k$ is the **spring constant** for the particular spring. If a force of 2,000 N is required to extend a certain spring to 4 cm longer than its natural length, how much work must be done to extend it that far?

***Solution***   Since $F(x) = kx = 2{,}000$ N when $x = 4$ cm, we must have $k = 2{,}000/4 = 500$ N/cm. The work done in extending the spring 4 cm is

$$W = \int_0^4 kx \, dx = k\frac{x^2}{2}\Big|_0^4 = 500 \, \frac{\text{N}}{\text{cm}} \times \frac{4^2 \text{ cm}^2}{2} = 4{,}000 \text{ N·cm} = 40 \text{ N·m.}$$

Forty newton-metres (joules) of work must be done to stretch the spring 4 cm.

---

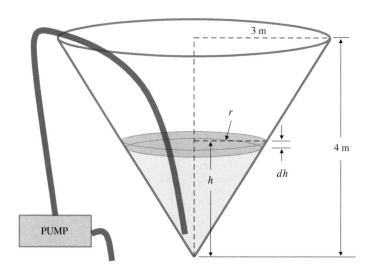

Figure 10.47   Pumping water out of a
conical tank

---

EXAMPLE 4   **(Work done to pump out a tank)**  Water fills a tank in the shape
of a right-circular cone with top radius 3 m and depth 4 m. How
much work must be done (against gravity) to pump all the water out of the tank over
the top edge of the tank?

*Solution*   A thin, disk-shaped slice of water at height $h$ above the vertex of the tank
has radius $r$ (see Figure 10.47), where $r = \frac{3}{4}h$ by similar triangles. The volume of this
slice is

$$dV = \pi r^2\, dh = \frac{9}{16}\, \pi h^2\, dh,$$

and its *weight* (the force of gravity on the mass of water in the slice) is

$$dF = \rho g\, dV = \frac{9}{16}\, \rho g\, \pi h^2\, dh.$$

The water in this disk must be raised (against gravity) a distance $(4 - h)$ m by the
pump. The work required to do this is

$$dW = \frac{9}{16}\, \rho g\, \pi (4 - h) h^2\, dh.$$

The total work that must be done to empty the tank is the sum (integral) of all these
elements of work for disks at depths between 0 and 4 m:

$$
\begin{aligned}
W &= \int_0^4 \frac{9}{16}\, \rho g\, \pi (4h^2 - h^3)\, dh \\
&= \frac{9}{16}\, \rho g\, \pi \left( \frac{4h^3}{3} - \frac{h^4}{4} \right)\Bigg|_0^4 \\
&= \frac{9\pi}{16} \times 1{,}000 \times 9.8 \times \frac{64}{3} \approx 3.69 \times 10^5 \text{ N·m.}
\end{aligned}
$$

---

EXAMPLE 5   **(Work to raise material into orbit)**  The gravitational force of
the earth on a mass $m$ located at height $h$ above the surface of the
earth is given by

$$F(h) = \frac{Km}{(R + h)^2},$$

where $R$ is the radius of the earth and $K$ is a constant that is independent of $m$ and $h$. Determine, in terms of $K$ and $R$, the work that must be done against gravity to raise an object from the surface of the earth to:

(a) a height $H$ above the surface of the earth, and

(b) an infinite height above the surface of the earth.

**Solution**   The work done to raise the mass $m$ from height $h$ to height $h + dh$ is

$$dW = \frac{Km}{(R + h)^2}\, dh.$$

(a) The total work to raise it from height $h = 0$ to height $h = H$ is

$$W = \int_0^H \frac{Km}{(R + h)^2}\, dh = \left.\frac{-Km}{R + h}\right|_0^H = Km\left(\frac{1}{R} - \frac{1}{R + H}\right).$$

If $R$ and $H$ are measured in metres and $F$ is measured in newtons, then $W$ is measured in newton-metres (N·m), or joules.

(b) The total work necessary to raise the mass $m$ to an infinite height is

$$W = \int_0^\infty \frac{Km}{(R + h)^2}\, dh = \lim_{H \to \infty} Km\left(\frac{1}{R} - \frac{1}{R + H}\right) = \frac{Km}{R}.$$

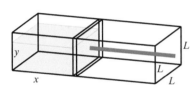

Figure 10.48   The piston in Example 6

**EXAMPLE 6**   One end of a horizontal tank with cross-section a square of edge length $L$ metres is fixed while the other end is a square piston free to travel without friction along the length of the tank. Between the piston and the fixed end there is some water in the tank; its depth depends on the position of the piston. (See Figure 10.48.)

(a) When the depth of the water is $y$ metres ($0 \le y \le L$), what force does it exert on the piston?

(b) If the piston is $X$ metres from the fixed end of the tank when the water depth is $L/2$ metres, how much work must be done to force the piston in further to halve that distance and hence cause the water level to increase to fill the available space? Assume no water leaks out but that trapped air can escape from the top of the tank.

**Solution**

(a) When the depth of water in the tank is $y$ m, a horizontal strip on the face of the piston at depth $z$ below the surface of the water ($0 \le z \le y$) and having height $dz$ has area $dA = L\, dz$. Since the pressure at depth $z$ is $\rho g z = 9{,}800 z$ N/m$^2$, the force of the water on the strip is $dF = 9{,}800\, Lz\, dz$ N. Thus, the force on the piston is

$$F = \int_0^y 9{,}800\, L\, z\, dz = 4{,}900\, L\, y^2 \text{ N}, \quad \text{where } 0 \le y \le L.$$

(b) If the distance from the fixed end of the tank to the piston is $x$ m when the water depth is $y$ m, then the volume of water in the tank is $V = Lxy$ m$^3$. But we are given that $V = L^2X/2$, so we have $u = LX/2$. Now the work done in moving the piston from $x$ to $x - dx$ is

$$dW = 4{,}900\, Ly^2(-dx) = -4{,}900\, L\, \frac{L^2X^2}{4x^2}\, dx.$$

Thus, the work done to move the piston from position $X$ to position $X/2$ is

$$W = -\int_X^{X/2} 4{,}900\, \frac{L^3X^2}{4}\frac{dx}{x^2}$$

$$= 4{,}900\, \frac{L^3X^2}{4}\left(\frac{2}{X} - \frac{1}{X}\right) = 1{,}225\, \text{N} \cdot \text{m}.$$

## Potential Energy and Kinetic Energy

The units of energy are the same as those of work (force × distance). Work done against a force may be regarded as storing up energy for future use or for conversion to other forms. Such stored energy is called **potential energy** (P.E.). For instance, in extending or compressing an elastic spring, we are doing work against the tension in the spring and hence storing energy in the spring. When work is done against a (variable) force $F(x)$ to move an object from $x = a$ to $x = b$, the energy stored is

$$\text{P.E.} = -\int_a^b F(x)\,dx.$$

Since the work is being done against $F$, the signs of $F(x)$ and $b - a$ are opposite, so the integral is negative; the explicit negative sign is included so that the calculated potential energy will be positive.

One of the forms of energy into which potential energy can be converted is **kinetic energy** (K.E.), the energy of motion. If an object of mass $m$ is moving with velocity $v$, it has kinetic energy

$$\text{K.E.} = \frac{1}{2}m\,v^2.$$

For example, if an object is raised and then dropped, it accelerates downward under gravity as more and more of the potential energy stored in it when it was raised is converted to kinetic energy.

Consider the change in potential energy stored in a mass $m$ as it moves along the $x$-axis from $a$ to $b$ under the influence of a force $F(x)$ depending only on $x$:

$$\text{P.E.}(b) - \text{P.E.}(a) = -\int_a^b F(x)\,dx.$$

(The change in P.E. is negative if $m$ is moving in the direction of $F$.) According to Newton's Second Law of Motion, the force $F(x)$ causes the mass $m$ to accelerate, with acceleration $dv/dt$ given by

$$F(x) = m\frac{dv}{dt} \qquad (\text{force} = \text{mass} \times \text{acceleration}).$$

By the Chain Rule we can rewrite $dv/dt$ in the form

$$\frac{dv}{dt} = \frac{dv}{dx}\frac{dx}{dt} = v\frac{dv}{dx},$$

so $F(x) = mv\dfrac{dv}{dx}$. Hence,

$$
\begin{aligned}
\text{P.E.}(b) - \text{P.E.}(a) &= -\int_a^b mv\frac{dv}{dx}\,dx \\
&= -m\int_{x=a}^{x=b} v\,dv \\
&= -\frac{1}{2}mv^2\bigg|_{x=a}^{x=b} \\
&= \text{K.E.}(a) - \text{K.E.}(b).
\end{aligned}
$$

It follows that

$$\text{P.E.}(b) + \text{K.E.}(b) = \text{P.E.}(a) + \text{K.E.}(a).$$

This shows that the total energy (potential + kinetic) remains constant as the mass $m$ moves under the influence of a force $F$, *depending only on position*. Such a force is said to be **conservative**, and the above result is called the **Law of Conservation of Energy**.

$$\overline{\text{EXAMPLE 7}}$$  **(Escape velocity)**  Use the result of Example 5 together with the following known values,

(a) the radius $R$ of the earth is about 6,400 km, or $6.4 \times 10^6$ m,

(b) the acceleration of gravity $g$ at the surface of the earth is about 9.8 m/s$^2$,

to determine the constant $K$ in the gravitational force formula of Example 5, and use this information to determine the escape velocity for a projectile fired vertically from the surface of the earth. The **escape velocity** is the (minimum) speed that such a projectile must have at firing to ensure that it will continue to move farther and farther away from the earth and not fall back.

*Solution*   According to the formula of Example 5, the force of gravity on a mass $m$ kg at the surface of the earth ($h = 0$) is

$$F = \frac{Km}{(R + 0)^2} = \frac{Km}{R^2}.$$

According to Newton's Second Law of Motion, this force is related to the acceleration of gravity ($g$) there by the equation $F = mg$. Thus,

$$\frac{Km}{R^2} = mg \quad \text{and} \quad K = gR^2.$$

According to the Law of Conservation of Energy, the projectile must have sufficient kinetic energy at firing to do the work necessary to raise the mass $m$ to infinite height. By the result of Example 5, this required energy is $Km/R$. If the initial velocity of the projectile is $v$, we want

$$\frac{1}{2}mv^2 \geq \frac{Km}{R}.$$

Thus, $v$ must satisfy

$$v \geq \sqrt{\frac{2K}{R}} = \sqrt{2gR} \approx \sqrt{2 \times 9.8 \times 6.4 \times 10^6} \approx 1.12 \times 10^4 \text{ m/s}.$$

Thus, the escape velocity is approximately 11.2 km/s and is independent of the mass $m$. In this calculation we have neglected any air resistance near the surface of the earth. Such resistance depends on velocity rather than on position, so it is not a conservative force. The effect of such resistance would be to use up (convert to heat) some of the initial kinetic energy and so raise the escape velocity.

## EXERCISES 10.6

**1.** A tank has a square base 2 m on each side and vertical sides 6 m high. If the tank is filled with water, find the total force exerted by the water (a) on the bottom of the tank and (b) on one of the four vertical walls of the tank.

**2.** A swimming pool 20 m long and 8 m wide has a sloping plane bottom so that the depth of the pool is 1 m at one end and 3 m at the other end. Find the total force exerted on the bottom if the pool is full of water.

**3.** A dam 200 m long and 24 m high presents a sloping face of 26 m slant height to the water in a reservoir behind the dam (Figure 10.49). If the surface of the water is level with the top of the dam, what is the total force of the water on the dam?

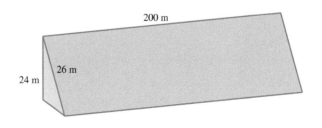

Figure 10.49

**4.** A pyramid with a square base, 4 m on each side and four equilateral triangular faces, sits on the level bottom of a lake at a place where the lake is 10 m deep. Find the total force of the water on each of the triangular faces.

**5.** A lock on a canal has a gate in the shape of a vertical rectangle 5 m wide and 20 m high. If the water on one side of the gate comes up to the top of the gate, and the water on the other side comes only 6 m up the gate, find the total force that must be exerted to hold the gate in place.

**6.** If 100 N·cm of work must be done to compress an elastic spring to 3 cm shorter than its natural length, how much work must be done to compress it 1 cm further?

**7.** Find the total work that must be done to pump all the water in the tank of Exercise 1 out over the top of the tank.

**8.** Find the total work that must be done to pump all the water in the swimming pool of Exercise 2 out over the top edge of the pool.

**9.** Find the work that must be done to pump all the water in a full hemispherical bowl of radius $a$ m to a height $h$ m above the top of the bowl.

**■ 10.** A horizontal cylindrical tank has radius $R$ m. One end of the tank is a fixed disk, but the other end is a circular piston of radius $R$ m free to travel along the length of the tank. There is some water in the tank between the piston and the fixed end; its depth depends on the position of the piston. What force does the water exert on the piston when the surface of the water is $y$ m $(-R \leq y \leq R)$ above the centre of the piston face? (See Figure 10.50.)

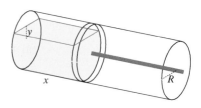

Figure 10.50

**■ 11.** Continuing the previous problem, suppose that when the piston is $X$ m from the fixed end of the tank the water level is at the centre of the piston face. How much work must be done to reduce the distance from the piston to the fixed end to $X/2$ m, and thus cause the water to fill the volume between the piston and the fixed end of the tank? As in Example 6, you can assume the piston can move without friction and that trapped air can escape. *Hint:* The technique used to solve part (b) of Example 6 is very difficult to apply here. Instead, calculate the work done to raise the water in half of the bottom half-cylinder of length $X$ so that it fills the top half-cylinder of length $X/2$.

**■ 12.** A bucket is raised vertically from ground level at a constant speed of 2 m/min by a winch. If the bucket weighs 1 kg and contains 15 kg of water when it starts up but loses water by leakage at a rate of 1 kg/min thereafter, how much work must be done by the winch to raise the bucket to a height of 10 m?

## 10.7 First-Order Differential Equations

This final section on applications of integration concentrates on application of the indefinite integral rather than of the definite integral. We can use the techniques of integration developed in Chapters 8 and 9 to solve certain kinds of first-order differential equations that arise in a variety of modelling situations. We have already seen some examples of applications of differential equations to modelling growth and decay phenomena in Section 6.4.

### Separable Equations

Consider the logistic equation introduced in Section 6.4 to model the growth of an animal population with a limited food supply:

$$\frac{dy}{dt} = ky\left(1 - \frac{y}{L}\right),$$

where $y(t)$ is the size of the population at time $t$, $k$ is a positive constant related to the fertility of the population, and $L$ is the steady-state population size that can be sustained by the available food supply. This equation has two particular solutions, $y = 0$ and $y = L$, that are constant functions of time.

The logistic equation is an example of a class of first-order differential equations called **separable equations** because when they are written in terms of differentials, they can be separated with only the dependent variable on one side of the equation and only the independent variable on the other. The logistic equation can be written in the form

$$\frac{L\,dy}{y(L - y)} = k\,dt$$

and solved by integrating both sides. Expanding the left side in partial fractions and integrating, we get

$$\int \left(\frac{1}{y} + \frac{1}{L - y}\right) dy = kt + C.$$

Assuming that $0 < y < L$, we therefore obtain

$$\ln y - \ln(L - y) = kt + C,$$

$$\ln\left(\frac{y}{L - y}\right) = kt + C.$$

We can solve this equation for $y$ by taking exponentials of both sides:

$$\frac{y}{L-y} = e^{kt+C} = C_1 e^{kt}$$

$$y = (L-y)C_1 e^{kt}$$

$$y = \frac{C_1 L e^{kt}}{1 + C_1 e^{kt}},$$

where $C_1 = e^C$.

Generally, separable equations are of the form

$$\frac{dy}{dx} = f(x)g(y).$$

We solve them by rewriting them in the form

$$\frac{dy}{g(y)} = f(x)\,dx$$

and integrating both sides. Note that the separable equation above will have a constant solution $y(x) = C$ for any constant $C$ satisfying $g(C) = 0$.

---

**EXAMPLE 1**   Solve the equation $\dfrac{dy}{dx} = \dfrac{x}{y}$.

**Solution**   We rewrite the equation in the form $y\,dy = x\,dx$ and integrate both sides to get

$$\frac{1}{2}y^2 = \frac{1}{2}x^2 + C_1,$$

or $y^2 - x^2 = C$, where $C = 2C_1$ is an arbitrary constant. The solution curves are rectangular hyperbolas. (See Figure 10.51.) Their asymptotes $y = x$ and $y = -x$ are also solutions corresponding to $C = 0$.

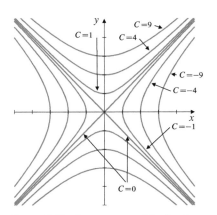

Figure 10.51   Some curves of the family $y^2 - x^2 = C$

---

**EXAMPLE 2**   Solve the initial-value problem

$$\begin{cases} \dfrac{dy}{dx} = x^2 y^3 \\ y(1) = 3. \end{cases}$$

**Solution**   Separating the differential equation gives $\dfrac{dy}{y^3} = x^2\,dx$. Thus,

$$\int \frac{dy}{y^3} = \int x^2\,dx, \qquad \text{so} \qquad \frac{-1}{2y^2} = \frac{x^3}{3} + C.$$

Since $y = 3$ when $x = 1$, we have $-\frac{1}{18} = \frac{1}{3} + C$ and $C = -\frac{7}{18}$. Substituting this value into the above solution and solving for $y$, we obtain

$$y(x) = \frac{3}{\sqrt{7 - 6x^3}}. \qquad \text{(Only the positive square root of } y^2 \text{ satisfies } y(1) = 3.)$$

This solution is valid for $x < \left(\frac{7}{6}\right)^{1/3}$. (See Figure 10.52.)

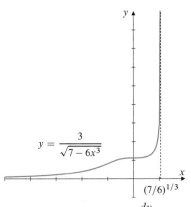

$y = \dfrac{3}{\sqrt{7 - 6x^3}}$

$(7/6)^{1/3}$

Figure 10.52   The solution of $\dfrac{dy}{dx} = x^2 y^3$ satisfying $y(1) = 3$

---

**EXAMPLE 3**    Solve the **integral equation** $y(x) = 3 + 2 \int_1^x t\, y(t)\, dt$.

*Solution*    Differentiating the integral equation with respect to $x$ gives

$$\frac{dy}{dx} = 2x\, y(x) \qquad \text{or} \qquad \frac{dy}{y} = 2x\, dx.$$

Thus, $\ln|y(x)| = x^2 + C$, and solving for $y$, $y(x) = C_1 e^{x^2}$. Putting $x = 1$ in the integral equation provides an initial value: $y(1) = 3 + 0 = 3$, so $C_1 = 3/e$ and

$$y(x) = 3e^{x^2 - 1}.$$

---

**EXAMPLE 4**    **(A solution concentration problem)**    Initially a tank contains 1,000 L of brine with 50 kg of dissolved salt. Brine containing 10 g of salt per litre is flowing into the tank at a constant rate of 10 L/min. If the contents of the tank are kept thoroughly mixed at all times, and if the solution also flows out at 10 L/min, how much salt remains in the tank at the end of 40 min?

*Solution*    Let $x(t)$ be the number of kilograms of salt in solution in the tank after $t$ min. Thus, $x(0) = 50$. Salt is coming into the tank at a rate of 10 g/L $\times$ 10 L/min $= 100$ g/min $= 1/10$ kg/min. At all times the tank contains 1,000 L of liquid, so the concentration of salt in the tank at time $t$ is $x/1{,}000$ kg/L. Since the contents flow out at 10 L/min, salt is being removed at a rate of $10x/1{,}000 = x/100$ kg/min. Therefore,

$$\frac{dx}{dt} = \text{rate in} - \text{rate out} = \frac{1}{10} - \frac{x}{100} = \frac{10 - x}{100}.$$

Although $x(t) = 10$ is a constant solution of the differential equation, it does not satisfy the initial condition $x(0) = 50$, so we will find other solutions by separating variables:

$$\frac{dx}{10 - x} = \frac{dt}{100}.$$

Integrating both sides of this equation, we obtain

$$-\ln|10 - x| = \frac{t}{100} + C.$$

Observe that $x(t) \neq 10$ for any finite time $t$ (since $\ln 0$ is not defined). Since $x(0) = 50 > 10$, it follows that $x(t) > 10$ for all $t > 0$. ($x(t)$ is necessarily continuous, so it cannot take any value less than 10 without somewhere taking the value 10 by the Intermediate-Value Theorem.) Hence, we can drop the absolute value from the solution above and obtain

$$\ln(x - 10) = -\frac{t}{100} - C.$$

Since $x(0) = 50$, we have $-C = \ln 40$ and

$$x = x(t) = 10 + 40e^{-t/100}.$$

After 40 min there will be $10 + 40e^{-0.4} \approx 36.8$ kg of salt in the tank.

---

EXAMPLE 5    **(A rate of reaction problem)** In a chemical reaction that goes to completion in solution, one molecule of each of two reactants, $A$ and $B$, combine to form each molecule of the product $C$. According to the law of mass action, the reaction proceeds at a rate proportional to the product of the concentrations of $A$ and $B$ in the solution. Thus, if there were initially present $a > 0$ molecules/cm$^3$ of $A$ and $b > 0$ molecules/cm$^3$ of $B$, then the number $x(t)$ of molecules/cm$^3$ of $C$ present at time $t$ thereafter is determined by the differential equation

$$\frac{dx}{dt} = k(a - x)(b - x).$$

This equation has constant solutions $x(t) = a$ and $x(t) = b$, neither of which satisfies the initial condition $x(0) = 0$. We find other solutions for this equation by separation of variables and the technique of partial fraction decomposition under the assumption that $b \neq a$:

$$\int \frac{dx}{(a - x)(b - x)} = k \int dt = kt + C.$$

Since

$$\frac{1}{(a - x)(b - x)} = \frac{1}{b - a}\left(\frac{1}{a - x} - \frac{1}{b - x}\right),$$

and since necessarily $x \leq a$ and $x \leq b$, we have

$$\frac{1}{b - a}\left(-\ln(a - x) + \ln(b - x)\right) = kt + C,$$

or

$$\ln\left(\frac{b - x}{a - x}\right) = (b - a)\,kt + C_1, \quad \text{where } C_1 = (b - a)C.$$

By assumption, $x(0) = 0$, so $C_1 = \ln(b/a)$ and

$$\ln\frac{a(b - x)}{b(a - x)} = (b - a)\,kt.$$

This equation can be solved for $x$ to yield $x = x(t) = \dfrac{ab(e^{(b-a)kt} - 1)}{be^{(b-a)kt} - a}$.

---

EXAMPLE 6    Find a family of curves, each of which intersects every parabola with equation of the form $y = Cx^2$ at right angles.

*Solution*    The family of parabolas $y = Cx^2$ satisfies the differential equation

$$\frac{d}{dx}\left(\frac{y}{x^2}\right) = \frac{d}{dx}C = 0;$$

that is,

$$x^2\frac{dy}{dx} - 2xy = 0 \quad \text{or} \quad \frac{dy}{dx} = \frac{2y}{x}.$$

Any curve that meets the parabolas $y = Cx^2$ at right angles must, at any point $(x, y)$ on it, have slope equal to the negative reciprocal of the slope of the particular parabola passing through that point. Thus, such a curve must satisfy

$$\frac{dy}{dx} = -\frac{x}{2y}.$$

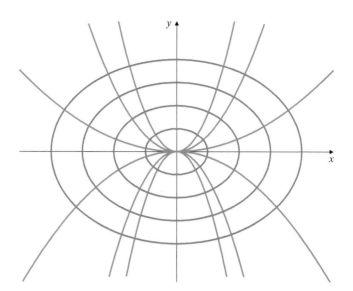

**Figure 10.53** The parabolas $y = C_1 x^2$ (blue) and the ellipses $x^2 + 2y^2 = C_2$ (red) intersect at right angles

Separation of the variables leads to $2y\,dy = -x\,dx$, and integration of both sides then yields $y^2 = -\frac{1}{2}x^2 + C_1$ or $x^2 + 2y^2 = C$, where $C = 2C_1$. This equation represents a family of ellipses centred at the origin. Each ellipse meets each parabola at right angles, as shown in Figure 10.53. When the curves of one family intersect the curves of a second family at right angles, each family is called the family of **orthogonal trajectories** of the other family.

## First-Order Linear Equations

A first-order **linear** differential equation is one of the type

$$\frac{dy}{dx} + p(x)y = q(x), \qquad (*)$$

where $p(x)$ and $q(x)$ are given functions, which we assume to be continuous. The equation is called **nonhomogeneous** unless $q(x)$ is identically zero. The corresponding **homogeneous** equation,

$$\frac{dy}{dx} + p(x)y = 0,$$

is separable and so is easily solved to give $y = K\,e^{-\mu(x)}$, where $K$ is any constant and $\mu(x)$ is any antiderivative of $p(x)$:

$$\mu(x) = \int p(x)\,dx \qquad \text{and} \qquad \frac{d\mu}{dx} = p(x).$$

There are two methods for solving the nonhomogeneous equation $(*)$. Both involve the function $\mu(x)$ defined above.

**METHOD I.    Using an Integrating Factor.**    Multiply equation $(*)$ by $e^{\mu(x)}$ (which is called an **integrating factor** for the equation) and observe that the left side is just the derivative of $e^{\mu(x)}y$; by the Product Rule

$$\frac{d}{dx}\left(e^{\mu(x)}y(x)\right) = e^{\mu(x)}\frac{dy}{dx} + e^{\mu(x)}\frac{d\mu}{dx}y(x)$$

$$= e^{\mu(x)}\left(\frac{dy}{dx} + p(x)y\right) = e^{\mu(x)}q(x).$$

Therefore, $e^{\mu(x)}\,y(x) = \int e^{\mu(x)}\,q(x)\,dx$, or

$$y(x) = e^{-\mu(x)} \int e^{\mu(x)} q(x)\, dx.$$

**METHOD II.  Variation of the Parameter.**   Start with the solution of the corresponding homogeneous equation, namely $y = K\,e^{-\mu(x)}$, and replace the constant (i.e., parameter) $K$ by an as yet unknown function $k(x)$ of the independent variable. Then substitute this expression for $y$ into the differential equation ($*$) and simplify:

$$\frac{d}{dx}\left(k(x)e^{-\mu(x)}\right) + p(x)k(x)e^{-\mu(x)} = q(x)$$
$$k'(x)e^{-\mu(x)} - \mu'(x)k(x)e^{-\mu(x)} + p(x)k(x)e^{-\mu(x)} = q(x),$$

which, since $\mu'(x) = p(x)$, reduces to

$$k'(x) = e^{\mu(x)}q(x).$$

Integrating the right side leads to the solution for $k(x)$ and thereby to the solution $y$ for ($*$).

---

**EXAMPLE 7**   Solve $\dfrac{dy}{dx} + \dfrac{y}{x} = 1$ for $x > 0$. Use both methods for comparison.

**Solution**   Here, $p(x) = 1/x$, so $\mu(x) = \int p(x)\,dx = \ln x$ (for $x > 0$).
METHOD I. The integrating factor is $e^{\mu(x)} = x$. We calculate

$$\frac{d}{dx}(xy) = x\frac{dy}{dx} + y = x\left(\frac{dy}{dx} + \frac{y}{x}\right) = x,$$

and so

$$xy = \int x\,dx = \frac{1}{2}x^2 + C.$$

Finally,

$$y = \frac{1}{x}\left(\frac{1}{2}x^2 + C\right) = \frac{x}{2} + \frac{C}{x}.$$

This is a solution of the given equation for any value of the constant $C$.

METHOD II. The corresponding homogeneous equation, $\dfrac{dy}{dx} + \dfrac{y}{x} = 0$, has solution $y = Ke^{-\mu(x)} = \dfrac{K}{x}$. Replacing the constant $K$ with the function $k(x)$ and substituting into the given differential equation we obtain

$$\frac{1}{x}k'(x) - \frac{1}{x^2}k(x) + \frac{1}{x^2}k(x) = 1,$$

so that $k'(x) = x$ and $k(x) = \dfrac{x^2}{2} + C$, where $C$ is any constant. Therefore,

$$y = \frac{k(x)}{x} = \frac{x}{2} + \frac{C}{x},$$

the same solution obtained by METHOD I.

*Remark*   Both methods really amount to the same calculations expressed in different ways. Use whichever one you think is easiest to understand. The remaining examples in this section will be done by using integrating factors, but variation of parameters will prove useful later on (Section 11.6) to deal with nonhomogeneous linear differential equations of second or higher order.

---

**EXAMPLE 8**   Solve $\dfrac{dy}{dx} + xy = x^3$.

*Solution*   Here, $p(x) = x$, so $\mu(x) = x^2/2$ and $e^{\mu(x)} = e^{x^2/2}$. We calculate

$$\frac{d}{dx}\left(e^{x^2/2}y\right) = e^{x^2/2}\frac{dy}{dx} + e^{x^2/2}xy = e^{x^2/2}\left(\frac{dy}{dx} + xy\right) = x^3 e^{x^2/2}.$$

Thus,

$$e^{x^2/2}\, y = \int x^3\, e^{x^2/2}\, dx \qquad \text{Let} \quad U = x^2, \qquad dV = x\, e^{x^2/2}\, dx.$$
$$\text{Then } dU = 2x\, dx, \qquad V = e^{x^2/2}.$$
$$= x^2\, e^{x^2/2} - 2\int x\, e^{x^2/2}\, dx$$
$$= x^2\, e^{x^2/2} - 2e^{x^2/2} + C,$$

and, finally, $y = x^2 - 2 + Ce^{-x^2/2}$.

---

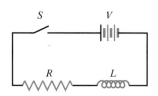

**Figure 10.54**   An inductance-resistance circuit

**EXAMPLE 9**   **(An inductance-resistance circuit)**   An electric circuit (see Figure 10.54) contains a constant DC voltage source of $V$ volts, a switch, a resistor of size $R$ ohms, and an inductor of size $L$ henrys. The circuit has no capacitance. The switch, initially open so that no current is flowing, is closed at time $t = 0$ so that current begins to flow at that time. If the inductance $L$ were zero, the current would suddenly jump from 0 amperes when $t < 0$ to $I = V/R$ amperes when $t > 0$. However, if $L > 0$ the current cannot change instantaneously; it will depend on time $t$. Let the current $t$ seconds after the switch is closed be $I(t)$ amperes. It is known that $I(t)$ satisfies the initial-value problem

$$\begin{cases} L\dfrac{dI}{dt} + RI = V \\ \quad I(0) = 0. \end{cases}$$

Find $I(t)$. What is $\lim_{t\to\infty} I(t)$? How long does it take after the switch is closed for the current to rise to 90% of its limiting value?

*Solution*   The DE can be written in the form $\dfrac{dI}{dt} + \dfrac{R}{L}I = \dfrac{V}{L}$. It is linear and has integrating factor $e^{\mu(t)}$, where

$$\mu(t) = \int \frac{R}{L}\, dt = \frac{Rt}{L}.$$

Therefore,

$$\frac{d}{dt}\left(e^{Rt/L}I\right) = e^{Rt/L}\left(\frac{dI}{dt} + \frac{R}{L}I\right) = e^{Rt/L}\frac{V}{L}$$
$$e^{Rt/L}I = \frac{V}{L}\int e^{Rt/L}\, dt = \frac{V}{R}e^{Rt/L} + C$$
$$I(t) = \frac{V}{R} + Ce^{-Rt/L}.$$

Since $I(0) = 0$, we have $0 = (V/R) + C$, so $C = -V/R$. Thus, the current flowing at any time $t > 0$ is

$$I(t) = \frac{V}{R}\left(1 - e^{-Rt/L}\right).$$

It is clear from this solution that $\lim_{t \to \infty} I(t) = V/R$; the *steady-state* current is the current that would flow if the inductance were zero.

$I(t)$ will be 90% of this limiting value when

$$\frac{V}{R}\left(1 - e^{-Rt/L}\right) = \frac{90}{100}\frac{V}{R}.$$

This equation implies that $e^{-Rt/L} = 1/10$, or $t = (L \ln 10)/R$. The current will grow to 90% of its limiting value in $(L \ln 10)/R$ seconds.

---

Our final example reviews a typical *stream of payments* problem of the sort considered in Section 10.7. This time we treat the problem as an initial-value problem for a differential equation.

**EXAMPLE 10**   A savings account is opened with a deposit of $A$ dollars. At any time $t$ years thereafter, money is being continually deposited into the account at a rate of $(C + Dt)$ dollars per year. If interest is also being paid into the account at a nominal rate of $100R$ percent per year, compounded continuously, find the balance $B(t)$ dollars in the account after $t$ years. Illustrate the solution for the data $A = 5,000$, $C = 1,000$, $D = 200$, $R = 0.13$, and $t = 5$.

*Solution*   As noted in Section 6.4, continuous compounding of interest at a nominal rate of $100R$ percent causes \$1.00 to grow to $e^{Rt}$ dollars in $t$ years. Without subsequent deposits, the balance in the account would grow according to the differential equation of exponential growth:

$$\frac{dB}{dt} = RB.$$

Allowing for additional growth due to the continual deposits, we observe that $B$ must satisfy the differential equation

$$\frac{dB}{dt} = RB + (C + Dt)$$

or, equivalently, $dB/dt - RB = C + Dt$. This is a linear equation for $B$ having $p(t) = -R$. Hence, we may take $\mu(t) = -Rt$ and $e^{\mu(t)} = e^{-Rt}$. We now calculate

$$\frac{d}{dt}\left(e^{-Rt} B(t)\right) = e^{-Rt}\frac{dB}{dt} - Re^{-Rt} B(t) = (C + Dt)e^{-Rt}$$

and

$$e^{-Rt} B(t) = \int (C + Dt)e^{-Rt}\, dt \qquad \text{Let} \quad U = C + Dt, \quad dV = e^{-Rt}\, dt.$$
$$\text{Then } dU = D\, dt, \qquad V = -e^{-Rt}/R.$$
$$= -\frac{C + Dt}{R} e^{-Rt} + \frac{D}{R}\int e^{-Rt}\, dt$$
$$= -\frac{C + Dt}{R} e^{-Rt} - \frac{D}{R^2} e^{-Rt} + K, \qquad (K = \text{constant}).$$

Hence,

$$B(t) = -\frac{C + Dt}{R} - \frac{D}{R^2} + Ke^{Rt}.$$

Since $A = B(0) = -\dfrac{C}{R} - \dfrac{D}{R^2} + K$, we have $K = A + \dfrac{C}{R} + \dfrac{D}{R^2}$ and

$$B(t) = \left(A + \frac{C}{R} + \frac{D}{R^2}\right)e^{Rt} - \frac{C + Dt}{R} - \frac{D}{R^2}.$$

For the illustration $A = 5{,}000$, $C = 1{,}000$, $D = 200$, $R = 0.13$, and $t = 5$, we obtain, using a calculator, $B(5) = 19{,}762.82$. The account will contain \$19,762.82, after five years, under these circumstances.

# EXERCISES 10.7

Solve the separable equations in Exercises 1–10.

**1.** $\dfrac{dy}{dx} = \dfrac{y}{2x}$

**2.** $\dfrac{dy}{dx} = \dfrac{3y - 1}{x}$

**3.** $\dfrac{dy}{dx} = \dfrac{x^2}{y^2}$

**4.** $\dfrac{dy}{dx} = x^2 y^2$

**5.** $\dfrac{dY}{dt} = tY$

**6.** $\dfrac{dx}{dt} = e^x \sin t$

**7.** $\dfrac{dy}{dx} = 1 - y^2$

**8.** $\dfrac{dy}{dx} = 1 + y^2$

**9.** $\dfrac{dy}{dt} = 2 + e^y$

**10.** $\dfrac{dy}{dx} = y^2(1 - y)$

Solve the linear equations in Exercises 11–16.

**11.** $\dfrac{dy}{dx} - \dfrac{2y}{x} = x^2$

**12.** $\dfrac{dy}{dx} + \dfrac{2y}{x} = \dfrac{1}{x^2}$

**13.** $\dfrac{dy}{dx} + 2y = 3$

**14.** $\dfrac{dy}{dx} + y = e^x$

**15.** $\dfrac{dy}{dx} + y = x$

**16.** $\dfrac{dy}{dx} + 2e^x y = e^x$

Solve the initial-value problems in Exercises 17–20.

**17.** $\begin{cases} \dfrac{dy}{dt} + 10y = 1 \\ y(1/10) = 2/10 \end{cases}$

**18.** $\begin{cases} \dfrac{dy}{dx} + 3x^2 y = x^2 \\ y(0) = 1 \end{cases}$

**19.** $\begin{cases} x^2 y' + y = x^2 e^{1/x} \\ y(1) = 3e \end{cases}$

**20.** $\begin{cases} y' + (\cos x)y = 2xe^{-\sin x} \\ y(\pi) = 0 \end{cases}$

Solve the integral equations in Exercises 21–24.

**21.** $y(x) = 2 + \displaystyle\int_0^x \dfrac{t}{y(t)}\, dt$

**22.** $y(x) = 1 + \displaystyle\int_0^x \dfrac{\left(y(t)\right)^2}{1 + t^2}\, dt$

**23.** $y(x) = 1 + \displaystyle\int_1^x \dfrac{y(t)\, dt}{t(t + 1)}$

**24.** $y(x) = 3 + \displaystyle\int_0^x e^{-y(t)}\, dt$

**25.** If $a > b > 0$ in Example 5, find $\lim_{t \to \infty} x(t)$.

**26.** If $b > a > 0$ in Example 5, find $\lim_{t \to \infty} x(t)$.

**27.** Why is the solution given in Example 5 not valid for $a = b$? Find the solution for the case $a = b$.

**28.** An object of mass $m$ falling near the surface of the earth is retarded by air resistance proportional to its velocity so that, according to Newton's Second Law of Motion,

$$m\frac{dv}{dt} = mg - kv,$$

where $v = v(t)$ is the velocity of the object at time $t$, and $g$ is the acceleration of gravity near the surface of the earth. Assuming that the object falls from rest at time $t = 0$, that is, $v(0) = 0$, find the velocity $v(t)$ for any $t > 0$ (up until the object strikes the ground). Show $v(t)$ approaches a limit as $t \to \infty$. Do you need the explicit formula for $v(t)$ to determine this limiting velocity?

**29.** Repeat Exercise 28 except assume that the air resistance is proportional to the square of the velocity so that the equation of motion is

$$m\frac{dv}{dt} = mg - kv^2.$$

**30.** Find the amount in a savings account after one year if the initial balance in the account was \$1,000, if the interest is paid continuously into the account at a nominal rate of 10% per annum, compounded continuously, and if the account is being continuously depleted (by taxes, say) at a rate of $y^2/1{,}000{,}000$ dollars per year, where $y = y(t)$ is the balance in the account after $t$ years. How large can the account grow? How long will it take the account to grow to half this balance?

**31.** Find the family of curves each of which intersects all of the hyperbolas $xy = C$ at right angles.

**32.** Repeat the solution concentration problem in Example 4, changing the rate of inflow of brine into the tank to 12 L/min but leaving all the other data as they were in that example. Note that the volume of liquid in the tank is no longer constant as time increases.

# CHAPTER REVIEW

## *Key Ideas*

- **What do the following phrases mean?**
  ◇ a solid of revolution
  ◇ a volume element
  ◇ the arc length of a curve
  ◇ the moment of a point mass $m$ about $x = 0$

◇ the centre of mass of a distribution of mass

◇ the centroid of a plane region

◇ a first-order separable differential equation

◇ a first-order linear differential equation

• **Let $D$ be the plane region $0 \le y \le f(x)$, $a \le x \le b$. Use integrals to represent the following:**

◇ the volume generated by revolving $D$ about the $x$-axis

◇ the volume generated by revolving $D$ about the $y$-axis

◇ the moment of $D$ about the $y$-axis

◇ the moment of $D$ about the $x$-axis

◇ the centroid of $D$

• **Let $C$ be the curve $y = f(x)$, $a \le x \le b$. Use integrals to represent the following:**

◇ the length of $C$

◇ the area of the surface generated by revolving $C$ about the $x$-axis

◇ the area of the surface generated by revolving $C$ about the $y$-axis

## Review Exercises

1. Figure 10.55 shows cross-sections along the axes of two circular spools. The left spool will hold 1,000 metres of thread if wound full with no bulging. How many metres of thread of the same size will the right spool hold?

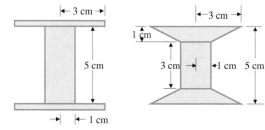

**Figure 10.55**

2. Water sitting in a bowl evaporates at a rate proportional to its surface area. Show that the depth of water in the bowl decreases at a constant rate, regardless of the shape of the bowl.

3. A barrel is 4 ft high and its volume is 16 cubic feet. Its top and bottom are circular disks of radius 1 ft, and its side wall is obtained by rotating the part of the parabola $x = a - by^2$ between $y = -2$ and $y = 2$ about the $y$-axis. Find, approximately, the values of the positive constants $a$ and $b$.

4. The solid in Figure 10.56 is cut from a vertical cylinder of radius 10 cm by two planes making angles of 60° with the horizontal. Find its volume.

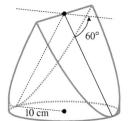

**Figure 10.56**

5. Find to 4 decimal places the value of the positive constant $a$ for which the curve $y = (1/a) \cosh ax$ has arc length 2 units between $x = 0$ and $x = 1$.

6. Find the area of the surface obtained by rotating the curve $y = \sqrt{x}$, $(0 \le x \le 6)$, about the $x$-axis.

7. Find the centroid of the plane region $x \ge 0$, $y \ge 0$, $x^2 + 4y^2 \le 4$.

8. A thin plate in the shape of a circular disk has radius 3 ft and constant areal density. A circular hole of radius 1 ft is cut out of the disk, centred 1 ft from the centre of the disk. Find the centre of mass of the remaining part of the disk.

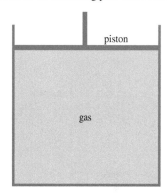

**Figure 10.57**

9. According to Boyle's Law, the product of the pressure and volume of a gas remains constant if the gas expands or is compressed isothermally. The cylinder in Figure 10.57 is filled with a gas that exerts a force of 1,000 N on the piston when the piston is 20 cm above the base of the cylinder. How much work is done by the piston if it compresses the gas isothermally by descending to a height of 5 cm above the base?

10. Suppose two functions $f$ and $g$ have the following property: for any $a > 0$, the solid produced by revolving the region of the $xy$-plane bounded by $y = f(x)$, $y = g(x)$, $x = 0$, and $x = a$ about the $x$-axis has the same volume as the solid produced by revolving the same region about the $y$-axis. What can you say about $f$ and $g$?

11. Find the equation of a curve that passes through the point $(2, 4)$ and has slope $3y/(x - 1)$ at any point $(x, y)$ on it.

12. Find a family of curves that intersect every ellipse of the form $3x^2 + 4y^2 = C$ at right angles.

13. The income and expenses of a seasonal business result in deposits and withdrawals from its bank account that correspond to a flow rate into the account of $\$P(t)$/year at time $t$ years, where $P(t) = 10{,}000 \sin(2\pi t)$. If the account earns interest at an instantaneous rate of 4% per year and has $8,000 in it at time $t = 0$, how much is in the account two years later?

## Challenging Problems

1. The curve $y = e^{-kx} \sin x$, $(x \ge 0)$, is revolved about the $x$-axis to generate a string of "beads" whose volumes decrease to the right if $k > 0$.

   (a) Show that the ratio of the volume of the $(n + 1)$st bead to that of the $n$th bead depends on $k$, but not on $n$.

   (b) For what value of $k$ is the ratio in part (a) equal to 1/2?

   (c) Find the total volume of all the beads as a function of the positive number $k$.

**2. (Conservation of earth)** A landscaper wants to create on level ground a ring-shaped pool having an outside radius of 10 m and a maximum depth of 1 m surrounding a hill that will be built up using all the earth excavated from the pool. (See Figure 10.58.) She decides to use a fourth-degree polynomial to determine the cross-sectional shape of the hill and pool bottom: at distance $r$ metres from the centre of the development the height above or below normal ground level will be

$$h(r) = a(r^2 - 100)(r^2 - k^2) \text{ metres,}$$

for some $a > 0$, where $k$ is the inner radius of the pool. Find $k$ and $a$ so that the requirements given above are all satisfied. How much earth must be moved from the pool to build the hill?

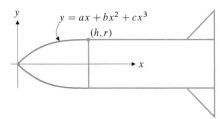

Figure 10.58

**3. (Rocket design)** The nose of a rocket is a solid of revolution of base radius $r$ and height $h$ that must join smoothly to the cylindrical body of the rocket. (See Figure 10.59.) Taking the origin at the tip of the nose and the $x$-axis along the central axis of the rocket, various nose shapes can be obtained by revolving the cubic curve

$$y = f(x) = ax + bx^2 + cx^3$$

about the $x$-axis. The cubic curve must have slope 0 at $x = h$, and its slope must be positive for $0 < x < h$. Find the particular cubic curve that maximizes the volume of the nose. Also show that this choice of the cubic makes the slope $dy/dx$ at the origin as large as possible and, hence, corresponds to the bluntest nose.

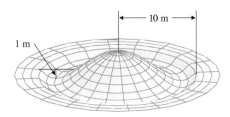

Figure 10.59

**4. (Quadratic splines)** Let $A = (x_1, y_1)$, $B = (x_2, y_2)$, and $C = (x_3, y_3)$ be three points with $x_1 < x_2 < x_3$. A function $f(x)$ whose graph passes through the three points is a *quadratic spline* if $f(x)$ is a quadratic function on $[x_1, x_2]$ and a possibly different quadratic function on $[x_2, x_3]$, and the two quadratics have the same slope at $x_2$. For this problem, take $A = (0, 1)$, $B = (1, 2)$, and $C = (3, 0)$.

(a) Find a one-parameter family $f(x, m)$ of quadratic splines through $A$, $B$, and $C$, having slope $m$ at $B$.

(b) Find the value of $m$ for which the length of the graph $y = f(x, m)$ between $x = 0$ and $x = 3$ is minimum. What is this minimum length? Compare it with the length of the polygonal line $ABC$.

**5.** A concrete wall in the shape of a circular ring must be built to have maximum height 2 m, inner radius 15 m, and width 1 m at ground level, so that its outer radius is 16 m. (See Figure 10.60.) Built on level ground, the wall will have a curved top with height at distance $15 + x$ metres from the centre of the ring given by the cubic function

$$f(x) = x(1 - x)(ax + b) \text{ m,}$$

which must not vanish anywhere in the open interval $(0, 1)$. Find the values of $a$ and $b$ that minimize the total volume of concrete needed to build the wall.

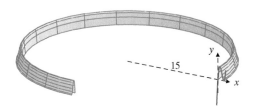

Figure 10.60

**6. (The volume of an $n$-dimensional ball)** Euclidean $n$-dimensional space consists of *points* $(x_1, x_2, \ldots, x_n)$ with $n$ real coordinates. By analogy with the 3-dimensional case, we call the set of such points that satisfy the inequality $x_1^2 + x_2^2 + \cdots + x_n^2 \leq r^2$ the $n$-dimensional *ball* centred at the origin. For example, the 1-dimensional ball is the interval $-r \leq x_1 \leq r$, which has *volume* (i.e., *length*) $V_1(r) = 2r$. The 2-dimensional ball is the disk $x_1^2 + x_2^2 \leq r^2$, which has *volume* (i.e., *area*)

$$V_2(r) = \pi r^2 = \int_{-r}^{r} 2\sqrt{r^2 - x^2}\, dx$$
$$= \int_{-r}^{r} V_1\left(\sqrt{r^2 - x^2}\right) dx.$$

The 3-dimensional ball $x_1^2 + x_2^2 + x_3^2 \leq r^2$ has volume

$$V_3(r) = \frac{4}{3}\pi r^3 = \int_{-r}^{r} \pi \left(\sqrt{r^2 - x^2}\right)^2 dx$$
$$= \int_{-r}^{r} V_2\left(\sqrt{r^2 - x^2}\right) dx.$$

By analogy with these formulas, the volume $V_n(r)$ of the $n$-dimensional ball of radius $r$ is the integral of the volume of the $(n-1)$-dimensional ball of radius $\sqrt{r^2 - x^2}$ from $x = -r$ to $x = r$:

$$V_n(r) = \int_{-r}^{r} V_{n-1}\left(\sqrt{r^2 - x^2}\right) dx.$$

Using a computer algebra program, calculate $V_4(r)$, $V_5(r)$, $\ldots$, $V_{10}(r)$, and guess formulas for $V_{2n}(r)$ (the even-dimensional balls) and $V_{2n+1}(r)$ (the odd-dimensional balls). If your computer algebra software is sufficiently powerful, you may be able to verify your guesses by induction. Otherwise, use them to predict $V_{11}(r)$ and $V_{12}(r)$, then check your predictions by starting from $V_{10}(r)$.

**7. (Buffon's needle problem)** A horizontal flat surface is ruled with parallel lines 10 cm apart, as shown in Figure 10.61. A needle 5 cm long is dropped at random onto the surface. Find the probability that the needle intersects one of the lines. *Hint:* Let the "lower" end of the needle (the end further down the page in the figure) be considered the reference point. (If both ends are the same height, use the left end.) Let $y$ be the distance from the reference point to the nearest line above it, and let $\theta$ be the angle between the needle and the line extending to the right of the reference point in the figure. What are the possible values of $y$ and $\theta$? In a plane with Cartesian coordinates $\theta$ and $y$, sketch the region consisting of all points $(\theta, y)$ corresponding to possible positions of the needle. Also sketch the region corresponding to those positions for which the needle crosses one of the parallel lines. The required probability is the area of the second region divided by the area of the first.

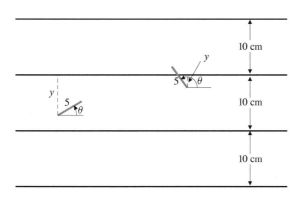

**Figure 10.61**

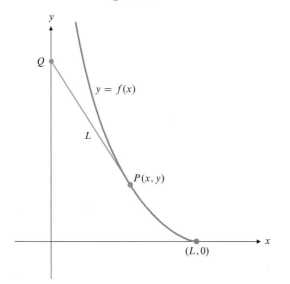

**Figure 10.62**

**8. (The path of a trailer)** Find the equation $y = f(x)$ of a curve in the first quadrant of the $xy$-plane, starting from the point $(L, 0)$, and having the property that if the tangent line to the curve at $P$ meets the $y$-axis at $Q$, then the length of $PQ$ is the constant $L$. (See Figure 10.62. This curve is called a **tractrix** after the Latin participle *tractus*, meaning *dragged*. It is the path of the rear end $P$ of a trailer of length $L$, originally lying along the $x$-axis, as the trailer is pulled (dragged) by a tractor $Q$ moving along the $y$-axis away from the origin.)

**9. (Approximating the surface area of an ellipsoid)** A physical geographer studying the flow of streams around oval stones needed to calculate the surface areas of many such stones that he modelled as ellipsoids:

$$\frac{x^2}{a^2} + \frac{y^2}{b^2} + \frac{z^2}{c^2} = 1.$$

He wanted a simple formula for the surface area so that he could implement it in a spreadsheet containing the measurements $a$, $b$, and $c$ of the stones. Unfortunately, there is no exact formula for the area of a general ellipsoid in terms of elementary functions. However, there are such formulas for ellipsoids of revolution, where two of the three semi-axes are equal. These ellipsoids are called spheroids; an *oblate spheroid* (like the earth) has its two longer semi-axes equal; a *prolate spheroid* (like an American football) has its two shorter semi-axes equal. A reasonable approximation to the area of a general ellipsoid can be obtained by linear interpolation between these two.

To be specific, assume the semi-axes are arranged in decreasing order $a \geq b \geq c$, and let the surface area be $S(a, b, c)$.

(a) Calculate $S(a, a, c)$, the area of an oblate spheroid.

(b) Calculate $S(a, c, c)$, the area of a prolate spheroid.

(c) Construct an approximation for $S(a, b, c)$ that divides the interval from $S(a, a, c)$ to $S(a, c, c)$ in the same ratio that $b$ divides the interval from $a$ to $c$.

(d) Approximate the area of the ellipsoid

$$\frac{x^2}{9} + \frac{y^2}{4} + z^2 = 1$$

using the above method.

# CHAPTER 11

# Ordinary Differential Equations

Differential equations are classified in several ways. The most significant classification is based on the number of variables with respect to which derivatives appear in the equation. An **ordinary differential equation (ODE)** is one that involves derivatives with respect to only one variable. Both of the examples given above are ordinary differential equations. A **partial differential equation (PDE)** is one that involves partial derivatives of the unknown function with respect to more than one variable. For example, the **one-dimensional wave equation**

$$\frac{\partial^2 u}{\partial t^2} = c^2 \frac{\partial^2 u}{\partial x^2}$$

models the lateral displacement $u(x,t)$ at position $x$ at time $t$ of a stretched vibrating string. We will not discuss partial differential equations in this chapter.

Differential equations are also classified with respect to **order**. The order of a differential equation is the order of the highest-order derivative present in the equation. The one-dimensional wave equation is a second-order PDE. The following example records the order of two ODEs.

---

**EXAMPLE 1**
$$\frac{d^2 y}{dx^2} + x^3 y = \sin x \qquad \text{has order 2,}$$

$$\frac{d^3 y}{dx^3} + 4x \left(\frac{dy}{dx}\right)^2 = y \frac{d^2 y}{dx^2} + e^y \qquad \text{has order 3.}$$

---

Like any equation, a differential equation can be written in the form $F = 0$, where $F$ is a function. For an ODE, the function $F$ can depend on the independent variable (usually called $x$ or $t$), the unknown function (usually $y$), and any derivatives of the unknown function up to the order of the equation. For instance, an $n$th-order ODE can be written in the form

$$F(x, y, y', y'', \ldots, y^{(n)}) = 0.$$

An important special class of differential equations consists of those that are **linear**. An $n$th-order linear ODE has the form

$$a_n(x)y^{(n)}(x) + a_{n-1}(x)y^{(n-1)}(x) + \cdots$$
$$+ a_2(x)y''(x) + a_1(x)y'(x) + a_0(x)y(x) = f(x).$$

Each term in the expression on the left side is the product of a *coefficient* that is a function of $x$, and a second factor that is either $y$ or one of the derivatives of $y$. The term on the right does not depend on $y$; it is called the **nonhomogeneous term**. Observe that no term on the left side involves any power of $y$ or its derivatives other than the first power, and $y$ and its derivatives are never multiplied together.

A linear ODE is said to be **homogeneous** if all of its terms involve the unknown function $y$, that is, if $f(x) = 0$. If $f(x)$ is not identically zero, the equation is **nonhomogeneous**.

---

**EXAMPLE 2**  In Example 1 the first DE, $\dfrac{d^2 y}{dx^2} + x^3 y = \sin x$, is linear. Here, the coefficients are $a_2(x) = 1$, $a_1(x) = 0$, $a_0(x) = x^3$, and the nonhomogeneous term is $f(x) = \sin x$. Although it can be written in the form

$$\frac{d^3 y}{dx^3} + 4x \left(\frac{dy}{dx}\right)^2 - y \frac{d^2 y}{dx^2} - e^y = 0,$$

the second equation is *not linear* (we say it is **nonlinear**) because the second term involves the square of a derivative of $y$, the third term involves the product of $y$ and one of its derivatives, and the fourth term is not $y$ times a function of $x$. The equation

$$(1 + x^2)\frac{d^3 y}{dx^3} + \sin x \frac{d^2 y}{dx^2} - 4\frac{dy}{dx} + y = 0$$

is a linear equation of order 3. The coefficients are $a_3(x) = 1 + x^2$, $a_2(x) = \sin x$, $a_1(x) = -4$, and $a_0(x) = 1$. Since $f(x) = 0$, this equation is *homogeneous*.

---

The following theorem states that any *linear combination* of solutions of a linear, homogeneous DE is also a solution. This is an extremely important fact about linear, homogeneous DEs.

**THEOREM**

**1**

If $y = y_1(x)$ and $y = y_2(x)$ are two solutions of the linear, homogeneous DE

$$a_n y^{(n)} + a_{n-1} y^{(n-1)} + \cdots + a_2 y'' + a_1 y' + a_0 y = 0,$$

then so is the linear combination

$$y = A y_1(x) + B y_2(x)$$

for any values of the constants $A$ and $B$.

**PROOF**  We are given that

$$a_n y_1^{(n)} + a_{n-1} y_1^{(n-1)} + \cdots + a_2 y_1'' + a_1 y_1' + a_0 y_1 = 0 \qquad \text{and}$$
$$a_n y_2^{(n)} + a_{n-1} y_2^{(n-1)} + \cdots + a_2 y_2'' + a_1 y_2' + a_0 y_2 = 0.$$

Multiplying the first equation by $A$ and the second by $B$ and adding the two gives

$$a_n(A y_1^{(n)} + B y_2^{(n)}) + a_{n-1}(A y_1^{(n-1)} + B y_2^{(n-1)})$$
$$+ \cdots + a_2(A y_1'' + B y_2'') + a_1(A y_1' + B y_2') + a_0(A y_1 + B y_2) = 0.$$

Thus, $y = A y_1(x) + B y_2(x)$ is also a solution of the equation.

---

The same kind of proof can be used to verify the following theorem.

**THEOREM**

**2**

If $y = y_1(x)$ is a solution of the linear, homogeneous equation

$$a_n y^{(n)} + a_{n-1} y^{(n-1)} + \cdots + a_2 y'' + a_1 y' + a_0 y = 0$$

and $y = y_2(x)$ is a solution of the linear, nonhomogeneous equation

$$a_n y^{(n)} + a_{n-1} y^{(n-1)} + \cdots + a_2 y'' + a_1 y' + a_0 y = f(x),$$

then $y = y_1(x) + y_2(x)$ is also a solution of the same linear, nonhomogeneous equation.

We will make extensive use of the two theorems above when we discuss second-order linear equations in Sections 11.4–11.6.

---

**EXAMPLE 3**

Verify that $y = \sin 2x$ and $y = \cos 2x$ satisfy the DE $y'' + 4y = 0$. Find a solution $y(x)$ of that DE that satisfies the *initial conditions* $y(0) = 2$ and $y'(0) = -4$.

***Solution*** If $y = \sin 2x$, then $y'' = \dfrac{d}{dx}(2\cos 2x) = -4\sin 2x = -4y$. Thus, $y'' + 4y = 0$. A similar calculation shows that $y = \cos 2x$ also satisfies the DE. Since the DE is linear and homogeneous, the function

$$y = A\sin 2x + B\cos 2x$$

is a solution for any values of the constants $A$ and $B$. We want $y(0) = 2$, so we need $2 = A\sin 0 + B\cos 0 = B$. Thus, $B = 2$. Also,

$$y' = 2A\cos 2x - 2B\sin 2x.$$

We want $y'(0) = -4$, so $-4 = 2A\cos 0 - 2B\sin 0 = 2A$. Thus, $A = -2$ and the required solution is $y = -2\sin 2x + 2\cos 2x$.

***Remark*** Let $P_n(r)$ be the $n$th-degree polynomial in the variable $r$ given by

$$P_n(r) = a_n(x)r^n + a_{n-1}(x)r^{n-1} + \cdots + a_2(x)r^2 + a_1(x)r + a_0(x),$$

with coefficients depending on the variable $x$. We can write the $n$th-order linear ODE with coefficients $a_k(x)$, $(0 \le k \le n)$, and nonhomogeneous term $f(x)$ in the form

$$P_n(D)y(x) = f(x),$$

where $D$ stands for the *differential operator* $d/dx$. The left side of the equation above denotes the application of the $n$th-order differential operator

$$P_n(D) = a_n(x)D^n + a_{n-1}(x)D^{n-1} + \cdots + a_2(x)D^2 + a_1(x)D + a_0(x)$$

to the function $y(x)$. For example,

$$a_k(x)D^k y(x) = a_k(x)\frac{d^k y}{dx^k}.$$

It is often useful to write linear DEs in terms of differential operators in this way.

***Remark*** Unfortunately, the term *homogeneous* is used in more than one way in the study of differential equations. Certain ODEs that are not necessarily linear are called homogeneous for a different reason than the one applying for linear equations above. We will encounter equations of this type in Section 11.2.

## EXERCISES 11.1

In Exercises 1–10, state the order of the given DE and whether it is linear or nonlinear. If it is linear, is it homogeneous or nonhomogeneous?

**1.** $\dfrac{dy}{dx} = 5y$

**2.** $\dfrac{d^2 y}{dx^2} + x = y$

**3.** $y\dfrac{dy}{dx} = x$

**4.** $y''' + xy' = x\sin x$

**5.** $y'' + x\sin x\, y' = y$

**6.** $y'' + 4y' - 3y = 2y^2$

**7.** $\dfrac{d^3 y}{dt^3} + t\dfrac{dy}{dt} + t^2 y = t^3$

**8.** $\cos x\dfrac{dx}{dt} + x\sin t = 0$

**9.** $y^{(4)} + e^x y'' = x^3 y'$

**10.** $x^2 y'' + e^x y' = \dfrac{1}{y}$

**11.** Verify that $y = \cos x$ and $y = \sin x$ are solutions of the DE $y'' + y = 0$. Are any of the following functions solutions? (a) $\sin x - \cos x$, (b) $\sin(x + 3)$, (c) $\sin 2x$. Justify your answers.

**12.** Verify that $y = e^x$ and $y = e^{-x}$ are solutions of the DE $y'' - y = 0$. Are any of the following functions solutions? (a) $\cosh x = \frac{1}{2}(e^x + e^{-x})$, (b) $\cos x$, (c) $x^e$. Justify your answers.

**13.** $y_1 = \cos(kx)$ is a solution of $y'' + k^2 y = 0$. Guess and verify another solution $y_2$ that is not a multiple of $y_1$. Then find a solution that satisfies $y(\pi/k) = 3$ and $y'(\pi/k) = 3$.

**14.** $y_1 = e^{kx}$ is a solution of $y'' - k^2 y = 0$. Guess and verify another solution $y_2$ that is not a multiple of $y_1$. Then find a solution that satisfies $y(1) = 0$ and $y'(1) = 2$.

**15.** Find a solution of $y'' + y = 0$ that satisfies $y(\pi/2) = 2y(0)$ and $y(\pi/4) = 3$. *Hint:* See Exercise 11.

**16.** Find two values of $r$ such that $y = e^{rx}$ is a solution of $y'' - y' - 2y = 0$. Then find a solution of the equation that

satisfies $y(0) = 1$, $y'(0) = 2$.

**17.** Verify that $y = x$ is a solution of $y'' + y = x$, and find a solution $y$ of this DE that satisfies $y(\pi) = 1$ and $y'(\pi) = 0$. *Hint:* Use Exercise 11 and Theorem 2.

**18.** Verify that $y = -e$ is a solution of $y'' - y = e$, and find a solution $y$ of this DE that satisfies $y(1) = 0$ and $y'(1) = 1$. *Hint:* Use Exercise 12 and Theorem 2.

## 11.2    Solving First-Order Equations

In this section we will develop techniques for solving several types of first-order ODEs, specifically,

1.  separable equations,
2.  linear equations,
3.  homogeneous equations, and
4.  exact equations.

Most first-order equations are of the form

$$\frac{dy}{dx} = f(x, y).$$

Solving such differential equations typically involves integration; indeed, the process of solving a DE is called *integrating* the DE. Nevertheless, solving DEs is usually more complicated than just writing down an integral and evaluating it. The only kind of DE that can be solved that way is the simplest kind of first-order, linear DE that can be written in the form

$$\frac{dy}{dx} = f(x).$$

The solution is then just the antiderivative of $f$:

$$y = \int f(x)\, dx.$$

### Separable Equations

The next simplest kind of equation to solve is a so-called **separable equation**. A separable equation is one of the form

$$\frac{dy}{dx} = f(x)g(y),$$

where the derivative $dy/dx$ is a product of a function of $x$ alone times a function of $y$ alone, rather than a more general function of the two variables $x$ and $y$.

> **A thorough discussion of separable equations with examples and exercises can be found in Section 10.7; we will not repeat it here. If you have not studied that material, please do so now.**

## First-Order Linear Equations

A first-order linear differential equation is one of the type

$$\frac{dy}{dx} + p(x)y = q(x),$$

where $p(x)$ and $q(x)$ are given functions, which we assume to be continuous. The equation is *homogeneous* (in the sense described in Section 11.1) provided that $q(x) = 0$ for all $x$. In that case, the given linear equation is separable,

$$\frac{dy}{y} = -p(x)\,dx,$$

which can be solved by integrating both sides. Nonhomogeneous first-order linear equations can be solved by a procedure involving the calculation of an integrating factor.

> **The technique for solving first-order linear differential equations, along with several examples and exercises, can be found in Section 10.7. If you have not studied that material, please do so now.**

## First-Order Homogeneous Equations

A first-order DE of the form

$$\frac{dy}{dx} = f\left(\frac{y}{x}\right)$$

is said to be **homogeneous**. This is a *different* use of the term homogeneous from that in the previous section, which applied only to linear equations. Here, homogeneous refers to the fact that $y/x$, and therefore $g(x, y) = f(y/x)$ is *homogeneous of degree 0* in the sense described. Such a homogeneous equation can be transformed into a separable equation (and therefore solved) by means of a change of dependent variable. If we set

$$v = \frac{y}{x}, \qquad \text{or equivalently} \qquad y = xv(x),$$

then we have

$$\frac{dy}{dx} = v + x\,\frac{dv}{dx},$$

and the original differential equation transforms into

$$\frac{dv}{dx} = \frac{f(v) - v}{x},$$

which is separable.

---

**EXAMPLE 1**  Solve the equation

$$\frac{dy}{dx} = \frac{x^2 + xy}{xy + y^2}.$$

*Solution*  The equation is homogeneous. (Divide the numerator and denominator of the right-hand side by $x^2$ to see this.) If $y = vx$ the equation becomes

$$v + x\,\frac{dv}{dx} = \frac{1 + v}{v + v^2} = \frac{1}{v},$$

or

$$x \frac{dv}{dx} = \frac{1 - v^2}{v}.$$

Separating variables and integrating, we calculate

$$\int \frac{v \, dv}{1 - v^2} = \int \frac{dx}{x} \qquad \text{Let } u = 1 - v^2$$

$$-\frac{1}{2} \int \frac{du}{u} = \int \frac{dx}{x}$$

$$-\ln|u| = 2\ln|x| + C_1 = \ln C_2 x^2 \qquad (C_1 = \ln C_2)$$

$$\frac{1}{|u|} = C_2 x^2$$

$$|1 - v^2| = \frac{C_3}{x^2} \qquad (C_3 = 1/C_2)$$

$$\left| 1 - \frac{y^2}{x^2} \right| = \frac{C_3}{x^2}.$$

The solution is best expressed in the form $x^2 - y^2 = C_4$. However, near points where $y \neq 0$, the equation can be solved for $y$ as a function of $x$.

## Exact Equations

A first-order differential equation expressed in differential form as

$$M(x, y) \, dx + N(x, y) \, dy = 0,$$

which is equivalent to $\dfrac{dy}{dx} = -\dfrac{M(x, y)}{N(x, y)}$, is said to be **exact** if the left-hand side is the differential of a function $\phi(x, y)$:

$$d\phi(x, y) = M(x, y) \, dx + N(x, y) \, dy.$$

The function $\phi$ is called an **integral function** of the differential equation. The level curves $\phi(x, y) = C$ of $\phi$ are the **solution curves** of the differential equation. For example, the differential equation

$$x \, dx + y \, dy = 0$$

has solution curves given by

$$x^2 + y^2 = C$$

since $d(x^2 + y^2) = 2(x \, dx + y \, dy) = 0$.

*Remark*   The condition that the differential equation $M \, dx + N \, dy = 0$ should be exact is just the condition that the vector field

$$\mathbf{F} = M(x, y) \, \mathbf{i} + N(x, y) \, \mathbf{j}$$

should be *conservative*; the integral function of the differential equation is then the potential function of the vector field.

A **necessary condition** for the exactness of the DE $M\,dx + N\,dy = 0$ is that

$$\frac{\partial M}{\partial y} = \frac{\partial N}{\partial x};$$

this just says that the mixed partial derivatives $\dfrac{\partial^2 \phi}{\partial x \partial y}$ and $\dfrac{\partial^2 \phi}{\partial y \partial x}$ of the integral function $\phi$ must be equal.

Once you know that an equation is exact, you can often guess the integral function. In any event, $\phi$ can always be found by the same method used to find the potential of a conservative vector field.

---

**EXAMPLE 2**    Verify that the DE

$$(2x + \sin y - ye^{-x})\,dx + (x\cos y + \cos y + e^{-x})\,dy = 0$$

is exact and find its solution curves.

**Solution**   Here, $M = 2x + \sin y - ye^{-x}$ and $N = x\cos y + \cos y + e^{-x}$. Since

$$\frac{\partial M}{\partial y} = \cos y - e^{-x} = \frac{\partial N}{\partial x},$$

the DE is exact. We want to find $\phi$ so that

$$\frac{\partial \phi}{\partial x} = M = 2x + \sin y - ye^{-x} \quad \text{and} \quad \frac{\partial \phi}{\partial y} = N = x\cos y + \cos y + e^{-x}.$$

Integrate the first equation with respect to $x$, being careful to allow the constant of integration to depend on $y$:

$$\phi(x, y) = \int (2x + \sin y - ye^{-x})\,dx = x^2 + x\sin y + ye^{-x} + C_1(y).$$

Now substitute this expression into the second equation:

$$x\cos y + \cos y + e^{-x} = \frac{\partial \phi}{\partial y} = x\cos y + e^{-x} + C_1'(y).$$

Thus, $C_1'(y) = \cos y$, and $C_1(y) = \sin y + C_2$. (It is because the original DE was exact that the equation for $C_1'(y)$ turned out to be independent of $x$; this had to happen or we could not have found $C_1$ as a function of $y$ only.) Choosing $C_2 = 0$, we find that $\phi(x, y) = x^2 + x\sin y + ye^{-x} + \sin y$ is an integral function for the given DE. The solution curves for the DE are the level curves

$$x^2 + x\sin y + ye^{-x} + \sin y = C.$$

---

## Integrating Factors

Any ordinary differential equation of order 1 and degree 1 can be expressed in differential form: $M\,dx + N\,dy = 0$. However, this latter equation will usually not be exact. It *may* be possible to multiply the equation by an **integrating factor** $\mu(x, y)$ so that the resulting equation

$$\mu(x, y)\,M(x, y)\,dx + \mu(x, y)\,N(x, y)\,dy = 0$$

is exact. In general, such integrating factors are difficult to find; they must satisfy the partial differential equation

$$M(x, y)\frac{\partial \mu}{\partial y} - N(x, y)\frac{\partial \mu}{\partial x} = \mu(x, y)\left(\frac{\partial N}{\partial x} - \frac{\partial M}{\partial y}\right),$$

which follows from the necessary condition for exactness stated above. We will not try to solve this equation here.

Sometimes it happens that a differential equation has an integrating factor depending on only one of the two variables. Suppose, for instance, that $\mu(x)$ is an integrating factor for $M\,dx + N\,dy = 0$. Then $\mu(x)$ must satisfy the ordinary differential equation

$$N(x, y) \frac{d\mu}{dx} = \mu(x)\left(\frac{\partial M}{\partial y} - \frac{\partial N}{\partial x}\right),$$

or

$$\frac{1}{\mu(x)}\frac{d\mu}{dx} = \frac{\dfrac{\partial M}{\partial y} - \dfrac{\partial N}{\partial x}}{N(x, y)}.$$

This equation can be solved (by integration) for $\mu$ as a function of $x$ alone *provided that the right-hand side is independent of $y$.*

**EXAMPLE 3**   Show that $(x + y^2)\,dx + xy\,dy = 0$ has an integrating factor depending only on $x$, find it, and solve the equation.

**Solution**   Here $M = x + y^2$ and $N = xy$. Since

$$\frac{\dfrac{\partial M}{\partial y} - \dfrac{\partial N}{\partial x}}{N(x, y)} = \frac{2y - y}{xy} = \frac{1}{x}$$

does not depend on $y$, the equation has an integrating factor depending only on $x$. This factor is given by $d\mu/\mu = dx/x$. Evidently, $\mu = x$ is a suitable integrating factor; if we multiply the given differential equation by $x$, we obtain

$$0 = (x^2 + xy^2)\,dx + x^2 y\,dy = d\left(\frac{x^3}{3} + \frac{x^2 y^2}{2}\right).$$

The solution is therefore $2x^3 + 3x^2 y^2 = C$.

**Remark**   Of course, it may be possible to find an integrating factor depending on $y$ instead of $x$. See Exercises 17–19 below. It is also possible to look for integrating factors that depend on specific combinations of $x$ and $y$, for instance, $xy$. See Exercise 20.

## EXERCISES 11.2

See Section 10.7 for exercises on separable equations and linear equations.

Solve the homogeneous differential equations in Exercises 1–6.

**1.** $\dfrac{dy}{dx} = \dfrac{x + y}{x - y}$

**2.** $\dfrac{dy}{dx} = \dfrac{xy}{x^2 + 2y^2}$

**3.** $\dfrac{dy}{dx} = \dfrac{x^2 + xy + y^2}{x^2}$

**4.** $\dfrac{dy}{dx} = \dfrac{x^3 + 3xy^2}{3x^2 y + y^3}$

**5.** $x\dfrac{dy}{dx} = y + x\cos^2\left(\dfrac{y}{x}\right)$

**6.** $\dfrac{dy}{dx} = \dfrac{y}{x} - e^{-y/x}$

**7.** Find an equation of the curve in the $xy$-plane that passes through the point $(2, 3)$ and has, at every point $(x, y)$ on it, slope $2x/(1 + y^2)$.

**8.** Repeat Exercise 7 for the point $(1, 3)$ and slope $1 + (2y/x)$.

**9.** Show that the change of variables $\xi = x - x_0$, $\eta = y - y_0$ transforms the equation

$$\frac{dy}{dx} = \frac{ax + by + c}{ex + fy + g}$$

into the homogeneous equation

$$\frac{d\eta}{d\xi} = \frac{a\xi + b\eta}{e\xi + f\eta},$$

provided $(x_0, y_0)$ is the solution of the system

$$ax + by + c = 0$$
$$ex + fy + g = 0.$$

**10.** Use the technique of Exercise 9 to solve the equation
$$\frac{dy}{dx} = \frac{x + 2y - 4}{2x - y - 3}.$$

Show that the DEs in Exercises 11–14 are exact, and solve them.

**11.** $(xy^2 + y)\,dx + (x^2y + x)\,dy = 0$

**12.** $(e^x \sin y + 2x)\,dx + (e^x \cos y + 2y)\,dy = 0$

**13.** $e^{xy}(1 + xy)\,dx + x^2 e^{xy}\,dy = 0$

**14.** $\left(2x + 1 - \dfrac{y^2}{x^2}\right) dx + \dfrac{2y}{x}\,dy = 0$

Show that the DEs in Exercises 15–16 admit integrating factors that are functions of $x$ alone. Then solve the equations.

**15.** $(x^2 + 2y)\,dx - x\,dy = 0$

**16.** $(xe^x + x \ln y + y)\,dx + \left(\dfrac{x^2}{y} + x \ln x + x \sin y\right) dy = 0$

**17.** What condition must the coefficients $M(x, y)$ and $N(x, y)$ satisfy if the equation $M\,dx + N\,dy = 0$ is to have an integrating factor of the form $\mu(y)$, and what DE must the integrating factor satisfy?

**18.** Find an integrating factor of the form $\mu(y)$ for the equation

$$2y^2(x + y^2)\,dx + xy(x + 6y^2)\,dy = 0,$$

and hence solve the equation. *Hint:* See Exercise 17.

**19.** Find an integrating factor of the form $\mu(y)$ for the equation $y\,dx - (2x + y^3 e^y)\,dy = 0$, and hence solve the equation. *Hint:* See Exercise 17.

**20.** What condition must the coefficients $M(x, y)$ and $N(x, y)$ satisfy if the equation $M\,dx + N\,dy = 0$ is to have an integrating factor of the form $\mu(xy)$, and what DE must the integrating factor satisfy?

**21.** Find an integrating factor of the form $\mu(xy)$ for the equation

$$\left(x \cos x + \frac{y^2}{x}\right) dx - \left(\frac{x \sin x}{y} + y\right) dy = 0,$$

and hence solve the equation. *Hint:* See Exercise 20.

## 11.3   Existence, Uniqueness, and Numerical Methods

A general first-order differential equation of the form

$$\frac{dy}{dx} = f(x, y)$$

specifies a slope $f(x, y)$ at every point $(x, y)$ in the domain of $f$, and therefore represents a **slope field**. Such a slope field can be represented graphically by drawing short line segments of the indicated slope at many points in the $xy$-plane. Slope fields resemble vector fields, but the segments are usually drawn having the same length and without arrowheads. Figure 11.1 portrays the slope field for the differential equation

$$\frac{dy}{dx} = x - y.$$

Solving a typical initial-value problem

$$\begin{cases} \dfrac{dy}{dx} = f(x, y) \\ y(x_0) = y_0 \end{cases}$$

involves finding a function $y = \phi(x)$ such that

$$\phi'(x) = f\big(x, \phi(x)\big) \qquad \text{and} \qquad \phi(x_0) = y_0.$$

The graph of the equation $y = \phi(x)$ is a curve passing through $(x_0, y_0)$ that is tangent to the slope-field at each point. Such curves are called **solution curves** of the differential equation. Figure 11.1 shows four solution curves for $y' = x - y$ corresponding to the initial conditions $y(0) = C$, where $C = -2, -1, 0,$ and $1$.

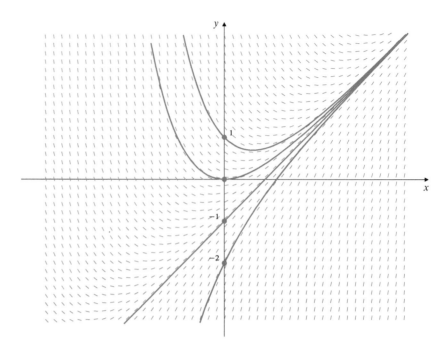

Figure 11.1    The slope field for the DE $y' = x - y$ and four solution curves for this DE

The DE $y' = x - y$ is linear and can be solved explicitly by the method of Section 11.2. Indeed, the solution satisfying $y(0) = C$ is $y = x - 1 + (C + 1)e^{-x}$. Most differential equations of the form $y' = f(x, y)$ cannot be solved for $y$ as an explicit function of $x$, so we must use numerical approximation methods to find the value of a solution function $\phi(x)$ at particular points.

## Existence and Uniqueness of Solutions

Even if we cannot calculate an explicit solution of an initial-value problem, it is important to know when the problem has a solution and whether that solution is unique.

**THEOREM**

**3**

**An existence and uniqueness theorem for first-order initial-value problems**

Suppose that $f(x, y)$ and $f_2(x, y) = (\partial/\partial y) f(x, y)$ are continuous on a rectangle $R$ of the form $a \leq x \leq b$, $c \leq y \leq d$, containing the point $(x_0, y_0)$ in its interior. Then there exists a number $\delta > 0$ and a *unique* function $\phi(x)$ defined and having a continuous derivative on the interval $(x_0 - \delta, x_0 + \delta)$ such that $\phi(x_0) = y_0$ and $\phi'(x) = f(x, \phi(x))$ for $x_0 - \delta < x < x_0 + \delta$. In other words, the initial-value problem

$$\begin{cases} \dfrac{dy}{dx} = f(x, y) \\ y(x_0) = y_0 \end{cases} \qquad (*)$$

has a unique solution on $(x_0 - \delta, x_0 + \delta)$.

We give only an outline of the proof here. Any solution $y = \phi(x)$ of the initial-value problem $(*)$ must also satisfy the **integral equation**

$$\phi(x) = y_0 + \int_{x_0}^{x} f(t, \phi(t)) \, dt, \qquad (**)$$

and, conversely, any solution of the integral equation $(**)$ must also satisfy the initial-value problem $(*)$. A sequence of approximations $\phi_n(x)$ to a solution of $(**)$ can be constructed as follows:

$$\phi_0(x) = y_0$$

$$\phi_{n+1}(x) = y_0 + \int_{x_0}^{x} f\left(t, \phi_n(t)\right) dt \qquad \text{for} \quad n = 0, 1, 2, \ldots$$

(These are called **Picard iterations.**) The proof of Theorem 3 involves showing that

$$\lim_{n \to \infty} \phi_n(x) = \phi(x)$$

exists on an interval $(x_0 - \delta, x_0 + \delta)$ and that the resulting limit $\phi(x)$ satisfies the integral equation $(**)$. The details can be found in more advanced texts on differential equations and analysis.

*Remark* Some initial-value problems can have nonunique solutions. For example, the functions $y_1(x) = x^3$ and $y_2(x) = 0$ both satisfy the initial-value problem

$$\begin{cases} \dfrac{dy}{dx} = 3y^{2/3} \\ y(0) = 0. \end{cases}$$

In this case $f(x, y) = 3y^{2/3}$ is continuous on the whole $xy$-plane. However, $\partial f / \partial y = 2y^{-1/3}$ is not continuous on the $x$-axis and is therefore not continuous on any rectangle containing $(0, 0)$ in its interior. The conditions of Theorem 3 are not satisfied, and the initial-value problem has a solution, but not a unique one.

*Remark* The unique solution $y = \phi(x)$ to the initial-value problem $(*)$ guaranteed by Theorem 3 may not be defined on the whole interval $[a, b]$ because it can "escape" from the rectangle $R$ through the top or bottom edges. Even if $f(x, y)$ and $(\partial / \partial y) f(x, y)$ are continuous on the whole $xy$-plane, the solution may not be defined on the whole real line. For example,

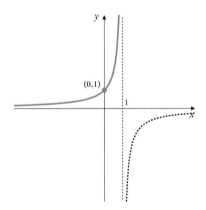

$$y = \frac{1}{1 - x} \qquad \text{satisfies the initial-value problem} \qquad \begin{cases} \dfrac{dy}{dx} = y^2 \\ y(0) = 1 \end{cases}$$

**Figure 11.2** The solution to $y' = y^2$, $y(0) = 1$ is the part of the curve $y = 1/(1 - x)$ to the left of the vertical asymptote at $x = 1$

but only for $x < 1$. Starting from $(0, 1)$, we can follow the solution curve as far as we want to the left of $x = 0$, but to the right of $x = 0$ the curve recedes to $\infty$ as $x \to 1-$. (See Figure 11.2.) It makes no sense to regard the part of the curve to the right of $x = 1$ as part of the solution curve to the initial-value problem.

## Numerical Methods

Suppose that the conditions of Theorem 3 are satisfied, so we know that the initial-value problem

$$\begin{cases} \dfrac{dy}{dx} = f(x, y) \\ y(x_0) = y_0 \end{cases}$$

has a unique solution $y = \phi(x)$ on some interval containing $x_0$. Even if we cannot solve the differential equation and find $\phi(x)$ explicitly, we can still try to find approximate values $y_n$ for $\phi(x_n)$ at a sequence of points

$$x_0, \quad x_1 = x_0 + h, \quad x_2 = x_0 + 2h, \quad x_3 = x_0 + 3h, \quad \ldots$$

starting at $x_0$. Here, $h > 0$ (or $h < 0$) is called the **step size** of the approximation scheme. In the remainder of this section we will describe three methods for constructing the approximations $\{y_n\}$:

1. the Euler method,
2. the improved Euler method, and
3. the fourth-order Runge–Kutta method.

Each of these methods starts with the given value of $y_0$ and provides a formula for constructing $y_{n+1}$ when you know $y_n$. The three methods are listed above in increasing order of the complexity of their formulas, but the more complicated formulas produce much better approximations for any given step size $h$.

The **Euler method** involves approximating the solution curve $y = \phi(x)$ by a polygonal line (a sequence of straight line segments joined end to end), where each segment has horizontal length $h$ and slope determined by the value of $f(x, y)$ at the end of the previous segment. Thus, if $x_n = x_0 + nh$, then

$$y_1 = y_0 + f(x_0, y_0)h$$
$$y_2 = y_1 + f(x_1, y_1)h$$
$$y_3 = y_2 + f(x_2, y_2)h$$

and, in general,

**Iteration formulas for Euler's method**

$$x_{n+1} = x_n + h, \qquad y_{n+1} = y_n + hf(x_n, y_n).$$

**EXAMPLE 1**    Use Euler's method to find approximate values for the solution of the initial-value problem

$$\begin{cases} \dfrac{dy}{dx} = x - y \\ y(0) = 1 \end{cases}$$

on the interval $[0, 1]$ using

(a)  5 steps of size $h = 0.2$, and

(b)  10 steps of size $h = 0.1$.

Calculate the error at each step, given that the problem (which involves a linear equation and so can be solved explicitly) has solution $y = \phi(x) = x - 1 + 2e^{-x}$.

*Solution*

(a)  Here we have $f(x, y) = x - y$, $x_0 = 0$, $y_0 = 1$, and $h = 0.2$, so that

$$x_n = \frac{n}{5}, \qquad y_{n+1} = y_n + 0.2(x_n - y_n),$$

and the error is $e_n = \phi(x_n) - y_n$ for $n = 0, 1, 2, 3, 4,$ and 5. The results of the calculation, which was done easily using a computer spreadsheet program, are presented in Table 1.

Table 1.    Euler approximations with $h = 0.2$

| $n$ | $x_n$ | $y_n$ | $f(x_n, y_n)$ | $y_{n+1}$ | $e_n = \phi(x_n) - y_n$ |
|---|---|---|---|---|---|
| 0 | 0.0 | 1.000 000 | −1.000 000 | 0.800 000 | 0.000 000 |
| 1 | 0.2 | 0.800 000 | −0.600 000 | 0.680 000 | 0.037 462 |
| 2 | 0.4 | 0.680 000 | −0.280 000 | 0.624 000 | 0.060 640 |
| 3 | 0.6 | 0.624 000 | −0.024 000 | 0.619 200 | 0.073 623 |
| 4 | 0.8 | 0.619 200 | 0.180 800 | 0.655 360 | 0.079 458 |
| 5 | 1.0 | 0.655 360 | 0.344 640 | | 0.080 399 |

The exact solution $y = \phi(x)$ and the polygonal line representing the Euler approximation are shown in Figure 11.3. The approximation lies below the solution curve, as is reflected in the positive values in the last column of Table 1, representing the error at each step.

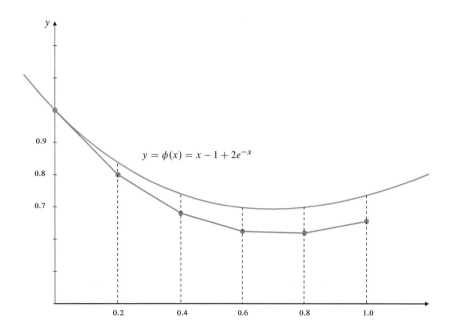

**Figure 11.3**    The solution $y = \phi(x)$ to $y' = x - y$, $y(0) = 1$ and an Euler approximation to it on $[0, 1]$ with step size $h = 0.2$

(b)  Here we have $h = 0.1$, so that

$$x_n = \frac{n}{10}, \qquad y_{n+1} = y_n + 0.1(x_n - y_n)$$

for $n = 0, 1, \ldots, 10$. Again we present the results in tabular form:

**Table 2.**   Euler approximations with $h = 0.1$

| $n$ | $x_n$ | $y_n$ | $f(x_n, y_n)$ | $y_{n+1}$ | $e_n = \phi(x_n) - y_n$ |
|---|---|---|---|---|---|
| 0 | 0.0 | 1.000 000 | −1.000 000 | 0.900 000 | 0.000 000 |
| 1 | 0.1 | 0.900 000 | −0.800 000 | 0.820 000 | 0.009 675 |
| 2 | 0.2 | 0.820 000 | −0.620 000 | 0.758 000 | 0.017 462 |
| 3 | 0.3 | 0.758 000 | −0.458 000 | 0.712 200 | 0.023 636 |
| 4 | 0.4 | 0.712 200 | −0.312 200 | 0.680 980 | 0.028 440 |
| 5 | 0.5 | 0.680 980 | −0.180 980 | 0.662 882 | 0.032 081 |
| 6 | 0.6 | 0.662 882 | −0.062 882 | 0.656 594 | 0.034 741 |
| 7 | 0.7 | 0.656 594 | 0.043 406 | 0.660 934 | 0.036 577 |
| 8 | 0.8 | 0.660 934 | 0.139 066 | 0.674 841 | 0.037 724 |
| 9 | 0.9 | 0.674 841 | 0.225 159 | 0.697 357 | 0.038 298 |
| 10 | 1.0 | 0.697 357 | 0.302 643 | | 0.038 402 |

Observe that the error at the end of the first step is about one-quarter of the error at the end of the first step in part (a), but the final error at $x = 1$ is only about half as large as in part (a). This behaviour is characteristic of Euler's method.

If we decrease the step size $h$, it takes more steps ($n = |x - x_0|/h$) to get from the starting point $x_0$ to a particular value $x$ where we want to know the value of the solution. For Euler's method it can be shown that the error at each step decreases on average proportionally to $h^2$, but the errors can accumulate from step to step, so the error at $x$ can be expected to decrease proportionally to $nh^2 = |x - x_0|h$. This is consistent with the results of Example 1. Decreasing $h$ and so increasing $n$ is costly in terms of computing resources, so we would like to find ways of reducing the error without decreasing the step size. This is similar to developing better techniques than the Trapezoid Rule for evaluating definite integrals numerically.

The **improved Euler method** is a step in this direction. The accuracy of the Euler method is hampered by the fact that the slope of each segment in the approximating polygonal line is determined by the value of $f(x, y)$ at one endpoint of the segment. Since $f$ varies along the segment, we would expect to do better by using, say, the average value of $f(x, y)$ at the two ends of the segment, that is, by calculating $y_{n+1}$ from the formula

$$y_{n+1} = y_n + h \frac{f(x_n, y_n) + f(x_{n+1}, y_{n+1})}{2}.$$

Unfortunately, $y_{n+1}$ appears on both sides of this equation, and we can't usually solve the equation for $y_{n+1}$. We can get around this difficulty by replacing $y_{n+1}$ on the right side by its Euler approximation $y_n + hf(x_n, y_n)$. The resulting formula is the basis for the improved Euler method.

> **Iteration formulas for the improved Euler method**
>
> $x_{n+1} = x_n + h$
>
> $u_{n+1} = y_n + h\, f(x_n, y_n)$
>
> $y_{n+1} = y_n + h\, \dfrac{f(x_n, y_n) + f(x_{n+1}, u_{n+1})}{2}.$

**EXAMPLE 2**    Use the improved Euler method with $h = 0.2$ to find approximate values for the solution to the initial-value problem of Example 1 on $[0, 1]$. Compare the errors with those obtained by the Euler method.

**Solution**    Table 3 summarizes the calculation of five steps of the improved Euler method for $f(x, y) = x - y$, $x_0 = 0$, and $y_0 = 1$.

Table 3.    Improved Euler approximations with $h = 0.2$

| $n$ | $x_n$ | $y_n$ | $u_{n+1}$ | $y_{n+1}$ | $e_n = \phi(x_n) - y_n$ |
|---|---|---|---|---|---|
| 0 | 0.0 | 1.000 000 | 0.800 000 | 0.840 000 | 0.000 000 |
| 1 | 0.2 | 0.840 000 | 0.712 000 | 0.744 800 | −0.002 538 |
| 2 | 0.4 | 0.744 800 | 0.675 840 | 0.702 736 | −0.004 160 |
| 3 | 0.6 | 0.702 736 | 0.682 189 | 0.704 244 | −0.005 113 |
| 4 | 0.8 | 0.704 244 | 0.723 395 | 0.741 480 | −0.005 586 |
| 5 | 1.0 | 0.741 480 | 0.793 184 | | −0.005 721 |

Observe that the errors are considerably less than one-tenth those obtained in Example 1(a). Of course, more calculations are necessary at each step, but the number of evaluations of $f(x, y)$ required is only twice the number required for Example 1(a). As for numerical integration, if $f$ is complicated, it is these function evaluations that constitute most of the computational "cost" of computing numerical solutions.

**Remark**    It can be shown for well-behaved functions $f$ that the error at each step in the improved Euler method is bounded by a multiple of $h^3$ rather than $h^2$ as for the (unimproved) Euler method. Thus, the cumulative error at $x$ can be bounded by a constant times $|x - x_0|h^2$. If Example 2 is repeated with 10 steps of size $h = 0.1$, the error at $n = 10$ (i.e., at $x = 1$) is $-0.001\,323$, which is about one-fourth the size of the error at $x = 1$ with $h = 0.2$.

The **fourth-order Runge–Kutta method** further improves upon the improved Euler method, but at the expense of requiring more complicated calculations at each step. It requires four evaluations of $f(x, y)$ at each step, but the error at each step is less than a constant times $h^5$, so the cumulative error decreases like $h^4$ as $h$ decreases. Like the improved Euler method, this method involves calculating a certain kind of average slope for each segment in the polygonal approximation to the solution to the initial-value problem. We present the appropriate formulas below but cannot derive them here.

**Iteration formulas for the Runge–Kutta method**

$$x_{n+1} = x_n + h$$
$$p_n = f(x_n, y_n)$$
$$q_n = f\left(x_n + \frac{h}{2}, y_n + \frac{h}{2}p_n\right)$$
$$r_n = f\left(x_n + \frac{h}{2}, y_n + \frac{h}{2}q_n\right)$$
$$s_n = f(x_n + h, y_n + hr_n)$$
$$y_{n+1} = y_n + h\frac{p_n + 2q_n + 2r_n + s_n}{6}.$$

**EXAMPLE 3**   Use the fourth-order Runge–Kutta method with $h = 0.2$ to find approximate values for the solution to the initial-value problem of Example 1 on $[0, 1]$. Compare the errors with those obtained by the Euler and improved Euler methods.

*Solution*   Table 4 summarizes the calculation of five steps of the Runge–Kutta method for $f(x, y) = x - y$, $x_0 = 0$, and $y_0 = 1$ according to the formulas above. The table does not show the values of the intermediate quantities $p_n, q_n, r_n$, and $s_n$, but columns for these quantities were included in the spreadsheet in which the calculations were made.

Table 4.   Fourth-order Runge–Kutta approximations with $h = 0.2$

| $n$ | $x_n$ | $y_n$ | $e_n = \phi(x_n) - y_n$ |
|---|---|---|---|
| 0 | 0.0 | 1.000 000 | 0.000 000 0 |
| 1 | 0.2 | 0.837 467 | −0.000 005 2 |
| 2 | 0.4 | 0.740 649 | −0.000 008 5 |
| 3 | 0.6 | 0.697 634 | −0.000 010 4 |
| 4 | 0.8 | 0.698 669 | −0.000 011 3 |
| 5 | 1.0 | 0.735 770 | −0.000 011 6 |

The errors here are about 1/500 of the size of the errors obtained with the improved Euler method and about 1/7,000 of the size of the errors obtained with the Euler method. This great improvement was achieved at the expense of doubling the number of function evaluations required in the improved Euler method and quadrupling the number required in the Euler method. If we use 10 steps of size $h = 0.1$ in the Runge–Kutta method, the error at $x = 1$ is reduced to $-6.664\,82 \times 10^{-7}$, which is less than 1/16 of its value when $h = 0.2$.

Our final example shows what can happen with numerical approximations to a solution that is unbounded.

**EXAMPLE 4**   Obtain approximations at $x = 0.4$, $x = 0.8$, and $x = 1.0$ for solutions to the initial-value problem

$$\begin{cases} y' = y^2 \\ y(0) = 1 \end{cases}$$

using all three methods described above, and using step sizes $h = 0.2$, $h = 0.1$, and $h = 0.05$ for each method. What do the results suggest about the values of the solution at these points? Compare the results with the actual solution $y = 1/(1 - x)$.

*Solution* The various approximations are calculated using the various formulas described above for $f(x, y) = y^2$, $x_0 = 0$, and $y_0 = 1$. The results are presented in Table 5.

Table 5. Comparing methods and step sizes for $y' = y^2$, $y(0) = 1$

|  | $h = 0.2$ | $h = 0.1$ | $h = 0.05$ |
|---|---|---|---|
| Euler |  |  |  |
| $x = 0.4$ | 1.488 000 | 1.557 797 | 1.605 224 |
| $x = 0.8$ | 2.676 449 | 3.239 652 | 3.793 197 |
| $x = 1.0$ | 4.109 124 | 6.128 898 | 9.552 668 |
| Improved Euler |  |  |  |
| $x = 0.4$ | 1.640 092 | 1.658 736 | 1.664 515 |
| $x = 0.8$ | 4.190 396 | 4.677 726 | 4.897 519 |
| $x = 1.0$ | 11.878 846 | 22.290 765 | 43.114 668 |
| Runge–Kutta |  |  |  |
| $x = 0.4$ | 1.666 473 | 1.666 653 | 1.666 666 |
| $x = 0.8$ | 4.965 008 | 4.996 663 | 4.999 751 |
| $x = 1.0$ | 41.016 258 | 81.996 399 | 163.983 395 |

Little useful information can be read from the Euler results. The improved Euler results suggest that the solution exists at $x = 0.4$ and $x = 0.8$, but likely not at $x = 1$. The Runge–Kutta results confirm this and suggest that $y(0.4) = 5/3$ and $y(0.8) = 5$, which are the correct values provided by the actual solution $y = 1/(1 - x)$. They also suggest very strongly that the solution "blows up" at (or near) $x = 1$.

## EXERCISES 11.3

A computer is almost essential for doing most of these exercises. The calculations are easily done with a spreadsheet program in which formulas for calculating the various quantities involved can be replicated down columns to automate the iteration process.

**1.** Use the Euler method with step sizes (a) $h = 0.2$, (b) $h = 0.1$, and (c) $h = 0.05$ to approximate $y(2)$ given that $y' = x + y$ and $y(1) = 0$.

**2.** Repeat Exercise 1 using the improved Euler method.

**3.** Repeat Exercise 1 using the Runge–Kutta method.

**4.** Use the Euler method with step sizes (a) $h = 0.2$ and (b) $h = 0.1$ to approximate $y(2)$ given that $y' = xe^{-y}$ and $y(0) = 0$.

**5.** Repeat Exercise 4 using the improved Euler method.

**6.** Repeat Exercise 4 using the Runge–Kutta method.

**7.** Use the Euler method with (a) $h = 0.2$, (b) $h = 0.1$, and (c) $h = 0.05$ to approximate $y(1)$ given that $y' = \cos y$ and $y(0) = 0$.

**8.** Repeat Exercise 7 using the improved Euler method.

**9.** Repeat Exercise 7 using the Runge–Kutta method.

**10.** Use the Euler method with (a) $h = 0.2$, (b) $h = 0.1$, and (c) $h = 0.05$ to approximate $y(1)$ given that $y' = \cos(x^2)$ and $y(0) = 0$.

**11.** Repeat Exercise 10 using the improved Euler method.

**12.** Repeat Exercise 10 using the Runge–Kutta method.

Solve the integral equations in Exercises 13–14 by rephrasing them as initial-value problems.

**13.** $y(x) = 2 + \int_1^x \left( y(t) \right)^2 dt$. *Hint:* Find $\dfrac{dy}{dx}$ and $y(1)$.

**14.** $u(x) = 1 + 3 \int_2^x t^2 u(t) \, dt$. *Hint:* Find $\dfrac{du}{dx}$ and $u(2)$.

**15.** The methods of this section can be used to approximate definite integrals numerically. For example,

$$ I = \int_a^b f(x) \, dx $$

is given by $I = y(b)$, where

$$ y' = f(x), \quad \text{and} \quad y(a) = 0. $$

Show that one step of the Runge–Kutta method with $h = b - a$ gives the same result for $I$ as Simpson's Rule (Section 9.4) with two subintervals of length $h/2$.

**16.** If $\phi(0) = A \geq 0$ and $\phi'(x) \geq k\phi(x)$ on $[0, X]$, where $k > 0$ and $X > 0$ are constants, show that $\phi(x) \geq Ae^{kx}$ on $[0, X]$. *Hint:* Calculate $(d/dx)(\phi(x)/e^{kx})$.

**17.** Consider the three initial-value problems

| | | |
|---|---|---|
| (A) | $u' = u^2$ | $u(0) = 1$ |
| (B) | $y' = x + y^2$ | $y(0) = 1$ |
| (C) | $v' = 1 + v^2$ | $v(0) = 1$ |

(a) Show that the solution of (B) remains between the solutions of (A) and (C) on any interval $[0, X]$ where solutions of all three problems exist. *Hint:* We must have $u(x) \geq 1$, $y(x) \geq 1$, and $v(x) \geq 1$ on $[0, X]$. (Why?) Apply the result of Exercise 16 to $\phi = y - u$ and to $\phi = v - y$.

(b) Find explicit solutions for problems (A) and (C). What can you conclude about the solution to problem (B)?

 (c) Use the Runge–Kutta method with $h = 0.05$, $h = 0.02$, and $h = 0.01$ to approximate the solution to (B) on $[0, 1]$. What can you conclude now?

# 11.4   Differential Equations of Second Order

The general second-order ordinary differential equation is of the form

$$F\left(\frac{d^2y}{dx^2}, \frac{dy}{dx}, y, x\right) = 0$$

for some function $F$ of four variables. When such an equation can be solved explicitly for $y$ as a function of $x$, the solution typically involves two integrations and therefore two arbitrary constants. A unique solution usually results from prescribing the values of the solution $y$ and its first derivative $y' = dy/dx$ at a particular point. Such a prescription constitutes an **initial-value problem** for the second-order equation.

## Equations Reducible to First Order

A second-order equation of the form

$$F\left(\frac{d^2y}{dx^2}, \frac{dy}{dx}, x\right) = 0$$

that does not involve the unknown function $y$ explicitly (except through its derivatives) can be reduced to a first-order equation by a change of dependent variable; if $v = dy/dx$, then the equation can be written

$$F\left(\frac{dv}{dx}, v, x\right) = 0.$$

This first-order equation in $v$ may be amenable to the techniques described in earlier sections. If an explicit solution $v = v(x)$ can be found and integrated, then the function

$$y = \int v(x)\,dx$$

is an explicit solution of the given equation.

---

**EXAMPLE 1**   Solve the initial-value problem

$$\frac{d^2y}{dx^2} = x\left(\frac{dy}{dx}\right)^2, \qquad y(0) = 1, \qquad y'(0) = -2.$$

***Solution***   If we let $v = dy/dx$, the given differential equation becomes

$$\frac{dv}{dx} = xv^2,$$

which is a separable first-order equation. Thus,

$$\frac{dv}{v^2} = x\,dx$$

$$-\frac{1}{v} = \frac{x^2}{2} + \frac{C_1}{2}$$

$$v = -\frac{2}{x^2 + C_1}.$$

The initial condition $y'(0) = -2$ implies that $v(0) = -2$ and so $C_1 = 1$. Therefore,

$$y = -2 \int \frac{dx}{x^2 + 1} = -2 \tan^{-1} x + C_2.$$

The initial condition $y(0) = 1$ implies that $C_2 = 1$, so the solution of the given initial-value problem is $y = 1 - 2 \tan^{-1} x$.

A second-order equation of the form

$$F\left(\frac{d^2 y}{dx^2}, \frac{dy}{dx}, y\right) = 0$$

that does not explicitly involve the independent variable $x$ can be reduced to a first-order equation by a change of both dependent and independent variables. Again let $v = dy/dx$, but regard $v$ as a function of $y$ rather than $x$: $v = v(y)$. Then

$$\frac{d^2 y}{dx^2} = \frac{dv}{dx} = \frac{dv}{dy}\frac{dy}{dx} = v\frac{dv}{dy}$$

by the Chain Rule. Hence, the given differential equation becomes

$$F\left(v\frac{dv}{dy}, v, y\right) = 0,$$

which is a first-order equation for $v$ as a function of $y$. If this equation can be solved for $v = v(y)$, there still remains the problem of solving the separable equation $(dy/dx) = v(y)$ for $y$ as a function of $x$.

**EXAMPLE 2**  Solve the equation $y\dfrac{d^2 y}{dx^2} = \left(\dfrac{dy}{dx}\right)^2$.

*Solution*  The change of variable $dy/dx = v(y)$ leads to the equation

$$yv\frac{dv}{dy} = v^2,$$

which is separable, $dv/v = dy/y$, and has solution $v = C_1 y$. The equation

$$\frac{dy}{dx} = C_1 y$$

is again separable and leads to

$$\frac{dy}{y} = C_1\,dx$$
$$\ln|y| = C_1 x + C_2$$
$$y = \pm e^{C_1 x + C_2} = C_3 e^{C_1 x}.$$

## Second-Order Linear Equations

The most frequently encountered ordinary differential equations arising in applications are second-order linear equations. The general second-order linear equation is of the form

$$a_2(x)\frac{d^2 y}{dx^2} + a_1(x)\frac{dy}{dx} + a_0(x)y = f(x).$$

As remarked in Section 11.1, if $f(x) = 0$ identically, then we say that the equation is **homogeneous**. If the coefficients $a_2(x)$, $a_1(x)$, and $a_0(x)$ are continuous on an interval and $a_2(x) \neq 0$ there, then the homogeneous equation

$$a_2(x)\frac{d^2y}{dx^2} + a_1(x)\frac{dy}{dx} + a_0(x)y = 0$$

has a general solution of the form

$$y_h = C_1 y_1(x) + C_2 y_2(x),$$

where $y_1(x)$ and $y_2(x)$ are two **independent** solutions, that is, two solutions with the property that $C_1 y_1(x) + C_2 y_2(x) = 0$ for all $x$ in the interval only if $C_1 = C_2 = 0$. (We will not prove this here.)

Whenever one solution, $y_1(x)$, of a homogeneous linear second-order equation is known, another independent solution (and therefore the general solution) can be found by substituting $y = v(x)y_1(x)$ into the differential equation. This leads to a first-order, linear, separable equation for $v'$.

---

**EXAMPLE 3**    Show that $y_1 = e^{-2x}$ is a solution of $y'' + 4y' + 4y = 0$, and find the general solution of this equation.

***Solution***    Since $y_1' = -2e^{-2x}$ and $y_1'' = 4e^{-2x}$, we have

$$y_1'' + 4y_1' + 4y_1 = e^{-2x}(4 - 8 + 4) = 0,$$

so $y_1$ is indeed a solution of the given differential equation. To find the general solution, try $y = y_1 v = e^{-2x}v(x)$. We have

$$y' = -2e^{-2x}v + e^{-2x}v'$$
$$y'' = 4e^{-2x}v - 4e^{-2x}v' + e^{-2x}v''.$$

Substituting these expressions into the given DE, we obtain

$$0 = y'' + 4y' + 4y$$
$$= e^{-2x}(4v - 4v' + v'' - 8v + 4v' + 4v) = e^{-2x}v''.$$

Thus, $y = y_1 v$ is a solution provided $v''(x) = 0$. This equation for $v$ has the general solution $v = C_1 + C_2 x$, so the given equation has the general solution

$$y = C_1 e^{-2x} + C_2 x e^{-2x} = C_1 y_1(x) + C_2 y_2(x),$$

where $y_2 = xe^{-2x}$ is a second solution of the DE, independent of $y_1$.

---

By Theorem 2 of Section 11.1, the general solution of the second-order, linear, nonhomogeneous equation (with $f(x) \neq 0$) is of the form

$$y = y_p(x) + y_h(x),$$

where $y_p(x)$ is any particular solution of the nonhomogeneous equation, and $y_h(x)$ is the general solution (as described above) of the corresponding homogeneous equation. In Section 11.6 we will discuss the solution of nonhomogeneous linear equations. First, however, in Section 11.5 we concentrate on some special classes of homogeneous, linear equations.

## EXERCISES 11.4

**1.** Show that $y = e^x$ is a solution of $y'' - 3y' + 2y = 0$, and find the general solution of this DE.

**2.** Show that $y = e^{-2x}$ is a solution of $y'' - y' - 6y = 0$, and find the general solution of this DE.

**3.** Show that $y = x$ is a solution of $x^2 y'' + 2xy' - 2y = 0$ on the interval $(0, \infty)$, and find the general solution on this interval.

**4.** Show that $y = x^2$ is a solution of $x^2 y'' - 3xy' + 4y = 0$ on the interval $(0, \infty)$, and find the general solution on this interval.

**5.** Show that $y = x$ is a solution of the differential equation $x^2 y'' - (2x + x^2)y' + (2 + x)y = 0$, and find the general solution of this equation.

**6.** Show that $y = x^{-1/2} \cos x$ is a solution of the Bessel equation with $\nu = 1/2$:

$$x^2 y'' + xy' + \left(x^2 - \frac{1}{4}\right) y = 0.$$

Find the general solution of this equation.

**First-order systems**

**7.** A system of $n$ first-order, linear, differential equations in $n$ unknown functions $y_1, y_2, \cdots, y_n$ is written

$$y_1' = a_{11}(x)y_1 + a_{12}(x)y_2 + \cdots + a_{1n}(x)y_n + f_1(x)$$
$$y_2' = a_{21}(x)y_1 + a_{22}(x)y_2 + \cdots + a_{2n}(x)y_n + f_2(x)$$
$$\vdots$$
$$y_n' = a_{n1}(x)y_1 + a_{n2}(x)y_2 + \cdots + a_{nn}(x)y_n + f_n(x).$$

Such a system is called an $n \times n$ **first-order linear system** and can be rewritten in vector-matrix form as $\mathbf{y}' = \mathcal{A}(x)\mathbf{y} + \mathbf{f}(x)$, where

$$\mathbf{y}(x) = \begin{pmatrix} y_1(x) \\ \vdots \\ y_n(x) \end{pmatrix}, \quad \mathbf{f}(x) = \begin{pmatrix} f_1(x) \\ \vdots \\ f_n(x) \end{pmatrix},$$

$$\mathcal{A}(x) = \begin{pmatrix} a_{11}(x) & \cdots & a_{1n}(x) \\ \vdots & \ddots & \vdots \\ a_{n1}(x) & \cdots & a_{nn}(x) \end{pmatrix}.$$

Show that the second-order, linear equation $y'' + a_1(x)y' + a_0(x)y = f(x)$ can be transformed into a $2 \times 2$ first-order system with $y_1 = y$ and $y_2 = y'$ having

$$\mathcal{A}(x) = \begin{pmatrix} 0 & 1 \\ -a_0(x) & -a_1(x) \end{pmatrix}, \quad \mathbf{f}(x) = \begin{pmatrix} 0 \\ f(x) \end{pmatrix}.$$

**8.** Generalize Exercise 7 to transform an $n$th-order linear equation

$$y^{(n)} + a_{n-1}(x)y^{(n-1)} + a_{n-2}(x)y^{(n-2)} + \cdots + a_0(x)y = f(x)$$

into an $n \times n$ first-order system.

**9.** If $\mathcal{A}$ is an $n \times n$ constant matrix, and if there exists a scalar $\lambda$ and a nonzero constant vector $\mathbf{v}$ for which $\mathcal{A}\mathbf{v} = \lambda\mathbf{v}$, show that $\mathbf{y} = C_1 e^{\lambda x} \mathbf{v}$ is a solution of the homogeneous system $\mathbf{y}' = \mathcal{A}\mathbf{y}$.

**10.** Show that the determinant $\begin{vmatrix} 2 - \lambda & 1 \\ 2 & 3 - \lambda \end{vmatrix}$ is zero for two distinct values of $\lambda$. For each of these values find a nonzero vector $\mathbf{v}$ that satisfies the condition $\begin{pmatrix} 2 & 1 \\ 2 & 3 \end{pmatrix} \mathbf{v} = \lambda\mathbf{v}$. Hence, solve the system

$$y_1' = 2y_1 + y_2, \qquad y_2' = 2y_1 + 3y_2.$$

## 11.5    Linear Differential Equations with Constant Coefficients

A differential equation of the form

$$a\,y'' + b\,y' + cy = 0, \qquad (*)$$

where $a$, $b$, and $c$ are constants and $a \neq 0$, is said to be a **linear, homogeneous, second-order equation with constant coefficients**.

> **A thorough discussion of techniques for solving such equations, together with examples, exercises, and applications to the study of simple and damped harmonic motion, can be found in Section 6.7; we will not repeat that discussion here. If you have not studied it, please do so now.**

We will, however, extend the treatment to cover linear, constant-coefficient differential equations of higher order.

## Constant-Coefficient Equations of Higher Order

Because in most applications of equation (∗) the dependent variable represents time, we will, as we did in Section 6.7, regard $y$ as a function of $t$ rather than $x$, so that the prime symbol ($'$) denotes the derivative $d/dt$. The basic result of Section 6.7 was that the function $y = e^{rt}$ was a solution of (∗) provided that $r$ satisfies the **auxiliary equation**

$$ar^2 + br + c = 0. \qquad (**)$$

The auxiliary equation is quadratic and can have either

(a) two distinct real roots, $r_1$ and $r_2$ (if $b^2 > 4ac$), in which case (∗) has general solution $y = C_1 e^{r_1 t} + C_2 e^{r_2 t}$,

(b) a single repeated real root $r$ (if $b^2 = 4ac$), in which case (∗) has general solution $y = (C_1 + C_2 t)e^{rt}$, or

(c) a pair of complex conjugate roots, $r = k \pm i\omega$ with $k$ and $\omega$ real (if $b^2 < 4ac$), in which case (∗) has general solution $y = e^{kt}(C_1 \cos(\omega t) + C_2 \sin(\omega t))$.

The situation is analogous for higher-order linear, homogeneous DEs with constant coefficients. We describe the procedure without offering any proofs. If

$$P_n(r) = a_n r^n + a_{n-1} r^{n-1} + \cdots + a_2 r^2 + a_1 r + a_0$$

is a polynomial of degree $n$ with constant coefficients $a_j$, $(0 \le j \le n)$, and $a_n \ne 0$, then the DE

$$P_n(D)y = 0, \qquad (†)$$

where $D = d/dt$ can be solved by substituting $y = e^{rt}$ and obtaining the *auxiliary equation* $P_n(r) = 0$. This polynomial equation has $n$ roots (see Appendix II) some of which may be equal and some or all of which can be complex. If the coefficients of the polynomial $P_n(r)$ are all real, then any complex roots must occur in complex conjugate pairs $k \pm i\omega$ (with the same multiplicity), where $k$ and $\omega$ are real.

The general solution of (†) can be expressed as a *linear combination* of $n$ independent particular solutions

$$y = C_1 y_1(t) + C_2 y_2(t) + \cdots + C_n y_n(t),$$

where the $C_j$ are arbitrary constants. The independent solutions $y_1, y_2, \ldots, y_n$ are constructed as follows:

1. If $r_1$ is a $k$-fold real root of the auxiliary equation (i.e., if $(r - r_1)^k$ is a factor of $P_n(r)$), then

$$e^{r_1 t}, \quad t e^{r_1 t}, \quad t^2 e^{r_1 t}, \quad \ldots, \quad t^{k-1} e^{r_1 t}$$

are $k$ independent solutions of (†).

2. If $r = a + ib$ and $r = a - ib$ (where $a$ and $b$ are real) constitute a $k$-fold pair of complex conjugate roots of the auxiliary equation (i.e., if $[(r - a)^2 + b^2]^k$ is a factor of $P_n(r)$), then

$$e^{at} \cos bt, \quad t e^{at} \cos bt, \quad \ldots, \quad t^{k-1} e^{at} \cos bt,$$
$$e^{at} \sin bt, \quad t e^{at} \sin bt, \quad \ldots, \quad t^{k-1} e^{at} \sin bt$$

are $2k$ independent solutions of (†).

*Remark*   There is a simple explanation for such solutions, even though some treatments make them seem needlessly experimental. They arise because the operator polynomial is factorable, and the factors are commutative,

$$P_n(D)y = a_n(D - r_1)(D - r_2)\dots(D - r_n)y = 0.$$

Being commutative, any factor, $(D - r_k)$, can be placed first in the order of application to $y$. Thus, if $(D - r_k)y_k = 0$, then $y_k$ must be a solution and every factor contributes a solution, $C_k e^{r_k x}$. The contributions of each factor are additive, because the operators are linear. For distinct roots, $r_k$, this captures all possible solutions.

However, for roots occurring $m$ times things are more complicated. Suppose the root $r_k$ appears $m$ times. If $y_k$ represents the contributions of these $m$ factors to the general solution, then

$$(D - r_k)^m y_k = 0.$$

But

$$(D-r_k)^m y_k(t) = (D-r_k)^{m-1}(D-r_k)e^{r_k t}\underbrace{e^{-r_k t}y_k(t)}_{u_k(t)} = (D-r_k)^{m-1}e^{r_k t}Du_k(t)$$

because, for any function $f(t)$, $(D - r_k)e^{r_k t}f(t) = D(e^{r_k t}f(t)) - r_k e^{r_k t}f(t) = 0 + e^{r_k t}Df(t)$. We can repeat this argument $m - 1$ more times to obtain

$$(D - r_k)^m y_k = e^{r_k t}D^m u_k(t) = 0,$$

Thus,

$$D^m u_k(t) = e^{-r_k t}(D - r_k)^m y_k(t) = 0,$$

and so $u_k(t)$ must be a polynomial of degree at most $m - 1$: $u_k(t) = P_{m-1}(t)e^{r_k t}$. Similarly, the trigonometric solutions arise from complex roots and Euler's formula.

**EXAMPLE 1**   Solve   (a) $y^{(4)} - 16y = 0$ and   (b) $y^{(5)} - 2y^{(4)} + y^{(3)} = 0$.

*Solution*   The auxiliary equation for (a) is $r^4 - 16 = 0$, which factors down to $(r - 2)(r + 2)(r^2 + 4) = 0$ and, hence, has roots $r = 2, -2, 2i$, and $-2i$. Thus, the DE (a) has general solution

$$y = C_1 e^{2t} + C_2 e^{-2t} + C_3 \cos(2t) + C_4 \sin(2t)$$

for arbitrary constants $C_1, C_2, C_3$, and $C_4$.

The auxiliary equation for (b) is $r^5 - 2r^4 + r^3 = 0$, which factors to $r^3(r-1)^2 = 0$, and so has roots $r = 0, 0, 0, 1, 1$. The general solution of the DE (b) is

$$y = C_1 + C_2 t + C_3 t^2 + C_4 e^t + C_5 t e^t,$$

where $C_1, \dots, C_5$ are arbitrary constants.

**EXAMPLE 2**   What are the order and the general solution of the constant-coefficient, linear, homogeneous DE whose auxiliary equation is

$$(r + 4)^3(r^2 + 4r + 13)^2 = 0?$$

*Solution*   The auxiliary equation has degree 7, so the DE is of seventh order. Since $r^2 + 4r + 13 = (r + 2)^2 + 9$, which has roots $-2 \pm 3i$, the DE must have the general solution

$$\begin{aligned} y = & C_1 e^{-4t} + C_2 t e^{-4t} + C_3 t^2 e^{-4t} \\ & + C_4 e^{-2t} \cos(3t) + C_5 e^{-2t} \sin(3t) + C_6 t e^{-2t} \cos(3t) + C_7 t e^{-2t} \sin(3t). \end{aligned}$$

## Euler (Equidimensional) Equations

A homogeneous, linear equation of the form

$$ax^2 \frac{d^2 y}{dx^2} + bx \frac{dy}{dx} + cy = 0$$

is called an **Euler equation** or an **equidimensional equation**, the latter term being appropriate since all the terms in the equation have the same dimension (i.e., they are measured in the same units), provided that the constants $a$, $b$, and $c$ all have the same dimension. The coefficients of an Euler equation are *not constant,* but there is a technique for solving these equations that is similar to that for solving equations with constant coefficients, so we include a brief discussion of these equations in this section. As in the case of constant-coefficient equations, we assume that the constants $a$, $b$, and $c$ are real numbers and that $a \neq 0$. Even so, the leading coefficient, $ax^2$, does vanish at $x = 0$ (which is called a **singular point** of the equation), and this can cause solutions to fail to be defined at $x = 0$. We will solve the equation in the interval $x > 0$; the same solution will also hold for $x < 0$ provided we replace $x$ by $|x|$ in the solution.

Let us search for solutions in $x > 0$ given by powers of $x$; if

$$y = x^r, \qquad \frac{dy}{dx} = rx^{r-1}, \qquad \frac{d^2 y}{dx^2} = r(r-1)x^{r-2},$$

then the Euler equation becomes

$$\big(ar(r-1) + br + c\big)x^r = 0.$$

This will be satisfied for all $x > 0$, provided that $r$ satisfies the **auxiliary equation**

$$ar(r-1) + br + c = 0 \quad \text{or, equivalently,} \quad ar^2 + (b-a)r + c = 0.$$

As for constant-coefficient equations, there are three possibilities.

**CASE I.**   If $(b-a)^2 \geq 4ac$, then the auxiliary equation has two real roots:

$$r_1 = \frac{a - b + \sqrt{(b-a)^2 - 4ac}}{2a},$$
$$r_2 = \frac{a - b - \sqrt{(b-a)^2 - 4ac}}{2a}.$$

In this case, the Euler equation has the general solution

$$y = C_1 x^{r_1} + C_2 x^{r_2}, \qquad (x > 0).$$

The general solution is usually quoted in the form

$$y = C_1 |x|^{r_1} + C_2 |x|^{r_2},$$

which is valid in any interval not containing $x = 0$ and may even be valid on intervals containing the origin if, for example, $r_1$ and $r_2$ are nonnegative integers.

---

EXAMPLE 3    Solve the initial-value problem

$$2x^2\,y'' - xy' - 2y = 0, \qquad y(1) = 5, \qquad y'(1) = 0.$$

*Solution*    The auxiliary equation is $2r(r-1) - r - 2 = 0$, that is, $2r^2 - 3r - 2 = 0$, or $(r-2)(2r+1) = 0$, and has roots $r = 2$ and $r = -(1/2)$. Thus, the general solution of the differential equation (valid for $x > 0$) is

$$y = C_1 x^2 + C_2 x^{-1/2}.$$

The initial conditions imply that

$$5 = y(1) = C_1 + C_2 \quad \text{and} \quad 0 = y'(1) = 2C_1 - \frac{1}{2}C_2.$$

Therefore, $C_1 = 1$ and $C_2 = 4$, and the initial-value problem has solution

$$y = x^2 + \frac{4}{\sqrt{x}}, \qquad (x > 0).$$

---

**CASE II.**    If $(b-a)^2 = 4ac$, then the auxiliary equation has one double root, namely, the root $r = (a-b)/2a$. It is left to the reader to verify that in this case the transformation $y = x^r v(x)$ leads to the general solution

$$y = C_1 x^r + C_2 x^r \ln x, \qquad (x > 0),$$

or, more generally,

$$y = C_1 |x|^r + C_2 |x|^r \ln|x|, \qquad (x \neq 0).$$

**CASE III.**    If $(b-a)^2 < 4ac$, then the auxiliary equation has complex conjugate roots:

$$r = \alpha \pm i\beta, \qquad \text{where} \quad \alpha = \frac{a-b}{2a}, \quad \beta = \frac{\sqrt{4ac - (b-a)^2}}{2a}.$$

The corresponding powers $x^r$ can be expressed in real form in a manner similar to that used for constant coefficient equations; we have

$$x^{\alpha \pm i\beta} = e^{(\alpha \pm i\beta)\ln x} = e^{\alpha \ln x}\left[\cos(\beta \ln x) \pm i \sin(\beta \ln x)\right]$$
$$= x^\alpha \cos(\beta \ln x) \pm i x^\alpha \sin(\beta \ln x).$$

Accordingly, the Euler equation has the general solution

$$y = C_1 |x|^\alpha \cos(\beta \ln|x|) + C_2 |x|^\alpha \sin(\beta \ln|x|).$$

---

EXAMPLE 4    Solve the DE $x^2 y'' - 3xy' + 13y = 0$.

*Solution*    The DE has the auxiliary equation $r(r-1) - 3r + 13 = 0$, that is, $r^2 - 4r + 13 = 0$, which has roots $r = 2 \pm 3i$. The DE, therefore, has the general solution

$$y = C_1 x^2 \cos(3\ln|x|) + C_2 x^2 \sin(3\ln|x|).$$

---

*Remark*    Euler equations can be transformed into constant-coefficient equations by using a simple change of variable. See Exercise 14 for the details. In terms of the new variable the operator is factorable, and the factors are commutative, therefore all solution forms follow according to the previous remark. Transforming the resulting solutions back in terms of the original variable brings us to the solutions above.

## EXERCISES 11.5

Exercises involving the solution of second-order, linear, homogeneous equations with constant coefficients can be found at the end of Section 6.7.

Find general solutions of the DEs in Exercises 1–4.

**1.** $y''' - 4y'' + 3y' = 0$

**2.** $y^{(4)} - 2y'' + y = 0$    **3.** $y^{(4)} + 2y'' + y = 0$

**4.** $y^{(4)} + 4y^{(3)} + 6y'' + 4y' + y = 0$

**5.** Show that $y = e^{2t}$ is a solution of

$$y''' - 2y' - 4y = 0$$

(where $'$ denotes $d/dt$), and find the general solution of this DE.

**6.** Write the general solution of the linear, constant-coefficient DE having auxiliary equation $(r^2 - r - 2)^2(r^2 - 4)^2 = 0$.

Find general solutions to the Euler equations in Exercises 7–12.

**7.** $x^2 y'' - xy' + y = 0$    **8.** $x^2 y'' - xy' - 3y = 0$

**9.** $x^2 y'' + xy' - y = 0$    **10.** $x^2 y'' - xy' + 5y = 0$

**11.** $x^2 y'' + xy' = 0$    **12.** $x^2 y'' + xy' + y = 0$

**!** **13.** Solve the DE $x^3 y''' + xy' - y = 0$ in the interval $x > 0$.

**14.** Show that the change of variables $x = e^t$, $z(t) = y(e^t)$, transforms the Euler equation

$$ax^2 \frac{d^2 y}{dx^2} + bx \frac{dy}{dx} + cy = 0$$

into the constant-coefficient equation

$$a \frac{d^2 z}{dt^2} + (b - a)\frac{dz}{dt} + cz = 0.$$

**15.** Use the transformation $x = e^t$ of the previous exercise to solve the Euler equation

$$x^2 \frac{d^2 y}{dx^2} - x \frac{dy}{dx} + 2y = 0, \qquad (x > 0).$$

## 11.6 Nonhomogeneous Linear Equations

We now consider the problem of solving the nonhomogeneous second-order differential equation

$$a_2(x)\frac{d^2 y}{dx^2} + a_1(x)\frac{dy}{dx} + a_0(x)y = f(x). \qquad (*)$$

We assume that two independent solutions, $y_1(x)$ and $y_2(x)$, of the corresponding homogeneous equation

$$a_2(x)\frac{d^2 y}{dx^2} + a_1(x)\frac{dy}{dx} + a_0(x)y = 0$$

are known. The function $y_h(x) = C_1 y_1(x) + C_2 y_2(x)$, which is the general solution of the homogeneous equation, is called the **complementary function** for the nonhomogeneous equation. Theorem 2 of Section 11.1 suggests that the general solution of the nonhomogeneous equation is of the form

$$y = y_p(x) + y_h(x) = y_p(x) + C_1 y_1(x) + C_2 y_2(x),$$

where $y_p(x)$ is any **particular solution** of the nonhomogeneous equation. All we need to do is find *one solution* of the nonhomogeneous equation, and we can write the general solution.

There are two common methods for finding a particular solution $y_p$ of the nonhomogeneous equation $(*)$:

1. the method of undetermined coefficients, and
2. the method of variation of parameters.

The first of these hardly warrants being called a *method*; it just involves making an educated guess about the form of the solution as a sum of terms with unknown coefficients and substituting this guess into the equation to determine the coefficients. This method works well for simple DEs, especially ones with constant coefficients. The nature of the *guess* depends on the nonhomogeneous term $f(x)$, but can also be affected by the solution of the corresponding homogeneous equation. A few examples will illustrate the ideas involved.

---

**EXAMPLE 1**    Find the general solution of $y'' + y' - 2y = 4x$.

*Solution*    Because the nonhomogeneous term $f(x) = 4x$ is a first-degree polynomial, we "guess" that a particular solution can be found that is also such a polynomial. Thus, we try

$$y = Ax + B, \qquad y' = A, \qquad y'' = 0.$$

Substituting these expressions into the given DE, we obtain

$$0 + A - 2(Ax + B) = 4x \qquad \text{or}$$
$$-(2A + 4)x + (A - 2B) = 0.$$

This latter equation will be satisfied for all $x$ provided $2A + 4 = 0$ and $A - 2B = 0$. Thus, we require $A = -2$ and $B = -1$; a particular solution of the given DE is

$$y_p(x) = -2x - 1.$$

Since the corresponding homogeneous equation $y'' + y' - 2y = 0$ has auxiliary equation $r^2 + r - 2 = 0$ with roots $r = 1$ and $r = -2$, the given DE has the general solution

$$y = y_p(x) + C_1 e^x + C_2 e^{-2x} = -2x - 1 + C_1 e^x + C_2 e^{-2x}.$$

---

**EXAMPLE 2**    Find general solutions of the equations (where $'$ denotes $d/dt$)

(a)    $y'' + 4y = \sin t$,
(b)    $y'' + 4y = \sin(2t)$,
(c)    $y'' + 4y = \sin t + \sin(2t)$.

*Solution*

(a)  Let us look for a particular solution of the form

$$y = A \sin t + B \cos t \qquad \text{so that}$$
$$y' = A \cos t - B \sin t$$
$$y'' = -A \sin t - B \cos t.$$

Substituting these expressions into the DE $y'' + 4y = \sin t$, we get

$$-A \sin t - B \cos t + 4A \sin t + 4B \cos t = \sin t,$$

which is satisfied for all $x$ if $3A = 1$ and $3B = 0$. Thus, $A = 1/3$ and $B = 0$. Since the homogeneous equation $y'' + 4y = 0$ has general solution $y = C_1 \cos(2t) + C_2 \sin(2t)$, the given nonhomogeneous equation has the general solution

$$y = \frac{1}{3} \sin t + C_1 \cos(2t) + C_2 \sin(2t).$$

(b) Motivated by our success in part (a), we might be tempted to try for a particular solution of the form $y = A \sin(2t) + B \cos(2t)$, but that won't work, because this function is a solution of the homogeneous equation, so we would get $y'' + 4y = 0$ for any choice of $A$ and $B$. In this case it is useful to try

$$y = At \sin(2t) + Bt \cos(2t).$$

We have

$$
\begin{aligned}
y' &= A \sin(2t) + 2At \cos(2t) + B \cos(2t) - 2Bt \sin(2t) \\
&= (A - 2Bt) \sin(2t) + (B + 2At) \cos(2t) \\
y'' &= -2B \sin(2t) + 2(A - 2Bt) \cos(2t) + 2A \cos(2t) \\
&\quad - 2(B + 2At) \sin(2t) \\
&= -4(B + At) \sin(2t) + 4(A - Bt) \cos(2t).
\end{aligned}
$$

Substituting into $y'' + 4y = \sin(2t)$ leads to

$$-4(B + At) \sin(2t) + 4(A - Bt) \cos(2t) + 4At \sin(2t) + 4Bt \cos(2t)$$
$$= \sin(2t).$$

Observe that the terms involving $t \sin(2t)$ and $t \cos(2t)$ cancel out, and we are left with

$$-4B \sin(2t) + 4A \cos(2t) = \sin(2t),$$

which is satisfied for all $x$ if $A = 0$ and $B = -1/4$. Hence, the general solution for part (b) is

$$y = -\frac{1}{4}t \cos(2t) + C_1 \cos(2t) + C_2 \sin(2t).$$

(c) Since the homogeneous equation is the same for (a), (b), and (c), and the non-homogeneous term in equation (c) is the sum of the nonhomogeneous terms in equations (a) and (b), the sum of particular solutions of (a) and (b) is a particular solution of (c). (This is because the equation is *linear*.) Thus, the general solution of equation (c) is

$$y = \frac{1}{3}\sin t - \frac{1}{4}t \cos(2t) + C_1 \cos(2t) + C_2 \sin(2t).$$

We summarize the appropriate forms to try for particular solutions of constant-coefficient equations as follows:

> **Trial solutions for constant-coefficient equations**
>
> Let $A_n(x)$, $B_n(x)$, and $P_n(x)$ denote the $n$th-degree polynomials
>
> $$A_n(x) = a_0 + a_1 x + a_2 x^2 + \cdots + a_n x^n$$
> $$B_n(x) = b_0 + b_1 x + b_2 x^2 + \cdots + b_n x^n$$
> $$P_n(x) = p_0 + p_1 x + p_2 x^2 + \cdots + p_n x^n.$$
>
> To find a particular solution $y_p(x)$ of the second-order linear, constant-coefficient, nonhomogeneous DE
>
> $$a_2 \frac{d^2 y}{dx^2} + a_1 \frac{dy}{dx} + a_0 y = f(x),$$
>
> use the following forms:
>
> If $f(x) = P_n(x)$,                     try $y_p = x^m A_n(x)$.
> If $f(x) = P_n(x)e^{rx}$,                 try $y_p = x^m A_n(x)e^{rx}$.
> If $f(x) = P_n(x)e^{rx}\cos(kx)$, try $y_p = x^m e^{rx}[A_n(x)\cos(kx) + B_n(x)\sin(kx)]$.
> If $f(x) = P_n(x)e^{rx}\sin(kx)$, try $y_p = x^m e^{rx}[A_n(x)\cos(kx) + B_n(x)\sin(kx)]$,
>
> where $m$ is the smallest of the integers 0, 1, and 2, that ensures that no term of $y_p$ is a solution of the corresponding homogeneous equation
>
> $$a_2 \frac{d^2 y}{dx^2} + a_1 \frac{dy}{dx} + a_0 y = 0.$$

## Resonance

For $\lambda > 0$, $\lambda \neq 1$, the solution $y_\lambda(t)$ of the initial-value problem

$$\begin{cases} y'' + y = \sin(\lambda t) \\ \quad y(0) = 0 \\ \quad y'(0) = 1 \end{cases}$$

can be determined by first looking for a particular solution of the DE having the form $y = A\sin(\lambda t)$, and then adding the complementary function $y = B\cos t + C\sin t$. The calculations give $A = 1/(1 - \lambda^2)$, $B = 0$, $C = (1 - \lambda - \lambda^2)/(1 - \lambda^2)$, so

$$y_\lambda(t) = \frac{\sin(\lambda t) + (1 - \lambda - \lambda^2)\sin t}{1 - \lambda^2}.$$

For $\lambda = 1$ the nonhomogeneous term in the DE is a solution of the homogeneous equation $y'' + y = 0$, so we must try for a particular solution of the form $y = At\cos t + Bt\sin t$. In this case, the solution of the initial-value problem is

$$y_1(t) = \frac{3\sin t - t\cos t}{2}.$$

(This solution can also be found by calculating $\lim_{\lambda \to 1} y_\lambda(t)$ using l'Hôpital's Rule.) Observe that this solution is unbounded; the amplitude of the oscillations becomes larger and larger as $t$ increases. In contrast, the solutions $y_\lambda(t)$ for $\lambda \neq 1$ are bounded for all $t$, although they can become quite large for some values of $t$ if $\lambda$ is close to 1. The graphs of the solutions $y_{0.9}(t)$, $y_{0.95}(t)$, and $y_1(t)$ on the interval $-10 \leq t \leq 100$ are shown in Figure 11.4.

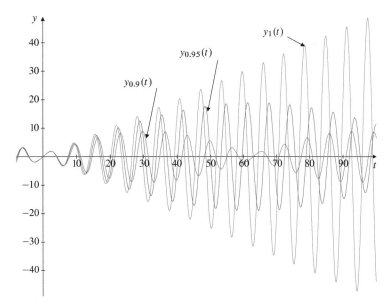

**Figure 11.4**    Resonance

The phenomenon illustrated here is called **resonance**. Vibrating mechanical systems have natural frequencies at which they will vibrate. If you try to force them to vibrate at a different frequency, the amplitude of the vibrations will themselves vary sinusoidally over time, producing an effect known as **beats**. The amplitudes of the beats can grow quite large, and the period of the beats lengthens as the forcing frequency approaches the natural frequency of the system. If the system has no resistive damping (the one illustrated here has no damping), then forcing vibrations at the natural frequency will cause the system to vibrate at ever increasing amplitudes.

As a concrete example, if you push a child on a swing, the swing will rise highest if your pushes are timed to have the same frequency as the natural frequency of the swing. Resonance is used in the design of tuning circuits of radios; the circuit is tuned (usually by a variable capacitor) so that its natural frequency of oscillation is the frequency of the station being tuned in. The circuit then responds much more strongly to the signal received from that station than to others on different frequencies.

## Variation of Parameters

A more formal method for finding a particular solution $y_p(x)$ of the nonhomogeneous equation

$$a_2(x)\frac{d^2y}{dx^2} + a_1(x)\frac{dy}{dx} + a_0(x)y = f(x) \tag{$*$}$$

when we know two independent solutions, $y_1(x)$ and $y_2(x)$, of the corresponding homogeneous equation is to replace the constants in the complementary function by functions, that is, search for $y_p$ in the form

$$y_p = u_1(x)y_1(x) + u_2(x)y_2(x).$$

Requiring $y_p$ to satisfy the given nonhomogeneous DE ($*$) provides one equation that must be satisfied by the two unknown functions $u_1$ and $u_2$. We are free to require them to satisfy a second equation also. To simplify the calculations below, we choose this second equation to be

$$u_1'(x)y_1(x) + u_2'(x)y_2(x) = 0.$$

Now we have

$$y_p' = u_1'y_1 + u_1y_1' + u_2'y_2 + u_2y_2' = u_1y_1' + u_2y_2'$$
$$y_p'' = u_1'y_1' + u_1y_1'' + u_2'y_2' + u_2y_2''.$$

Substituting these expressions into the given DE, we obtain

$$a_2(u'_1 y'_1 + u'_2 y'_2) + u_1(a_2 y''_1 + a_1 y'_1 + a_0 y_1) + u_2(a_2 y''_2 + a_1 y'_2 + a_0 y_2)$$
$$= a_2(u'_1 y'_1 + u'_2 y'_2) = f(x),$$

because $y_1$ and $y_2$ satisfy the homogeneous equation. Therefore, $u'_1$ and $u'_2$ satisfy the pair of equations

$$u'_1(x)y_1(x) + u'_2(x)y_2(x) = 0,$$
$$u'_1(x)y'_1(x) + u'_2(x)y'_2(x) = \frac{f(x)}{a_2(x)}.$$

We can solve these two equations for the unknown functions $u'_1$ and $u'_2$ by Cramer's Rule, or otherwise, and obtain

$$u'_1 = -\frac{y_2(x)}{W(x)} \frac{f(x)}{a_2(x)}, \qquad u'_2 = \frac{y_1(x)}{W(x)} \frac{f(x)}{a_2(x)},$$

where $W(x)$, called the **Wronskian** of $y_1$ and $y_2$, is the determinant

$$W(x) = \begin{vmatrix} y_1(x) & y_2(x) \\ y'_1(x) & y'_2(x) \end{vmatrix}.$$

Then $u_1$ and $u_2$ can be found by integration.

---

**EXAMPLE 3**    Find the general solution of $y'' + y = \tan x$.

*Solution*    The homogeneous equation $y'' + y = 0$ has general solution

$$y_h = C_1 \cos x + C_2 \sin x.$$

A particular solution $y_p(x)$ of the nonhomogeneous equation can be found in the form

$$y_p = u_1(x) \cos x + u_2(x) \sin x,$$

where $u_1$ and $u_2$ satisfy

$$u'_1(x) \cos x + u'_2(x) \sin x = 0$$
$$-u'_1(x) \sin x + u'_2(x) \cos x = \tan x.$$

Solving these equations for $u'_1(x)$ and $u'_2(x)$, we obtain

$$u'_1(x) = -\frac{\sin^2 x}{\cos x}, \qquad u'_2(x) = \sin x.$$

Therefore,

$$u_1(x) = -\int \frac{\sin^2 x}{\cos x} \, dx = \int (\cos x - \sec x) \, dx = \sin x - \ln(\sec x + \tan x)$$
$$u_2(x) = -\cos x.$$

Hence, $y_p = \sin x \cos x - \cos x \ln(\sec x + \tan x) - \cos x \sin x = -\cos x \ln(\sec x + \tan x)$ is a particular solution of the nonhomogeneous equation, and the general solution is

$$y = C_1 \cos x + C_2 \sin x - \cos x \ln(\sec x + \tan x).$$

Note that no arbitrary constants were included when we integrated $u'_1$ and $u'_2$ to produce $u_1$ and $u_2$ as they would have produced terms in the general solution that are already included in $y_h$.

*Remark* This method for solving the nonhomogeneous equation is called the **method of variation of parameters**. It is completely general and extends to higher-order equations in a reasonable way, but it can be computationally somewhat difficult. We would not likely have been able to "guess" the form of the particular solution in the above example, so we could not have used the method discussed earlier in this section to solve this equation.

## Maple Calculations

Maple has a `dsolve` routine for solving (some) differential equations and initial-value problems. This routine takes as input a DE and, if desired, initial conditions for it. We illustrate for the equation $y'' + 2y' + 5y = 25t + 20$ (assuming that the independent variable is $t$):

```
>    DE := (D@@2)(y)(t)+2*D(y)(t)+5*y(t)=25*t+20;
```

$$DE := D^{(2)}(y)(t) + 2D(y)(t) + 5y(t) = 25t + 20$$

```
>    dsolve(DE, y(t));
```

$$y(t) = e^{(-t)} \sin(2t) \_C2 + e^{(-t)} \cos(2t) \_C1 + 2 + 5t$$

Note Maple's use of $\_C1$ and $\_C2$ for arbitrary constants. For an initial-value problem we supply the DE and its initial conditions to `dsolve` as a single list or set argument enclosed in square brackets or braces:

```
>    dsolve([DE, y(0)=3, D(y)(0)=-2], y(t));
```

$$y(t) = -3e^{(-t)} \sin(2t) + e^{(-t)} \cos(2t) + 2 + 5t$$

You might think that this output indicates that $y$ has been defined as a function of $t$ and you can find a decimal value for, say, $y(1)$ by giving the input `evalf(y(1))`. But this won't work. In fact, the output of the `dsolve` is just an equation with left side the symbol $y(t)$. We can, however, use this output to define $y$ as a function of $t$ as follows:

```
>    y := unapply(op(2,%),t);
```

$$y := t \rightarrow -3e^{(-t)} \sin(2t) + e^{(-t)} \cos(2t) + 2 + 5t$$

The `op(2,%)` in the `unapply` command refers to the second operand of the previous result (i.e., the right side of equation output from the `dsolve`). `unapply(f,t)` converts an expression `f` to a function of $t$. To confirm:

```
>    evalf(y(1));
```

$$5.843372646$$

## EXERCISES 11.6

Find general solutions for the nonhomogeneous equations in Exercises 1–12 by the method of undetermined coefficients.

**1.** $y'' + y' - 2y = 1$

**2.** $y'' + y' - 2y = x$

**3.** $y'' + y' - 2y = e^{-x}$

**4.** $y'' + y' - 2y = e^{x}$

**5.** $y'' + 2y' + 5y = x^2$

**6.** $y'' + 4y = x^2$

**7.** $y'' - y' - 6y = e^{-2x}$

**8.** $y'' + 4y' + 4y = e^{-2x}$

**9.** $y'' + 2y' + 2y = e^x \sin x$

**10.** $y'' + 2y' + 2y = e^{-x} \sin x$

**11.** $y'' + y' = 4 + 2x + e^{-x}$

**12.** $y'' + 2y' + y = xe^{-x}$

**13.** Repeat Exercise 3 using the method of variation of parameters.

**14.** Repeat Exercise 4 using the method of variation of parameters.

**15.** Find a particular solution of the form $y = Ax^2$ for the Euler equation $x^2 y'' + xy' - y = x^2$, and hence obtain the general solution of this equation on the interval $(0, \infty)$.

**16.** For what values of $r$ can the Euler equation $x^2 y'' + xy' - y = x^r$ be solved by the method of Exercise 15? Find a particular solution for each such $r$.

**17.** Try to guess the form of a particular solution for $x^2 y'' + xy' - y = x$, and hence obtain the general solution for this equation on the interval $(0, \infty)$.

In Exercises 18–20, find the general solution on the interval $(0, \infty)$ of the given DE using variation of parameters.

**18.** $x^2 y'' + xy' - y = x$      **19.** $y'' - 2y' + y = \dfrac{e^x}{x}$

**20.** $y'' + 4y' + 4y = \dfrac{e^{-2x}}{x^2}$

**21.** Consider the nonhomogeneous, linear equation

$$x^2 y'' - (2x + x^2)y' + (2 + x)y = x^3.$$

Use the fact that $y_1(x) = x$ and $y_2(x) = xe^x$ are independent solutions of the corresponding homogeneous

equation (see Exercise 5 of Section 11.4) to find the general solution of this nonhomogeneous equation.

**22.** Consider the nonhomogeneous, Bessel equation

$$x^2 y'' + xy' + \left( x^2 - \frac{1}{4} \right) y = x^{3/2}.$$

Use the fact that $y_1(x) = x^{-1/2} \cos x$ and $y_2(x) = x^{-1/2} \sin x$ are independent solutions of the corresponding homogeneous equation (see Exercise 6 of Section 11.4) to find the general solution of this nonhomogeneous equation.

# Answers to Odd-Numbered Exercises

## Chapter 1

Section 1.1, page 10

1. The solution is $(x_1, x_2) = (-8, 3)$, or simply $(-8, 3)$.

3. $(4/7, 9/7)$

5. Replace row 2 by its sum with 3 times row 3, and then replace row 1 by its sum with $-5$ times row 3.

7. The solution set is empty.

9. $(4, 8, 5, 2)$      11. Inconsistent

13. $(5, 3, -1)$      15. Consistent

17. The three lines have one point in common.

19. $h \neq 2$      21. All $h$

23. Mark a statement True only if the statement is *always* true. Giving you the answers here would defeat the purpose of the true–false questions, which is to help you learn to read the text carefully. The *Study Guide* will tell you where to look for the answers, but you should not consult it until you have made an honest attempt to find the answers yourself.

25. $k + 2g + h = 0$

27. The row reduction of $\begin{bmatrix} 1 & 3 & f \\ c & d & g \end{bmatrix}$ to $\begin{bmatrix} 1 & 3 & f \\ 0 & d - 3c & g - cf \end{bmatrix}$ shows that $d - 3c$ must be nonzero, since $f$ and $g$ are arbitrary. Otherwise, for some choices of $f$ and $g$ the second row could correspond to an equation of the form $0 = b$, where $b$ is nonzero. Thus $d \neq 3c$.

29. Swap row 1 and row 2; swap row 1 and row 2.

31. Replace row 3 by row $3 + (-4)$ row 1; replace row 3 by row $3 + (4)$ row 1.

33. 
$$\begin{aligned} 4T_1 - \ \ T_2 \qquad\quad - \ \ T_4 &= 30 \\ -T_1 + 4T_2 - \ \ T_3 \qquad\quad &= 60 \\ -T_2 + 4T_3 - \ \ T_4 &= 70 \\ -T_1 \qquad\quad - \ \ T_3 + 4T_4 &= 40 \end{aligned}$$

Section 1.2, page 21

1. Reduced echelon form: a and b. Echelon form: d. Not echelon: c.

3. $\begin{bmatrix} 1 & 0 & -1 & -2 \\ 0 & 1 & 2 & 3 \\ 0 & 0 & 0 & 0 \end{bmatrix}$. Pivot cols 1 and 2: $\begin{bmatrix} 1 & 2 & 3 & 4 \\ 4 & 5 & 6 & 7 \\ 6 & 7 & 8 & 9 \end{bmatrix}$.

5. $\begin{bmatrix} \blacksquare & * \\ 0 & \blacksquare \end{bmatrix}, \begin{bmatrix} \blacksquare & * \\ 0 & 0 \end{bmatrix}, \begin{bmatrix} 0 & \blacksquare \\ 0 & 0 \end{bmatrix}$

7. $\begin{cases} x_1 = -5 - 3x_2 \\ x_2 \text{ is free} \\ x_3 = 3 \end{cases}$    9. $\begin{cases} x_1 = 4 + 5x_3 \\ x_2 = 5 + 6x_3 \\ x_3 \text{ is free} \end{cases}$

11. $\begin{cases} x_1 = \dfrac{4}{3}x_2 - \dfrac{2}{3}x_3 \\ x_2 \text{ is free} \\ x_3 \text{ is free} \end{cases}$

13. $\begin{cases} x_1 = 5 + 3x_5 \\ x_2 = 1 + 4x_5 \\ x_3 \text{ is free} \\ x_4 = 4 - 9x_5 \\ x_5 \text{ is free} \end{cases}$

*Note:* The *Study Guide* discusses the common mistake $x_3 = 0$.

15. **a.** Consistent, with a unique solution
    **b.** Inconsistent

17. $h = 7/2$

19. **a.** Inconsistent when $h = 2$ and $k \neq 8$
    **b.** A unique solution when $h \neq 2$
    **c.** Many solutions when $h = 2$ and $k = 8$

21. Read the text carefully, and write your answers before you consult the *Study Guide*. Remember, a statement is true only if it is true in all cases.

23. Yes. The system is consistent because with three pivots, there must be a pivot in the third (bottom) row of the coefficient matrix. The reduced echelon form cannot contain a row of the form $[0 \ \ 0 \ \ 0 \ \ 0 \ \ 0 \ \ 1]$.

25. If the coefficient matrix has a pivot position in every row, then there is a pivot position in the bottom row, and there is no room for a pivot in the augmented column. So, the system is consistent, by Theorem 2.

**27.** If a linear system is consistent, then the solution is unique if and only if *every column in the coefficient matrix is a pivot column; otherwise, there are infinitely many solutions.*

**29.** An underdetermined system always has more variables than equations. There cannot be more basic variables than there are equations, so there must be at least one free variable. Such a variable may be assigned infinitely many different values. If the system is consistent, each different value of a free variable will produce a different solution.

**31.** Yes, a system of linear equations with more equations than unknowns can be consistent. The following system has a solution ($x_1 = x_2 = 1$):

$$
\begin{aligned}
x_1 + x_2 &= 2 \\
x_1 - x_2 &= 0 \\
3x_1 + 2x_2 &= 5
\end{aligned}
$$

**33.** [M] $p(t) = 7 + 6t - t^2$

## Section 1.3, page 32

**1.** $\begin{bmatrix} -4 \\ 1 \end{bmatrix}, \begin{bmatrix} 5 \\ 4 \end{bmatrix}$

**3.**

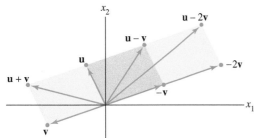

**5.** $x_1 \begin{bmatrix} 6 \\ -1 \\ 5 \end{bmatrix} + x_2 \begin{bmatrix} -3 \\ 4 \\ 0 \end{bmatrix} = \begin{bmatrix} 1 \\ -7 \\ -5 \end{bmatrix},$

$\begin{bmatrix} 6x_1 \\ -x_1 \\ 5x_1 \end{bmatrix} + \begin{bmatrix} -3x_2 \\ 4x_2 \\ 0 \end{bmatrix} = \begin{bmatrix} 1 \\ -7 \\ -5 \end{bmatrix}, \begin{bmatrix} 6x_1 - 3x_2 \\ -x_1 + 4x_2 \\ 5x_1 \end{bmatrix} = \begin{bmatrix} 1 \\ -7 \\ -5 \end{bmatrix}$

$$
\begin{aligned}
6x_1 - 3x_2 &= 1 \\
-x_1 + 4x_2 &= -7 \\
5x_1 \quad\;\;\; &= -5
\end{aligned}
$$

Usually the intermediate steps are not displayed.

**7.** $\mathbf{a} = \mathbf{u} - 2\mathbf{v}, \mathbf{b} = 2\mathbf{u} - 2\mathbf{v}, \mathbf{c} = 2\mathbf{u} - 3.5\mathbf{v}, \mathbf{d} = 3\mathbf{u} - 4\mathbf{v}$

**9.** $x_1 \begin{bmatrix} 0 \\ 4 \\ -1 \end{bmatrix} + x_2 \begin{bmatrix} 1 \\ 6 \\ 3 \end{bmatrix} + x_3 \begin{bmatrix} 5 \\ -1 \\ -8 \end{bmatrix} = \begin{bmatrix} 0 \\ 0 \\ 0 \end{bmatrix}$

**11.** Yes, $\mathbf{b}$ is a linear combination of $\mathbf{a}_1, \mathbf{a}_2$, and $\mathbf{a}_3$.

**13.** No, $\mathbf{b}$ is *not* a linear combination of the columns of $A$.

**15.** Noninteger weights are acceptable, of course, but some simple choices are $0 \cdot \mathbf{v}_1 + 0 \cdot \mathbf{v}_2 = \mathbf{0}$, and

$1 \cdot \mathbf{v}_1 + 0 \cdot \mathbf{v}_2 = \begin{bmatrix} 7 \\ 1 \\ -6 \end{bmatrix}, 0 \cdot \mathbf{v}_1 + 1 \cdot \mathbf{v}_2 = \begin{bmatrix} -5 \\ 3 \\ 0 \end{bmatrix}$

$1 \cdot \mathbf{v}_1 + 1 \cdot \mathbf{v}_2 = \begin{bmatrix} 2 \\ 4 \\ -6 \end{bmatrix}, 1 \cdot \mathbf{v}_1 - 1 \cdot \mathbf{v}_2 = \begin{bmatrix} 12 \\ -2 \\ -6 \end{bmatrix}$

**17.** $h = -17$

**19.** Span $\{\mathbf{v}_1, \mathbf{v}_2\}$ is the set of points on the line through $\mathbf{v}_1$ and $\mathbf{0}$.

**21.** *Hint:* Show that $\begin{bmatrix} 2 & 2 & h \\ -1 & 1 & k \end{bmatrix}$ is consistent for all $h$ and $k$. Explain what this calculation shows about Span $\{\mathbf{u}, \mathbf{v}\}$.

**23.** Before you consult your *Study Guide*, read the entire section carefully. Pay special attention to definitions and theorem statements, and note any remarks that precede or follow them.

**25. a.** No, three     **b.** Yes, infinitely many
**c.** $\mathbf{a}_1 = 1 \cdot \mathbf{a}_1 + 0 \cdot \mathbf{a}_2 + 0 \cdot \mathbf{a}_3$

**27. a.** $5\mathbf{v}_1$ is the output of 5 day's operation of mine #1.
**b.** The total output is $x_1\mathbf{v}_1 + x_2\mathbf{v}_2$, so $x_1$ and $x_2$ should satisfy $x_1\mathbf{v}_1 + x_2\mathbf{v}_2 = \begin{bmatrix} 150 \\ 2825 \end{bmatrix}$.
**c.** [M] 1.5 days for mine #1 and 4 days for mine #2

**29.** $(1.3, .9, 0)$

**31. a.** $\begin{bmatrix} 10/3 \\ 2 \end{bmatrix}$
**b.** Add 3.5 g at $(0, 1)$, add .5 g at $(8, 1)$, and add 2 g at $(2, 4)$.

**33.** Review Practice Problem 1 and then *write* a solution. The *Study Guide* has a solution.

## Section 1.4, page 40

**1.** The product is not defined because the number of columns (2) in the $3 \times 2$ matrix does not match the number of entries (3) in the vector.

**3.** $A\mathbf{x} = \begin{bmatrix} 6 & 5 \\ -4 & -3 \\ 7 & 6 \end{bmatrix} \begin{bmatrix} 2 \\ -3 \end{bmatrix} = 2 \cdot \begin{bmatrix} 6 \\ -4 \\ 7 \end{bmatrix} - 3 \cdot \begin{bmatrix} 5 \\ -3 \\ 6 \end{bmatrix}$

$= \begin{bmatrix} 12 \\ -8 \\ 14 \end{bmatrix} + \begin{bmatrix} -15 \\ 9 \\ -18 \end{bmatrix} = \begin{bmatrix} -3 \\ 1 \\ -4 \end{bmatrix}$, and

$A\mathbf{x} = \begin{bmatrix} 6 & 5 \\ -4 & -3 \\ 7 & 6 \end{bmatrix} \begin{bmatrix} 2 \\ -3 \end{bmatrix} = \begin{bmatrix} 6 \cdot 2 + 5 \cdot (-3) \\ (-4) \cdot 2 + (-3) \cdot (-3) \\ 7 \cdot 2 + 6 \cdot (-3) \end{bmatrix}$

$= \begin{bmatrix} -3 \\ 1 \\ -4 \end{bmatrix}$. Show your work here and for Exercises 4–6, but thereafter perform the calculations mentally.

**5.** $5 \cdot \begin{bmatrix} 5 \\ -2 \end{bmatrix} - 1 \cdot \begin{bmatrix} 1 \\ -7 \end{bmatrix} + 3 \cdot \begin{bmatrix} -8 \\ 3 \end{bmatrix} - 2 \cdot \begin{bmatrix} 4 \\ -5 \end{bmatrix} = \begin{bmatrix} -8 \\ 16 \end{bmatrix}$

**7.** $\begin{bmatrix} 4 & -5 & 7 \\ -1 & 3 & -8 \\ 7 & -5 & 0 \\ -4 & 1 & 2 \end{bmatrix} \begin{bmatrix} x_1 \\ x_2 \\ x_3 \end{bmatrix} = \begin{bmatrix} 6 \\ -8 \\ 0 \\ -7 \end{bmatrix}$

**9.** $x_1 \begin{bmatrix} 3 \\ 0 \end{bmatrix} + x_2 \begin{bmatrix} 1 \\ 1 \end{bmatrix} + x_3 \begin{bmatrix} -5 \\ 4 \end{bmatrix} = \begin{bmatrix} 9 \\ 0 \end{bmatrix}$ and

$\begin{bmatrix} 3 & 1 & -5 \\ 0 & 1 & 4 \end{bmatrix} \begin{bmatrix} x_1 \\ x_2 \\ x_3 \end{bmatrix} = \begin{bmatrix} 9 \\ 0 \end{bmatrix}$

**11.** $\begin{bmatrix} 1 & 2 & 4 & -2 \\ 0 & 1 & 5 & 2 \\ -2 & -4 & -3 & 9 \end{bmatrix}, \mathbf{x} = \begin{bmatrix} x_1 \\ x_2 \\ x_3 \end{bmatrix} = \begin{bmatrix} 0 \\ -3 \\ 1 \end{bmatrix}$

**13.** Yes. (Justify your answer.)

**u** are here

**15.** The equation $A\mathbf{x} = \mathbf{b}$ is not consistent when $3b_1 + b_2$ is nonzero. (Show your work.) The set of $\mathbf{b}$ for which the equation *is* consistent is a line through the origin—the set of all points $(b_1, b_2)$ satisfying $b_2 = -3b_1$.

**17.** Only three rows contain a pivot position. The equation $A\mathbf{x} = \mathbf{b}$ does *not* have a solution for each $\mathbf{b}$ in $\mathbb{R}^4$, by Theorem 4.

**19.** The work in Exercise 17 shows that statement (d) in Theorem 4 is false. So all four statements in Theorem 4 are false. Thus, not all vectors in $\mathbb{R}^4$ can be written as a linear combination of the columns of $A$. Also, the columns of $A$ do *not* span $\mathbb{R}^4$.

**21.** The matrix $[\mathbf{v}_1 \ \mathbf{v}_2 \ \mathbf{v}_3]$ does not have a pivot in each row, so the columns of the matrix do not span $\mathbb{R}^4$, by Theorem 4. That is, $\{\mathbf{v}_1, \mathbf{v}_2, \mathbf{v}_3\}$ does not span $\mathbb{R}^4$.

**23.** Read the text carefully and try to mark each exercise statement True or False before you consult the *Study Guide*. Several parts of Exercises 23 and 24 are *implications* of the form

"If ⟨statement 1⟩, then ⟨statement 2⟩"

or equivalently,

"⟨statement 2⟩, if ⟨statement 1⟩"

Mark such an implication as True if ⟨statement 2⟩ is true in all cases when ⟨statement 1⟩ is true.

**25.** $c_1 = -3, c_2 = -1, c_3 = 2$

**27.** $Q\mathbf{x} = \mathbf{v}$, where $Q = [\mathbf{q}_1 \ \mathbf{q}_2 \ \mathbf{q}_3]$ and $\mathbf{x} = \begin{bmatrix} x_1 \\ x_2 \\ x_3 \end{bmatrix}$

*Note:* If your answer is the equation $A\mathbf{x} = \mathbf{b}$, you must specify what $A$ and $\mathbf{b}$ are.

**29.** *Hint:* Start with any $3 \times 3$ matrix $B$ in echelon form that has three pivot positions.

**31.** *Write* your solution before you check the *Study Guide*.

**33.** *Hint:* How many pivot columns does $A$ have? Why?

**35.** Given $A\mathbf{x}_1 = \mathbf{y}_1$ and $A\mathbf{x}_2 = \mathbf{y}_2$, you are asked to show that the equation $A\mathbf{x} = \mathbf{w}$ has a solution, where $\mathbf{w} = \mathbf{y}_1 + \mathbf{y}_2$. Observe that $\mathbf{w} = A\mathbf{x}_1 + A\mathbf{x}_2$ and use Theorem 5(a) with $\mathbf{x}_1$ and $\mathbf{x}_2$ in place of $\mathbf{u}$ and $\mathbf{v}$, respectively. That is, $\mathbf{w} = A\mathbf{x}_1 + A\mathbf{x}_2 = A(\mathbf{x}_1 + \mathbf{x}_2)$. So the vector $\mathbf{x} = \mathbf{x}_1 + \mathbf{x}_2$ is a solution of $\mathbf{w} = A\mathbf{x}$.

**37.** [M] The columns do not span $\mathbb{R}^4$.

**39.** [M] The columns span $\mathbb{R}^4$.

**41.** [M] Delete column 4 of the matrix in Exercise 39. It is also possible to delete column 3 instead of column 4.

## Section 1.5, page 48

**1.** The system has a nontrivial solution because there is a free variable, $x_3$.

**3.** The system has a nontrivial solution because there is a free variable, $x_3$.

**5.** $\mathbf{x} = \begin{bmatrix} x_1 \\ x_2 \\ x_3 \end{bmatrix} = x_3 \begin{bmatrix} 5 \\ -2 \\ 1 \end{bmatrix}$

**7.** $\mathbf{x} = \begin{bmatrix} x_1 \\ x_2 \\ x_3 \\ x_4 \end{bmatrix} = x_3 \begin{bmatrix} -9 \\ 4 \\ 1 \\ 0 \end{bmatrix} + x_4 \begin{bmatrix} 8 \\ -5 \\ 0 \\ 1 \end{bmatrix}$

**9.** $\mathbf{x} = x_2 \begin{bmatrix} 3 \\ 1 \\ 0 \end{bmatrix} + x_3 \begin{bmatrix} -2 \\ 0 \\ 1 \end{bmatrix}$

**11.** *Hint:* The system derived from the *reduced* echelon form is

$$\begin{aligned} x_1 - 4x_2 \qquad\quad + 5x_6 &= 0 \\ x_3 \quad - x_6 &= 0 \\ x_5 - 4x_6 &= 0 \\ 0 &= 0 \end{aligned}$$

The basic variables are $x_1$, $x_3$, and $x_5$. The remaining variables are free. The *Study Guide* discusses two mistakes that are often made on this type of problem.

**13.** $\mathbf{x} = \begin{bmatrix} 5 \\ -2 \\ 0 \end{bmatrix} + x_3 \begin{bmatrix} 4 \\ -7 \\ 1 \end{bmatrix} = \mathbf{p} + x_3\mathbf{q}$. Geometrically, the solution set is the line through $\begin{bmatrix} 5 \\ -2 \\ 0 \end{bmatrix}$ parallel to $\begin{bmatrix} 4 \\ -7 \\ 1 \end{bmatrix}$.

**15.** $\mathbf{x} = \begin{bmatrix} x_1 \\ x_2 \\ x_3 \end{bmatrix} = \begin{bmatrix} -2 \\ 1 \\ 0 \end{bmatrix} + x_3 \begin{bmatrix} 5 \\ -2 \\ 1 \end{bmatrix}$. The solution set is the

line through $\begin{bmatrix} -2 \\ 1 \\ 0 \end{bmatrix}$, parallel to the line that is the solution

set of the homogeneous system in Exercise 5.

**17.** Let $\mathbf{u} = \begin{bmatrix} -9 \\ 1 \\ 0 \end{bmatrix}$, $\mathbf{v} = \begin{bmatrix} 4 \\ 0 \\ 1 \end{bmatrix}$, $\mathbf{p} = \begin{bmatrix} -2 \\ 0 \\ 0 \end{bmatrix}$. The solution of

the homogeneous equation is $\mathbf{x} = x_2\mathbf{u} + x_3\mathbf{v}$, the plane
through the origin spanned by $\mathbf{u}$ and $\mathbf{v}$. The solution set of
the nonhomogeneous system is $\mathbf{x} = \mathbf{p} + x_2\mathbf{u} + x_3\mathbf{v}$, the
plane through $\mathbf{p}$ parallel to the solution set of the
homogeneous equation.

**19.** $\mathbf{x} = \mathbf{a} + t\mathbf{b}$, where $t$ represents a parameter, or

$\mathbf{x} = \begin{bmatrix} x_1 \\ x_2 \end{bmatrix} = \begin{bmatrix} -2 \\ 0 \end{bmatrix} + t \begin{bmatrix} -5 \\ 3 \end{bmatrix}$, or $\begin{cases} x_1 = -2 - 5t \\ x_2 = 3t \end{cases}$

**21.** $\mathbf{x} = \mathbf{p} + t(\mathbf{q} - \mathbf{p}) = \begin{bmatrix} 2 \\ -5 \end{bmatrix} + t \begin{bmatrix} -5 \\ 6 \end{bmatrix}$

**23.** It is important to read the text carefully and write your
answers. After that, check the *Study Guide*, if necessary.

**25.** $A\mathbf{v}_h = A(\mathbf{w} - \mathbf{p}) = A\mathbf{w} - A\mathbf{p} = \mathbf{b} - \mathbf{b} = \mathbf{0}$

**27.** When $A$ is the $3 \times 3$ zero matrix, *every* $\mathbf{x}$ in $\mathbb{R}^3$ satisfies
$A\mathbf{x} = \mathbf{0}$. So the solution set is all vectors in $\mathbb{R}^3$.

**29. a.** When $A$ is a $3 \times 3$ matrix with three pivot positions, the
equation $A\mathbf{x} = \mathbf{0}$ has no free variables and hence has no
nontrivial solution.

  **b.** With three pivot positions, $A$ has a pivot position in
each of its three rows. By Theorem 4 in Section 1.4, the
equation $A\mathbf{x} = \mathbf{b}$ has a solution for every possible $\mathbf{b}$.
The word "possible" in the exercise means that the only
vectors considered in this case are those in $\mathbb{R}^3$, because
$A$ has three rows.

**31. a.** When $A$ is a $3 \times 2$ matrix with two pivot positions, each
column is a pivot column. So the equation $A\mathbf{x} = \mathbf{0}$ has
no free variables and hence no nontrivial solution.

  **b.** With two pivot positions and three rows, $A$ cannot have
a pivot in every row. So the equation $A\mathbf{x} = \mathbf{b}$ cannot
have a solution for every possible $\mathbf{b}$ (in $\mathbb{R}^3$), by
Theorem 4 in Section 1.4.

**33.** One answer: $\mathbf{x} = \begin{bmatrix} 3 \\ -1 \end{bmatrix}$

**35.** Your example should have the property that the sum of the
entries in each row is zero. Why?

**37.** One answer is $A = \begin{bmatrix} 1 & -4 \\ 1 & -4 \end{bmatrix}$. The *Study Guide* shows how
to analyze the problem in order to construct $A$. If $\mathbf{b}$ is any
vector *not* a multiple of the first column of $A$, then the
solution set of $A\mathbf{x} = \mathbf{b}$ is empty and thus cannot be formed
by translating the solution set of $A\mathbf{x} = \mathbf{b}$. This does not
contradict Theorem 6, because that theorem applies when
the equation $A\mathbf{x} = \mathbf{b}$ has a nonempty solution set.

**39.** If $c$ is a scalar, then $A(c\mathbf{u}) = cA\mathbf{u}$, by Theorem 5(b) in
Section 1.4. If $\mathbf{u}$ satisfies $A\mathbf{x} = \mathbf{0}$, then $A\mathbf{u} = \mathbf{0}$,
$cA\mathbf{u} = c \cdot \mathbf{0} = \mathbf{0}$, and so $A(c\mathbf{u}) = \mathbf{0}$.

## Section 1.6, page 55

**1.** The general solution is $p_{Goods} = .875p_{Services}$, with $p_{Services}$
free. One equilibrium solution is $p_{Services} = 1000$ and
$p_{Goods} = 875$. Using fractions, the general solution could be
written $p_{Goods} = (7/8)p_{Services}$, and a natural choice of
prices might be $p_{Services} = 80$ and $p_{Goods} = 70$. Only the
*ratio* of the prices is important. The economic equilibrium
is unaffected by a proportional change in prices.

**3. a.**

| Output | C&M ↓ | F&P ↓ | Mach. ↓ | Input | Purchased By: |
|---|---|---|---|---|---|
| | .2 | .8 | .4 | → | C&M |
| | .3 | .1 | .4 | → | F&P |
| | .5 | .1 | .2 | → | Mach. |

Distribution of Output From:

  **b.** $\begin{bmatrix} .8 & -.8 & -.4 & 0 \\ -.3 & .9 & -.4 & 0 \\ -.5 & -.1 & .8 & 0 \end{bmatrix}$

  **c.** **[M]** $p_{Chemicals} = 141.7$, $p_{Fuels} = 91.7$, $p_{Machinery} = 100$.
To two significant figures, $p_{Chemicals} = 140$, $p_{Fuels} = 92$,
$p_{Machinery} = 100$.

**5.** $B_2S_3 + 6H_2O \rightarrow 2H_3BO_3 + 3H_2S$

**7.** $3NaHCO_3 + H_3C_6H_5O_7 \rightarrow Na_3C_6H_5O_7 + 3H_2O + 3CO_2$

**9.** **[M]** $15PbN_6 + 44CrMn_2O_8 \rightarrow$
$5Pb_3O_4 + 22Cr_2O_3 + 88MnO_2 + 90NO$

**11.** $\begin{cases} x_1 = 20 - x_3 \\ x_2 = 60 + x_3 \\ x_3 \text{ is free} \\ x_4 = 60 \end{cases}$  The largest value of $x_3$ is 20.

**13. a.** $\begin{cases} x_1 = x_3 - 40 \\ x_2 = x_3 + 10 \\ x_3 \text{ is free} \\ x_4 = x_6 + 50 \\ x_5 = x_6 + 60 \\ x_6 \text{ is free} \end{cases}$  **b.** $\begin{cases} x_2 = 50 \\ x_3 = 40 \\ x_4 = 50 \\ x_5 = 60 \end{cases}$

## Chapter 2

### Section 2.1, page 66

**1.** $\begin{bmatrix} -4 & 0 & 2 \\ -8 & 10 & -4 \end{bmatrix}$, $\begin{bmatrix} 3 & -5 & 3 \\ -7 & 6 & -7 \end{bmatrix}$, not defined,

$\begin{bmatrix} 1 & 13 \\ -7 & -6 \end{bmatrix}$

**3.** $\begin{bmatrix} -1 & 1 \\ -5 & 5 \end{bmatrix}$, $\begin{bmatrix} 12 & -3 \\ 15 & -6 \end{bmatrix}$

**5. a.** $A\mathbf{b}_1 = \begin{bmatrix} -7 \\ 7 \\ 12 \end{bmatrix}$, $A\mathbf{b}_2 = \begin{bmatrix} 4 \\ -6 \\ -7 \end{bmatrix}$,

$AB = \begin{bmatrix} -7 & 4 \\ 7 & -6 \\ 12 & -7 \end{bmatrix}$

**b.** $AB = \begin{bmatrix} -1 \cdot 3 + 2(-2) & -1(-2) + 2 \cdot 1 \\ 5 \cdot 3 + 4(-2) & 5(-2) + 4 \cdot 1 \\ 2 \cdot 3 - 3(-2) & 2(-2) - 3 \cdot 1 \end{bmatrix}$

$= \begin{bmatrix} -7 & 4 \\ 7 & -6 \\ 12 & -7 \end{bmatrix}$

**7.** $3 \times 7$    **9.** $k = 5$

**11.** $AD = \begin{bmatrix} 2 & 3 & 5 \\ 2 & 6 & 15 \\ 2 & 12 & 25 \end{bmatrix}$, $DA = \begin{bmatrix} 2 & 2 & 2 \\ 3 & 6 & 9 \\ 5 & 20 & 25 \end{bmatrix}$

Right-multiplication (that is, multiplication on the right) by $D$ multiplies each *column* of $A$ by the corresponding diagonal entry of $D$. Left-multiplication by $D$ multiplies each *row* of $A$ by the corresponding diagonal entry of $D$. The *Study Guide* tells how to make $AB = BA$, but you should try this yourself before looking there.

**13.** *Hint:* One of the two matrices is $Q$.

**15.** Answer the questions before looking in the *Study Guide*.

**17.** $\mathbf{b}_1 = \begin{bmatrix} 7 \\ 4 \end{bmatrix}$, $\mathbf{b}_2 = \begin{bmatrix} -8 \\ -5 \end{bmatrix}$

**19.** The third column of $AB$ is the sum of the first two columns of $AB$. Here's why. Write $B = [\ \mathbf{b}_1 \quad \mathbf{b}_2 \quad \mathbf{b}_3\ ]$. By definition, the third column of $AB$ is $A\mathbf{b}_3$. If $\mathbf{b}_3 = \mathbf{b}_1 + \mathbf{b}_2$, then $A\mathbf{b}_3 = A(\mathbf{b}_1 + \mathbf{b}_2) = A\mathbf{b}_1 + A\mathbf{b}_2$, by a property of matrix-vector multiplication.

**21.** The columns of $A$ are linearly dependent. Why?

**23.** *Hint:* Suppose $\mathbf{x}$ satisfies $A\mathbf{x} = \mathbf{0}$, and show that $\mathbf{x}$ must be $\mathbf{0}$.

**25.** *Hint:* Use the results of Exercises 23 and 24, and apply the associative law of multiplication to the product $CAD$.

**27.** $\mathbf{u}^T\mathbf{v} = \mathbf{v}^T\mathbf{u} = -2a + 3b - 4c$,

$\mathbf{u}\mathbf{v}^T = \begin{bmatrix} -2a & -2b & -2c \\ 3a & 3b & 3c \\ -4a & -4b & -4c \end{bmatrix}$,

$\mathbf{v}\mathbf{u}^T = \begin{bmatrix} -2a & 3a & -4a \\ -2b & 3b & -4b \\ -2c & 3c & -4c \end{bmatrix}$

**29.** *Hint:* For Theorem 2(b), show that the $(i, j)$-entry of $A(B + C)$ equals the $(i, j)$-entry of $AB + AC$.

**31.** *Hint:* Use the definition of the product $I_m A$ and the fact that $I_m\mathbf{x} = \mathbf{x}$ for $\mathbf{x}$ in $\mathbb{R}^m$.

**33.** *Hint:* First write the $(i, j)$-entry of $(AB)^T$, which is the $(j, i)$-entry of $AB$. Then, to compute the $(i, j)$-entry in $B^T A^T$, use the facts that the entries in row $i$ of $B^T$ are $b_{1i}, \ldots, b_{ni}$, because they come from column $i$ of $B$, and the entries in column $j$ of $A^T$ are $a_{j1}, \ldots, a_{jn}$, because they come from row $j$ of $A$.

**35.** **[M]** The answer here depends on the choice of matrix program. For MATLAB, use the `help` command to read about `zeros`, `ones`, `eye`, and `diag`.

**37.** **[M]** Display your results and report your conclusions.

**39.** **[M]** The matrix $S$ "shifts" the entries in a vector $(a, b, c, d, e)$ to yield $(b, c, d, e, 0)$. $S^5$ is the $5 \times 5$ zero matrix. So is $S^6$.

## Section 2.2, page 75

**1.** $\begin{bmatrix} 2 & -3 \\ -5/2 & 4 \end{bmatrix}$    **3.** $-\dfrac{1}{5}\begin{bmatrix} -5 & -5 \\ 7 & 8 \end{bmatrix}$ or

$\begin{bmatrix} 1 & 1 \\ -7/5 & -8/5 \end{bmatrix}$

**5.** $x_1 = 7$ and $x_2 = -9$

**7. a** and **b**: $\begin{bmatrix} -9 \\ 4 \end{bmatrix}$, $\begin{bmatrix} 11 \\ -5 \end{bmatrix}$, $\begin{bmatrix} 6 \\ -2 \end{bmatrix}$, and $\begin{bmatrix} 13 \\ -5 \end{bmatrix}$

**9.** Write out your answers before checking the *Study Guide*.

**11.** The proof can be modeled after the proof of Theorem 5.

**13.** $AB = AC \Rightarrow A^{-1}AB = A^{-1}AC \Rightarrow IB = IC \Rightarrow B = C$. No, in general, $B$ and $C$ can be different when $A$ is not invertible. See Exercise 10 in Section 2.1.

**15.** $D = C^{-1}B^{-1}A^{-1}$. Show that $D$ works.

**17.** $A = BCB^{-1}$

**19.** After you find $X = CB - A$, show that $X$ is a solution.

**21.** *Hint:* Consider the equation $A\mathbf{x} = \mathbf{0}$.

**23.** *Hint:* If $A\mathbf{x} = \mathbf{0}$ has only the trivial solution, then there are no free variables in the equation $A\mathbf{x} = \mathbf{0}$, and each column of $A$ is a pivot column.

**25.** *Hint:* Consider the case $a = b = 0$. Then consider the vector $\begin{bmatrix} -b \\ a \end{bmatrix}$, and use the fact that $ad - bc = 0$.

**27.** *Hint:* For part (a), interchange $A$ and $B$ in the box following Example 6 in Section 2.1, and then replace $B$ by the identity matrix. For parts (b) and (c), begin by writing

$A = \begin{bmatrix} \text{row}_1(A) \\ \text{row}_2(A) \\ \text{row}_3(A) \end{bmatrix}$

**29.** $\begin{bmatrix} -7 & 2 \\ 4 & -1 \end{bmatrix}$    **31.** $\begin{bmatrix} 8 & 3 & 1 \\ 10 & 4 & 1 \\ 7/2 & 3/2 & 1/2 \end{bmatrix}$

**33.** $A^{-1} = B = \begin{bmatrix} 1 & 0 & 0 & \cdots & 0 \\ -1 & 1 & 0 & & 0 \\ 0 & -1 & 1 & & \\ \vdots & & & \ddots & \vdots \\ 0 & 0 & \cdots & -1 & 1 \end{bmatrix}$. *Hint:* For

$j = 1, \ldots, n$, let $\mathbf{a}_j, \mathbf{b}_j$, and $\mathbf{e}_j$ denote the $j$th columns of $A$, $B$, and $I$, respectively. Use the facts that $\mathbf{a}_j - \mathbf{a}_{j+1} = \mathbf{e}_j$ and $\mathbf{b}_j = \mathbf{e}_j - \mathbf{e}_{j+1}$ for $j = 1, \ldots, n - 1$, and $\mathbf{a}_n = \mathbf{b}_n = \mathbf{e}_n$.

**35.** $\begin{bmatrix} 3 \\ -6 \\ 4 \end{bmatrix}$. Find this by row reducing $[\,A \quad \mathbf{e}_3\,]$.

**37.** $C = \begin{bmatrix} 1 & 1 & -1 \\ -1 & 1 & 0 \end{bmatrix}$

**39.** .27, .30, and .23 inch, respectively

**41.** [M] 12, 1.5, 21.5, and 12 newtons, respectively

## Chapter 3

### Section 3.1, page 81

**1.** 1    **3.** 0    **5.** −24    **7.** 4

**9.** 15. Start with row 3.

**11.** −18. Start with column 1 or row 4.

**13.** 6. Start with row 2 or column 2.

**15.** 24    **17.** −10

**19.** $ad - bc, cb - da$. Interchanging two rows changes the sign of the determinant.

**21.** $ad - bc, akd - bkc = k(ad - bc)$. Scaling a row by a constant $k$ multiplies the determinant by $k$.

**23.** $7a - 14b + 7c. - 7a + 14b - 7c$. Interchanging two rows changes the sign of the determinant.

**25.** 1    **27.** 1    **29.** $k$

**31.** 1. The matrix is upper or lower triangular, with only 1's on the diagonal. The determinant is 1, the product of the diagonal entries.

**33.** $\det EA = \det \begin{bmatrix} a + kc & b + kd \\ c & d \end{bmatrix}$
$= (a + kc)d - (b + kd)c$
$= ad + kcd - bc - kdc = (+1)(ad - bc)$
$= (\det E)(\det A)$

**35.** $\det EA = \det \begin{bmatrix} c & d \\ a & b \end{bmatrix} = cb - ad = (-1)(ad - bc)$
$= (\det E)(\det A)$

**37.** $5A = \begin{bmatrix} 15 & 5 \\ 20 & 10 \end{bmatrix}$; no

**39.** Hints are in the *Study Guide*.

**41.** The area of the parallelogram and the determinant of $[\,\mathbf{u} \quad \mathbf{v}\,]$ both equal 6. If $\mathbf{v} = \begin{bmatrix} x \\ 2 \end{bmatrix}$ for any $x$, the area is still 6. In each case the base of the parallelogram is unchanged, and the altitude remains 2 because the second coordinate of $\mathbf{v}$ is always 2.

**43.** [M] In general, $\det A^{-1} = 1/\det A$ as long as $\det A$ is nonzero.

**45.** [M] You can check your conjectures when you get to Section 3.2.

### Section 3.2, page 89

**1.** Interchanging two rows reverses the sign of the determinant.

**3.** Multiplying a row by 3 multiplies the determinant by 3.

**5.** −3    **7.** 0    **9.** −28    **11.** −48

**13.** 6    **15.** 21    **17.** 7    **19.** 14

**21.** Not invertible    **23.** Invertible

**25.** Linearly independent    **27.** See the *Study Guide*.

**29.** 16

**31.** *Hint:* Show that $(\det A)(\det A^{-1}) = 1$.

**33.** *Hint:* Use Theorem 6.

**35.** *Hint:* Use Theorem 6 and another theorem.

**37.** $\det AB = \det \begin{bmatrix} 6 & 0 \\ 17 & 4 \end{bmatrix} = 24$; $(\det A)(\det B) = 3 \cdot 8 = 24$

**39. a.** −12    **b.** −375    **c.** 4    **d.** $-\frac{1}{3}$    **e.** −27

**41.** $\det A = (a + e)d - (b + f)c = ad + ed - bc - fc$
$= (ad - bc) + (ed - fc) = \det B + \det C$

**43.** *Hint:* Compute $\det A$ by a cofactor expansion down column 3.

**45.** [M] See the *Study Guide* after you have made a conjecture about $A^T A$ and $A A^T$.

### Section 3.3, page 98

**1.** $\begin{bmatrix} 5/6 \\ -1/6 \end{bmatrix}$    **3.** $\begin{bmatrix} 4/5 \\ -3/10 \end{bmatrix}$    **5.** $\begin{bmatrix} 1/4 \\ 11/4 \\ 3/8 \end{bmatrix}$

**7.** $s \neq \pm\sqrt{3};\ x_1 = \dfrac{5s + 4}{6(s^2 - 3)}, x_2 = \dfrac{-4s - 15}{4(s^2 - 3)}$

**9.** $s \neq 0, 1;\ x_1 = \dfrac{7}{3(s - 1)}, x_2 = \dfrac{4s + 3}{6s(s - 1)}$

**11.** $\operatorname{adj} A = \begin{bmatrix} 0 & 1 & 0 \\ -5 & -1 & -5 \\ 5 & 2 & 10 \end{bmatrix}$, $A^{-1} = \dfrac{1}{5}\begin{bmatrix} 0 & 1 & 0 \\ -5 & -1 & -5 \\ 5 & 2 & 10 \end{bmatrix}$

**13.** $\operatorname{adj} A = \begin{bmatrix} -1 & -1 & 5 \\ 1 & -5 & 1 \\ 1 & 7 & -5 \end{bmatrix}$, $A^{-1} = \dfrac{1}{6}\begin{bmatrix} -1 & -1 & 5 \\ 1 & -5 & 1 \\ 1 & 7 & -5 \end{bmatrix}$

**15.** $\operatorname{adj} A = \begin{bmatrix} -1 & 0 & 0 \\ -1 & -5 & 0 \\ -1 & -15 & 5 \end{bmatrix}$, $A^{-1} = \dfrac{-1}{5}\begin{bmatrix} -1 & 0 & 0 \\ -1 & -5 & 0 \\ -1 & -15 & 5 \end{bmatrix}$

**17.** If $A = \begin{bmatrix} a & b \\ c & d \end{bmatrix}$, then $C_{11} = d, C_{12} = -c, C_{21} = -b$, $C_{22} = a$. The adjugate matrix is the transpose of cofactors:

$\operatorname{adj} A = \begin{bmatrix} d & -b \\ -c & a \end{bmatrix}$

Following Theorem 8, we divide by $\det A$; this produces the formula from Section 2.2.

**19.** 8    **21.** 3    **23.** 23

**25.** A $3 \times 3$ matrix $A$ is not invertible if and only if its columns are linearly dependent (by the Invertible Matrix Theorem). This happens if and only if one of the columns is in the plane spanned by the other two columns, which is equivalent to the condition that the parallelepiped determined by these columns has zero volume, which in turn is equivalent to the condition that $\det A = 0$.

**27.** 12    **29.** $\frac{1}{2} |\det [\mathbf{v}_1 \quad \mathbf{v}_2]|$

**31. a.** See Example 5.    **b.** $4\pi abc/3$

**33. [M]** In MATLAB, the entries in $B - \text{inv}(A)$ are approximately $10^{-15}$ or smaller. See the *Study Guide* for suggestions that may save you keystrokes as you work.

**35. [M]** MATLAB Student Version 4.0 uses 57,771 flops for $\text{inv}(A)$, and 14,269,045 flops for the inverse formula. The `inv(A)` command requires only about 0.4% of the operations for the inverse formula. The *Study Guide* shows how to use the `flops` command.

# Answers to Odd-Numbered Exercises

## Chapter 4

## Preliminaries

### Section 4.1    (page 108)

**1.** $0.\overline{2}$    **3.** $4/33$

**5.** $1/7 = 0.\overline{142857}$, $2/7 = 0.\overline{285714}$,
$3/7 = 0.\overline{428571}$, $4/7 = 0.\overline{571428}$,
$5/7 = 0.\overline{714285}$, $6/7 = 0.\overline{857142}$

**7.** $[0, 5]$    **9.** $(-\infty, -6) \cup (-5, \infty)$

**11.** $(-2, \infty)$    **13.** $(-\infty, -2)$

**15.** $(-\infty, 5/4]$    **17.** $(0, \infty)$

**19.** $(-\infty, 5/3) \cup (2, \infty)$    **21.** $[0, 2]$

**23.** $(-2, 0) \cup (2, \infty)$    **25.** $[-2, 0) \cup [4, \infty)$

**27.** $x = -3, \ 3$    **29.** $t = -1/2, \ -9/2$

**31.** $s = -1/3, \ 17/3$    **33.** $(-2, 2)$

**35.** $[-1, 3]$    **37.** $\left(\dfrac{5}{3}, 3\right)$

**39.** $[0, 4]$    **41.** $x > 1$

**43.** true if $a \geq 0$, false if $a < 0$

### Section 4.2    (page 114)

**1.** $\Delta x = 4$, $\Delta y = -3$, dist $= 5$

**3.** $\Delta x = -4$, $\Delta y = -4$, dist $= 4\sqrt{2}$

**5.** $(2, -4)$

**7.** circle, centre $(0, 0)$, radius 1

**9.** points inside and on circle, centre $(0, 0)$, radius 1

**11.** points on and above the parabola $y = x^2$

**13.** (a) $x = -2$, (b) $y = 5/3$

**15.** $y = x + 2$    **17.** $y = 2x + b$

**19.** above    **21.** $y = 3x/2$

**23.** $y = (7 - x)/3$    **25.** $y = \sqrt{2} - 2x$

**27.** 4, 3,

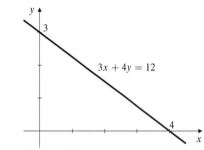

**29.** $\sqrt{2}, -2/\sqrt{3}$

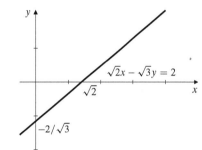

**31.** (a) $y = x - 1$, (b) $y = -x + 3$

**33.** $(2, -3)$    **37.** 5

**39.** $\$23,000$    **43.** $(-2, -2)$

**45.** $\left(\frac{1}{3}(x_1 + 2x_2), \frac{1}{3}(y_1 + 2y_2)\right)$

**47.** circle, centre $(2, 0)$, radius 4

**49.** perp. if $k = -8$, parallel if $k = 1/2$

## Chapter 5
## Differentiation

### Section 5.1    (page 122)

**1.** $y = 3x - 1$    **3.** $y = 8x - 13$

**5.** $y = 12x + 24$    **7.** $x - 4y = -5$

**9.** $x - 4y = -2$    **11.** $y = 2x_0 x - x_0^2$

**13.** no    **15.** yes, $x = -2$

**17.** yes, $x = 0$

**19.** (a) $3a^2$;    (b) $y = 3x - 2$ and $y = 3x + 2$

**21.** $(1, 1), \ (-1, 1)$    **23.** $k = 3/4$

**25.** horiz. tangent at $(0, 0)$, $(3, 108)$, $(5, 0)$

**27.** horiz. tangent at $(-0.5, 1.25)$, no tangents at $(-1, 1)$ and $(1, -1)$

**29.** horiz. tangent at $(0, -1)$

**31.** no, consider $y = x^{2/3}$ at $(0, 0)$

## Section 5.2   (page 129)

**1.**

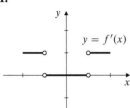

**3.**

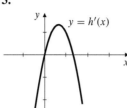

**5.** on $[-2, 2]$ except at $x = -1$ and $x = 1$

**7.** slope positive for $x < 1.5$, negative for $x > 1.5$; horizontal tangent at $x = 1.5$

**9.** singular points at $x = -1$, $0$, $1$, horizontal tangents at about $x = \pm 0.57$

**11.** (a) $y' = 2x - 3$, (b) $dy = (2x - 3)\,dx$

**13.** (a) $f'(x) = 3x^2$, (b) $df(x) = 3x^2\,dx$

**15.** (a) $g'(x) = -\dfrac{4}{(2+x)^2}$, (b) $dg(x) = -\dfrac{4}{(2+x)^2}\,dx$

**17.** (a) $F'(t) = \dfrac{1}{\sqrt{2t+1}}$, (b) $dF(t) = \dfrac{1}{\sqrt{2t+1}}\,dt$

**19.** (a) $y' = 1 - \dfrac{1}{x^2}$, (b) $dy = \left(1 - \dfrac{1}{x^2}\right)dx$

**21.** (a) $F'(x) = -\dfrac{x}{(1+x^2)^{3/2}}$, (b) $dF(x) = -\dfrac{x}{(1+x^2)^{3/2}}\,dx$

**23.** (a) $y' = -\dfrac{1}{2(1+x)^{3/2}}$, (b) $dy = -\dfrac{1}{2(1+x)^{3/2}}\,dx$

**25.** Define $f(0) = 0$, $f$ is not differentiable at $0$

**27.** at $x = -1$ and $x = -2$

**29.**

| $x$ | $\dfrac{f(x) - f(2)}{x - 2}$ | $x$ | $\dfrac{f(x) - f(2)}{x - 2}$ |
|---|---|---|---|
| 1.9 | −0.26316 | 2.1 | −0.23810 |
| 1.99 | −0.25126 | 2.01 | −0.24876 |
| 1.999 | −0.25013 | 2.001 | −0.24988 |
| 1.9999 | −0.25001 | 2.0001 | −0.24999 |

$$\dfrac{d}{dx}\left(\dfrac{1}{x}\right)\bigg|_{x=2} = -\dfrac{1}{4}$$

**31.** $x - 6y = -15$

**33.** $y = \dfrac{2}{a^2 + a} - \dfrac{2(2a + 1)}{(a^2 + a)^2}(t - a)$

**35.** $22t^{21}$, all $t$

**37.** $-(1/3)x^{-4/3}$, $x \neq 0$

**39.** $(119/4)s^{115/4}$, $s \geq 0$

**41.** $-16$

**43.** $1/(8\sqrt{2})$

**45.** $y = a^2 x - a^3 + \dfrac{1}{a}$

**47.** $y = 6x - 9$ and $y = -2x - 1$

**49.** $\dfrac{1}{2\sqrt{2}}$

**53.** $f'(x) = \frac{1}{3}x^{-2/3}$

## Section 5.3   (page 137)

**1.** $6x - 5$

**3.** $2Ax + B$

**5.** $\frac{1}{3}s^4 - \frac{1}{5}s^2$

**7.** $\frac{1}{3}t^{-2/3} + \frac{1}{2}t^{-3/4} + \frac{3}{5}t^{-4/5}$

**9.** $x^{2/3} + x^{-8/5}$

**11.** $\dfrac{5}{2\sqrt{x}} - \frac{3}{2}\sqrt{x} - \frac{5}{6}x^{3/2}$

**13.** $-\dfrac{2x + 5}{(x^2 + 5x)^2}$

**15.** $\dfrac{\pi^2}{(2 - \pi t)^2}$

**17.** $(4x^2 - 3)/x^4$

**19.** $-t^{-3/2} + (1/2)t^{-1/2} + (3/2)\sqrt{t}$

**21.** $-\dfrac{24}{(3 + 4x)^2}$

**23.** $\dfrac{1}{\sqrt{t}(1 - \sqrt{t})^2}$

**25.** $\dfrac{ad - bc}{(cx + d)^2}$

**27.** $10 + 70x + 150x^2 + 96x^3$

**29.** $2x(\sqrt{x} + 1)(5x^{2/3} - 2) + \dfrac{1}{2\sqrt{x}}(x^2 + 4)(5x^{2/3} - 2)$

$\quad + \dfrac{10}{3}x^{-1/3}(x^2 + 4)(\sqrt{x} + 1)$

**31.** $\dfrac{6x + 1}{(6x^2 + 2x + 1)^2}$

**33.** $-1$

**35.** $20$

**37.** $-\dfrac{1}{2}$

**39.** $-\dfrac{1}{18\sqrt{2}}$

**41.** $y = 4x - 6$

**43.** $(1, 2)$ and $(-1, -2)$

**45.** $\left(-\frac{1}{2}, \frac{4}{3}\right)$

**47.** $y = b - \dfrac{b^2 x}{4}$

**49.** $y = 12x - 16$, $y = 3x + 2$

**51.** $x/\sqrt{x^2 + 1}$

## Section 5.4   (page 142)

**1.** $12(2x + 3)^5$

**3.** $-20x(4 - x^2)^9$

**5.** $\dfrac{30}{t^2}\left(2 + \dfrac{3}{t}\right)^{-11}$

**7.** $\dfrac{12}{(5 - 4x)^2}$

**9.** $-2x\,\mathrm{sgn}\,(1 - x^2)$

**11.** $\begin{cases} 8 & \text{if } x > 1/4 \\ 0 & \text{if } x < 1/4 \end{cases}$

**13.** $\dfrac{-3}{2\sqrt{3x + 4}(2 + \sqrt{3x + 4})^2}$

**15.** $-\dfrac{5}{3}\left(1 - \dfrac{1}{(u - 1)^2}\right)\left(u + \dfrac{1}{u - 1}\right)^{-8/3}$

**17.**

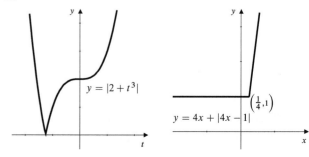

$y = |2 + t^3|$

$y = 4x + |4x - 1|$, $\left(\frac{1}{4}, 1\right)$

**23.** $(5 - 2x) f'(5x - x^2)$   **25.** $\dfrac{f'(x)}{\sqrt{3 + 2f(x)}}$

**27.** $\dfrac{1}{\sqrt{x}} f'(3 + 2\sqrt{x})$

**29.** $15 f'(4 - 5t) f'(2 - 3f(4 - 5t))$

**31.** $\dfrac{3}{2\sqrt{2}}$   **33.** $102$

**35.** $-6 \left(1 - \frac{15}{2}(3x)^4 \left((3x)^5 - 2\right)^{-3/2}\right)$
$\times \left(x + \left((3x)^5 - 2\right)^{-1/2}\right)^{-7}$

**37.** $y = 2^{3/2} - \sqrt{2}(x + 1)$   **39.** $y = \frac{1}{27} + \frac{5}{162}(x + 2)$

**41.** $\dfrac{x(x^4 + 2x^2 - 2)}{(x^2 + 1)^{5/2}}$   **43.** $857{,}592$

**45.** no; yes; both functions are equal to $x^2$.

## Section 5.5   (page 148)

**3.** $-3 \sin 3x$   **5.** $\pi \sec^2 \pi x$

**7.** $3 \csc^2(4 - 3x)$   **9.** $r \sin(s - rx)$

**11.** $2\pi x \cos(\pi x^2)$   **13.** $\dfrac{-\sin x}{2\sqrt{1 + \cos x}}$

**15.** $-(1 + \cos x) \sin(x + \sin x)$

**17.** $(3\pi/2) \sin^2(\pi x/2) \cos(\pi x/2)$

**19.** $a \cos 2at$   **21.** $2\cos(2x) + 2\sin(2x)$

**23.** $\sec^2 x - \csc^2 x$   **25.** $\tan^2 x$

**27.** $-t \sin t$   **29.** $1/(1 + \cos x)$

**31.** $2x \cos(3x) - 3x^2 \sin(3x)$

**33.** $2x[\sec(x^2) \tan^2(x^2) + \sec^3(x^2)]$

**35.** $-\sec^2 t \sin(\tan t) \cos(\cos(\tan t))$

**39.** $y = \pi - x, \; y = x - \pi$

**41.** $y = 1 - (x - \pi)/4, \; y = 1 + 4(x - \pi)$

**43.** $y = \dfrac{1}{\sqrt{2}} + \dfrac{\pi}{180\sqrt{2}}(x - 45)$

**45.** $\pm(\pi/4, 1)$   **49.** yes, $(\pi, \pi)$

**51.** yes, $(2\pi/3, (2\pi/3) + \sqrt{3}), (4\pi/3, (4\pi/3) - \sqrt{3})$

**53.** $2$   **55.** $1$

**57.** $1/2$

**59.** infinitely many, $0.336508, 0.161228$

## Section 5.6   (page 153)

**1.** $\begin{cases} y' = -14(3 - 2x)^6, \\ y'' = 168(3 - 2x)^5, \\ y''' = -1680(3 - 2x)^4 \end{cases}$

**3.** $\begin{cases} y' = -12(x - 1)^{-3}, \\ y'' = 36(x - 1)^{-4}, \\ y''' = -144(x - 1)^{-5} \end{cases}$

**5.** $\begin{cases} y' = \frac{1}{3}x^{-2/3} + \frac{1}{3}x^{-4/3}, \\ y'' = -\frac{2}{9}x^{-5/3} - \frac{4}{9}x^{-7/3} \\ y''' = \frac{10}{27}x^{-8/3} + \frac{28}{27}x^{-10/3} \end{cases}$

**7.** $\begin{cases} y' = \frac{5}{2}x^{3/2} + \frac{3}{2}x^{-1/2} \\ y'' = \frac{15}{4}x^{1/2} - \frac{3}{4}x^{-3/2} \\ y''' = \frac{15}{8}x^{-1/2} + \frac{9}{8}x^{-5/2} \end{cases}$

**9.** $y' = \sec^2 x, \; y'' = 2\sec^2 x \tan x, \; y''' = 4\sec^2 x \tan^2 x + 2\sec^4 x$

**11.** $y' = -2x \sin(x^2), \; y'' = -2\sin(x^2) - 4x^2 \cos(x^2), \; y''' = -12x \cos(x^2) + 8x^3 \sin(x^2)$

**13.** $(-1)^n n! x^{-(n+1)}$   **15.** $n!(2 - x)^{-(n+1)}$

**17.** $(-1)^n n! b^n (a + bx)^{-(n+1)}$

**19.** $f^{(n)} = \begin{cases} (-1)^k a^n \cos(ax) & \text{if } n = 2k \\ (-1)^{k+1} a^n \sin(ax) & \text{if } n = 2k + 1 \end{cases}$ where $k = 0, 1, 2, \ldots$

**21.** $f^{(n)} = (-1)^k [a^n x \sin(ax) - na^{n-1} \cos(ax)]$ if $n = 2k$, or $(-1)^k [a^n x \cos(ax) + na^{n-1} \sin(ax)]$ if $n = 2k + 1$, where $k = 0, 1, 2, \ldots$

**23.** $-\dfrac{1 \times 3 \times 5 \times \cdots \times (2n - 3)}{2^n} 3^n (1 - 3x)^{-(2n-1)/2},$ $(n = 2, 3, \ldots)$

## Section 5.7   (page 159)

**1.** $-0.0025, \; 0.4975$   **3.** $-1/40, \; -1/40$

**5.** $4\%$   **7.** $-4\%$

**9.** $1\%$   **11.** $6\%$

**13.** $8 \text{ ft}^2/\text{ft}$

**15.** $1/\sqrt{\pi A}$ units/square unit

**17.** $16\pi \text{ m}^3/\text{m}$

**19.** $\dfrac{dC}{dA} = \sqrt{\dfrac{\pi}{A}}$ length units/area unit

**21.** (a) 10,500 L/min, 3,500 L/min, (b) 7,000 L/min

**23.** decreases at $1/8$ pound/mi

**25.** (a) \$300, (b) $C(101) - C(100) = \$299.50$

**27.** (a) $-\$2.00$, (b) \$9.11

## Section 5.8   (page 166)

**1.** $c = \dfrac{a + b}{2}$   **3.** $c = \pm\dfrac{2}{\sqrt{3}}$

**9.** inc. $x > 0$, decr. $x < 0$

**11.** inc. on $(-\infty, -4)$ and $(0, \infty)$, decr. on $(-4, 0)$

**13.** inc. on $\left(-\infty, -\dfrac{2}{\sqrt{3}}\right)$ and $\left(\dfrac{2}{\sqrt{3}}, \infty\right)$, dec. on $\left(-\dfrac{2}{\sqrt{3}}, \dfrac{2}{\sqrt{3}}\right)$

**15.** inc. on $(-2, 0)$ and $(2, \infty)$; dec. on $(-\infty, -2)$ and $(0, 2)$

**17.** inc. on $(-\infty, 3)$ and $(5, \infty)$; dec. on $(3, 5)$

**19.** inc. on $(-\infty, \infty)$   **23.** $0.535898, \; 7.464102$

**25.** $0, \; -0.518784$

## Section 5.9   (page 171)

**1.** $\dfrac{1 - y}{2 + x}$   **3.** $\dfrac{2x + y}{3y^2 - x}$

**5.** $\dfrac{2 - 2xy^3}{3x^2 y^2 + 1}$   **7.** $-\dfrac{3x^2 + 2xy}{x^2 + 4y}$

**9.** $2x + 3y = 5$   **11.** $y = x$

**13.** $y = 1 - \dfrac{4}{4-\pi}\left(x - \dfrac{\pi}{4}\right)$

**15.** $y = 2 - x$

**17.** $\dfrac{2(y-1)}{(1-x)^2}$

**19.** $\dfrac{(2-6y)(1-3x^2)^2}{(3y^2-2y)^3} - \dfrac{6x}{3y^2-2y}$

**21.** $-a^2/y^3$

**23.** $0$

**25.** $-26$

## Section 5.10    (page 177)

**1.** $5x + C$

**3.** $\frac{2}{3}x^{3/2} + C$

**5.** $\frac{1}{4}x^4 + C$

**7.** $-\cos x + C$

**9.** $a^2 x - \frac{1}{3}x^3 + C$

**11.** $\frac{4}{3}x^{3/2} + \frac{9}{4}x^{4/3} + C$

**13.** $\frac{1}{12}x^4 - \frac{1}{6}x^3 + \frac{1}{2}x^2 - x + C$

**15.** $\frac{1}{2}\sin(2x) + C$

**17.** $\dfrac{-1}{1+x} + C$

**19.** $\frac{1}{3}(2x+3)^{3/2} + C$

**21.** $-\cos(x^2) + C$

**23.** $\tan x - x + C$

**25.** $(x + \sin x \cos x)/2 + C$

**27.** $y = \frac{1}{2}x^2 - 2x + 3$, all $x$

**29.** $y = 2x^{3/2} - 15$, $(x > 0)$

**31.** $y = \dfrac{A}{3}(x^3 - 1) + \dfrac{B}{2}(x^2 - 1) + C(x-1) + 1$, (all $x$)

**33.** $y = \sin x + (3/2)$, (all $x$)

**35.** $y = 1 + \tan x$, $-\pi/2 < x < \pi/2$

**37.** $y = x^2 + 5x - 3$, (all $x$)

**39.** $y = \dfrac{x^5}{20} - \dfrac{x^2}{2} + 8$, (all $x$)

**41.** $y = 1 + x - \cos x$, (all $x$)

**43.** $y = 3x - \dfrac{1}{x}$, $(x > 0)$

**45.** $y = -\dfrac{7\sqrt{x}}{2} + \dfrac{18}{\sqrt{x}}$, $(x > 0)$

## Section 5.11    (page 184)

**1.** (a) $t > 2$,    (b) $t < 2$,    (c) all $t$,    (d) no $t$,
(e) $t > 2$,    (f) $t < 2$,    (g) 2,    (h) 0

**3.** (a) $t < -2/\sqrt{3}$ or $t > 2/\sqrt{3}$,
(b) $-2/\sqrt{3} < t < 2/\sqrt{3}$,    (c) $t > 0$,    (d) $t < 0$,
(e) $t > 2/\sqrt{3}$ or $-2/\sqrt{3} < t < 0$,
(f) $t < -2/\sqrt{3}$ or $0 < t < 2/\sqrt{3}$,
(g) $\pm 12/\sqrt{3}$ at $t = \pm 2/\sqrt{3}$,    (h) 12

**5.** acc $= 9.8$ m/s$^2$ downward at all times;
max height $= 4.9$ m; ball strikes ground at 9.8 m/s

**7.** time 27.8 s; distance 771.6 m

**9.** $4h$ m, $\sqrt{2}v_0$ m/s

**11.** 400 ft

**13.** 0.833 km

**15.** $v = \begin{cases} 2t & \text{if } 0 < t \le 2 \\ 4 & \text{if } 2 < t < 8 \\ 20 - 2t & \text{if } 8 \le t < 10 \end{cases}$
$v$ is continuous for $0 < t < 10$.

$a = \begin{cases} 2 & \text{if } 0 < t < 2 \\ 0 & \text{if } 2 < t < 8 \\ -2 & \text{if } 8 < t < 10 \end{cases}$
$a$ is continuous except at $t = 2$ and $t = 8$.
Maximum velocity 4 is attained for $2 \le t \le 8$.

**17.** 7 s

**19.** 448 ft

## Review Exercises    (page 185)

**1.** $18x + 6$

**3.** $-1$

**5.** $6\pi x + 12y = 6\sqrt{3} + \pi$

**7.** $\dfrac{\cos x - 1}{(x - \sin x)^2}$

**9.** $x^{-3/5}(4 - x^{2/5})^{-7/2}$

**11.** $-2\theta \sec^2 \theta \tan \theta$

**13.** $20x^{19}$

**15.** $-\sqrt{3}$

**17.** $-2xf'(3 - x^2)$

**19.** $2f'(2x)\sqrt{g(x/2)} + \dfrac{f(2x)\,g'(x/2)}{4\sqrt{g(x/2)}}$

**21.** $f'(x + (g(x))^2)(1 + 2g(x)g'(x))$

**23.** $\cos x\, f'(\sin x)\, g(\cos x) - \sin x\, f(\sin x)\, g'(\cos x)$

**25.** $7x + 10y = 24$

**27.** $\dfrac{x^3}{3} - \dfrac{1}{x} + C$

**29.** $2\tan x + 3\sec x + C$

**31.** $4x^3 + 3x^4 - 7$

**33.** $I_1 = x\sin x + \cos x + C$, $I_2 = \sin x - x\cos x + C$

**35.** $y = 3x$

**37.** points $k\pi$ and $k\pi/(n+1)$ where $k$ is any integer

**39.** $(0,0)$, $(\pm 1/\sqrt{2}, 1/2)$, dist. $= \sqrt{3}/2$ units

**41.** (a) $k = g/R$

**43.** 15.3 m

**45.** 80 ft/s or about 55 mph

## Challenging Problems    (page 186)

**3.** (a) 0, (b) 3/8, (c) 12, (d) $-48$, (e) 3/7, (f) 21

**13.** $f(m) = C - (m - B)^2/(4A)$

**17.** (a) $3b^2 > 8ac$

**19.** (a) 3 s, (b) $t = 7$ s, (c) $t = 12$ s, (d) about 13.07 m/s$^2$, (e) 197.5 m, (f) 60.3 m

# Chapter 6
# Transcendental Functions

## Section 6.1    (page 193)

**1.** $f^{-1}(x) = x + 1$
$\mathcal{D}(f^{-1}) = \mathcal{R}(f) = \mathcal{R}(f^{-1}) = \mathcal{D}(f) = \mathbb{R}$

**3.** $f^{-1}(x) = x^2 + 1$, $\mathcal{D}(f^{-1}) = \mathcal{R}(f) = [0, \infty)$,
$\mathcal{R}(f^{-1}) = \mathcal{D}(f) = [1, \infty)$

**5.** $f^{-1}(x) = x^{1/3}$
$\mathcal{D}(f^{-1}) = \mathcal{R}(f) = \mathcal{R}(f^{-1}) = \mathcal{D}(f) = \mathbb{R}$

**7.** $f^{-1}(x) = -\sqrt{x}$,    $\mathcal{D}(f^{-1}) = \mathcal{R}(f) = [0, \infty)$,
$\mathcal{R}(f^{-1}) = \mathcal{D}(f) = (-\infty, 0]$

**9.** $f^{-1}(x) = \dfrac{1}{x} - 1$,    $\mathcal{D}(f^{-1}) = \mathcal{R}(f) = \{x : x \ne 0\}$,
$\mathcal{R}(f^{-1}) = \mathcal{D}(f) = \{x : x \ne -1\}$

**11.** $f^{-1}(x) = \dfrac{1-x}{2+x}$,

  $\mathcal{D}(f^{-1}) = \mathcal{R}(f) = \{x : x \neq -2\}$,
  $\mathcal{R}(f^{-1}) = \mathcal{D}(f) = \{x : x \neq -1\}$

**13.** $g^{-1}(x) = f^{-1}(x+2)$    **15.** $k^{-1}(x) = f^{-1}\left(-\dfrac{x}{3}\right)$

**17.** $p^{-1}(x) = f^{-1}\left(\dfrac{1}{x} - 1\right)$

**19.** $r^{-1}(x) = \dfrac{1}{4}\left(3 - f^{-1}\left(\dfrac{1-x}{2}\right)\right)$

**21.** $f^{-1}(x) = \begin{cases} \sqrt{x-1} & \text{if } x >= 1 \\ x-1 & \text{if } x < 1 \end{cases}$

**23.** $h^{-1}(x) = \begin{cases} \sqrt{x-1} & \text{if } x \geq 1 \\ \sqrt{1-x} & \text{if } x < 1 \end{cases}$

**25.** $g^{-1}(1) = 2$             **29.** $\left(f^{-1}\right)'(2) = 1/4$

**31.** 2.23362                    **33.** $\mathbb{R}$, 1

**35.** $c = 1$, $a$, $b$ arbitrary except $ab \neq 1$, or $c = -1$ and $a = b = 0$.

**37.** no

## Section 6.2   (page 197)

**1.** $\sqrt{3}$                  **3.** $x^6$

**5.** 3                          **7.** $-2x$

**9.** $x$                        **11.** 1

**13.** 1                         **15.** 2

**17.** $\log_a(x^4 + 4x^2 + 3)$  **19.** $4.728804\ldots$

**21.** $x = (\log_{10} 5)/(\log_{10}(4/5)) \approx -7.212567$

**23.** $x = 3^{1/5} = 10^{(\log_{10} 3)/5} \approx 1.24573$

**29.** $1/2$                     **31.** 0

**33.** $\infty$

## Section 6.3   (page 205)

**1.** $\sqrt{e}$                 **3.** $x^5$

**5.** $-3x$                      **7.** $\ln \dfrac{64}{81}$

**9.** $\ln\left(x^2(x-2)^5\right)$  **11.** $x = \dfrac{\ln 2}{\ln(3/2)}$

**13.** $x = \dfrac{\ln 5 - 9\ln 2}{2\ln 2}$  **15.** $0 < x < 2$

**17.** $3 < x < 7/2$             **19.** $5e^{5x}$

**21.** $(1-2x)e^{-2x}$           **23.** $\dfrac{3}{3x-2}$

**25.** $\dfrac{e^x}{1+e^x}$      **27.** $\dfrac{e^x - e^{-x}}{2}$

**29.** $e^{x+e^x}$               **31.** $e^x(\sin x + \cos x)$

**33.** $\dfrac{1}{x\ln x}$       **35.** $2x\ln x$

**37.** $(2\ln 5)5^{2x+1}$        **39.** $t^x x^t \ln t + t^{x+1} x^{t-1}$

**41.** $\dfrac{b}{(bs+c)\ln a}$

**43.** $x^{\sqrt{x}}\left(\dfrac{1}{\sqrt{x}}\left(\tfrac{1}{2}\ln x + 1\right)\right)$

**45.** $\sec x$                  **47.** $-\dfrac{1}{\sqrt{x^2+a^2}}$

**49.** $f^{(n)}(x) = e^{ax}(na^{n-1} + a^n x)$,   $n = 1,2,3,\ldots$

**51.** $y' = 2xe^{x^2}$,  $y'' = 2(1+2x^2)e^{x^2}$,
  $y''' = 4(3x + 2x^3)e^{x^2}$,  $y^{(4)} = 4(3 + 12x^2 + 4x^4)e^{x^2}$

**53.** $f'(x) = x^{x^2+1}(2\ln x + 1)$,
  $g'(x) = x^{x^x} x^x \left(\ln x + (\ln x)^2 + \dfrac{1}{x}\right)$;
  $g$ grows more rapidly than does $f$.

**55.** $f'(x) = f(x)\left(\dfrac{1}{x-1} + \dfrac{1}{x-2} + \dfrac{1}{x-3} + \dfrac{1}{x-4}\right)$

**57.** $f'(2) = \dfrac{556}{3675}$,   $f'(1) = \dfrac{1}{6}$

**59.** $f$ inc. for $x < 1$, dec. for $x > 1$

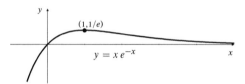

**61.** $y = ex$                  **63.** $y = 2e\ln 2(x-1)$

**65.** $-1/e^2$

**67.** $f'(x) = (A+B)\cos\ln x + (B-A)\sin\ln x$,
  $\int \cos\ln x\, dx = \dfrac{x}{2}(\cos\ln x + \sin\ln x)$,
  $\int \sin\ln x\, dx = \dfrac{x}{2}(\sin\ln x - \cos\ln x)$

**69.** (a) $F_{2B,-2A}(x)$;   (b) $-2e^x(\cos x + \sin x)$

## Section 6.4   (page 213)

**1.** 0                          **3.** 2

**5.** 0                          **7.** 0

**9.** 566                        **11.** 29.15 years

**13.** 160.85 years             **15.** 4,139 g

**17.** \$7,557.84                **19.** about 14.7 years

**21.** about 142

**23.** (a) $f(x) = Ce^{bx} - (a/b)$,
  (b) $y = (y_0 + (a/b))e^{bx} - (a/b)$

**25.** 22.35 °C                  **27.** 6.84 min

**31.** $(0, -(1/k)\ln(y_0/(y_0 - L)))$, solution $\to -\infty$

**33.** about 7,671 cases, growing at about 3,028 cases/week

## Section 6.5    (page 221)

**1.** $\pi/3$          **3.** $-\pi/4$

**5.** $0.7$            **7.** $-\pi/3$

**9.** $\dfrac{\pi}{2} + 0.2$        **11.** $2/\sqrt{5}$

**13.** $\sqrt{1 - x^2}$      **15.** $\dfrac{1}{\sqrt{1 + x^2}}$

**17.** $\dfrac{\sqrt{1 - x^2}}{x}$      **19.** $\dfrac{1}{\sqrt{2 + x - x^2}}$

**21.** $\dfrac{-\operatorname{sgn} a}{\sqrt{a^2 - (x - b)^2}}$      **23.** $\tan^{-1} t + \dfrac{t}{1 + t^2}$

**25.** $2x \tan^{-1} x + 1$

**27.** $\dfrac{\sqrt{1 - 4x^2} \sin^{-1} 2x - 2\sqrt{1 - x^2} \sin^{-1} x}{\sqrt{1 - x^2}\sqrt{1 - 4x^2} \left(\sin^{-1} 2x\right)^2}$

**29.** $\dfrac{x}{\sqrt{(1 - x^4)} \sin^{-1} x^2}$      **31.** $\sqrt{\dfrac{a - x}{a + x}}$

**33.** $\dfrac{\pi - 2}{\pi - 1}$

**37.** $\dfrac{d}{dx} \csc^{-1} x = -\dfrac{1}{|x|\sqrt{x^2 - 1}}$

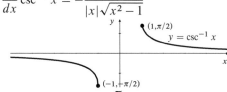

**39.** $\tan^{-1} x + \cot^{-1} x = -\dfrac{\pi}{2}$ for $x < 0$

**41.** cont. everywhere, differentiable except at $n\pi$ for integers $n$

**43.** continuous and differentiable everywhere except at odd multiples of $\pi/2$

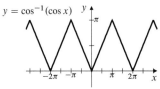      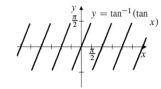

**49.** $\tan^{-1}\left(\dfrac{x - 1}{x + 1}\right) - \tan^{-1} x = \dfrac{3\pi}{4}$ on $(-\infty, -1)$

**51.** $f'(x) = 1 - \operatorname{sgn}(\cos x)$

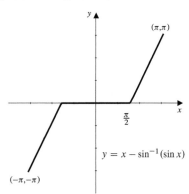

$y = x - \sin^{-1}(\sin x)$

**53.** $y = \dfrac{1}{3} \tan^{-1} \dfrac{x}{3} + 2 - \dfrac{\pi}{12}$

**55.** $y = 4 \sin^{-1} \dfrac{x}{5}$

## Section 6.6    (page 227)

**3.** $\tanh(x + y) = \dfrac{\tanh x + \tanh y}{1 + \tanh x \tanh y}$

$\tanh(x - y) = \dfrac{\tanh x - \tanh y}{1 - \tanh x \tanh y}$

**5.** $\dfrac{d}{dx} \sinh^{-1}(x) = \dfrac{1}{\sqrt{x^2 + 1}}$,

$\dfrac{d}{dx} \cosh^{-1}(x) = \dfrac{1}{\sqrt{x^2 - 1}}$,

$\dfrac{d}{dx} \tanh^{-1}(x) = \dfrac{1}{1 - x^2}$,

$\displaystyle\int \dfrac{dx}{\sqrt{x^2 + 1}} = \sinh^{-1}(x) + C$,

$\displaystyle\int \dfrac{dx}{\sqrt{x^2 - 1}} = \cosh^{-1}(x) + C \quad (x > 1)$,

$\displaystyle\int \dfrac{dx}{1 - x^2} = \tanh^{-1}(x) + C \quad (-1 < x < 1)$

**7.** (a) $\dfrac{x^2 - 1}{2x}$;  (b) $\dfrac{x^2 + 1}{2x}$;  (c) $\dfrac{x^2 - 1}{x^2 + 1}$;  (d) $x^2$

**9.** domain $(0, 1]$, range $[0, \infty)$, derivative $-1/(x\sqrt{1 - x^2})$

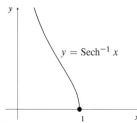

**11.** $f_{A,B} = g_{A+B, A-B}$;  $g_{C,D} = f_{(C+D)/2, (C-D)/2}$

**13.** $y = y_0 \cosh k(x - a) + \dfrac{v_0}{k} \sinh k(x - a)$

## Section 6.7    (page 234)

**1.** $y = Ae^{-5t} + Be^{-2t}$        **3.** $y = A + Be^{-2t}$

**5.** $y = (A + Bt)e^{-4t}$

**7.** $y = (A \cos t + B \sin t)e^{3t}$

**9.** $y = (A \cos 2t + B \sin 2t)e^{-t}$

**11.** $y = (A \cos \sqrt{2}t + B \sin \sqrt{2}t)e^{-t}$

**13.** $y = \dfrac{6}{7}e^{t/2} + \dfrac{1}{7}e^{-3t}$

**15.** $y = e^{-2t}(2 \cos t + 6 \sin t)$

**25.** $y = \dfrac{3}{10} \sin(10t)$, circ freq 10, freq $\dfrac{10}{2\pi}$, per $\dfrac{2\pi}{10}$, amp $\dfrac{3}{10}$

**33.** $y = e^{3-t}[2 \cos(2(t - 3)) + sin(2(t - 3))]$

**35.** $y = \dfrac{c}{k^2}(1 - \cos(kx)) + a \cos(kx) + \dfrac{b}{k} \sin(kx)$

*Review Exercises*    *(page 235)*

**1.** $1/3$          **3.** both limits are 0

**5.** max $1/\sqrt{2e}$, min $-1/\sqrt{2e}$

**7.** $f(x) = 3e^{(x^2/2)-2}$

**9.** (a) about 13.863%, (b) about 68 days

**11.** $e^{2x}$          **13.** y=x

**15.** 13.8165% approx.

**17.** $\cos^{-1} x = \frac{\pi}{2} - \sin^{-1} x$, $\cot^{-1} x = \text{sgn}\, x \sin^{-1}(1/\sqrt{x^2+1})$,
$\csc^{-1} x = \sin^{-1}(1/x)$

**19.** $15\,^{\circ}C$

# Chapter 7
# More Applications of Differentiation

*Section 7.1*    *(page 242)*

**1.** $32$ cm$^2$/min

**3.** increasing at $160\pi$ cm$^2$/s

**5.** (a) $1/(6\pi r)$ km/hr, (b) $1/(6\sqrt{\pi A})$ km/hr

**7.** $1/(180\pi)$ cm/s          **9.** 2 cm$^2$/s

**11.** increasing at 2 cm$^3$/s    **13.** increasing at rate 12

**15.** increasing at rate $2/\sqrt{5}$

**17.** $45\sqrt{3}$ km/h          **19.** 1/3 m/s, 5/6 m/s

**21.** 100 tonnes/day          **23.** $16\frac{4}{11}$ min after 3:00

**25.** $1/(18\pi)$ m/min

**27.** $9/(6250\pi)$ m/min, 4.64 m

**29.** 8 m/min          **31.** dec. at 126.9 km/h

**33.** 1/8 units/s          **35.** $\sqrt{3}/16$ m/min

**37.** (a) down at 24/125 m/s, (b) right at 7/125 m/s

**39.** dec. at 0.0197 rad/s          **41.** 0.047 rad/s

*Section 7.2*    *(page 252)*

**1.** 0.35173          **3.** 0.95025

**5.** 0.45340          **7.** 1.41421356237

**9.** 0.453397651516

**11.** 1.64809536561, 2.352392647658

**13.** 0.510973429389

**15.** infinitely many, 4.49340945791

**19.** max 1, min $-0.11063967219\ldots$

**21.** $x_1 = -a$, $x_2 = a = x_0$. Look for a root half way between $x_0$ and $x_1$

**23.** $x_n = (-1/2)^n \to 0$ (root) as $n \to \infty$.

*Section 7.3*    *(page 257)*

**1.** 3/4          **3.** $a/b$

**5.** 1          **7.** 1

**9.** 0          **11.** $-3/2$

**13.** 1          **15.** $-1/2$

**17.** $\infty$          **19.** $2/\pi$

**21.** $-2$          **23.** $a$

**25.** 1          **27.** $-1/2$

**29.** $e^{-2}$          **31.** 0

**33.** $f''(x)$

*Section 7.4*    *(page 264)*

**1.** abs min 1 at $x = -1$; abs max 3 at $x = 1$

**3.** abs min 1 at $x = -1$; no max

**5.** abs min $-1$ at $x = 0$; abs max 8 at $x = 3$; loc max 3 at $x = -2$

**7.** abs min $a^3 + a - 4$ at $x = a$; abs max $b^3 + b - 4$ at $x = b$

**9.** abs max $b^5 + b^3 + 2b$ at $x = b$; no min value

**11.** no max or min values

**13.** max 3 at $x = -2$, min 0 at $x = 1$

**15.** abs max 1 at $x = 0$; no min value

**17.** no max or min value

**19.** loc max at $x = -1$; loc min at $x = 1$

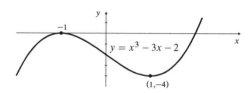

**21.** loc max at $x = \frac{3}{5}$; loc min at $x = 1$; critical point $x = 0$ is neither max nor min

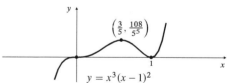

**23.** loc max at $x = -1$ and $x = 1/\sqrt{5}$; loc min at $x = 1$ and $x = -1/\sqrt{5}$

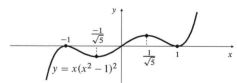

**25.** abs min at $x = 0$

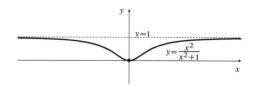

**27.** loc min at CP $x = -1$ and endpoint SP $x = \sqrt{2}$; loc max at CP $x = 1$ and endpoint SP $x = -\sqrt{2}$

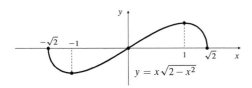

**29.** loc max at $x = 2n\pi - \dfrac{\pi}{3}$; loc min at $x = 2n\pi + \dfrac{\pi}{3}$ $(n = 0, \pm1, \pm2, \ldots)$

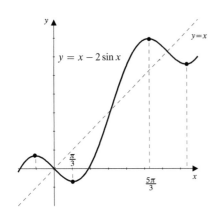

**31.** loc max at CP $x = \sqrt{3}/2$ and endpoint SP $x = -1$; loc min at CP $x = -\sqrt{3}/2$ and endpoint SP $x = 1$

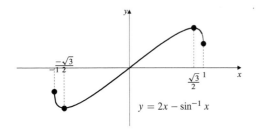

**33.** abs max at $x = 1/\ln 2$

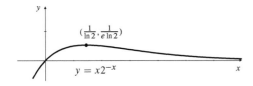

**35.** abs max at $x = e$

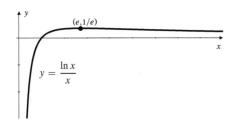

**37.** loc max at CP $x = 0$; abs min at SPs $x = \pm1$

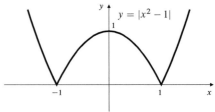

**39.** abs max at CPs $x = (2n + 1)\pi/2$; abs min at SPs $x = n\pi$ $(n = 0, \pm1, \pm2, \ldots)$

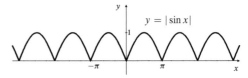

**41.** no max or min   **43.** max 2, min $-2$

**45.** has min, no max   **47.** yes, no

### Section 7.5   (page 268)

**1.** concave down on $(0, \infty)$

**3.** concave up on $\mathbb{R}$

**5.** concave down on $(-1, 0)$ and $(1, \infty)$; concave up on $(-\infty, -1)$ and $(0, 1)$; inflection $x = -1, 0, 1$

**7.** concave down on $(-1, 1)$; concave up on $(-\infty, -1)$ and $(1, \infty)$; inflection $x = \pm1$

**9.** concave down on $(-2, -2/\sqrt{5})$ and $(2/\sqrt{5}, 2)$; concave up on $(-\infty, -2)$, $(-2/\sqrt{5}, 2/\sqrt{5})$ and $(2, \infty)$; inflection $x = \pm2, \pm2/\sqrt{5}$

**11.** concave down on $(2n\pi, (2n + 1)\pi)$; concave up on $((2n - 1)\pi, 2n\pi)$, $(n = 0, \pm1, \pm2, \ldots)$; inflection $x = n\pi$

**13.** concave down on $\left(n\pi, (n + \tfrac{1}{2})\pi\right)$; concave up on $\left((n - \tfrac{1}{2})\pi, n\pi\right)$; inflection $x = n\pi/2$, $(n = 0, \pm1, \pm2, \ldots)$

**15.** concave down on $(0, \infty)$, up on $(-\infty, 0)$; inflection $x = 0$

**17.** concave down on $(-1/\sqrt{2}, 1/\sqrt{2})$, up on $(-\infty, -1/\sqrt{2})$ and $(1/\sqrt{2}, \infty)$; inflection $x = \pm1/\sqrt{2}$

**19.** concave down on $(-\infty, -1)$ and $(1, \infty)$; conc up on $(-1, 1)$; inflection $x = \pm1$

**21.** concave down on $(-\infty, 4)$, up on $(4, \infty)$; inflection $x = 4$

**23.** no concavity, no inflections

**25.** loc min at $x = 2$; loc max at $x = \tfrac{2}{3}$

**27.** loc min at $x = 1/\sqrt[4]{3}$; loc max at $-1/\sqrt[4]{3}$

**29.** loc max at $x = 1$; loc min at $x = -1$ (both abs)

**31.** loc (and abs) min at $x = 1/e$

**33.** loc min at $x = 0$; inflections at $x = \pm2$ (not discernible by Second Derivative Test)

**35.** abs min at $x = 0$; abs max at $x = \pm1/\sqrt{2}$

**39.** If $n$ is even, $f_n$ has a min and $g_n$ has a max at $x = 0$. If $n$ is odd, both have inflections at $x = 0$.

## Section 7.6   (page 275)

**1.** $49/4$

**3.** 20 and 40

**5.** $71.45$

**11.** $R^2$ sq. units

**13.** $2ab$ units$^2$

**15.** 50 cm$^2$

**17.** width $8 + 10\sqrt{2}$ m, height $4 + 5\sqrt{2}$ m

**19.** rebate \$250

**21.** point 5 km east of $A$

**25.** (a) 0 m, (b) $\pi/(4 + \pi)$ m

**27.** $8\sqrt{3}$ units

**29.** $\left[(a^{2/3} + b^{2/3})^3 + c^2\right]^{1/2}$ units

**31.** $3^{1/2}/2^{1/3}$ units

**33.** height $\dfrac{2R}{\sqrt{3}}$, radius $\sqrt{\dfrac{2}{3}} R$ units

**35.** base 2m $\times$ 2m, height 1 m

**37.** width $\dfrac{20}{4 + \pi}$ m, height $\dfrac{10}{4 + \pi}$ m

**41.** width $R$, depth $\sqrt{3}R$

**43.** $Q = 3L/8$

**45.** 750 cars

**47.** $\dfrac{5000}{\pi}$ m$^2$; semicircle

**49.** $\dfrac{3\sqrt{3}a}{4}$ cm

## Section 7.7   (page 282)

**1.** $6x - 9$

**3.** $2 - (x/4)$

**5.** $(7 - 2x)/27$

**7.** $\pi - x$

**9.** $(1/4) + (\sqrt{3}/2)(x - (\pi/6))$

**11.** about 8 cm$^2$

**13.** about 62.8 mi

**15.** $\sqrt{50} \approx \frac{99}{14} \approx 7.071429$, error $< 0$,
$|\text{error}| < \frac{1}{2744} \approx 0.0003644$, $(7.07106, 7.071429)$

**17.** $\sqrt[4]{85} \approx \frac{82}{27}$, error $< 0$, $|\text{error}| < \frac{1}{2 \times 3^6}$, $(3.03635, 3.03704)$

**19.** $\cos 46° \approx \dfrac{1}{\sqrt{2}}\left(1 - \dfrac{\pi}{180}\right) \approx 0.694765$, error $< 0$,
$|\text{error}| < \dfrac{1}{2\sqrt{2}}\left(\dfrac{\pi}{180}\right)^2$, $(0.694658, 0.694765)$

**21.** $\sin(3.14) \approx \pi - 3.14$, error $< 0$,
$|\text{error}| < (\pi - 3.14)^3/2 < 2.02 \times 10^{-9}$,
$(\pi - 3.14 - (\pi - 3.14)^3/2, \pi - 3.14)$

**23.** $(7.07106, 7.07108)$, $\sqrt{50} \approx 7.07107$

**25.** $(0.80891, 0.80921)$, $\sqrt[4]{85} \approx 0.80906$

**27.** $3 \le f(3) \le 13/4$

**29.** $g(1.8) \approx 0.6$, $|\text{error}| < 0.0208$

**31.** about 1,005 cm$^3$

# Chapter 8
# Integration

## Section 8.1   (page 289)

**1.** $1^3 + 2^3 + 3^3 + 4^3$

**3.** $3 + 3^2 + 3^3 + \cdots + 3^n$

**5.** $\dfrac{(-2)^3}{1^2} + \dfrac{(-2)^4}{2^2} + \dfrac{(-2)^5}{3^2} + \cdots + \dfrac{(-2)^n}{(n-2)^2}$

**7.** $\sum_{i=5}^{9} i$

**9.** $\sum_{i=2}^{99}(-1)^i i^2$

**11.** $\sum_{i=0}^{n} x^i$

**13.** $\sum_{i=1}^{n}(-1)^{i-1}/i^2$

**15.** $\sum_{i=1}^{100} \sin(i - 1)$

**17.** $n(n + 1)(2n + 7)/6$

**19.** $\dfrac{\pi(\pi^n - 1)}{\pi - 1} - 3n$

**21.** $\ln(n!)$

**23.** $400$

**25.** $(x^{2n+1} + 1)/(x + 1)$

**27.** $-4{,}949$

**31.** $2^m - 1$

**33.** $n/(n + 1)$

## Section 8.2   (page 295)

**1.** $3/2$ sq. units

**3.** 6 sq. units

**5.** $26/3$ sq. units

**7.** 15 sq. units

**9.** 4 sq. units

**11.** $32/3$ sq. units

**13.** $3/(2 \ln 2)$ sq. units

**15.** $\ln(b/a)$, follows from definition of ln

**17.** $0$

**19.** $\pi/4$

## Section 8.3   (page 301)

**1.** $L(f, P_8) = 7/4$, $\quad U(f, P_8) = 9/4$

**3.** $L(f, P_4) = \dfrac{e^4 - 1}{e^2(e - 1)} \approx 4.22$,
$U(f, P_4) = \dfrac{e^4 - 1}{e(e - 1)} \approx 11.48$

**5.** $L(f, P_6) = \dfrac{\pi}{6}(1 + \sqrt{3}) \approx 1.43$,
$U(f, P_6) = \dfrac{\pi}{6}(3 + \sqrt{3}) \approx 2.48$

**7.** $L(f, P_n) = \dfrac{n - 1}{2n}$, $U(f, P_n) = \dfrac{n + 1}{2n}$, $\int_0^1 x\, dx = \dfrac{1}{2}$

**9.** $L(f, P_n) = \dfrac{(n - 1)^2}{4n^2}$, $U(f, P_n) = \dfrac{(n + 1)^2}{4n^2}$,
$\int_0^1 x^3\, dx = \dfrac{1}{4}$

**11.** $\int_0^1 \sqrt{x}\, dx$

**13.** $\int_0^\pi \sin x\, dx$

**15.** $\int_0^1 \tan^{-1}x\, dx$

## Section 8.4   (page 306)

**1.** $0$

**3.** $8$

**5.** $(b^2 - a^2)/2$

**7.** $\pi$

**9.** $0$

**11.** $2\pi$

**13.** $0$

**15.** $(2\pi + 3\sqrt{3})/6$

**17.** $16$

**19.** $32/3$

**21.** $(4 + 3\pi)/12$

**23.** $\ln 2$

**25.** $\ln 3$

**27.** $4$

**29.** $1$

**31.** $\pi/2$

**33.** $1$

**35.** $11/6$

**37.** $\dfrac{\pi}{3} - \sqrt{3}$

**39.** $41/2$

**41.** $3/4$

**43.** $k = \bar{f}$

**Section 8.5   (page 312)**

**1.** $4$

**3.** $1$

**5.** $9$

**7.** $80\frac{4}{5}$

**9.** $\dfrac{2 - \sqrt{2}}{2\sqrt{2}}$

**11.** $(1/\sqrt{2}) - (1/2)$

**13.** $e^{\pi} - e^{-\pi}$

**15.** $(a^e - 1)/\ln a$

**17.** $\pi/2$

**19.** $\dfrac{\pi}{3}$

**21.** $\frac{1}{5}$ sq. units

**23.** $\frac{32}{3}$ sq. units

**25.** $\frac{1}{6}$ sq. units

**27.** $\frac{1}{3}$ sq. units

**29.** $\frac{1}{12}$ sq. units

**31.** $2\pi$ sq. units

**33.** $3$

**35.** $\frac{16}{3}$

**37.** $e - 1$

**39.** $\dfrac{\sin x}{x}$

**41.** $-2\dfrac{\sin x^2}{x}$

**43.** $\dfrac{\cos t}{1 + t^2}$

**45.** $(\cos x)/(2\sqrt{x})$

**47.** $f(x) = \pi e^{\pi(x-1)}$

**49.** $1/x^2$ is not continuous (or even defined) at $x = 0$, so the Fundamental Theorem cannot be applied over $[-1, 1]$. Since $1/x^2 > 0$ on its domain, we would expect the integral to be positive if it exists at all. (It doesn't.)

**51.** $F(x)$ has a maximum value at $x = 1$ but no minimum value.

**53.** $2$

**Section 8.6   (page 320)**

**1.** $-\frac{1}{2}e^{5-2x} + C$

**3.** $\frac{2}{9}(3x + 4)^{3/2} + C$

**5.** $-\frac{1}{32}(4x^2 + 1)^{-4} + C$

**7.** $\frac{1}{2}e^{x^2} + C$

**9.** $\frac{1}{2}\tan^{-1}\left(\frac{1}{2}\sin x\right) + C$

**11.** $2\ln\left|e^{x/2} - e^{-x/2}\right| + C = \ln\left|e^x - 2 + e^{-x}\right| + C$

**13.** $-\frac{2}{5}\sqrt{4 - 5s} + C$

**15.** $\frac{1}{2}\sin^{-1}\left(\dfrac{t^2}{2}\right) + C$

**17.** $-\ln(1 + e^{-x}) + C$

**19.** $-\frac{1}{2}(\ln\cos x)^2 + C$

**21.** $\frac{1}{2}\tan^{-1}\dfrac{x + 3}{2} + C$

**23.** $\frac{1}{8}\cos^8 x - \frac{1}{6}\cos^6 x + C$

**25.** $-\dfrac{1}{3a}\cos^3 ax + C$

**27.** $\frac{5}{16}x - \frac{1}{4}\sin 2x + \frac{3}{64}\sin 4x + \frac{1}{48}\sin^3 2x + C$

**29.** $\frac{1}{5}\sec^5 x + C$

**31.** $\frac{2}{3}(\tan x)^{3/2} + \frac{2}{7}(\tan x)^{7/2} + C$

**33.** $\frac{3}{8}\sin x - \frac{1}{4}\sin(2\sin x) + \frac{1}{32}\sin(4\sin x) + C$

**35.** $\frac{1}{3}\tan^3 x + C$

**37.** $-\frac{1}{9}\csc^9 x + \frac{2}{7}\csc^7 x - \frac{1}{5}\csc^5 x + C$

**39.** $\frac{14}{3}\sqrt{17} + \frac{2}{3}$

**41.** $3\pi/16$

**43.** $\ln 2$

**45.** $2,\ 2(\sqrt{2} - 1)$

**47.** $\pi/32$ sq. units

**Section 8.7   (page 325)**

**1.** $\dfrac{1}{6}$ sq. units

**3.** $\dfrac{64}{3}$ sq. units

**5.** $\dfrac{125}{12}$ sq. units

**7.** $\dfrac{1}{2}$ sq. units

**9.** $\dfrac{5}{12}$ sq. units

**11.** $\dfrac{15}{8} - 2\ln 2$ sq. units

**13.** $\dfrac{\pi}{2} - \dfrac{1}{3}$ sq. units

**15.** $\dfrac{4}{3}$ sq. units

**17.** $2\sqrt{2}$ sq. units

**19.** $1 - \pi/4$ sq. units

**21.** $(\pi/8) - \ln\sqrt{2}$ sq. units

**23.** $(4\pi/3) - 2\ln(2 + \sqrt{3})$ sq. units

**25.** $(4/\pi) - 1$ sq. units

**27.** $\dfrac{4}{3}$ sq. units

**29.** $\dfrac{e}{2} - 1$ sq. units

**Review Exercises   (page 326)**

**1.** sum is $n(n + 2)/(n + 1)^2$

**3.** $20/3$

**5.** $4\pi$

**7.** $0$

**9.** $2$

**11.** $\sin(t^2)$

**13.** $-4e^{\sin(4s)}$

**15.** $f(x) = -\frac{1}{2}e^{(3/2)(1-x)}$

**17.** $9/2$ sq. units

**19.** $3/10$ sq. units

**21.** $(3\sqrt{3}/4) - 1$ sq. units

**23.** $(\frac{1}{6}\sin(2x^3 + 1) + C$

**25.** $98/3$

**27.** $(\pi/8) - (1/2)\tan^{-1}(1/2)$

**29.** $-\cos\sqrt{2s + 1} + C$

**31.** min $-\pi/4$, no max

**35.** $x_1 = \dfrac{\sqrt{3} - 1}{2\sqrt{3}}, \quad x_2 = \dfrac{\sqrt{3} + 1}{2\sqrt{3}}$

# Chapter 9
# Techniques of Integration

**Section 9.1   (page 333)**

**1.** $x\sin x + \cos x + C$

**3.** $\dfrac{1}{\pi}x^2\sin\pi x + \dfrac{2}{\pi^2}x\cos\pi x - \dfrac{2}{\pi^3}\sin\pi x + C$

**5.** $\frac{1}{4}x^4\ln x - \frac{1}{16}x^4 + C$

**7.** $x\tan^{-1}x - \frac{1}{2}\ln(1 + x^2) + C$

**9.** $\left(\frac{1}{2}x^2 - \frac{1}{4}\right)\sin^{-1}x + \frac{1}{4}x\sqrt{1 - x^2} + C$

**11.** $\frac{7}{8}\sqrt{2} + \frac{3}{8}\ln(1 + \sqrt{2})$

**13.** $\frac{1}{13}e^{2x}(2\sin 3x - 3\cos 3x) + C$

**15.** $\ln(2 + \sqrt{3}) - \dfrac{\pi}{6}$

**17.** $x\tan x - \ln|\sec x| + C$

**19.** $\dfrac{x}{2}\left[\cos(\ln x) + \sin(\ln x)\right] + C$

**21.** $\ln x\left(\ln(\ln x) - 1\right) + C$

**23.** $x \cos^{-1} x - \sqrt{1 - x^2} + C$

**25.** $\dfrac{2\pi}{3} - \ln(2 + \sqrt{3})$

**27.** $\frac{1}{2}(x^2 + 1)\left(\tan^{-1} x\right)^2 - x \tan^{-1} x + \frac{1}{2}\ln(1 + x^2) + C$

**29.** $\dfrac{1 + e^{-\pi}}{2}$ square units

**31.** $I_n = x(\ln x)^n - n I_{n-1}$,
$I_4 = x\left[(\ln x)^4 - 4(\ln x)^3 + 12(\ln x)^2 - 24(\ln x) + 24\right] + C$

**33.** $I_n = -\dfrac{1}{n}\sin^{n-1} x \cos x + \dfrac{n-1}{n} I_{n-2}$,

$I_6 = \dfrac{5x}{16} - \cos x \left[\frac{1}{6}\sin^5 x + \frac{5}{24}\sin^3 x + \frac{5}{16}\sin x\right] + C$,

$I_7 = -\cos x \left[\frac{1}{7}\sin^6 x + \frac{6}{35}\sin^4 x + \frac{8}{35}\sin^2 x + \frac{16}{35}\right] + C$

**35.** $I_n = \dfrac{x}{2a^2(n-1)(x^2 + a^2)^{n-1}} + \dfrac{2n - 3}{2a^2(n-1)} I_{n-1}$,

$I_3 = \dfrac{x}{4a^2(x^2 + a^2)^2} + \dfrac{3x}{8a^4(x^2 + a^2)} + \dfrac{3}{8a^5}\tan^{-1}\dfrac{x}{a} + C$

**37.** Any conditions which guarantee that
$f(b)g'(b) - f'(b)g(b) = f(a)g'(a) - f'(a)g(a)$
will suffice.

### Section 9.2   (page 342)

**1.** $1/2$

**3.** $1/2$

**5.** $3 \times 2^{1/3}$

**7.** $3/2$

**9.** $3$

**11.** $\pi$

**13.** $1/2$

**15.** diverges to $\infty$

**17.** $2$

**19.** diverges

**21.** $0$

**23.** $1$ sq. unit

**25.** $2\ln 2$ square units

**29.** $2$

**31.** diverges to $\infty$

**33.** converges

**35.** diverges to $\infty$

**37.** diverges to $\infty$

**39.** diverges

**41.** diverges to $\infty$

### Section 9.3   (page 349)

**1.** $T_4 = 4.75$,
$M_4 = 4.625$,
$T_8 = 4.6875$,
$M_8 = 4.65625$,
$T_{16} = 4.671875$
Actual errors:
$I - T_4 \approx -0.0833333$,
$I - M_4 \approx \phantom{-}0.0416667$,
$I - T_8 \approx -0.0208333$,
$I - M_8 \approx \phantom{-}0.0104167$,
$I - T_{16} \approx -0.0052083$
Error estimates:
$|I - T_4| \le 0.0833334$,
$|I - M_4| \le 0.0416667$,
$|I - T_8| \le 0.0208334$,
$|I - M_8| \le 0.0104167$,
$|I - T_{16}| \le 0.0052084$

**3.** $T_4 = 0.9871158$,
$M_4 = 1.0064545$,
$T_8 = 0.9967852$,
$M_8 = 1.0016082$,
$T_{16} = 0.9991967$
Actual errors:
$I - T_4 \approx \phantom{-}0.0128842$,
$I - M_4 \approx -0.0064545$,
$I - T_8 \approx \phantom{-}0.0032148$,
$I - M_8 \approx -0.0016082$,
$I - T_{16} \approx \phantom{-}0.0008033$
Error estimates:
$|I - T_4| \le 0.020186$,
$|I - M_4| \le 0.010093$,
$|I - T_8| \le 0.005047$,
$|I - M_8| \le 0.002523$,
$|I - T_{16}| \le 0.001262$

**5.** $T_4 = 46$, $T_8 = 46.7$

**7.** $T_4 = 3,000$ km$^2$, $T_8 = 3,400$ km$^2$

**9.** $T_4 \approx 2.02622$,   $M_4 \approx 2.03236$,
$T_8 \approx 2.02929$,   $M_8 \approx 2.02982$,
$T_{16} \approx 2.029555$

**11.** $M_8 \approx 1.3714136$,   $T_{16} \approx 1.3704366$,   $I \approx 1.371$

### Section 9.4   (page 354)

**1.** $S_4 = S_8 = I$,   Errors $= 0$

**3.** $S_4 \approx 1.0001346$,   $S_8 \approx 1.0000083$,
$I - S_4 \approx -0.0001346$,   $I - S_8 \approx -0.0000083$

**5.** $46.93$

**7.** For $f(x) = e^{-x}$:
$|I - S_4| \le 0.000022$, $|I - S_8| \le 0.0000014$;
for $f(x) = \sin x$,
$|I - S_4| \le 0.00021$,
$|I - S_8| \le 0.000013$

**9.** $S_4 \approx 2.0343333$,   $S_8 \approx 2.0303133$,
$S_{16} \approx 2.0296433$

# Chapter 10
# Applications of Integration

### Section 10.1   (page 363)

**1.** $\dfrac{\pi}{5}$ cu. units

**3.** $\dfrac{3\pi}{10}$ cu. units

**5.** (a) $\dfrac{16\pi}{15}$ cu. units,   (b) $\dfrac{8\pi}{3}$ cu. units

**7.** (a) $\dfrac{27\pi}{2}$ cu. units,   (b) $\dfrac{108\pi}{5}$ cu. units

**9.** (a) $\dfrac{15\pi}{4} - \dfrac{\pi^2}{8}$ cu. units,   (b) $\pi(2 - \ln 2)$ cu. units

**11.** $\dfrac{10\pi}{3}$ cu. units

**13.** about $35\%$

**15.** $\dfrac{\pi h}{3}\left(b^2 - 3a^2 + \dfrac{2a^3}{b}\right)$ cu. units

**17.** $\dfrac{\pi}{3}(a-b)^2(2a+b)$ cu. units

**19.** $\dfrac{4\pi ab^2}{3}$ cu. units

**21.** (a) $\pi/2$ cu. units,   (b) $2\pi$ cu. units

**23.** $k > 2$                    **25.** yes; no; $a^2b/2$ cm$^3$

**27.** Vol. of ball $= \int_0^R kr^2\,dr = \dfrac{kR^3}{3}$; $k = 4\pi$

**29.** about $1,537$ cu. units    **31.** $R = \dfrac{h\sin\alpha}{\sin\alpha + \cos 2\alpha}$

### Section 10.2   (page 367)

**1.** $6$ m$^3$                    **3.** $\pi/3$ units$^3$

**5.** $132$ ft$^3$                 **7.** $\pi a^2 h/2$ cm$^3$

**9.** $3z^2$ sq. units            **11.** $\dfrac{16r^3}{3}$ cu. units

**13.** $72\pi$ cm$^3$              **15.** $\pi r^2(a+b)/2$ cu. units

**17.** $\dfrac{16,000}{3}$ cu. units    **19.** $12\pi\sqrt{2}$ in$^3$

**21.** approx $97.28$ cm$^3$

### Section 10.3   (page 374)

**1.** $2\sqrt{5}$ units            **3.** $52/3$ units

**5.** $(2/27)(13^{3/2} - 8)$ units

**7.** $6$ units                    **9.** $(e^2 + 1)/4$ units

**11.** $\sinh a$ units
**13.** $\ln(1 + \sqrt{2}) - \ln\sqrt{3}$ units

**15.** $\ln(e^2 + e^{-2})$ units    **17.** $6a$ units

**19.** $1.0338$ units              **21.** $1.0581$

**23.** $(10^{3/2} - 1)\pi/27$ sq. units

**25.** $\dfrac{64\pi}{81}\left[\dfrac{(13/4)^{5/2} - 1}{5} - \dfrac{(13/4)^{3/2} - 1}{3}\right]$ sq. units

**27.** $2\pi\left(\sqrt{2} + \ln(1 + \sqrt{2})\right)$ sq. units

**29.** $2\pi\left(\dfrac{255}{16} + \ln 4\right)$ sq. units

**31.** $4\pi^2 ab$ sq. units

**33.** $8\pi\left(1 + \dfrac{\ln(2 + \sqrt{3})}{2\sqrt{3}}\right)$ sq. units

**35.** $s = \dfrac{5}{\pi}\sqrt{4 + \pi^2}\,E\left(\dfrac{\pi}{\sqrt{4 + \pi^2}}\right)$

**37.** $k > -1$
**39.** (a) $\pi$ cu. units;   (c) "Covering" a surface with paint requires putting on a layer of constant thickness. Far enough to the right, the horn is thinner than any prescribed constant, so it can contain less paint than would be necessary to paint its surface.

### Section 10.4   (page 381)

**1.** mass $\dfrac{2L}{\pi}$; centre of mass at $\bar{s} = \dfrac{L}{2}$

**3.** $m = \frac{1}{4}\pi\sigma_0 a^2$;   $\bar{x} = \bar{y} = \dfrac{4a}{3\pi}$

**5.** $m = \dfrac{256k}{15}$;   $\bar{x} = 0$,   $\bar{y} = \dfrac{16}{7}$

**7.** $m = \dfrac{ka^3}{2}$;   $\bar{x} = \dfrac{2a}{3}$,   $\bar{y} = \dfrac{a}{2}$

**9.** $m = \int_a^b \sigma(x)\big(g(x) - f(x)\big)\,dx$;
$M_{x=0} = \int_a^b x\sigma(x)\big(g(x) - f(x)\big)\,dx$,   $\bar{x} = M_{x=0}/m$,
$M_{y=0} = \frac{1}{2}\int_a^b \sigma(x)\big((g(x))^2 - (f(x))^2\big)\,dx$,
$\bar{y} = M_{y=0}/m$

**11.** Mass is $\frac{8}{3}\pi R^4$ kg.  The centre of mass is along the line through the centre of the ball perpendicular to the plane, at a distance $R/10$ m from the centre of the ball on the side opposite the plane.

**13.** $m = \frac{1}{8}\pi\rho_0 a^4$;   $\bar{x} = 16a/(15\pi)$,   $\bar{y} = 0$, $\bar{z} = 8a/15$

**15.** $m = \frac{1}{3}k\pi a^3$;   $\bar{x} = 0$,     $\bar{y} = \dfrac{3a}{2\pi}$

**17.** about $5.57C/k^{3/2}$

### Section 10.5   (page 386)

**1.** $\left(\dfrac{4r}{3\pi}, \dfrac{4r}{3\pi}\right)$

**3.** $\left(\dfrac{\sqrt{2} - 1}{\ln(1 + \sqrt{2})}, \dfrac{\pi}{8\ln(1 + \sqrt{2})}\right)$

**5.** $\left(0, \dfrac{9\sqrt{3} - 4\pi}{4\pi - 3\sqrt{3}}\right)$      **7.** $\left(\dfrac{19}{9}, -\dfrac{1}{3}\right)$

**9.** The centroid is on the axis of symmetry of the hemisphere half way between the base plane and the vertex.
**11.** The centroid is on the axis of the cone, one-quarter of the cone's height above the base plane.

**13.** $\left(\dfrac{\pi}{2}, \dfrac{\pi}{8}\right)$                  **15.** $\left(\dfrac{2r}{\pi}, \dfrac{2r}{\pi}\right)$

**17.** $(8/9, 11/9)$                **19.** $(0, 2/(3(\pi + 2)))$

**21.** $(1, -2)$                    **23.** $\dfrac{5\pi}{3}$ cu. units

**25.** $(0.71377, 0.26053)$          **27.** $\left(1, \frac{1}{5}\right)$

**29.** $\bar{x} = \dfrac{M_{x=0}}{A}$, $\bar{y} = \dfrac{M_{y=0}}{A}$,
where $A = \displaystyle\int_c^d \big(g(y) - f(y)\big)\,dy$,
$M_{x=0} = \frac{1}{2}\displaystyle\int_c^d \big((g(y))^2 - (f(y))^2\big)\,dy$,
$M_{y=0} = \displaystyle\int_c^d y\big(g(y) - f(y)\big)\,dy$

**31.** diamond orientation, edge upward

## Section 10.6   (page 393)

**1.** (a) 235,200 N,   (b) 352,800 N

**3.** $6.12 \times 10^8$ N          **5.** $8.92 \times 10^6$ N

**7.** $7.056 \times 10^5$ N·m

**9.** $2450\pi a^3 \left( a + \dfrac{8h}{3} \right)$ N·m

**11.** $\dfrac{19{,}600}{3} XR^3$ N·m

## Section 10.7   (page 404)

**1.** $y^2 = Cx$          **3.** $x^3 - y^3 = C$

**5.** $Y = Ce^{t^2/2}$

**7.** $y = \pm 1, \quad y = \dfrac{Ce^{2x} - 1}{Ce^{2x} + 1}$

**9.** $y = -\ln\left(Ce^{-2t} - \frac{1}{2}\right)$     **11.** $y = x^3 + Cx^2$

**13.** $y = \frac{3}{2} + Ce^{-2x}$          **15.** $y = x - 1 + Ce^{-x}$

**17.** $y = (1 + e^{1-10t})/10$          **19.** $y = (x+2)e^{1/x}$

**21.** $y = \sqrt{4 + x^2}$          **23.** $y = \dfrac{2x}{1+x}, \ (x > 0)$

**25.** $b$

**27.** If $a = b$ the given solution is indeterminate $0/0$; in this case the solution is $x = a^2 kt/(1 + akt)$.

**29.** $v = \sqrt{\dfrac{mg}{k}}, \quad v = \sqrt{\dfrac{mg}{k}} \dfrac{e^{2\sqrt{kg/mt}} - 1}{e^{2\sqrt{kg/mt}} + 1}, \quad v \to \sqrt{\dfrac{mg}{k}}$

**31.** the hyperbolas $x^2 - y^2 = C$

## Review Exercises   (page 405)

**1.** about 833 m

**3.** $a \approx 1.1904$, $b \approx 0.0476$

**5.** $a = 2.1773$          **7.** $\left( \frac{8}{3\pi}, \frac{4}{3\pi} \right)$

**9.** about 27,726 N·cm          **11.** $y = 4(x - 1)^3$

**13.** \$8, 798.85

## Challenging Problems   (page 405)

**1.** (b) $\ln 2/(2\pi)$, (c) $\pi/(4k(k^2 + 1))$

**3.** $y = (r/h^3)x^3 - 3(r/h^2)x^2 + 3(r/h)x$

**5.** $b = -a = 27/2$          **7.** $1/\pi$

**9.** (a) $S(a,a,c) = 2\pi a^2 + \dfrac{2\pi ac^2}{\sqrt{a^2 - c^2}} \ln\left( \dfrac{a + \sqrt{a^2 - c^2}}{c} \right).$

(b) $S(a,c,c) = 2\pi c^2 + \dfrac{2\pi a^2 c}{\sqrt{a^2 - c^2}} \cos^{-1}\left( \dfrac{c}{a} \right).$

(c) $S(a,b,c) \approx \dfrac{b-c}{a-c} S(a,a,c) + \dfrac{a-b}{a-c} S(a,c,c).$

(d) $S(3, 2, 1) \approx 49.595.$

# Chapter 11
# Ordinary Differential Equations

## Section 11.1   (page 411)

**1.** 1, linear, homogeneous     **3.** 1, nonlinear

**5.** 2, linear, homogeneous

**7.** 3, linear, nonhomogeneous

**9.** 4, linear, homogeneous

**11.** (a) and (b) are solutions, (c) is not

**13.** $y_2 = \sin(kx)$, $y = -3(\cos(kx) + (3/k)\sin(kx))$

**15.** $y = \sqrt{2}(\cos x + 2\sin x)$

**17.** $y = x + \sin x + (\pi - 1)\cos x$

## Section 11.2   (page 416)

**1.** $2\tan^{-1}(y/x) = \ln(x^2 + y^2) + C$

**3.** $y = x\tan(\ln|x| + C)$     **5.** $y = x\tan^{-1}(\ln|Cx|)$

**7.** $y^3 + 3y - 3x^2 = 24$          **11.** $2xy + x^2 y^2 = C$

**13.** $xe^{xy} = C$          **15.** $\ln|x| - \frac{y}{x^2} = C$

**17.** $\dfrac{\mu'(y)}{\mu(y)} = \dfrac{1}{M}\left( \dfrac{\partial N}{\partial x} - \dfrac{\partial M}{\partial y} \right)$ must depend only on $y$.

**19.** $\dfrac{1}{M}\left( \dfrac{\partial N}{\partial x} - \dfrac{\partial M}{\partial y} \right)$ must depend only on $y$.

$x - y^2 e^y = Cy^2$

**21.** $\dfrac{1}{\mu}\dfrac{d\mu}{dx} = \dfrac{\dfrac{\partial N}{\partial x} - \dfrac{\partial M}{\partial y}}{xM - yN}$ must depend only on $xy$;

$\dfrac{\sin x}{y} - \dfrac{y}{x} = C$

## Section 11.3   (page 424)

**1.** (a) 1.97664, (b) 2.187485, (c) 2.306595

**3.** (a) 2.436502, (b) 2.436559, (c) 2.436563

**5.** (a) 1.097897, (b) 1.098401

**7.** (a) 0.89441, (b) 0.87996, (c) 0.872831

**9.** (a) 0.865766, (b) 0.865769, (c) 0.865769

**11.** (a) 0.898914, (b) 0.903122, (c) 0.904174

**13.** $y = 2/(3 - 2x)$

**17.** (b) $u = 1/(1-x)$, $v = \tan(x + \frac{\pi}{4})$. $y(x)$ is defined at least on $[0, \pi/4)$ and satisfies $1/(1-x) \leq y(x) \leq \tan(x+\frac{\pi}{4})$ there.

## Section 11.4   (page 428)

**1.** $y = C_1 e^x + C_2 e^{2x}$          **3.** $y = C_1 x + \dfrac{C_2}{x^2}$

**5.** $y = C_1 x + C_2 x e^x$

## Section 11.5  (page 433)

**1.** $y = C_1 + C_2 e^t + C_3 e^{3t}$

**3.** $y = C_1 \cos t + C_2 \sin t + C_3 t \cos t + C_4 t \sin t$

**5.** $y = C_1 e^{2t} + C_2 e^{-t} \cos t + C_3 e^{-t} \sin t$

**7.** $y = Ax + Bx \ln x$      **9.** $y = Ax + \dfrac{B}{x}$

**11.** $y = A + B \ln x$

**13.** $y = C_1 x + C_2 x \ln x + C_3 x (\ln x)^2$

**15.** $y = C_1 x \cos(\ln x) + C_2 x \sin(\ln x)$

## Section 11.6  (page 439)

**1.** $y = -\dfrac{1}{2} + C_1 e^x + C_2 e^{-2x}$

**3.** $y = -\dfrac{1}{2} e^{-x} + C_1 e^x + C_2 e^{-2x}$

**5.** $y = -\dfrac{2}{125} - \dfrac{4x}{25} + \dfrac{x^2}{5} + C_1 e^{-x} \cos(2x) + C_2 e^{-x} \sin(2x)$

**7.** $y = -\dfrac{1}{5} x e^{-2x} + C_1 e^{-2x} + C_2 e^{3x}$

**9.** $y = \dfrac{1}{8} e^x (\sin x - \cos x) + e^{-x}(C_1 \cos x + C_2 \sin x)$

**11.** $y = 2x + x^2 - x e^{-x} + C_1 + C_2 e^{-x}$

**15.** $y_p = \dfrac{x^2}{3}, \quad y = \dfrac{x^2}{3} + C_1 x + \dfrac{C_2}{x}$

**17.** $y = \dfrac{1}{2} x \ln x + C_1 x + \dfrac{C_2}{x}$

**19.** $y = C_2 e^x + C_2 x e^x + x e^x \ln x$

**21.** $y = -x^2 + C_1 x + C_2 x e^x$

# Index